PHYSICAL SCIENCE

FOUNDATIONS

1ST EDITION

BRIGHAM YOUNG UNIVERSITY

COLLEGE OF PHYSICAL AND MATHEMATICAL SCIENCES

BYU ACADEMIC PUBLISHING

BYU ACADEMIC PUBLISHING

PHYSICAL SCIENCE
FOUNDATIONS

COLLEGE OF PHYSICAL AND MATHEMATICAL SCIENCES

Physical Science 100 Textbook Committee Chair
J. Ward Moody

Authors:
Chapters 1-7, 10, 11
J. Ward Moody

Chapters 8, 9, 25
M. Jeannette Lawler

Chapters 12-14, 17-19, 21, 22, 24
Juliana Boerio-Goates

Chapters 15-16
R. Steven Turley

Chapters 20, 23
David V. Dearden

Chapters 26-31
Bart J. Kowallis

Chapters 32-34
Michael D. Joner

Author Assistant
Robert Snyder

Study Guide Assistants
Robert Snyder, Christopher Hallstrom

BYU ACADEMIC PUBLISHING

Publisher
Roger Reynolds

Associate Publisher
Brent Laker

Managing Editor
Jennifer Berry

Assistant Managing Editor
Kent Minson

Text Editor
Jennifer Berry

Illustrations
Christopher Henderson, Kent Minson, Kelli Rane, Jennifer Berry

Primary Photographer
Kelli Rane

Typesetting
Jennifer Berry, Kent Minson

Proofreaders
Cindy Busard, Christopher Hallstrom, Brent Laker, Kent Minson

Printer
BYU Print and Mail Production Center

CONTENTS

PREFACE

We live in a physical universe. As such, we are governed by physical laws. The discovery, comprehension and application of these laws, which make up "physical science," are among humanity's greatest triumphs. In comprehending these laws, we have the added benefit of seeing tangible manifestations of the power, majesty, order, and design of our Creator.

The rise of physical science has changed enormously how we view the natural universe. Many ancient people understood the world around them through mythological story. To them the world functioned at the will of gods who made things happen according to their fancies. We today recognize nature as an entity governed by processes that function according to law. If one can find the laws that govern the world, then one can predict how the world will work. In 1969 when the engines of the Saturn V moon rocket roared to life , it was with the full expectation that, as a result of complicated maneuvers based on the laws of motion, men would land on the moon and return safely. People respect science because it works.

Physical science is founded on ideas first and technical detail second. The ideas such as *matter is made of molecules, forces cause acceleration when unopposed,* or *the continents drift about on the surface of earth* are often remarkably simple and straight-forward. A college student need not understand the detailed technical justifications to be adequately familiar with these fundamental ideas and how they shape their lives.

One of our goals with this text is to show how just a few fundamental concepts can be used as a foundation to understand much of the complexity that exists in the universe; indeed, this is one of the great beauties of modern science. In this book we have attempted to lay out the key ideas that form the foundation of physics, chemistry, geology, and astronomy. Given our intent to structure a text that can comfortably be used in a single semester, careful consideration has been given to what is truly essential. Also, our topic selection has been guided by considering the basic physical and chemical processes that undergird astronomy and geology. Along the way, we hope to provide a "big picture" that shows how physics, chemistry, geology and astronomy are all closely interrelated. Much of the excitement of science today takes place in these interesting areas where the disciplines overlap.

Many ideas in this book will be familiar, like Newton's laws of motion or the periodic table of elements. Other ideas like Archimedes' principle of buoyancy, metallic bonding, the techniques of geological dating or finding distances to galaxies, may be new. We have attempted to weave these ideas together into a coherent presentation that ties new developments back to well-established principles. In the process, we hope to give the reader a basic description of the universe, some rules that govern it, and some useful experience with the scientific method of thinking.

As you read this text, we hope you are filled with some of the sense of awe and wonder science has instilled in us. We hope you strengthen your scientific reasoning skills and improve your ability to gather and evaluate evidence in many fields of endeavor. As you enhance your appreciation of the physical universe, we hope your faith will be strengthened in the ultimate Author of the universe we have endeavored to describe.

We in the College of Physical and Mathematical

Sciences at Brigham Young University owe a debt of gratitude to many people who have made this book possible. We are indebted to William Dibble, Jae Ballif, John Merrill, Grant Mason, Kenneth Hamblin, Richard Snow, Dana Griffen, and James Thorne, who all wrote portions of earlier texts from which this one derives. We are indebted to Jennifer Berry and her wonderful staff of illustrators, editors and photographers who have made the book presentable and interesting. We are grateful to Dean Earl Woolley and Associate Dean Dana Griffen of the College of Physical and Mathematical Sciences and the chairs and staff of the departments of Physics and Astronomy, Chemistry and Biochemistry, and Geology for continued support and patience throughout the project. We especially thank BYU Academic Publishing for investing the resources and talent necessary to make this project a success.

J. Ward Moody
Juliana Boerio-Goates
Bart J. Kowallis
M. Jeannette Lawler
Michael D. Joner
R. Steven Turley
David V. Dearden

PHYSICAL SCIENCE

FOUNDATIONS

CHAPTER 1

KNOWLEDGE, SCIENCE, AND THE UNIVERSE

The important thing is not to stop questioning. Curiosity has its own reason for existing. One cannot help but be in awe when he contemplates the mysteries of eternity, of life, of the marvelous structure of reality. It is enough if one tries merely to comprehend a little of this mystery every day. Never lose a holy curiosity.

~ Albert Einstein

You are a born explorer. Right from the cradle, your natural curiosity led you to explore the world around you. You looked at something you didn't understand, and then instinctively tried to grab it, feel it, touch it, taste it. These experiences taught you that candy tastes good and touching a hot stove can be painful! In a remarkably short amount of time you learned and remembered an enormous body of important facts about what to embrace and what to avoid. Even at this young age, and without any training in the sciences, you were participating in a scientific process of experimentation.

The process scientists follow in the lab, known formally as the "scientific method," is the same process you followed while conducting experiments as a toddler. Just as you measured the outcomes of your explorations by the sensations they created, scientists evaluate laboratory experiments by the results they observe and measure. The scientific method, therefore, is a familiar, natural extension of your innate curiosity and ability to scrutinize the world with a scientific eye.

We need tools like the scientific method because actually *knowing* what is true and accurate is not as straight-forward as you might think. For example, a few decades ago medical researchers designed and built an artificial eye. A blind patient was fitted with electric probes that were surgically connected directly to his brain. When the probes were stimulated, his brain picked up signals and he could "see" crude patterns. The patterns were not of physical objects, but if the patient had always been blind, and if he had not been told by his physician-researchers what was happening, how would he have known whether those patterns represented real objects or not?

LEARNING OBJECTIVES

When you finish this chapter you should be able to

• Identify and describe the four ways we learn.

• Discuss the scientific method and how it generates knowledge.

• Describe six basic assumptions the scientific method rests upon.

• Identify the four interactions of nature and the scope of their influence.

• Identify the realm covered by the physical sciences.

1–1 SHARED SOURCES OF KNOWLEDGE

We often uncritically assume that we know something without realizing that we build our own knowledge from information that is presented to us. Much of our knowledge is made from signals channeled to our brains by our eyes, ears, hands, etc. while other knowledge comes to us in less physical ways. And although we all live in the same world, each of us weighs differently the value and validity of information being supplied to us. This creates a view of the real world that is unique to each of us. In essence, every person is a philosopher, creating his or her own worldview from shared sources of knowledge.

What are these "shared sources of knowledge?" The four most often identified are: **authority, intuition, reason,** and **sensory data**.

Authority

Learning through "authority" means you place your faith in the knowledge possessed by another person or source and accept it as true, even though you yourself have not had the experiences through which your accepted authority gained their knowledge. The authority could be a parent, scholar, historian, reporter, leader, the scriptures, or any of a number of other sources. In cases of conflicting claims of knowledge between competing authorities, we may give

3

precedence to those that come to us from antiquity and thus have been tested by time, or to those that are held to be true by the greatest number and so have been validated by the most "witnesses." Perhaps we might give greater weight to knowledge from a prestigious source, someone with a special perspective, such as an

- **Authority**
An accepted source of expert information or advice.

Figure 1.1
Much of our learning comes from following authority.

astronomer telling us about the stars. Much, possibly the majority, of our knowledge comes from authority because our own sphere of experience is so limited compared to the world at large.

The strength of this source of knowledge is that it allows us to accept and learn from the experience of others, so that we do not have to experience all things ourselves. Its weakness is that sources of authority can often conflict with each other and we cannot resolve competing claims of truth without reference to one of the other sources. How do we know which sources of authority to trust?

- **Intuition**
The act or faculty of knowing or sensing without the use of rational processes; immediate cognition.

Intuition

We define "intuition" as knowledge imparted to us through methods outside of our five physical senses. Inspiration and revelation are in this category, as are "hunches" or "feelings" or a "belief" that something is correct or true. Because intuitive experiences often come after contemplating questions relating to the meaning and purpose of life, intuition is often regarded as a religious type of knowledge. However, the scientific process benefits from intuition as well. Albert Einstein and other great scientists have freely acknowledged that intu-

- **Reason**
The capacity for logical, rational, and analytic thought; intelligence.

itive thinking was the genesis of many of their ideas. Einstein unashamedly confessed that intuition guided his scientific judgment.

The inner experiences of intuition may be impossible to articulate or quantify scientifically, but nonetheless, they are deeply felt, convincing, and direct. Individuals who experience this source of knowledge often alter their lives and perform deeds that the other sources of knowledge seldom inspire.

Intuition's greatest strength is that it may be knowledge from the giver of life Himself who knows all things. But although several individuals may experience the same intuitive event, each will have their own interpretation that may be difficult to describe to someone else. It is this privateness, this inaccessibility to public scrutiny, that is the weakness of intuitive knowledge. How do we know that our intuition is true and if so, that our interpretation of it is correct?

Figure 1.2
Intuitive learning is direct and pure but personal. Great moments of learning often come with an intuitive "flash of insight."

Reason

Reason is knowledge derived from an internally consistent system of assumptions and conclusions. An example of reason, in its ideal form as a source of knowledge, is the mathematical proof. Begin with basic assumptions, such as Euclid's five postulates of geometry, and proceed to logical, inescapable, and indisputable conclusions. You can write the conclusions down, describe the process by which they are obtained, and subject the argument to public scrutiny. These are the strengths of reason.

The weakness of reason lies in the problem

Figure 1.3
Reason builds conclusions from basic assumptions.

of identifying the assumptions that are the basis for the argument. If the assumptions are reliable, then the conclusions will be reliable. If an assumption is false then some of that system of reasoning is false as well and it must be rebuilt upon a new assumption. The question then becomes, how do we know if our assumptions are true?

Sensory Data

We define sensory data or "sensation" as experience obtained through the five senses of sight, hearing, touch, taste, and smell. Sensation gives us the knowledge of our immediate surroundings necessary to function in everyday life. Sensation's strength is its ability to portray the world accurately. Sensory data is so reliable that we nearly always assume it is true. But all sensation is filtered through our senses and, in the modern world, it may additionally be filtered through instruments like cameras and TV and can be altered from reality in the process.

Sensory data is not direct knowledge in the same way that intuition is thought to be direct. Sensed data represent the *appearance* of things, and from that we as individuals infer the reality behind the appearance. Perhaps you have had the delight of being fooled by a magician. He showed you his empty hands and then a second later produced a bird in them, seemingly from nowhere! Most of us have heard about, or even experienced, a "virtual reality" room. In such rooms individuals can be outfitted with sensors

that track their every move. They might wear goggles that tell their eyes and ears they are moving through a jungle or climbing a mountain when it really isn't so.

A weakness, then, of the senses is that they can be tricked or fooled. In addition, their sensitivity and accuracy can diminish over time or through injury. How do we know if what we sense is always accurate?

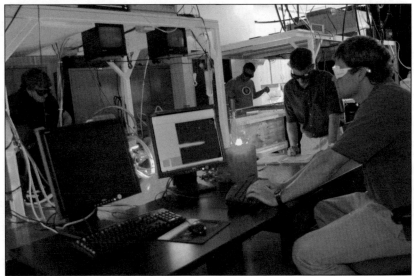

Figure 1.4
Sensory data taken under carefully controlled conditions tells us how the universe acts. Here data is being obtained on the behavior of light at short time-scales in Dr. Justin Peatross's lab at Brigham Young University.

1–2   THE SCIENTIFIC METHOD

The "scientific method" is a way to obtain knowledge. It uses all four methods of learning. Authority is very important as evidenced by library shelves filled with technical papers and books. No scientist would properly start researching without first reading what others have learned from their experiments and studies. Science successfully done adds to the pool of authoritative knowledge and wisdom.

In deciding which studies to pursue and how to pursue them, scientists are often guided by intuition and authority. Nonetheless, the "scientific method" of obtaining knowledge relies mostly on the other two ways of learning: reason and sensory data.

You may have been taught the scientific method through a science fair project in high school. If so, you probably first made a **hypothesis** about something and then designed an experiment to test it. A hypothesis is usually a "first guess," a reasoned conjecture about what

* **Sensory Data**
Knowledge obtained through the senses.

* **Hypothesis**
A tentative explanation for an observation, phenomenon, or scientific problem that can be tested by further investigation.

might be happening, based on intuition and the limited knowledge at hand. As an example, Albert Einstein began his Special Theory of Relativity by first hypothesizing that nothing can travel faster than the speed of light in empty space.

Hypotheses are tested through sensory data obtained in experiments. After sufficient testing the hypothesis will be refined, focused, possibly combined with other hypotheses, and emerge as a **theory**. For example, the Special Theory of Relativity builds upon the now well-proven hypothesis that nothing travels faster than the speed of light. It quantifies the consequences of this in mathematical reasoning that makes specific, measurable predictions about how things behave when their movement approaches the speed of light. Theories generally possess a greater level of mature detail than hypotheses do.

Theories that have been proven accurate and never witnessed to be contradicted are often called "**laws**," such as Newton's laws of motion or the law of gravity. Laws are theories that are so well tested and proven that further testing is suspended. They are *assumed* to be true, and are placed in the foundation of scientific knowledge. No law is hard and fast, however. Sometimes unexpected discoveries call long-standing laws into question, leading to true revolutions in science.

Science uses reason based upon its laws, theories, and hypotheses to create **models** of reality. These models often take the form of mathematical equations that describe the physical reality of a hypothetical world. The predictions of the models are tested against the outcome of experiments, and models that don't work are revised or rejected. If successful models cannot be built upon the theories, then the theories themselves are called into question. Models that do work are kept and tested again. As they pass more tests, faith in their accuracy and truthfulness increases.

Models "passing tests" means that their predictions were verified with sensory data. Researchers can hypothesize and reason, but if investigation does not yield sensory data, it is not science. In conducting research, we start with sensory data, reason out an explanatory model, design experiments to test it, and gather data through experimentation. As mentioned

• Theory
A set of statements or principles devised to explain a group of facts or phenomena, especially one that has been repeatedly tested or is widely accepted and can be used to make predictions about natural phenomena.

• Law
A well-tested theory, so firm as to be unquestioned by science.

• Model
A schematic description of a system, theory, or phenomenon that accounts for its known or inferred properties and may be used for further study of its characteristics.

• Existence
The fact or state of having actual or real being.

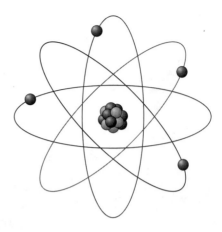

Figure 1.5
Models are used to represent reality. Science leads us to truth by building models and refining them through theory and data.

earlier, the parts of the model that do not work are discarded while those that do work are retained and refined. The cycle is repeated with the faith that the process is progressing toward an enlarged view of truth regarding the tested ideas and gathered data. The process begins and ends with data.

The scientific method is a priceless tool, which, when powered by curiosity, helps us efficiently comprehend our complex world. It helps our curious minds formulate important "why" and "how" questions. It helps us sift through clouds of variables and possible answers to find a relatively few laws and principles through which a broad range of phenomena can be understood. When our thinking skills are equal to our curiosity, the scientific method can help us reach true and accurate knowledge.

1–3 SIX "SELF-EVIDENT TRUTHS"

As previously stated, all reasoning must rest upon assumptions, and the scientific method is not an exception. It assumes basic philosophical ideals as a foundation. What are these basic assumptions of science? We do not know that there has ever been a definitive set established. But there are some assumptions that are so logical and basic we present them here as six "self-evident truths."

1. **Existence:** There exists a physical world separate and distinct from our minds which is comprehensible through our senses and which

is governed by certain generalities called the "laws of nature."

Earlier in this chapter we questioned the absolute validity of information obtained through our senses because senses can be deceived. The Chinese philosopher Chuang Tsu illustrated the dilemma with the following story:

Once upon a time, I, Chuang Tsu dreamed I was a butterfly, flying happily here and there, enjoying life without knowing who I was. Suddenly I woke up and I was indeed Chuang Tsu. Did Chuang Tsu dream he was a butterfly or did the butterfly dream he was Chuang Tsu?[1]

Perhaps you, too, have had dreams that were so vivid that after awakening you were puzzled for a moment about what was real. In essence the assumption of existence asserts that Chuang Tsu is, indeed, a Chinese philosopher and not a butterfly, and the reality around him is the same as the reality that surrounds us. Each of us might see this reality a little differently because of who we are. But regardless of how we understand it, a single, unique, reality is there, existing independent of us.

Figure 1.6
Existence: The universe is wonderful and real!

2. **Causality:** Events in the physical universe have natural causes which always precede them in time and that can be explained rationally in terms of the laws of nature.

Science has never proven that it is impossible to travel back in time. However, someone traveling to the past could possibly kill their own parents before the traveler was born, thus setting up a violation of reason. The assumption of causality guides us to reject any hypothesis or theory that leads to the possibility of a result existing in time before its cause does. The cause must always precede the effect. Science asserts that time travel to the past is not possible without constraints on it that ensure causality is never violated.

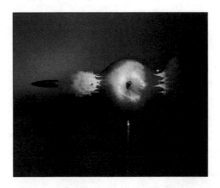

Figure 1.7
Causality: Can the apple burst before the bullet strikes it? No!

3. **Position Symmetry:** The laws of nature are the same everywhere in the universe.

The universe is a huge entity. A beam of light takes over 100,000 years to cross the Milky Way Galaxy alone. We have no hope at present of ever traveling to the far side of the Galaxy, conducting experiments, and returning. Yet we want to use the law of gravity to explain how galaxies behave. We therefore assume that the law of gravity—and all laws of nature—hold true for all matter everywhere in the Universe while acknowledging that we cannot prove this through experimentation.

4. **Time Symmetry:** The laws of nature have remained the same through time. They are the

♦ **Causality**
Cause must always precede the effect.

♦ **Position Symmetry**
The laws of the universe are not different at different locations.

Figure 1.8
Position Symmetry: The laws of nature are the same in our galaxy as they are in this galaxy and everywhere in the universe.

◆ **Time Symmetry**
The laws of the universe do not change with time.

◆ **Principle of Noncontradiction**
Of two contradictory propositions, both cannot be true.

◆ **Occam's Razor**
Simpler explanations are more likely to be true than complex ones.

Figure 1.9
Time Symmetry: The laws of nature as deduced by Galileo in Italy 400 years ago have not changed with time.

same now as they were in the distant past, and they will be the same in the future.

In the absence of time travel, we cannot visit past epochs and conduct experiments in those time periods. We still want to use the laws of nature to explain how the universe has behaved in the past and—more importantly—learn how it will unfold into the future. Indeed, science is a means of predicting the future through understanding universal laws. For this to be true, those laws must be eternally true.

5. **Principle of Noncontradiction:** Of two contradictory propositions, both cannot be true.

When based on different assumptions, reason can lead to different conclusions. When two conclusions contradict each other, at least one conclusion, and possibly both, is wrong. Otherwise logic and reason wouldn't hold true and the basic scientific methodology would be invalid. The principle of non-contradiction leads

us to identify areas of science where more data must be gathered and theories and assumptions refined to remove the contradictions.

6. **Occam's Razor:** If alternative explanations of any phenomenon are available, where each are logical and explain the phenomenon equally well, then the simplest explanation shall be chosen. Explanatory principles or factors are not to be multiplied beyond necessity. On the other hand, explanations cannot be too simple; they must be adequate to explain consistently the available data.

Of all the self-evident truths, Occam's razor is perhaps the hardest to quantify. Yet it is also likely the brightest guiding beacon. Great scientists of antiquity formulated a brilliant theory of the universe in which the Earth stood motionless in the center and the stars and planets all whirled about it in the heavens. A model based on this theory, called the Ptolemaic cosmology, said the Sun, the Moon, and planets all orbited about the Earth on two circles (see *Figure 1.10*). This model was accurate for its day in predicting when and where a planet would appear in the sky.

As measurements of planetary positions became more precise, the Ptolemaic model was changed to fit the data by including more circular paths for the planets to move on. Soon the long-accepted Ptolemaic model became an entangled collection of circles connected to circles connected to even more circles that was complex beyond reason. Nicholas Copernicus saw that if the sun were at the center of the solar system and the Earth moved around it, the complex arrangement of circles could be discarded in favor of a simple, single orbital path for each planet.

Figure 1.10
A drawing of the complex Ptolemaic model and the simpler Copernican model. Noncontradition and Occam's razor: Only one of the competing models of the solar system can be true. The simpler Copernican model is correct.

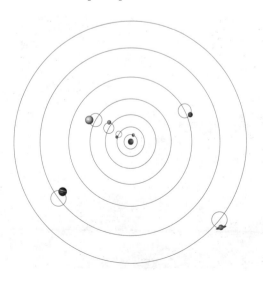
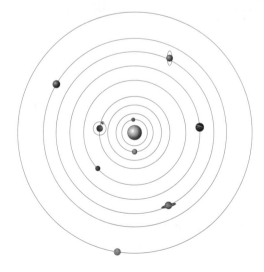

The simplicity of this new scheme correctly guided mankind to the truth. The incorrect assumption that the Sun and planets orbited about the Earth was replaced by the correct and much simpler assumption that the Earth and planets orbited about the Sun.

1–4   THE UNIVERSE AROUND US

We have described the methods used by scientists to find answers to questions about our world and universe. We shall now briefly describe, as the last part of this introduction, the realms of the universe that science has examined. These realms may be viewed as a map of the topics we will discuss in this book. The nature of each realm and the specific laws and forces that govern within it will be elaborated on in subsequent chapters.

Interactions and Force

Whether we are looking at microscopic objects nearby, or large bodies halfway across the universe, all things are made of matter and energy organized differently and rather uniquely on different lengths and scales. This organization is governed by the influence of **interactions** that give rise to **forces**.

We know of four interactions in nature, the **strong nuclear**, the **electromagnetic**, the **weak nuclear**, and **gravity**. Forces are felt by matter in accordance with attributes possessed by the matter. The nuclear forces act on nucleons and quarks, the electromagnetic force acts on charged particles, and gravity acts on mass. In some structures these four interactions may be at work simultaneously with similar or opposing effects.

The relative strengths of these interactions are surprisingly diverse. If two protons are placed side by side and the forces on them are measured, the strong nuclear force acting on the protons is 100 times greater than the electromagnetic force, 10^{13} times greater than the nuclear weak force, and 10^{38} times greater than gravity (*see Table 1.1*). The strong nuclear force is the most powerful force known but its range (and that of the weak nuclear force) is so short the electromagnetic force dominates by the time we have increased in scale to the size of an atom.

- **Interaction**
Any of four fundamental ways in which elementary particles and bodies can influence each other.

- **Force**
A push or pull on an object.

- **Strong Nuclear Interaction**
The interaction between nucleons that gives rise to the strong force.

- **Electromagnetic Interaction**
The interaction between charged objects that gives rise to the electromagnetic force.

- **Weak Nuclear Interaction**
The interaction between nucleons that gives rise to the weak force.

- **Gravity**
The interaction between anything with mass that gives rise to the gravitational force.

POWERS OF 10 NOTATION

The universe covers a huge range in sizes that are often difficult to represent using ordinary numbers. To overcome this problem, we use a shorthand system called "scientific" or "powers of ten" notation. The cumbersome zeros of a large number are condensed into a "factor of 10" which is 10 raised to an exponent. The exponent indicates how many zeros are needed to properly represent the number. Positive exponents represent places to the left of the decimal while negative exponents represent places to the right. For example:

10^1 = 10 (ten)
10^2 = 100 (one hundred)
10^3 = 1,000 (one thousand)
10^6 = 1,000,000 (one million)
10^9 = 1,000,000,000 (one billion)
10^{12} = 1,000,000,000,000 (one trillion)
10^0 = 1 (one)
10^{-1} = 0.1 (one tenth)

10^{-6} = 0.000001 (one millionth).
These values are read "ten to the first," "ten to the second," on down to "ten to the minus sixth."

Since real values rarely are even powers of ten, we typically must multiply the factor of 10 by a value between 1 and 10 as follows.

5×10^5 = 500,000
1.23456×10^3 = 1,234.56
9.87×10^{-7} = 0.000000987

These would be read "five times ten to the fifth," "one point two three four five six times ten to the third," and "nine point eight seven times ten to the minus seventh" respectively.

- **Atomic Nuclei**
The positively charged central region of an atom, composed of protons and neutrons.

- **Proton**
A composite, strongly interacting particle made up of three quarks. The proton carries a positive electrical charge and is a constituent part of the nucleus of atoms.

- **Neutron**
A composite, strongly-interacting particle made up of three quarks, but which carries no net electrical charge. Neutrons are a constituent part of the nucleus of atoms.

- **Nucleon**
A generic name for either a proton or a neutron.

- **Quark**
The elementary particles of which protons and neutrons consist. A proton and a neutron each consist of three quarks.

- **Radioactive**
A term referring to atoms whose nuclei can spontaneously change under the influence of the weak nuclear force.

- **Electron**
An elementary particle in atoms having a negative charge. Electrons are located outside atomic nuclei.

- **Element**
A substance composed of atoms which have an identical number of protons in each nucleus. Elements cannot be reduced to simpler substances by normal chemical means.

- **Atom**
The fundamental unit of an element.

- **Molecule**
A microscopic structure usually made up of more than one atom.

The electromagnetic force dominates the world in which we live. Weak gravity, which increases slowly and steadily with increasing mass, becomes the dominant force when the sizes we are considering are as large as a planet or larger. This is illustrated by *Figure 1.11*. The nuclear weak force is the only one that does not dominate at any scale length. The realms over which each of these forces dominates is described in the following sections.

The Realm of the Nuclear Forces

We start at a scale size of approximately 10^{-15}m. Are there structures smaller than this? There may be, but if so, we do not as yet have the ability to measure them. **Atomic nuclei** are this size and are comprised of **protons** and **neutrons**, which we together call **nucleons**. Nucleons are so small that it would take one million million (or 10^{12}) lined up next to each other to reach across the head of a pin. They are so dense that a pinhead-size ball made of nucleons packed next to each other would weigh about a million tons. No crane could lift it!

A well-tested model theorizes that protons and neutrons are each comprised of more fundamental particles called **quarks**. The strong nuclear force acts on quarks, binding them together into nucleons and also binding the nucleons together into atomic nuclei. The nuclear weak force, on the other hand, attempts to break nuclei apart. Nuclei that are susceptible to being broken apart this way are termed **radioactive**.

The electromagnetic force is also present in atomic nuclei as a repulsion between positively charged protons. Atomic nuclei do not fly apart

only because the strong nuclear force is more powerful than the electromagnetic force. In addition, only protons feel the repulsive electromagnetic force, while both neutrons and protons feel the attractive strong nuclear force.

The Realm of the Electromagnetic Force

Surrounding atomic nuclei are **electrons** held in place by their attraction to the nuclear protons. Together the electrons and nuclei constitute **atoms**. The average distance of the outermost electrons from the nucleus is about 10^{-10}m, meaning an atom is approximately 100,000 times larger than its nucleus and is mostly empty space. If a nucleus were the size of a ballpoint pen tip, its surrounding atom would be the size of a football field! Atoms, in a variety of combinations, make up matter as we know it. The tiniest speck of dust visible to the unaided eye contains about 10^{18} atoms. A sample of air the size of a sugar cube has about the same number.

The atoms of each of the nearly 100 **elements** found in nature have a unique number of protons and electrons. The lightest element, hydrogen, has one of each. The next lightest element, helium, has two protons, two neutrons and two electrons. The atoms of each successive element increase with each step by one proton, one electron, and usually one or several neutrons.

Atoms join together in small groups called **molecules**. Most individual molecules contain fewer than 50 atoms. The common table sugar molecule contains 12 carbon atoms, 22 hydrogen atoms, and 11 oxygen atoms. Some sub-

Table 1.1 – The Four Forces of Nature

Force	Relative Strength	Range	Acts Upon
Nuclear Strong	10^{38}	Atomic Nuclei 10^{-15}m	Nucleons
Electromagnetic	10^{36}	Earth Diameter 10^{7}m	Charged Matter
Nuclear Weak	10^{25}	Atomic Nuclei 10^{-15}m	Nucleons
Gravity	1	Entire Universe 10^{26}m	Mass

Their strengths vary with distance from each other. The relative strength listed here is what is felt by two protons sitting side-by-side (approximately 10^{-15}m apart).

stances, like nylon for example, have long molecular chains that may contain a million atoms or more. Molecular sizes vary from 10^{-10}m to 10^{-8}m or larger. Even the largest molecules are too small to be seen under the most powerful optical microscope.

Objects from 10^{-7}m to 10^4m in size are large numbers of atoms and molecules arranged together. We will call these arrangements "molecular complexes." Molecular complexes can be simple in structure like a shovel full of dirt, in which the individual molecules are just piled against each other and have no real connection beyond proximity. Other arrangements of molecules can be as complex as the human body where the individual parts not only interact in a marvelous manner but the absence of a small amount of needed material (proteins, vitamins, etc.) will cause other parts of the body to drastically change their functions. The realm of molecular complexes is the world we live in.

The Realm of Gravity

As molecular complexes increase in mass, they are eventually held together by gravity instead of electromagnetism. Since gravity always pulls matter inward toward the center of the distribution, objects held together by gravity tend to have a spherical or circular shape.

Earth has the shape of a ball with a radius of almost 6400 km (4000 miles). This is so large we do not generally notice that the level of a lake curves downward to be about 16 feet lower five miles away than it is at our feet. Earth is a member of the **solar system,** which consists of the Sun, nine planets and their moons, thousands of asteroids and comets, and an untold number of smaller pieces of rock and ice. The Sun's gravity keeps all of these bodies orbiting about it in a circular disk. The average distance from the Sun to the farthest planet Pluto is 6.0×10^{12}m, or the distance light can travel in about 6 hours.

Like the atom, the solar system is mainly empty space. If the sun were an orange on the 50-yard line of a football field, Earth would be a BB ten yards away and Pluto would be a grain of sand in the seats at the top of the stadium. On this scale all the material in the entire solar system combined would form a ball that is smaller than a grapefruit.

As large as the solar system is, it is dwarfed

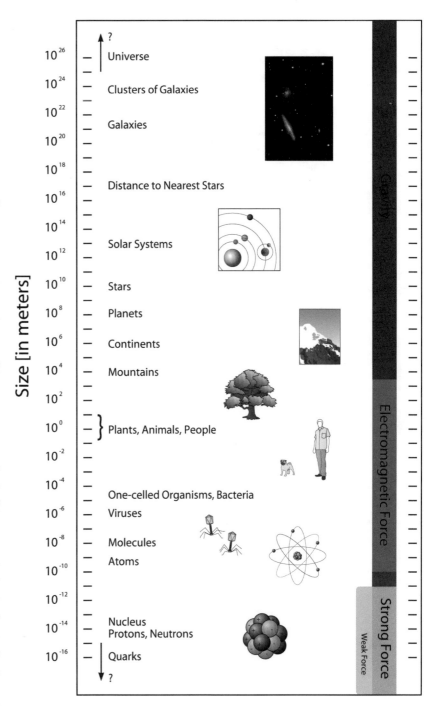

by the enormity of the Milky Way Galaxy in which it resides. This huge structure is a circular disk of over 200 billion stars held together by their mutual gravity. It measures about 10^{21}m from edge to edge, which is the distance light can travel in 100,000 years. If the entire solar system were a marble on the 50-yard line of a football field in Provo Utah, then the edge of the galaxy would be in Moscow, Russia! The nearest stars would be like a half-dozen grains of sand spread throughout the football stadium. The vastness and emptiness of it all is staggering. Such distances seem unreal in part because the

Figure 1.11

The organization and character of the universe is determined by forces from the four interactions of nature.

• **Solar System**

The sun and all planets, comets, asteroids, and other bodies that orbit about it under the pull of gravity.

Milky Way Galaxy seen on a moonless night seems to be crowded with stars. That so many stars are visible attests to their great brightness and prolific abundance.

Finally, we come to the realm of visible galaxies that populate the vastness of the universe itself. The deepest image from the Hubble Space Telescope suggests there are at least 50 billion galaxies averaging over 100 billion stars each. These are spread throughout the 10^{26}m of visible space in clusters of 10 to 10,000 members or more. Evidence strongly suggests that the universe itself had a beginning almost 14 billion years ago in an event of nearly incomprehensible magnitude called the "Big Bang."

As you study the realms described above, try to learn not just what they are but *how* we know of them. Distinguish between the parts that are well known and those for which our knowledge is more tentative and developing. Pay attention to the reasoning and assumptions involved. Let your own intuitive heart guide you through the huge body of authority, evidence, and reason the knowledge is built upon. Knowing the world around us through the physical sciences is a triumphant elevation of the human mind and spirit.

References

1. Chuang Tsu, *Inner Chapters*, p. 48, translated by Gia-Fu Feng and Jane English, Vintage Books, Random House, New York, NY, 1974 .

Chapter Framework

A. Four Ways We Learn
  1. Authority
  2. Intuition
  3. Reason
  4. Sensory Data

B. The Scientific Method
  1. Hypothesis
  2. Theory
  3. Laws
  4. Models

C. Six "Self-Evident Truths"
  1. Existence
  2. Causality
  3. Position Symmetry
  4. Time Symmetry
  5. Principle of Noncontradiction
  6. Occam's Razor

D. Interaction and Forces
  1. Four Interactions in Nature
     a. *Strong nuclear*
     b. *Electromagnetic*
     c. *Weak nuclear*
     d. *Gravity*
  2. The Realm of Nuclear Forces
     a. *Atomic nuclei—protons, neutrons—and smaller*
  3. The Realm of the Electromagnetic Force
     a. *Electrons, protons, and atomic nuclei*
     b. *Atoms*
     c. *Molecules*
     d. *Molecular complexes*
  4. The Realm of Gravity
     a. *Earth*
     b. *Solar System*
     c. *Milky Way Galaxy*
     d. *Universe*

Comprehension

True/False

1. _____ Protons and neutrons together form atomic nuclei.
2. _____ Occam's razor states that complex explanations are more likely to be true than simple explanations.
3. _____ Intuition is the act or faculty of knowing or sensing outside the five physical senses.
4. _____ A *law*, such as Newton's Law of motion, can never be proved wrong.
5. _____ The laws on Mars are slightly different then the laws on Earth due to the differences in each planet's composition.

Fill in the Blank

1. The Principle of _____ states that of two contradictory propositions, both cannot be true.
2. Electromagnetic Interaction: The interaction between _____ objects that gives rise to the electromagnetic force.
3. Electrons and nuclei together form a(n) _____.
4. A _____ is a set of statements or principles devised from a well-proven hypothesis, and used to make predictions about natural phenomenon.
5. Atoms join into groups called _____.

Matching

1. _____ Cause must always precede the effect.
2. _____ A substance made of atoms, all of which contain the same number of protons.
3. _____ The laws of the universe are not different at different locations.
4. _____ An accepted source of expert information or advice.
5. _____ The force that arises from the interactions of anything with mass.
6. _____ A well-tested theory, so firm as to be unquestioned by science.
7. _____ A push or pull on an object.
8. _____ A world separate and distinct from our minds that actually exists.
9. _____ Any of four fundamental ways in which elementary particles and bodies can influence each other.
10. _____ A tentative explanation for an observation, phenomenon, or scientific problem that can be tested by further investigation.
11. _____ The capacity for logical, rational, and analytic thought; intelligence.
12. _____ A schematic description of a system, theory, or phenomenon that accounts for its known or inferred properties and may be used for further study of its characteristics.
13. _____ The interaction between nucleons that holds them together.
14. _____ The laws of the universe do not change with time.
15. _____ Knowledge obtained through seeing, hearing, touching, tasting, and smelling.

a. *Time Symmetry*
b. *Model*
c. *Reason*
d. *Interaction*
e. *Sensory Data*
f. *Law*
g. *Position Symmetry*
h. *Authority*
i. *Force*
j. *Causality*
k. *Element*
l. *Hypothesis*
m. *Strong Nuclear Interaction*
n. *Existence*
o. *Gravity*

Analysis

1. Which of the following is not one of the four ways of learning?

   a) Authority   b) Sensory Data
   c) Discovery   d) Reason

2. Which of the following forces is electrical?

   a) Weight of a book
   b) The force exerted by a book on a table
   c) Gravitational force of Earth

d) Force keeping the moon in orbit

e) Force keeping the solar system together

Synthesis

1. Some people might say that they "know" the following statements are true. In each case, identify which of the four primary sources of knowledge they base their assertions on.

   a) How did Pythagoras know the squared lengths of a right triangle's legs equals the squared length of the hypotenuse ($A^2 + B^2 = C^2$, the Pythagorean Theorem)?

   b) God exists.

   c) Prescriptions written by doctors cure people because they are experts in medicine.

   d) Water is made up of molecules.

   e) The Earth spins on its axis once every 24 hours.

   f) Lowering taxes will stimulate the economy.

   g) My great-great-grandfather was a kind man.

2. Which of the "self evident truths" best applies to each statement?

   a) You can vote for a politician who argues for a tax decrease or for one who argues for increasing services in society, but not both—the two ideas oppose one another.

   b) You want to know if gravity exists on Pluto.

   c) You want to analyze light that left a distant star 100,000 years ago.

   d) You must solve a murder based on the details from a crime scene.

   e) You are in a comatose state and experience dreams that seem very real.

   f) The phone rings before you pick it up and say hello.

3. When Kent got up this morning, he found the refrigerator door open. Use your understanding of Occam's razor to rank the following explanations from most to least likely, and explain why.

   a) A tornado swept through the kitchen at night and pulled open the door.

   b) His fridge has suddenly developed a faulty magnetic seal.

   c) His roommate, who just left for class, forgot to close it.

   d) A goblin lives under the fridge and got hungry during the night. He opened the door, but didn't know how to close the fridge when he was done.

4. Write down the classes you are taking this semester and decide which way of learning pertains most to each of them. (For example, an introductory Econ class might be heavily weighted towards authority, whereas a graduate physics course might be more weighted towards reason.)

5. Contrast the authority, intuition, reason, and sensory data in stories and articles on the front page of a current newspaper against those on the editorial page.

6. The weight of an object on the moon is only one-sixth of its weight on the earth. Why does this not violate position symmetry?

7. If there were different forces present at the beginning of the universe than the ones we observe now, would this violate time symmetry?

8. Describe in your own words what a hypothesis, theory, law, and model are. Give examples of each.

9. Describe how scientific methods can be used in the following situations:

   a) Building an automobile

   b) Dating fossils on the slopes of Mt. Timpanogos

   c) Deciding where to build a house

10. Using an analogy or a numerical value, contrast the size of the nucleus and the size of the atom.

11. Using an analogy or a numerical value, contrast the distances between stars, the size of the galaxy, and the distance between galaxies.

12. Describe the organization of the universe. Show how clusters of galaxies are ultimately composed of the simplest entities we know about.

13. Describe six "self-evident truths" assumed by many scientist and explain what each one means.

14. Pick 5 objects that exemplify different levels of organization observed in the universe. Put the objects in order of size, beginning with the smallest. Explain how each is held together and where it fits into the levels of organization described in the text. Identify the basic forces which dominate in each object.

15. Conspiracy theories are fairly common currently (e.g., the moon landing was a hoax, there are aliens from space hidden in New Mexico, etc.). Explain how you can differentiate between reliable and suspect claims on the basis of how they use scientific methods.

Effective Studying

For many freshmen, adapting to the university's standard of studying is very difficult. Many college students did well in high school without ever really taking notes or studying. Generally, they must develop better study skills to do well at the university level. There are many resources available to help you develop the necessary learning habits.

Taking Notes

- Write things down in your own words.

- Review your notes daily.

- Attend class with the mindset that you will ultimately teach someone else the material. Tests are simply a way of teaching the teacher what you have learned.

- Develop a system of abbreviations so you can take notes faster.

- Some people find it helpful to leave room in their notes, so they can add notes later as they review.

- It may be helpful to rewrite or type your notes each week, so you can keep them organized and have an extra chance to review them.

Reading Texts

- Read assignments before class. This will make lectures easier to understand and, especially, more enjoyable.

- If your textbooks have comprehension questions at the end of the chapters, read through them to check your understanding.

- Change textbook headings into questions and attempt to answer the questions while reading.

- Read first and highlight later.

- Take reading notes in the margins of your text or in a notebook for the class.

Study Groups

- Form study groups with classmates from your learning community.

- Discuss what you are studying with others to sharpen your understanding.

- Study groups are more effective if you prepare beforehand.

- Try the "round robin" approach. Each person in the group can quiz others on the material. This allows everyone to review by listening and instructing, which helps to commit the material to memory.

- Limit your study groups to four or five people.

- Meet with study groups regularly, not just before tests.

- Find a quiet and convenient place to meet. You can schedule rooms online or at the computers by the library information desk.

Studying

- Focus your study on what you don't know. An effective way of doing this is to keep an "I don't understand…" note card handy.

- Study for each class every day.

- Find interesting things about what you are learning.

- Study somewhere comfortable for you, but avoid sitting or laying on your bed! Most people like to study somewhere quiet where they can focus and won't be interrupted, such as the library.

- Keep your study area clean and organized.

- Many find it helpful to take short breaks during study sessions.

Courtesy of Freshman Academy, BYU.

LAWS GOVERNING MOTION

CHAPTER 2

*If I have made any valuable discoveries,
it has been owing more to patient
attention than to any other talent.*

~ Isaac Newton

Our world is not static; it is constantly changing. People walk, clouds drift, rain falls, cars travel, and flowers grow. What would life and living be if we and the world in which we live did not change and progress from one state to another? A world without change is impossible to imagine.

Regardless of the type of change, in each and every instance when change happens, something moves. Whether it is whole objects changing locations or individual objects reforming their shapes, change and motion are intertwined. Stop for a moment and look around. Can you see even one example of a change occurring without motion being involved? The motion may be slow and subtle, like a tree growing. Or the moving objects may be tiny particles too small to see, like electrons moving about on an electric sign. But in all cases, without exception, if something changed, it or some part of it moved.

Understanding motion is fundamental to truly understanding the world around us. With a scientific eye we therefore ask, "What is the nature of motion? Does it take place in a haphazard way? Does it follow a set of well-defined rules? If so, what are those rules?"

Simple examples are often the most instructive. Let's start looking for answers to these ques-

tions by imagining that there is a soccer ball resting motionless in your front yard. You kick it and it bounces down the street, going slower and slower until finally coming to a complete stop a few houses away. Thinking for a moment, you draw a few conclusions about why the ball moved like it did.

First, the ball remained motionless until you kicked it. So you might naturally conclude that nothing will go from being at rest to moving unless there is some sort of force, like a kick, applied to it. This is reasonable, and as it turns out, correct. But why did the ball stop? Perhaps, you surmise, it quit moving because the force from your kick faded out. Indeed, more than two thousand years ago the great Greek philosopher Aristotle wrote:

> *The moving body comes to a standstill when the force which pushes it along can no longer so act as to push it.*[1]

But reflecting for a minute, you conclude that Aristotle's statement cannot be entirely true. Yes, a force is necessary to get a ball to start moving. However, a kick lasts for just a fraction of a second and a ball will stay in motion for a much longer period of time, well after the kick is over.

LEARNING OBJECTIVES

When you finish this chapter you should be able to
- Describe Newton's three laws of motion and how they work together.
- Identify what "state of motion" and "acceleration" are and describe how they relate to each other.
- Explain the relationship between force, mass, and acceleration.
- Use Newton's laws of motion to predict what will happen in simple interactions.

There must be more to this than Aristotle's explanation.

Aristotle, in fact, was in error. While a force of some kind is necessary to create motion, force is not necessary to sustain it. Albert Einstein and Leopold Infeld, in their book *The Evolution of Physics*, explain as follows:

> *"Consider a body at rest, where there is no motion at all. To change the position of such a body it is necessary to exert some influence upon it, to push it or lift it, or let other bodies, such as horses or steam engines, act upon it. Our intuitive idea is that motion is connected with acts of pushing, lifting, or pulling. Repeated experience would make us risk the further statement that we must push harder if we wish to move the body faster. It seems natural to conclude that the stronger the action exerted on a body, the greater will be its speed. A four-horse carriage goes faster than a carriage drawn by only two horses. Intuition thus tells us that speed is essentially connected with action.*
>
> *It is a familiar fact to readers of detective fiction that a false clue muddles the story and postpones the solution. The method of reasoning dictated by intuition was wrong and led to false ideas of motion which were held for centuries.*
>
> *. . . But where does intuition go wrong? . . .*
>
> *Suppose that someone going along a level road with a pushcart suddenly stops pushing. The cart will go on moving for a short distance before coming to rest. We ask: how is it possible to increase this distance? There are various ways, such as oiling the wheels, and making the road very smooth. The more easily the wheels turn and the smoother the road, the longer the cart will go on moving. And just what has been done by the oiling and smoothing? Only this: the external influences have been made smaller. The effect of what is called friction has been diminished . . ."*[2]

Friction is a force or "external influence," that pushes against the motion of the cart. If the cart in the above example were on a perfectly

Aristotle

Aristotle's concept of force being necessary to sustain all motion was thought to be true for nearly 2,000 years.

Galileo Galilei

Galileo understood the law of inertia several decades before Isaac Newton.

♦ **State of Motion**

The condition of an object when no unbalanced forces act upon it. A state of motion always refers to being at rest or in uniform motion.

♦ **Inertia**

The tendency to resist changing a state of motion.

flat, smooth road and all friction were entirely absent, the cart would roll on forever. Similarly, after a soccer ball is kicked it would roll down the street forever if its motion were never opposed by friction or by obstacles in its path. The brilliant Italian scientist Galileo Galilei understood this. In his book, *Discourses and Mathematical Demonstrations Concerning the Two New Sciences,* he wrote:

> . . . [A]ny velocity once imparted to a moving body will be rigidly maintained as long as the external causes of acceleration or retardation are removed* . . .

This basic understanding of motion—that it persists until external forces alter it—was reasonably established as a correct principle by the mid 1600s.

The great early 18th century natural philosopher and mathematician Sir Isaac Newton built upon this foundation. In 1687, at the urging of colleagues, he wrote *Principia Mathematica,* arguably the greatest single work of science ever produced. In it, he laid out what have come to be called Newton's Laws of Motion.

2–1   THE FIRST LAW OF MOTION

The first of Newton's laws, sometimes called **The Law of Inertia,** is a refined statement of the conclusion of Galileo. It can be stated as follows:

> *Every object in a state of rest, or in a state of uniform motion in a straight line with unchanging speed, will stay in that state of rest or of uniform motion, until compelled to do otherwise by forces acting upon it.*

This law establishes a similarity between objects at rest and objects in uniform motion; both respond to force in exactly the same way. It may seem odd that there should be any similarity. What could be more different in the state of motion of an object than moving along ver-

sus standing still? The difference, as it turns out, is in the observer's perspective, and is not a change of the moving object's true physical condition.

For example, if you hold a rock in your hand while you are riding along in a car at freeway speeds, then the rock is "at rest," with respect to you. However, it is not at rest with respect to an observer standing on the shoulder of the freeway watching the car, you, and the rock speeding past. That person would say your handheld rock is moving at 70 miles per hour.

It isn't reasonable that there should be a different law describing the behavior of the rock when you ride with it as opposed to when it is in a car moving past. The rock will obey the same laws of nature regardless of what *you* are doing! Indeed, there *is* no difference, and Newton's first law of motion applies exactly the same to objects in uniform motion as to those at rest. We will refer to either condition (moving uniformly or being at rest) as the object's **state of motion.** Newton's first law can be restated to say that if an object has changed its state of motion, then a force was responsible. In this sense, it *defines* what a force is—something that can change an object's state of motion.

It should be obvious that an object at rest remains at rest if it is left alone, yet the consequences can sometimes be startling. A fun example is pulling a tablecloth off a fully set dinner table and leaving the dinner service undisturbed. The plates and goblets on the table are at rest and will remain at rest unless the tablecloth "compels" them to do otherwise. If the tablecloth is sufficiently smooth, a quick jerk will break the frictional grip it has on the dinner service, which then remains undisturbed as the cloth flies away. A less entertaining manifestation of the law occurs when a stopped car with passengers is struck from behind. The passengers' heads momentarily remain at rest while the car and the rest of their bodies are compelled to move forward by the force of the impact, sometimes with a harmful effect as shown in *Figure 2.2.*

The above examples illustrate **inertia**. A moving object wants to keep moving. An object at rest wants to remain at rest. In both cases the objects are said to possess inertia—the tendency to not change the *status quo.*

The First Law is not obvious because the objects we deal with in everyday life are not free

---

* Galileo reasoned that if a ball rolling downhill gained speed, and a ball rolling uphill lost speed, then a ball rolling on a perfectly flat surface would roll forever at the same speed. In this way he was able to separate the effects of gravity and friction from the natural motion of a moving ball.

SIR ISAAC NEWTON

Isaac Newton (1642–1727) was born on Christmas Day, a weak and frail child. His father, a poor farmer who could not sign his own name, died a few months before Newton's birth. His mother had remarried by the time Newton was three years old, and left him to live with his grandmother. She rejoined him when he was 14 and tried to make a farmer of him, but Newton was already preoccupied with mathematics. At age 18 he enrolled at Cambridge University and began work for the Bachelor of Arts degree. But in 1665 and 1666 Cambridge was closed because of the plague and Newton retreated to his home in Lincolnshire for the duration. It was there that many of the ideas were born that would revolutionize our concept of the world—ideas that justly brought Newton such great fame.

Newton was a complex character who seemed haunted by insecurity, possibly stemming from his childhood. In his lifetime he would develop a powerful new understanding of light and color, invent a new kind of reflecting telescope which had significant advantages over earlier instruments, and explain the motions of the heavens. He would also write some 650,000 words on the subject of alchemy and some 1,300,000 words on Biblical and theological topics (Boorstin, *The Discoverers*, p. 407). He was a Unitarian, but a fellow of Trinity College and found it best, at last, to leave Cambridge to become Master of the Mint from which he drew a comfortable salary. He became president of the Royal Society in 1703, was knighted by Queen Anne in 1705, and for the remainder of his life dominated intellectual life in England.

Alexander Pope summarizes the tribute to Newton with this couplet:

Nature and Nature's laws lay hid in night:
God said, "Let Newton be!" and all was light.

One can juxtapose this with Newton's modest (and, some would say, uncharacteristic) statement to Robert Hooke, "If I have seen further than others it is by standing upon the shoulders of Giants."

Newton shared with Pythagoras a fascination with mathematics as the key to understanding the world. Newton's approach was to summarize his observations of nature into general mathematical statements. To deal with motion and change he had to invent a whole new mathematics, the calculus (which he called the theory of "fluxions"). Although he was a creative genius who was constantly introducing new ideas and explanations, in his own mind he "frame[ed] no hypotheses," meaning that he only summarized in the

Sir Isaac Newton

In 1687 Isaac Newton published in the book *Principia Mathematica* the three laws of motion that bear his name.

formulas what could be confirmed experimentally. He made no attempt to explain the physical reasons that caused the formulas to work.

Newton's great contribution was the ability to see the world in a new way. It occurred to him, after watching an apple fall, that gravitation was not strictly a terrestrial phenomenon, but rather a universal one. He looked at the moon, saw what everyone had seen before him—and suddenly realized that the moon, just like the apple, was a falling object! True, it was moving sideways in its orbit as it fell, thus always missing the earth, but it was falling, pulled toward the earth by the same gravity that pulled the apple toward the earth's center. And with that insight Newton removed the distinction between celestial and terrestrial phenomena.

From Newton's time forward, the bodies of the universe and their motions, be they planets, moons, or atoms, were to be accounted for by universal laws that could be observed in experiments on earth, summarized in mathematical formulae, and then applied, to both understand and predict all the phenomena of the universe. The laws would predict the future of each body in a decisive, deterministic way. In the hands of Newton's followers and the French philosophers who followed Descartes, the world began to assume the characteristics of a giant clockwork whose motions could, in principle, be predicted and which were, therefore, "predestined." This view would dominate the philosophy of science until the twentieth century, when it was discovered that atomic particles do not obey Newton's laws of motion. The modifications to Newton's laws revealed an unpredictable randomness in the world that breaks the deterministic grip that otherwise would rule.

Newton's gift to science was to establish that we can find the laws of nature and use them to understand the system and predict its future. This was, and is, a very powerful idea.

from the influence of forces. Gravity seeks to pull everything down to the earth. Friction acts against motion and, if not opposed by other forces, causes objects to change their state of motion by losing forward speed. Newton and Galileo had the insight to understand that the actual motion of objects on the earth were governed by forces of friction and gravity, but if these forces could be eliminated or cancelled out, their motion would always obey the First Law.

We can test the validity of the First Law by considering the motion of objects in situations where friction is greatly reduced. One can imagine, for example, that an ice skater could glide on forever without ever slowing down if friction between the blades of the ice skates and the ice could be eliminated totally (*Figure 2.1*).

Figure 2.1
An ice skater could go on forever without effort if friction were not present.

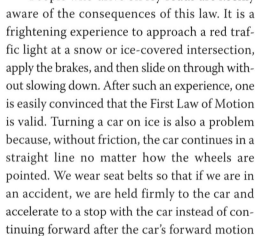

- **Velocity**
The speed and direction of a moving body.

- **Acceleration**
When an object either speeds up or slows down or changes direction.

- **Deceleration**
Acceleration against the direction of motion.

- **Centripetal Acceleration**
The acceleration of turning or changing the direction of motion.

Figure 2.2
Both drivers lose their heads in a rear-end collision. Why?

People who drive on icy roads are keenly aware of the consequences of this law. It is a frightening experience to approach a red traffic light at a snow or ice-covered intersection, apply the brakes, and then slide on through without slowing down. After such an experience, one is easily convinced that the First Law of Motion is valid. Turning a car on ice is also a problem because, without friction, the car continues in a straight line no matter how the wheels are pointed. We wear seat belts so that if we are in an accident, we are held firmly to the car and accelerate to a stop with the car instead of continuing forward after the car's forward motion ends, striking the dashboard or windshield. (*Figure 2.2*).

Successfully driving a car around a corner illustrates another consequence of the law. Let's say a car makes a left turn at a modest speed. In the process a package placed next to the driver slides across the seat to the door. It may seem to a passenger sitting in the back seat that the package has moved outward under the influence of a force, but the truth is that the package, acting in strict accordance with the First Law of Motion, is simply moving straight ahead while the car changes its state of motion under the influence of an inward force! (*Figure 2.3*)

Figure 2.3
Why does the passenger feel "thrown" to the outside of a turn?

2–2 ACCELERATION

The state of motion of an object is given by its **velocity,** which is its speed and direction of motion. **Acceleration** is when the velocity of an object *changes.* Acceleration happens when the object either increases its speed, decreases its speed, or changes the direction in which it is heading. Speeding up is called an **acceleration,** slowing down is called a **deceleration,** and a change in direction is called a **centripetal acceleration,** or acceleration toward the center of a circle. In general, though, a change from uniform motion of any kind is termed an acceleration (*Figures 2.4 and 2.5*).

It is important not to confuse velocity with acceleration. Velocity is distance covered per unit of time, and has a measurement like "miles per hour" or "meters per second." Acceleration is the rate at which speed or direction changes, and has a measurement like "miles per hour per second" or "meters per second per second." This second expression is awkward and is usually converted to "meters per second^2" which is read "meters per second squared."

As an example of how velocity and accel-

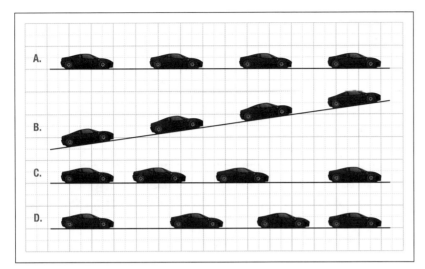

⇦ **Figure 2.4**

Successive pictures, taken at equal time intervals, of a car in four different kinds of motion. Why do we say that the car is accelerating in c and d but not in a and b?

Figure 2.5 ⇧

The puck slides in a circle on an air-hockey table without friction. How do you know it is accelerating? In what direction is the force exerted on the puck by the string?

eration are related, suppose a car is heading due west at 50 miles per hour. The driver then accelerates so that the car is going 70 miles per hour four seconds later. During this change in velocity it accelerated at a rate of 5 miles per hour per second (50 miles per hour + 5 miles per hour per second × 4 seconds = 70 miles per hour). Now suppose the car is traveling at 10 miles per hour and accelerates to 25 miles per hour in five seconds. Its acceleration in this case is 3 miles per hour per second. If it slowed from 50 to 40 miles per hour in 2 seconds the acceleration would be −5 miles per hour per second; the negative sign denoting deceleration.

2-3 FORCE

The intuitive definition of force is that it is a push or pull exerted on one object by another. As previously stated, a more exact definition is offered by the First Law of Motion: force is anything that causes acceleration. All accelerations are caused by forces. If you ever witness an acceleration, you can know with complete certainty that a force of some kind made it happen.

But the corollary is not true. If a force is present it does not have to cause an acceleration. If another force balances it out, there will be a **net force** of zero and no resulting change in the state of motion. Each of us experiences this every day. Gravity exerts a force on you, pulling you toward the ground. But as you sit motionless in your chair you do not accelerate toward the ground because the chair pushes back with an equal force. So the net force on you is zero and

you do not change your state of motion. Therefore, it is more accurate to say accelerations are caused by **unbalanced forces,** the amount of any force that is not cancelled out by other, competing forces.

Unbalanced forces are acting whenever an object moves faster, slower, changes direction, or experiences any combination of speed and direction change. The kind of acceleration caused by a particular force depends on the direction of the force. If a force pushes on an object in the same direction as its motion, the object speeds up like the pitched ball of *Figure 2.6*. It slows down if the force opposes its motion. Lateral forces cause a change in direction with the object turning toward the direction of the force as shown in *Figure 2.5*. The strength of forces is measured in pounds (lb) in the English system of units and newtons (N) in the metric system. A newton is approximately one quarter of a pound.

• **Net Force**

The sum of all the forces present on a body.

• **Unbalanced Forces**

The portion of the total force that is unopposed by other forces and so will cause an acceleration.

Figure 2.6

Both pitcher and catcher exert forces that accelerate the baseball. In which direction is each force applied?

2–4   MASS

Forces cause accelerations, but what determines the *amount* of acceleration? The strength of the force is, of course, a major factor. Stronger forces produce greater accelerations. If a particular force causes an object to accelerate from 20 to 30 miles per hour in 10 seconds, a force twice as strong would cause the same change in half the time. A force half as strong would take 20 seconds to produce the same acceleration.

There is also another factor to be considered. Suppose you run out of gas driving your compact car to work and coast to the side of the road near a pickup truck, which is also out of gas. You and the driver of the pickup truck decide to combine efforts and push one of the vehicles to the nearest gas station. With little thought you both choose to push the compact car, because you know that pushing the pickup would be a lot harder. In other words, an equal amount of pushing force will make the smaller vehicle accelerate more than the larger vehicle.

The property of an object that determines how much it will accelerate in response to an applied force is called **mass**. If mass is larger (*e.g.* the truck), acceleration will be less than if mass is smaller (the car). The smaller the mass, the greater the acceleration will be.

Mass does not depend on location. A particular force applied to a mass causes the same amount of acceleration no matter where the object is located, be it on the surface of Earth, in interstellar space, or anywhere else (*Figure 2.7*). If the same object experiences different accelerations at different places, it is not because the mass has changed, it is because the forces acting on it are different.

Mass should not be confused with **weight**. Weight is a measure of the force of gravity on a particular mass. Weight *does* change with location. This concept is explained more fully in Chapter 3.

2–5   THE SECOND LAW OF MOTION

Exactly how an object accelerates in response to a force is described by Newton's Second Law of Motion. Stated in mathematical terms, this law is:

Force = mass × acceleration

or just

F = ma

The First Law establishes the effects of force and is *qualitative,* or in others words just a *description* of the effect of force. The Second Law is *quantitative*. It says exactly *how much* the state of motion of an object of mass "m" changes when acted upon by a force of magnitude "F." The significance of this law cannot be overstated. It was the first universal principle to be discovered that enables changes observed in our physical world to be described in mathematical terms.

Suppose an object has a mass of 100 kilograms. If it is pushed by a force that causes it to accelerate at a rate of 5 meters per second every second, then the Second Law tells us the force is 100 × 5 = 500 newtons. If the object was originally at rest and this force was in effect for ten

Sidebar

♦ **Mass**
A measure of how a body resists accelerating.

♦ **Weight**
A measure of the force of gravity pulling on an object.

Figure 2.7
A space shuttle (or any object) will accelerate the same for a given force, regardless of location.

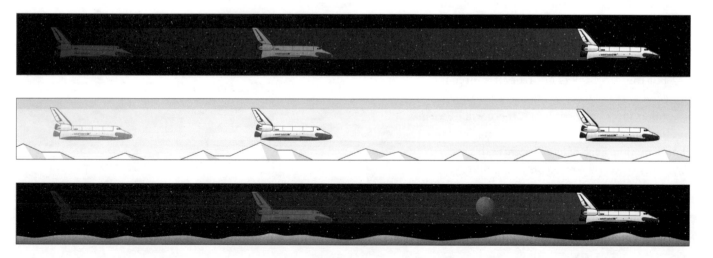

STANDARDS OF MEASUREMENT

As we have already noted in this chapter, mass is the property of objects that determines how much they accelerate in response to a force. To be useful, the concept of mass must be made quantitative. We want to know, for example, whether a sack of potatoes has a mass of one kilogram or two kilograms. Quantities of mass are defined by comparison to some arbitrarily defined standard. The standard measurement of one kilogram has been decreed to be the mass of a specific piece of platinum-iridium which is kept under the watchful care of the Bureau Internationals des Poids et Measures at Sevres, near Paris, France. If you want to know if you have one kilogram of potatoes, you must directly or indirectly compare the mass of your potatoes with the mass of this piece of metal.

Obviously, neither you nor your grocer are going to take that sack of potatoes to France to make sure you're getting exactly one kilogram of spuds. Still, grocers, manufacturers, the Post Office, and even serious dieters, as well as scientists in all disciplines, are vitally concerned about exact weights and measures. To make the process of weighing objects and keeping the weighing standards both exact and practical, copies of the standard kilogram are supplied to government bureaus of standards around the world. Those bureaus, in turn, make exact-weight copies—some of which are split in halves, quarters, etc. You may have seen a box of "weights" in a chemistry laboratory which is the result of this process. One way to compare your potatoes to the standard mass is to place potatoes and standard mass on opposite sides of a balance (scales) and let gravity serve as a standard force. Put your potatoes on one side and keep adding standard masses to the other until balance is achieved. Now add up the standard masses you have used and this will be equal to the mass of the potatoes. You have made your comparison (accurately but indirectly) with the standard kilogram secured in a bell jar in that science repository near Paris.

Length and time must also be given quantitative meaning by comparison to standards. For many years the standard meter was the official measurement of a long bar of metal kept with the standard kilogram in France. The ancient measure of time, when there were no clocks, was done by imprecisely measuring where the sun was in the sky. The invention of clocks allowed greater accuracy, and was soon followed by the "invention" of the "second," which was defined as 1/84,600th of a day. Today we have more precise standards of time and distance which are based on certain characteristics of atoms, rather than the gear-cutting precision of a watch maker. The equations we present in this book are usually presented in a form which requires that a certain consistent set of units be adopted when using the equation. The metric system uses meters, centimeters, and millimeters for length, seconds for time, and kilograms for mass; the English system in popular use in the United States uses feet and inches to measure length, seconds for time, and slugs for mass. Almost all civilized nations have adopted the metric system.

Standard Kilogram

The unit of mass, the kilogram (kg), remains the only base unit in the International System of Units which is still defined in terms of a physical artifact. The standard was manufactured in 1879. It is stored in an evacuated chamber near Paris.

---

seconds, the object will emerge with a velocity of 50 meters per second.

A useful reformulation of this law is:

$$a = F/m$$

This way of writing the Second Law more clearly shows that the acceleration of an object is proportional to force and inversely proportional to mass. If you double the force on an object without changing its mass, the acceleration doubles. If you have two objects, the first of which has twice the mass of the second, and the same force is applied to both of them, the first will accelerate at half the rate as the second. Can you see how this is described by the Second Law?

2–6   THE THIRD LAW OF MOTION

The crowning observation of Newton that completed his fundamental laws of motion, was his statement that **forces occur only when *two* things interact with each other**. Nothing in isolation can exert a force on itself. A car can accelerate only if its wheels touch the road and push against it. If there is no interaction between the tires and the pavement, there is no force and the car does not accelerate. A boat cannot accelerate forward unless its propeller churns against the water. An airplane flies only because the angled propeller blades, or the turbine blades in jet aircraft, push the air behind them as they rotate. The forces that accelerate a rocket result from the contact between the rocket itself and the fuel that is burnt inside it and thrust out behind (*Figure 2.8*).

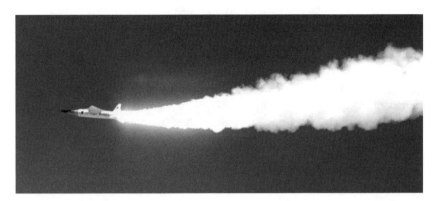

Figure 2.8
This experimental NASA aircraft accelerates forward only because it pushes equally on the exhaust accelerating backwards behind it.

In every interaction two forces arise, one on each of the two interacting bodies. The magnitude of each force is the same but they are oppositely directed. This is the Third Law of Motion and can be stated as follows:

All forces result from interactions between pairs of objects, each object exerting a force on the other. The two resulting forces have the same strength and act in exactly opposite directions.

If you are familiar with this law you might have expected to read "For every action there is an opposite and equal reaction." We avoid using this common phrase because it seems to imply that one force starts the interaction and the other arises as a result. That is not what the Third Law says. The Third Law says that a single-

Figure 2.9
Log rolling requires an understanding of the third law of motion. Can you see why?

sided force cannot exist. When two objects interact, each feels the same force on it but in opposite directions.

In cases where the interacting objects are of comparable mass, the two forces are both readily apparent from the accelerations they cause. For example, as a man steps from a small rowboat to a dock, he is accelerated toward the dock and the boat is accelerated in the opposite direction. When a rifle is fired the slug accelerates from the barrel while the firearm recoils in the opposite direction.

However, if one object has considerably more mass than the other, its resulting acceleration can be so small the force on it *seems* negligible. When you start to walk the force that accelerates you comes from the interaction between your foot and the floor. You push on the floor with your legs and the resulting interaction manifests itself as a forward force on you and a backward force on the floor. As you accelerate forward, the floor accelerates backward. But when have you ever noticed a floor accelerating backward?

The floor is firmly attached to the building, which is attached to Earth. So the floor's effective mass is that of Earth itself. By the Third Law we can write*:

Force of you on the Earth = Force of the Earth on you

The Second Law allows us to substitute mass times acceleration in place of force. So we have:

Earth's mass × Earth's acceleration = Your mass × your acceleration

Earth's mass is 10^{23} times greater than your mass. So by the above equation its acceleration will be 10^{23} times *less* than yours. This amount is too small to be measured, let alone noticed as you sprint to class!

Now, consider what will happen if you step on a banana peel. A slick peel will not cling to the floor, (as cartoons and comics have demonstrated for more than a century). Therefore, the

---

* Strictly speaking we should write

    Force of you on Earth = −Force of Earth on you

The "−" sign in front of a force indicates that it is oppositely directed. Here we are considering only the strength of the force and not its direction, and so we ignore the negative sign.

banana peel will have to be considered for its own mass alone. Now the equation is:

Force of you on the banana peel = Force of the banana peel on you

or

$$\text{Banana peel's mass} \times \text{banana peel's acceleration} = \text{Your mass} \times \text{your acceleration}$$

This time the banana peel, having 1/1000 of your mass, accelerates backward 1000 times more than you accelerate forward. Expecting to go forward, you instead fall flat as the banana peel flies away behind you!

These examples illustrate the interconnectedness of the laws of motion. The Third Law of Motion is a rule about forces. It applies to motion only to the extent that forces and motion are related through the Second Law. The Third Law allows us to equate the forces between any two objects and the Second Law allows us to change the equation to one of masses and accelerations. In this way, the accelerations can be solved and the resulting motion completely understood.

Notice that the laws of motion do not address the nature of forces themselves. They give no information about how forces arise in the first place, nor how strong they will be for any given interaction. This information is expressed by force laws which are unique for each of the four interactions of nature. Gravity is considered in Chapter 3, electromagnetism in Chapter 4, and the nuclear forces in Chapter 25.

References

1. Aristotle, *Mechanics,* 350 BCE.

2. A. Einstein and L. Infield, "The Evolution of Physics" Simon and Schuster, 630 Fifth Avenue, New York, NY, 1938 pp. 6–8.

Chapter Framework

A. Introduction
1. Motion and change
2. Force creates motion

B. The First Law of Motion
1. State of motion
2. Changing a state of motion
3. Inertia

C. Acceleration
1. Change of velocity
2. Speed up
3. Slow down
4. Change direction

D. Force
1. Unbalanced forces
2. Cause of acceleration

E. Mass
1. Mass and acceleration
2. Mass and force
3. Mass and weight

F. The Second Law of Motion
1. F=ma
2. Acceleration proportional to force
3. Acceleration inversely proportional to mass

G. The Third Law of Motion
1. Forces come in pairs
2. Equal strength and opposite direction
3. No single-sided forces

Comprehension

True/False

1. _____ The laws of nature are treated differently for an object in uniform motion and an object at rest.

2. _____ If an object changes its state of motion then it must be accelerating.

3. _____ When an astronaut travels to the moon, his or her weight changes. Therefore, the astronaut's mass must also change.

4. _____ For an object to change its state of motion, an unbalanced force must act on it.

5. _____ Objects that interact to form forces always exert the same force on one another.

Matching
(Choose the law that is most apparent in each scenario)

a. 1st Law
b. 2nd Law
c. 3rd Law

1. _____ A boat glides through the water on a lake at constant speed in a straight line.

2. _____ An airplane circles the airport at a constant speed while waiting to land.

3. _____ A marathon runner begins running faster just before crossing the finish line.

4. _____ Comparing all forces that arise when a book sits on a table.

5. _____ Describing the motion of a bench in the park.

6. _____ Comparing the forces responsible for accelerating a bullet and the recoil of a gun.

7. _____ A hot air balloon rising straight up at a constant speed.

8. _____ A submarine falling straight towards the ocean bottom at a constant speed.

9. _____ Describing the forces created as two boxers' gloves come in contact.

Fill in the blank

1. _____ understood the law of inertia several decades before Newton.

2. If an applied force remains constant, and the object's _____ increases, a smaller acceleration will result.

3. _____ is the speed and direction of a moving object.

4. Acceleration is when the _____ of an object changes.

Analysis

1. Which of the following is correct for rocket propulsion? (You should find it helpful to know that rocket motors function perfectly well in the vacuum of space where there is no air.)

    a) The rocket shoots out gases which push on the air. The air pushing back on the rocket moves the rocket.

    b) The rocket pushes back on its own exhaust gases. These gases pushing on the rocket are responsible for the acceleration of the rocket.

    c) The motion of the exhaust gases leaves a vacuum in the air which occurs in the region in the front of the rocket. The air in this reduced pressure region pulls the rocket forward.

    d) The gases expelled from the rear of the rocket cause lower pressure regions behind the rocket. This low pressure pushes the rocket. This effect is particularly effective in a vacuum where there is zero pressure in front of the rocket.

2. When a body is acted upon by a single constant unbalanced force,

    a) it will move with a constant speed in the direction of the force.

    b) it will experience a constant acceleration in the direction of the force.

    c) it will accelerate in a direction perpendicular to the force.

    d) its resulting acceleration will increase at a constant rate.

3. If an object is moving in a straight line at a constant speed, which of the following **must** be true?

    a) there is a constant force acting in the direction the object is moving.

    b) there is a steadily increasing force acting in the direction the object is moving.

    c) the total force on the object is zero.

    d) the body is experiencing no frictional forces.

Synthesis

1. Restate Newton's laws in your own words.

2. If velocity is zero, does acceleration have to be zero? If acceleration is zero, does velocity need to be zero? Give an example to illustrate your answers.

3. If there is a constant net force on an object that starts out at rest, what happens to its speed?

4. When you drive, the engine generates a constant force as long as you give the car a constant amount of gas. Why doesn't your car accelerate at a constant rate like described in the previous question?

5. Give an example of a situation where it is important to use Newton's Third Law.

6. A rubber chicken thrown into the road hits a car moving 60 mph.

   a) Upon contact, does the car or the chicken experience the greater force?

   b) Does the car or the chicken experience the greatest acceleration?

   c) Using Newton's Second and Third Law reconcile your answers for (a) and (b).

7. What two forces on Earth make Newton's First Law difficult to see? How do they prevent most objects from traveling in uniform motion?

8. How do force and mass affect acceleration?

9. A semi-truck going 70 mph runs into a patch of black ice and glides across the ice. No unbalanced forces (such as friction) are present on the truck.

   a) What type of motion does the truck experience after encountering the ice?

   b) What law applies to the scenario?

   c) If the patch of completely frictionless ice extended in front of the truck for six miles, what is the truck's speed right before reaching the end of the ice patch?

10. During a football game, a wide receiver that only weighs 160 lbs catches the football on a short curl route. From the receiver's blind side, a 270-lb line backer running full speed hits the receiver causing the linebacker's speed to slightly decrease and knocking the receiver into the stands.

   a) What type of motion does the linebacker experience when hitting the receiver?

   b) What type of motion does the receiver experience when hit by the linebacker?

   c) Compare the accelerations of the two players.

Use Newton's 2nd and 3rd laws to explain your answers.

11. A rocket in space has a constant unbalanced force on it. The force is applied to the rocket indefinitely.

   a) Describe the rocket's motion. What will happen to rocket's speed?

   b) Which of Newton's laws apply to this scenario?

   c) If the unbalanced force comes from a rocket engine that ejects gases from the rocket, how does this change your answers for (a)?

12. Lindsay pushes the back of a tricycle that her sister, Sunny, sits on. They both head straight home with progressively increasing speed.

   a) Analyze the motion of the tricycle by doing the following:

      i. Describe the tricycle's motion. Is it uniform or accelerated?

      ii. Identify which law(s) of motion apply.

      iii. Identify all forces that are acting on the tricycle and which of these forces influence the tricycle's motion. A labeled diagram with arrows representing forces is often helpful here.

      iv. Compare the size of relevant forces. Are the forces balanced or unbalanced?

   b) Use Newton's 3rd law to compare the size of the force Lindsay exerts on the tricycle to the force the tricycle exerts on Lindsay. Explain how the tricycle and Lindsay can both be speeding up in the same direction taking into account the 3rd law.

   c) If Sunny jumps off the tricycle while Lindsay keeps pushing with the same force, what will happen?

13. In a car crash between a small car and an SUV, the occupants of the small car are much more likely to be injured. Use Newton's laws to explain why.

14. Use Newton's laws to explain how safety features in cars like seat belts, crumple-zones (places where the car's frame is designed to bend in a crash), and air bags reduce the risk of injury in a crash.

15. A boy is standing on a skateboard at rest. The boy jumps forward off of the skateboard.

   a) Which of Newton's Laws apply to this situation?

   b) What happens to the boy and to the skateboard?

   c) What would happen if the boy jumped off sideways? Why are the situations different?

THE GRAVITATIONAL INTERACTION

Millions saw the apple fall,
but Newton asked why.

~ Bernard Baruch

Everything moves in accordance with the laws of motion, under the influence of forces, while the forces themselves arise from interactions. In the days of Aristotle, it was generally thought that there were two fundamental interactions, gravity and levity. Gravity caused things to somehow fall to Earth, and levity caused things to somehow rise to the heavens. Rocks, it was believed, possessed gravity and therefore naturally descended to Earth when dropped in order to be with other similar material. Fire, on the other hand, was said to possess levity, because it always leaped skyward, yearning to return to its home, the eternal burnings of heaven, which was the ancients' explanation for the stars.

It was a good beginning. The theory of levity would disappear under the gaze of scientific inquiry to reemerge as the buoyant force to be discussed in chapter 6. Instead of being a fundamental interaction itself, the buoyant force results from how forces from the electromagnetic and gravitational interactions spread throughout a fluid. The ancient concept of gravity, though, has turned out to be a fundamental interaction, giving us insights into the nature of space and time beyond anything imagined by the Greeks when they first conceived of it!

In this chapter we will consider gravity. We will examine its strength and behavior on the objects here on Earth's surface. We will study how it changes with mass and distance and how it keeps the Moon orbiting Earth. At the end of the chapter we will discuss the nature of gravitational interaction itself, and how it gives rise to forces.

3-1   FALLING OBJECTS

You probably have hiked to a mountaintop or up to the brink of a steep cliff and thrown a rock off into space, watching and listening as it fell, trying to hear it hit bottom. There is something fascinating about seeing a rock fall away under the pure influence of wind and gravity. Did you notice how it moved as it fell? Did it seem to fall at a constant speed or did fall faster with time? From the perspective of looking down from the top of a cliff, it may have been hard to tell.

There is a law describing how the force of gravity changes with mass and distance. This law, discovered by Isaac Newton, is used with his Laws of Motion, discussed in Chapter 2, to predict how bodies move under gravity's influ-

LEARNING OBJECTIVES

When you finish this chapter you should be able to

- Describe the motion of objects falling in the absence of friction.
- Describe how the acceleration of gravity affects bodies with initial upward or sideways motion.
- Discuss how gravity explains orbiting bodies.
- Differentiate between mass and weight.
- Describe the universal law of gravitation and discuss how it was discovered.
- Use the universal law of gravitation to predict the forces felt by bodies of different mass near the surface of Earth.
- Describe how Henry Cavendish determined the universal gravitational constant.
- State briefly the physical interpretation of gravity put forth by Einstein.

ence. Because all objects on Earth feel a force from gravity, Newton had to disentangle its effects from the motion he witnessed around him before he could derive the Laws of Motion. He could not do this without understanding gravity's effect, so his knowledge of both the laws of gravity and motion emerged at the same time.

The rock you tossed over the cliff fell with increasing speed. If we could make careful measurements, we would find that if nothing such as air friction opposed its fall, the increase in speed would be the constant value of 9.8 m/sec each second. After one second of falling its speed would be 9.8 m/sec. After 2 seconds it would be 19.6 m/sec. After 3 seconds it would be 29.4 m/sec, and so on. The speed would increase at a rate of 9.8 m/sec every second it fell unimpeded. This rate of acceleration is designated by the symbol **g**. In more familiar units **g** is 32 feet/sec^2 or about 22 miles/hour/sec.

Table 3.1 on the next page lists the acceleration rates of and distances covered for an object falling unopposed by friction for 10 seconds. (How friction changes this table is considered in Chapter 5.) Notice that the value in the acceleration column does not change with time

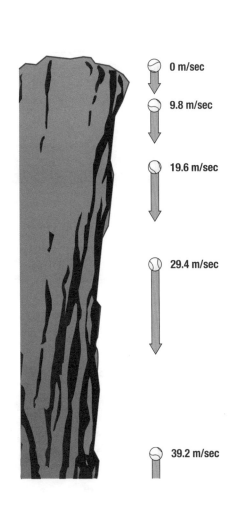

0 m/sec

9.8 m/sec

19.6 m/sec

29.4 m/sec

39.2 m/sec

Figure 3.1
Objects fall with increasing speed but constant acceleration if there is no friction.

because **g** is constant. Under this steady acceleration a speed of 220 miles per hour is reached in only 10 seconds!

3–2 UNIFORM ACCELERATION

The Second Law of Motion says that for all objects accelerating under the influence of any force, the relation

$$F = m \times a$$

holds true. For objects accelerating under the influence of gravity, we can write

$$F = m \times g$$

Let's examine that equation. In the previous chapter we talked about how acceleration arises from forces applied to objects of a given mass. In that discussion "m" was always fixed and we considered how "F" and "a" were proportional to each other: increase the force and the acceleration would also increase by the same factor. In the example we are discussing here the mass of the rock falling off a cliff is constant and so is its acceleration. Therefore by the Second Law of Motion the force on it must also be constant. A 10 kg rock tossed off a cliff will experience an acceleration of 9.8 m/sec every second and will therefore feel a force of 98 newtons. The force on it will be 98 newtons all the way to the bottom of the cliff.

Tossing a rock off a cliff is a simple act. Yet it teaches us that the force of gravity is constant for any given object as it falls, at least over the height of a typical cliff. If the acceleration had increased near the bottom of the cliff, then the force would have been greater at the bottom than at the top.

Now imagine throwing a ball straight up with an initial speed of 35 m/sec (about 80 miles/hr). Instead of speeding up, the ball moves slower as it rises since the force of gravity is opposing its motion. The amount of acceleration is the same as before because the strength of the gravitational force does not depend on whether the ball is going up or down. After 1 second of upward motion, the ball's speed is 35–9.8 = 25.2 m/sec. At the end of another second the speed has been reduced to 25.2–9.8 = 15.4 m/sec; after 3 seconds, it is 5.6 m/sec; and after just 4 seconds in the air,

Figure 3.2

The acceleration caused by gravity is constant regardless of the direction of motion. The rate a cannonball slows while traveling upward is the same rate it speeds up when coming down.

Gravity

Velocity

Table 3.1 – *A Falling Body in the Absence of Friction*

The distance, velocity, and acceleration of a falling body in the absence of friction. Velocity is presented in units of miles per hour as well as in the more standard units of meters per second.

Time (seconds)	Distance (meters)	Velocity (m/sec)	Velocity (miles/hr)	Acceleration (m/sec²)
0	0	0	0	9.8
1	4.9	9.8	22	9.8
2	19.6	19.6	44	9.8
3	44.1	29.4	66	9.8
4	78.4	39.2	88	9.8
5	122.5	49.0	110	9.8
6	176.4	58.8	132	9.8
7	240.1	68.6	154	9.8
8	313.6	78.4	176	9.8
9	396.9	88.2	198	9.8
10	490.0	98.0	220	9.8

its direction has changed and its speed is now 4.2 m/sec *downward*. From here the ball's downward speed increases each second by 9.8 m/sec.

Now suppose the ball is thrown horizontally instead of vertically, with an initial speed of 15 m/sec as indicated in *Figure 3.3*. This time it follows a curved path as it falls. Curved motion appears more complicated, but can be simplified by separating the path of the ball into horizontal and vertical components. At the end of the first second, the ball is still moving horizontally with a speed of 15 m/sec, but in addition it is falling with a vertical speed of 9.8 m/sec downward. After another second, the downward speed has increased to 19.6 m/sec, while the horizontal motion remains unchanged. As things progress the horizontal part of the motion never changes, while the downward velocity continues to increase at the rate of 9.8 m/sec every second because the force of gravity pulls only in that direction. This change in the downward speed of the ball is the same as if the ball had no initial motion at all. It may not be obvious, but two balls positioned at the same height, with one dropped at the same instant as the second ball is thrown horizontally, will hit the ground at the same time because the downward acceleration on both is the same.

In all three examples, dropping a rock, throwing a ball into the air, and throwing a ball horizontally, the initial velocities are all differ-ent but the accelerations, and therefore the way the velocities change, are all the same.

3-3 WEIGHT AND ACCELERATION

Now suppose you were to drop both a basketball-sized boulder and a baseball-sized rock from the same height. You might expect the boulder to drop more rapidly than the rock, because it is much heavier. But upon dropping the two rocks you find that, despite their great difference in size and weight, their accelerations are exactly the same. Their weights do not affect how they accelerate!

Look again at Newton's Second Law of Motion. The large boulder has greater mass than the smaller rock so it is harder to accelerate. Yet they both accelerate at the same rate so the force on the boulder has to be greater than the force on the rock. Thus the simple act of tossing a rock and a boulder off a cliff teaches us that the force of gravity is proportional to the mass of the object being attracted.

You are familiar with this, of course. More massive things weigh more and **weight** just refers to the force of gravity on an object. Weight and mass are exactly proportional. If the mass of one object is two times the mass of another,

• **Weight**
The force of gravity on an object.

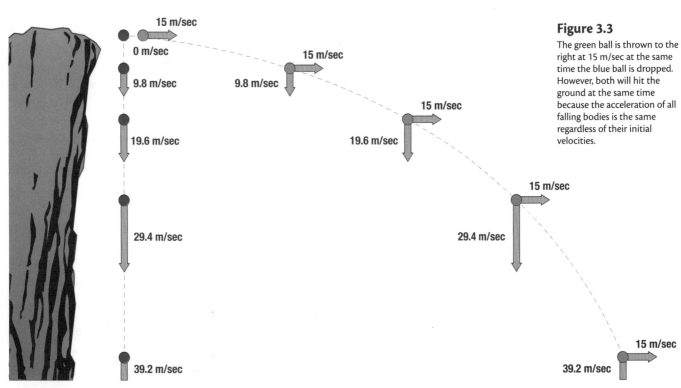

Figure 3.3
The green ball is thrown to the right at 15 m/sec at the same time the blue ball is dropped. However, both will hit the ground at the same time because the acceleration of all falling bodies is the same regardless of their initial velocities.

its weight is exactly twice as great. When you step on a scale, you are really measuring the force of gravity on you. This is an acceptable mass estimate only because of this proportionality.*

We must point out that objects all fall at the same rate of acceleration, regardless of their weight, only if the resistance from air can be ignored. The effect of air friction, considered in more detail in chapter 5, will cause lighter objects, like a leaf, to accelerate more slowly than a heavier rock. But even light objects such as feathers and leaves have exactly the same acceleration when they fall in the absence of air resistance. Any two objects, lead weights or popcorn, when dropped in a vacuum simultaneously from the same height, will hit the ground at the same time, traveling at the same speed.

Hopefully you made certain no one was at the base of the cliff before tossing the boulder off! You know from experience, of course, that a falling boulder lands with more force than a small rock does and could cause serious injury. The above discussion just quantifies this common sense.

Figure 3.4
In the absence of friction all objects fall with the same acceleration regardless of their mass.

3–4 CIRCULAR MOTION AND THE MOON'S ORBIT

The Italian scientist Galileo Galilei, so the story goes, proved that all objects fell at the same rate by dropping two unequal masses off the leaning Tower of Pisa. He probably did not do that actual experiment but he did know gravity's acceleration is constant for all things, and so did Newton, experimenting a century later, in a much more science-friendly society. But how do you go from this beginning to a law describing the force of gravity?

A popular but rather absurd legend claims that Newton saw an apple fall in his orchard and thus "discovered" gravity. What Newton did was look with a questioning mind at falling objects like apples and other things and then ask if the interaction that made these common things fall was the same interaction that held the Moon in its orbit. Up to that time the motion of the

Moon was considered to be unrelated to the way things were affected by gravity on Earth. The Moon was thought to be embedded in some mysterious cosmic material that kept it firmly in place, much like a marble affixed inside a spinning sphere of glass centered on the Earth.

Newton used rigorous mathematics to show that if the following two hypotheses were true, then the interaction of gravity alone was responsible for pulling apples to Earth and holding the Moon in its orbit:

1. The force of Earth's gravity on the Moon is perpendicular to the Moon's motion.

2. The force of gravity diminishes with distance as $1/d^2$ where "d" is the distance between the centers of any two gravitating bodies; Earth and an apple on the one hand, or Earth and the Moon on the other.

Our Moon circles Earth in an almost perfect circle every 27.3 days. Its speed is roughly uniform but the direction of travel is constantly curving in accordance with a centripetal acceleration pointed at Earth. In Chapter 2 we learned that when an object changes its direction of travel there must be a net sideways force acting on it. It doesn't matter if it is a ball twirled on the end of a string, a child on a merry-go-round, a car turning a circular corner or the Moon in its orbit. All experience an acceleration caused by a force directed toward the center of the circular path.

Newton pointed out that if a cannon on the edge of a cliff were fired horizontally, the cannonball would accelerate downward in an arc, like the green ball in *Figure 3.3*. If the projectile were fired faster, it would travel farther horizontally before hitting the ground. In a wonderful intuitive leap, Newton pointed out that if the cannonball were fired fast enough from a tall-enough mountain, that it would *never* hit the ground, because Earth's round surface would curve away at the same rate the cannonball fell. The cannonball would be forever falling but its forward velocity would never let it land; it would be in orbit! The Moon was doing just that. Its forward speed is such that it always remains the same distance from Earth.

Newton realized that to calculate the orbital acceleration of the moon and have it agree with the value of **g**, only a force law that diminished as the distance squared would work. The Moon's

---

* Actually, you are measuring the force of the scale pushing back on you, which is equal to the force of gravity pulling down on you so long as you are standing still. Read more on this in Chapter 5.

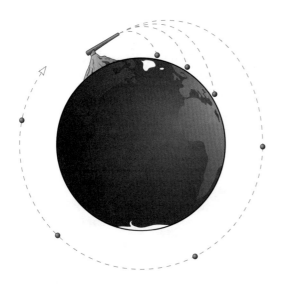

Figure 3.5
Going in orbit or falling to the ground only depends on how much horizontal velocity the projectile has.

centripetal acceleration is 1/3,600 the acceleration of an object falling near Earth's surface, so Earth's pull on the Moon must be only 1/3,600 as strong as it would be if the Moon were moved to the Earth's surface. The Moon is 60 times farther from Earth's center than Earth's surface is, so gravity diminishes as $1/60^2 = 1/3600$.

3–5 GRAVITY AND THE THIRD LAW OF MOTION

Newton's Third Law of Motion says that two forces arise from any interaction between bodies, one force acting on each of the bodies. Throwing a rock off a cliff clearly shows the acceleration from the force of Earth on the rock. What about Earth itself? The rock is pulling up on Earth at the same time Earth is pulling down. Does Earth accelerate toward the rock in response? Yes. But as we discussed in Chapter 2, Newton's Second Law tells us the amount of acceleration on Earth is inversely proportional to its mass and therefore is so tiny it can hardly be measured, much less observed.

But consider the Moon. Its gravity pulls on Earth with the same force that Earth's gravity is pulling on it. With a mass of only 1.2% of Earth's mass, the Moon does most of the accelerating. But while the Moon's mass is considerably less than Earth's, it is still enough to make Earth accelerate noticeably. As a result, as Earth circles the Sun it wobbles in and out of its orbit,

pulled always toward whichever side the Moon is on. Another noticeable effect is lunar tides. Ocean surfaces bulge upward, causing high tides, as the Moon passes overhead pulling the water that direction.

Newton understood that gravity between two objects depends on the mass of both objects, not just one or the other. By looking at the symmetry inherent in the Third Law of Motion, Newton inferred that if the force of gravity on a boulder falling to Earth was proportional to the mass of the boulder, then Earth's mass ought to be proportional to the force as well. He theorized that just as rocks with half the mass feel half the force, a planet with half the mass would create a gravitational attraction that is also half as strong. With this realization, the foundation for a universal law of gravity was finally complete.

3–6 THE LAW OF UNIVERSAL GRAVITATION

In sections 3–5 and 3–4 we determined the following two important facts. First, the force of gravity is proportional to both the masses of the objects on which it acts. Second, this force weakens as the square of the distance between their centers.

With these insights, Newton suggested the rule called the **Law of Universal Gravitation**, or just the **Law of Gravity**. It can be stated as follows:

> Every object in the universe attracts every other object by a long-range gravitational interaction that obeys Newton's Third Law. The strength of the attractive force, F, varies with the masses, M and m, of the two objects and the distance, d, between their centers according to the relationship

$$F = GmM/d^2$$

The number G that appears in the equation is the **gravitational constant.** G relates the amount of mass to the strength of the force. In Newton's day no one knew the value of G. It can only be found through experiment and is so small, 6.67×10^{-11} in the metric system of units, that the mutual attractive gravitational force between two 100-kilogram balls placed 30 centimeters apart is equivalent to the weight of only

• **The Law of Gravity**

The mathematical formula $F=GmM/d^2$ which describes the strength of the force of gravity between two objects of mass M and m separated between their centers by the distance d.

• **Gravitational Constant**

A number relating the strength of the gravitational force to the masses being attracted and their distance apart.

0.01 grams of mass. Only if one of the interacting objects has a large mass, like Earth, does the force become appreciable.

The first public test of Newton's universal law of gravity (and his laws of motion as well) came when he used them to successfully calculate the time and place of the return of a comet which the great English astronomer, Sir Edmund Halley, suspected was orbiting the Sun. When "Halley's" comet appeared just as Newton had predicted, the science of using mathematics based on universal laws to know future motion was born.

Using the heavens as a testing ground was successful. But one could still argue that gravity emanated only from the Sun and planets and was not present in ordinary objects, such as buildings or rocks. It was a leap of faith for Newton to hypothesize, without being able at that time to prove it, that a force of gravity universally exists between any and all objects that have mass. This aspect of the law was not confirmed until more than 70 years after Newton's death by Henry Cavendish (1731–1810), who developed a method of measuring the minute gravitational attraction between such ordinary objects as two large lead balls.

In Newton's day no one knew what the mass of Earth was. So there were two unknown values, G and M, in any formula expressing the force of Earth's gravity. An experiment was needed to measure the force of gravity between two known masses so that the value of G would be the only unknown value and could be calculated. In the late 1700s the shy, eccentric Cavendish did just that.

Cavendish used two small gold or platinum spheres mounted on opposite ends of a lightweight metal bar suspended in the middle by a very fine wire. The wire had a mirror mounted in the middle of it. A focused light beam reflected off the mirror and onto a scale across the room. As two large lead spheres were brought near the small spheres, the gravitational attraction between the small and large spheres twisted the wire just enough to move the light spot on the scale. The spot's movement could then be seen by observers. In this way the force required to twist the wire was determined, the force between the large and small spheres was inferred, and the Universal Law of Gravitation was used to calculate G from $G = Fd^2/Mm$.

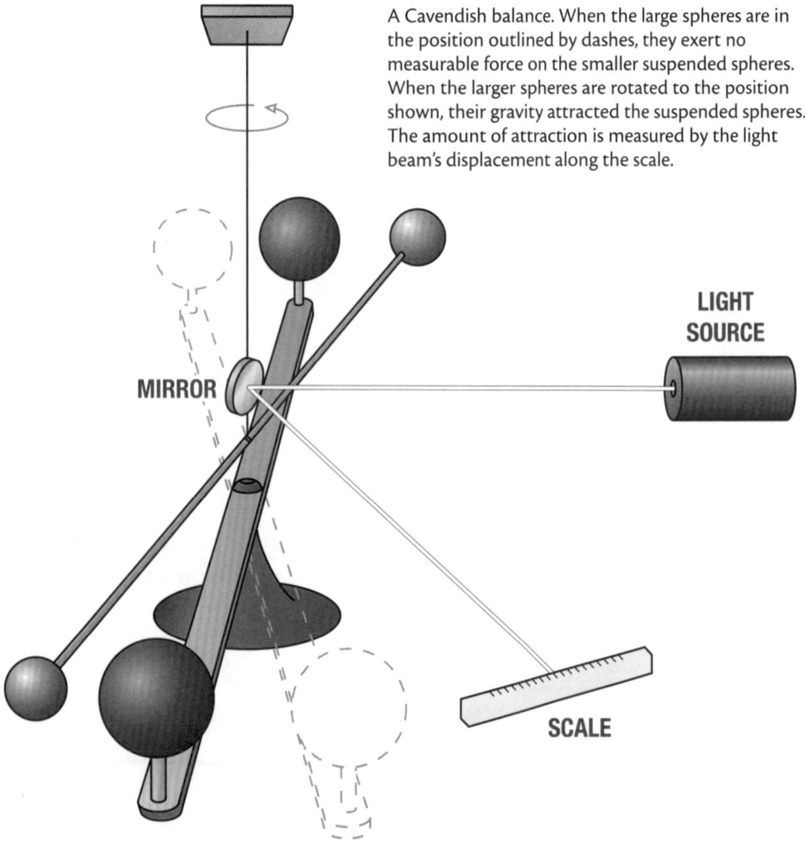

Figure 3.6

A Cavendish balance. When the large spheres are in the position outlined by dashes, they exert no measurable force on the smaller suspended spheres. When the larger spheres are rotated to the position shown, their gravity attracted the suspended spheres. The amount of attraction is measured by the light beam's displacement along the scale.

3-7 ACCELERATION REVISITED

There is a final point regarding the value of the acceleration of gravity, **g,** that needs to be cleared up. At the beginning of the chapter we found that **g** did not change for a rock as it fell off a cliff. Every second its velocity increased by the same amount. From this we concluded the force on the rock was the same at the top of the cliff as at the bottom. But the Law of Gravity clearly says the force of gravity gets stronger as the distance between objects decreases. Therefore **g** should be larger at the bottom of the cliff than at the top!

As it turns out, the force of gravity *is* stronger at the base of the cliff than at the top by the amount that the Law of Gravity predicts, but the effect is very slight. For example, a beach at sea-level is 6,378 km from Earth's center. The top of a one-kilometer high cliff by this beach is 6,379 km from Earth's center. The difference in the force felt by a one kilogram rock between the bottom and the top of the cliff is

$$\frac{G\left(\begin{array}{c}\text{mass of}\\\text{Earth}\end{array}\right)(1\text{ kg})}{(6378)^2} - \frac{G\left(\begin{array}{c}\text{mass of}\\\text{Earth}\end{array}\right)(1\text{ kg})}{(6379)^2} = 0.0027 \text{ newtons}$$

This amount of difference can be easily measured with sensitive instruments but is too slight to be noticed without them. It is better to say the height of a cliff, even one 10 miles high, is too short to sample a *significant* difference in the force of gravity and the resultant acceleration. We will therefore treat the gravitational force and the value of **g** as being constant "near Earth's surface" and only consider the $1/d^2$ decrease when examining objects located at distances from Earth's surface far greater than any we would encounter in normal life, such as rocket ships, satellites and the Moon.*

Treating a value as being constant because it does not change significantly over the area of interest is a common practice in science. Many fundamental values in nature such as G, the speed of light, the mass and charge of electrons, etc. are thought to be constant because all measurements of them find the same value within the parameters allowed by experimental error. They probably are truly constant, but scientists still conduct experiments to make certain they don't change with time or place. Other constants, like **g** or the speed of sound, vary a little depending on circumstances, but they will be considered constants in this text.

3-8 GRAVITY AND CURVED SPACE-TIME

Newton's Universal Law of Gravity was an enormous advancement in scientific inquiry as well as in our understanding of the interactions governing the universe. The Law of Gravity gave rise to the science of celestial mechanics, which allowed scientists to predict positions of planets, times of eclipses, and even the tides with greater accuracy than before. The "theory" of gravity soon became "law" and its truthfulness ceased to be questioned.

---

* In making this assumption we are accepting an error of about 0.5%. Earth is not a perfect sphere, Its poles are about 21 km closer to its center than is sea level at the Equator. This causes the gravitational force and acceleration to change slightly from place to place. Gravity is about 0.5% percent stronger at Earth's North and South Poles than at the Equator and slightly smaller (about 0.03% per kilometer) at higher elevations.

Newton and others realized, though, that this law gave no insights into how gravity could act across empty space. When the Moon was thought to be embedded in a cosmic material there was no problem; forces in this material kept the Moon in orbit. But with the law of gravitation arose the notion that such a binding material need not exist. Space could be empty and still, somehow, transmit a force between objects that do not touch. How is that possible?

Albert Einstein (1879–1955) proposed in 1915 a radical model for gravity in his general theory of relativity. Bothered by gravity being a "spooky action at a distance" he sought to derive the Law of Gravity from principles that gave insight into why it arose. He started by pointing out that Newton set up two independent ways of defining mass. The first was with his Second Law, F = ma, which allows mass to be measured by seeing how an object accelerates when pushed. The second was with the Law of Gravity, which allows mass to be measured by seeing how much force Earth exerts on the same object. Nothing in Newton's laws requires that those masses have the same value. Einstein, guided by Occam's razor, *postulated* that it would be simpler if those masses were the same, a fact that has now been verified by experiment to high precision.

This postulate led to the prediction that space and matter are interconnected. Exactly how it does this is beyond the scope of this textbook. Nonetheless, it is insightful to show how the general theory of relativity explains the cause of gravity through Newton's laws of motion, particularly the First Law.

Recall that the First Law says objects drifting in empty space go straight without accelerating. Einstein theorized that orbiting objects are doing just that, going straight through space and time. However a large body like Earth *affects the space and time surrounding it,* causing them to "curve." When the Moon moves, it follows the straightest possible path through *curved* space and time, which happens to be an orbit. Massive objects extend a gravitational influence by altering the space that surrounds them!

The curving takes place in the four dimensions of space and time and is impossible to visualize fully. It can be illustrated in two dimensions by stretching a rubber sheet across a wire hoop and placing a heavy ball bearing in the middle,

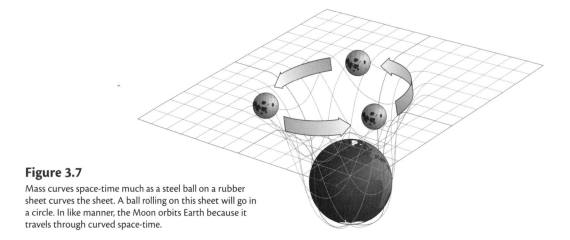

Figure 3.7

Mass curves space-time much as a steel ball on a rubber sheet curves the sheet. A ball rolling on this sheet will go in a circle. In like manner, the Moon orbits Earth because it travels through curved space-time.

as shown by *Figure 3.7*. The ball bearing causes the sheet to sag so that a smaller bead rolling on the edge will naturally curve around in a circle. By analogy, the Moon bends in a circle around Earth, following the curve in space and time placed there by Earth.

An extraordinary claim like this demands extraordinary proof. Predictions of this theory have been tested in laboratories worldwide, passing each and every time. The global positioning system used by navigators and hikers uses this theory to create accurate positions. Perhaps the most stark and irrefutable demonstration is *Figure 3.8*, which shows the image of a cluster of galaxies containing an incredible amount of mass. Light from more distant galaxies serendipitously located behind the cluster curves through the space surrounding it, forming the arcs seen surrounding the cluster. Curved space and time is the only possible explanation for this visual phenomenon.

The amount of mass density determines the amount of curvature. Extreme density leads to extreme space curvature and this in turn leads to the concept of black holes, a subject covered in Chapter 33.

If you consider the idea of curved space and

time to be incomprehensible, you are in good company. It is not entirely clear to even the most advanced thinkers exactly what this means physically, so don't be distressed. We do know, though, that the theory works beautifully and tells us there is much to be learned about the nature of mass, space, and time.

Figure 3.8

An image of the dense galaxy cluster ABell 2218. There are distant galaxies located behind the cluster. Light from these galaxies bends as it passes by the cluster because the cluster's mass curves the space-time surrounding it. The bent light is seen as arcs on the sides of the cluster.

Chapter Framework

A. Falling Objects
1. **g** = acceleration caused by gravity
2. **g** = $9.8 m/sec^2$ = $32 ft/sec^2$ = $22 mi/hr/sec$

B. Uniform Acceleration
1. F = m × g
2. Gravity causes a constant downward acceleration
3. Gravity and horizontal motion

C. Weight and Acceleration
1. Relationship between mass and weight
2. Acceleration is independent of mass and weight

D. Circular Motion and the Moon's Orbit
1. Newton, an apple, and the Moon
2. Gravity acts perpendicular to the Moon's velocity
3. Gravity diminishes as $1/distance^2$
4. Falling and orbiting

E. Gravity and the Third Law of Motion
1. Gravity depends on the mass of both objects

F. The Law of Universal Gravitation
1. F = GmM/d2
2. The gravitational constant
3. Predicting "Halley's Comet"
4. Henry Cavendish

G. Acceleration Revisited
1. Changes in **g**
2. Constants and significance difference

H. Gravity and Curved Space-Time
1. Albert Einstein
2. How mass affects space-time

Comprehension

True/False
1. _____ A small ball is dropped from the edge of a cliff. One-tenth of a second later a much heavier ball is dropped from the same position. Ignoring the effects of air friction, the second ball overtakes the first.
2. _____ Although the moon is so far away, it's gravitational pull still affects Earth.
3. _____ The force of gravity increases between objects as they get farther away from each other.
4. _____ Because the Moon orbits Earth at a constant speed, it travels in uniform motion.
5. _____ A cannon ball weighs more, requiring much less force to "fall" towards Earth at the same rate as a marble.

Fill in the Blank
1. Newton and Cavendish both contributed to proving the _____.
2. An object with great enough mass can cause a _____ in space and time.

3. The moon orbits because it has a _____ force acting on it.

Matching
1. _____ The force of gravity on an object.
2. _____ The mathematical formula $F=GMm/d^2$ that describes the strength of the force of gravity between two objects of mass M and m separated between their centers by the distance d.
3. _____ The symbol representing the acceleration caused by gravity. It is equal to 22 mi/hour per second or 32 ft/second per second or 9.8 m/sec per second depending on the units.

a. *g*
b. *Weight*
c. *The Law of Gravity*

Analysis

1. If a feather and a brick are dropped at the same height in a vacuum, then
   a) the brick hits the ground first.
   b) they hit at the same time.
   c) the feather hits the ground first.

2. When is the force of gravity greatest on a rock?
   a) when at the top of a cliff.
   b) when it is falling down the cliff.
   c) when it is just about to hit the ground.
   d) when it is resting on the ground.

3. Jane throws a rock horizontally off a cliff. How fast is the rock traveling downward after 5 seconds?
   a) 22 mph
   b) 88 mph
   c) 110 mph
   d) 132 mph

4. Using the Principle of Position Symmetry, the gravitational force on an object near another planet would
   a) be less than on the object than if it were near the earth.
   b) be the same on the object as if it were near the earth.
   c) be greater on object than if it were near the earth.
   d) depend on the masses of the planet and the object and the the square of the distance.

5. A baseball player throws a baseball horizontally at 100 mph. You drop a penny at the exact same height immediately after the ball leaves the baseball player's hand, Air friction is negligible. Which of the following is true?
   a) The baseball has greater velocity than the penny.
   b) The penny hits the ground first.
   c) The baseball has a greater force on it than the penny.
   d) They both have the same acceleration.
   e) Two of the above are true.

Synthesis

1. Why does an object weigh less on the surface of the moon than on Earth's surface?

2. The Sun has much more mass than Earth (about 330,000 times as much). Why aren't we pulled toward the Sun with 330,000 times as much force as we are toward Earth?

3. Compare the weights of an object in four locations:

   a) On the Earth's surface.

   b) In orbit around the Earth at an altitude of about 100 miles.

   c) On the moon's surface.

   d) Outside the solar system far from any planet.

4. How does the mass of the object in the previous exercise change as it is taken to the same three locations?

5. Compare the definitions of weight and mass. Why does the weight of an object change from place to place while the mass does not?

6. A cannonball, originally at rest, and a marble, originally at rest, are dropped in a vacuum from the same height at the same time.

   a) What happens when they are dropped? Compare the speed and acceleration of the cannonball with that of the marble.

   b) Is the gravitational force of attraction larger on the cannonball than it is on the marble? Justify your answer using a fundamental law.

   c) Does the cannonball require a larger force to provide the same acceleration as the marble? Justify your answer using the Second Law of Motion.

   d) Show that your answers to (a), (b), and (c) are consistent with each other.

7. How many forces are acting on the moon? What force keeps the moon moving around the Earth?

8. A penny and a feather fall toward the earth in a vacuum tube. They begin falling at the same time.

   a) Describe what would be observed.

   b) Which of Newton's laws apply to this scenario?

   c) Use the laws of motion that you listed in (b) to explain what would occur.

9. A ride at an amusement park straps you into a seat and raises you 400 feet above the ground. Once you reach the top, you are dropped. Near the bottom, a spring slows your descent.

   a) What forces act on you during the ride? When is each force acting on you?

   b) What laws of motion would be relevant as you travel from the top to the bottom of the ride?

   c) What is the rate of your acceleration when you are in the middle of the ride? What law tells you the rate of acceleration?

   d) In the middle of the ride, you feel weightless. Explain why.

   e) What is the direction of the net force at the bottom?

10. Two identical encyclopedias are dropped. Encyclopedia A is dropped from five feet off the ground and Encyclopedia B is dropped from ten feet off the ground. Encyclopedia B is dropped first. When Encyclopedia B reaches exactly five feet above the ground, Encyclopedia A is dropped.

    a) Which encyclopedia has the greater force and thus the greater acceleration acting on it?

    b) Which encyclopedia hits the ground first?

    c) When Encyclopedia B hits the ground does it have double, triple, or quadruple the speed of Encyclopedia A? (Hint: compare the two encyclopedias' rates of acceleration and the distance that they travel.)

    d) Both Encyclopedia A's and B's covers hit the ground face down. Does Encyclopedia A or Encyclopedia B exert the greater force on the ground?

11. You take your 20-lb bowling ball on a trip with you to the distant planet Sophia. The planet Sophia has double the mass and half the diameter of Earth. Answer the following questions about the bowling ball.

    a) What is the ball's mass on Sophia?

    b) Relative to Earth, what is the bowling ball's weight?

    c) Using the Law of Universal Gravitation, explain how your answers in (a) and (b) are consistent with one another.

    d) If dropped on the planet Sophia, how does the bowling ball's acceleration compare to its acceleration on Earth?

    e) You and your bowling buddies decide to race your bowling balls by dropping them from the same height somewhere on Sophia. Your friend's ball weighs 25 lbs on Earth, a mere fraction of what your ball weighs on Sophia. Which ball hits first?

    f) Which principle of symmetry from Chapter 1 applies to this question?

Connecting with the Aims of a BYU Education

*"The Mission of Brigham Young University—founded, supported, and
guided by The Church of Jesus Christ of Latter-day Saints—
is to assist individuals in their quest for perfection and eternal life."*

— BYU Mission Statement

As you begin to settle into a routine for the semester, it is the perfect time to evaluate your schedule to make sure that you are maximizing your opportunity here at BYU. It is very easy to become swamped with homework, papers, and tests, but the Aims of a BYU Education encompass much more than simply achieving a passing grade. To paraphrase Mark Twain, do not let your schooling interfere with your education. Are you connecting with the Aims?

A BYU Education should be:

- Spiritually strengthening,
- Intellectually enlarging, and
- Character building, leading to
- Lifelong learning and service.

How can you achieve the Aims?

Success requires significant individual planning and effort. The following goals can help you.

- Be willing to participate in learning community events—this will help build a sense of community with the other students in your classes, create positive relationships with faculty members, and provide ways for you to enhance your university experience.
- Commit to live the Honor Code.
- Actively participate in establishing and maintaining community standards in the classroom and your residence.
- Desire to grow spiritually through learning and service.

More ideas for achieving the Aims

Students who succeed have specific priorities. Periodically, take time to evaluate yourself in each of the following areas and decide where you can improve.

Value the university experience

- Know why you came to the university.

- Integrate the spiritual and secular in your learning.
- Commit to a solid academic effort.
- Feel confident that you can succeed.
- Understand and adhere to the Honor Code.

Place academics as a top priority

- Attend all classes.
- Read assigned materials before class.
- Study diligently.
- Plan how you will use your time.
- Prepare multiple drafts of papers.
- Find class lectures stimulating. (This requires coming prepared!)
- Say "no" to social activities when you should study.

Build your character

- Make spiritual growth a priority.
- Develop and maintain a healthy lifestyle.
- Establish a financial path to graduation.
- Limit work to 20 hours per week.
- Maintain positive relationships with family members.
- Be flexible.
- Handle difficulties effectively.
- Seek help when you need it.
- Interact with faculty and other students outside of class.
- Serve others.

Courtesy of Freshman Academy, BYU.

CHAPTER 4

THE ELECTROMAGNETIC INTERACTION

"[Because] the cathode rays are deflected by an electrostatic force as if they were negatively electrified, and are acted on by a magnetic force in just the way in which this force would act on a [moving] negatively electrified body, . . . I can see no escape from the conclusion that they are charges of negative electricity carried by particles of matter."

~ J. J. Thompson (1897)

That some objects can become "electrified" or "charged" when rubbed against certain other materials has intrigued and mystified people since at least the days of ancient Greece. One of the earliest Greek philosopher-scientists, Thales of Miletus (625–546 BC), wrote that stones of amber, after being rubbed with wool or fur, attracted straw and bits of feathers. In 1600 William Gilbert (1544–1603), physician to Queen Elizabeth I of England, interpreted this attraction as being part of a family of phenomena he collectively called "electrification" after *elektron*, the Greek word for amber. Gilbert hypothesized that all matter contained "electricity." He theorized that exchanging electricity somehow results in an attraction.

Electrification is easy to demonstrate. Run a plastic comb through your hair on a dry day then hold the comb close to some lint or tiny shreds of paper. Chances are good that the lint or paper bits will leap to the comb. Another experiment requires a little more courage. Simply put on shoes with rubber soles and shuffle your feet across a rug or carpet. Then touch a door knob or one of the exposed screws on a nearby wall light switch. You may receive a slight electrical shock (and maybe even an unnerving "zap" sound). A moving car may become elec-

trified from air friction, which explains why you might sometimes feel a shock as you exit the car and touch one of its metal parts.

Figure 4.1
Electrification happens all the time.

You can explore electrification by rubbing one end of a hard rubber rod with a piece of fur. Hang the rod from a string without allowing anything to touch the rubbed end. Rub a second rubber rod and hold it near the first. The hanging rod will move away, repelled by the held rod. This repulsion occurs even when the rods are some distance apart. If the rods are brought closer together the repulsion is stronger, showing that this interaction has a strength-distance relationship like gravity.

Material other than rubber and amber can

LEARNING OBJECTIVES

When you finish this chapter you should be able to

- Describe how positively and negatively charged objects interact with each other.

- Discuss the electrical model of matter.

- Discuss some of the history of how we came to understand the electromagnetic force.

- Define and discuss the electrical force law.

- Describe what conductors, insulators, and electrical currents are.

- Describe how the force of friction arises.

- Describe magnetic interactions and their relationship to the electric force.

also be electrified by rubbing. Two glass rods rubbed with silk will become charged and repel each other just like the rubber rods. But bring a charged glass rod near a suspended charged rubber rod and instead of repelling they will *attract* one another (*Figure 14.2*). The attractive force will increase as they are brought closer together. Unlike gravity, the force from electrification—which we will just call the "electric force" for short—can be either attractive or repulsive. In general, charged rods made of the same material will always repel each other. Some of these will be attracted to a charged rubber rod and some will be repelled by it. Those that are attracted to the charged rubber rod will always be repelled by a charged glass rod and vice versa.

Objects attracted to an electrified rubber rod are said to be **positively charged**, while

those attracted to the glass are **negatively charged**. These terms were coined by Benjamin Franklin (1706–1790) who experimented with electricity in the years preceding the American Revolution. Following William Gilbert's lead, Franklin hypothesized electricity to be a type of invisible fluid present in all matter. He thought that rubbing different surfaces together caused the fluid to flow, leaving some objects with more and some with less than their natural share. In Franklin's hypothetical model, matter with too little fluid was "negative," or missing some of this fluid, while matter with an excess of fluid was "positive."*

Franklin refined his invisible fluid model through experiments in which he created "static"

Figure 4.2
A charged glass rod and a charged rubber rod will attract each other when close together.

*Many scientists wish that Franklin had reversed those terms for, as you will read, it was later found that the negatively charged substances gain, not lose, charged particles.

(unmoving) electricity by using rubbing materials and techniques described above. He stored this electricity in Leyden jars, which are specially designed glass bottles that served the same purpose as modern batteries do. Franklin could then dispense the saved electrical charge in small amounts for careful study or, if desired, discharge the entire charge at once in a shower of sparks.

Benjamin Franklin

Franklin was not only renowned as a statesman, but was also an accomplished scientist.

Augustin de Coulomb

Discovered that forces between charged bodies are proportional to the charges on them.

♦ **Electric Force Law**

The mathematical formula F=kqQ/d2 which describes the strength of the force between two objects of charge Q and q separated between their centers by the distance d.

♦ **Electric Force Constant**

A number relating the strength of the electric force to the charges involved and their distance apart.

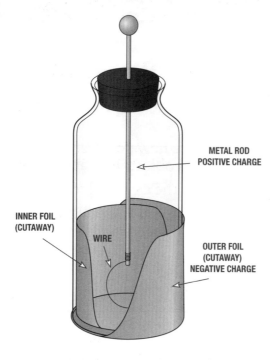

Figure 4.3

Static electricity was stored in Leyden Jars. Benjamin Franklin used them to show the connection between lightning and static electricity.

The similarity between flying sparks and lightning resulted in his famous—and highly dangerous—experiment in which he flew a kite in a thunderstorm. Franklin wanted to determine if lightning was just a more magnificent manifestation of static electricity. The connection between lightning and electricity may seem apparent to anyone taught about it since elementary school, but the biggest sparks Franklin could make with his Leydon jars in his laboratory were less than an inch long, while lightning flashes could be several miles in length, so the connection was not necessarily obvious. Franklin captured electricity from a key attached to the high-flying kite's string and successfully stored it in a Leyden jar. Experiments he performed later showed that his "captured lightning" behaved in his laboratory exactly like static electricity obtained from rubbing. They were different manifestations of the same phenomenon.

4–1   THE ELECTRIC FORCE LAW

By the end of the 18th century electricity was being modeled in two ways. One was Franklin's model, which assumed matter had a single charged fluid part embedded in an oppositely charged, less mobile part. According to this model the fluid could flow in or out of objects, leaving them positively or negatively charged. A second model hypothesized the existence of two oppositely charged fluids, either one of which could flow in or out of otherwise neutral matter. In 1785 Charles Augustin de Coulomb (1736–1806) experimentally determined a force law that worked equally well with either model. de Coulomb used a torsion balance similar to that used by Henry Cavendish for gravity to discover that the force between charged bodies is proportional to the charges on them, and that force decreases with the distance squared, just like the gravitational force.

This **Electric Force Law** can thus be summarized:

Pairs of objects with similar charges repel each other and pairs with dissimilar charges attract each other with forces, F, that obey Newton's Third Law. The strength of F depends on the net charges, q and Q, on the objects and the distance, d, between them, according to the relationship

$$F = kQq/d^2$$

The letter "k" represents a number called the **electrical force constant**. Like the constant

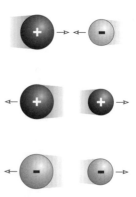

Figure 4.4

Every charged object is attracted or repelled by every other charged object through the electrical interaction. Objects of opposite charge attract each other. Objects of like charge repel each other.

"G" in the Law of Gravity, it must be measured experimentally. But unlike G, the value of k is relatively large, with a value of about 9×10^9 in the metric system. This means a small amount of charge is needed to generate the same amount of force created by a huge amount of mass. For example rubbing a rod with fur separates only about 1 part out of every 10^{12} of the charged material. If *all* the charged material were separated out of the fur and into the rod and the fur and rod were placed on opposite ends of a football field, the attraction between them would have a force of about 10^{13} tons. The electrical force can be strong indeed!

4-2 THE ELECTRICAL MODEL OF MATTER

After many decades of experiments, Benjamin Franklin's single fluid hypothesis of electricity emerged as the better model. Scientists then turned their attention to understanding what the fluid was made of, how it was able to flow, and if it was composed of measurable particles. In 1897 the English physicist J. J. Thomson (1856–1940) investigated these questions by devising a Nobel-prize-winning experiment that literally tore atoms apart and examined the pieces that emerged.

Thomson used a mostly evacuated cylindrical tube filled with a low-density gas*. Metal plates were placed in both ends of the tube and connected through the glass to battery terminals (see *Figure 4.5*). The plates were connected to batteries so that one was charged positively and the other was charged negatively. Thomson increased the charge difference between the plates until a faint, glowing beam arose between them. This beam was examined to see if it obeyed Newton's Laws of Motion. It did, proving that electricity had to have mass. Scientists repeating this experiment later determined that the beam was composed of two types of material, a negative, light-massed substance flowing

---

*These tubes, also called "Crooks tubes," had been invented and used earlier by many people, including William Crooks, after whom they are named. The version used by Thomson had been patented by Thomas Edison six years earlier. Although he was not the inventor, Thomson had the insight to use these tubes to examine fundamental questions about electricity. Often in science it is the people who come after the original invention or model who use it in its most insightful way.

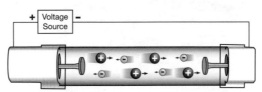

Figure 4.5
The glowing beam in a discharge tube is negative and positive parts of atoms moving in opposite directions.

to the positive plate and a heavier, positive substance flowing the opposite way to the negative plate.

Thomson correctly decided that the atoms of gas in the tube were being broken apart into charged fragments by the electric interaction. He further discovered that regardless of the type of gas used in the tube, the negative fragments always had the same charge and mass. The positive fragments, however, retained the mass properties of the original gas. From the results of his experiment Thomson put together the model of the atom which will be discussed in Chapter 15.

Thomson's results clearly suggested Franklin's "electrical fluid" was a stream of particles. He called those particles "corpuscles," a term later abandoned in favor of the word **electrons**. His experiment was not absolutely conclusive though. It was still possible to explain the glowing beam as a stream of pure material that could be divided into infinitely small pieces without losing its nature and properties. After all, other physical quantities, such as force and speed, can have any value, and there was no guiding principle that demanded electrical charge be different. Confirmation of the particle nature of charge finally came in 1910, when the American physicist Robert Millikan (1868–1953) devised an "oil-drop experiment" that isolated and measured the charge on individual particles.

In the oil-drop experiment, Millikan first sprayed light oil through an atomizer to form a mist. Friction between the emerging oil droplets and the atomizer spout caused each droplet to become negatively charged for the same reason rubbing a rod with fur negatively charges the rod. The oil drops were sprayed into the space between charged electric plates (*Figure 4.6*) and allowed to fall under the force of gravity. Selected drops were carefully examined through an eye-

J. J. Thompson

Thompson used a gas discharge tube to determine that electricity had mass.

♦ Electron
The basic negative charge-carrying particle in an atom.

Robert Millikan

Developed a way to measure the charge of individual electrons.

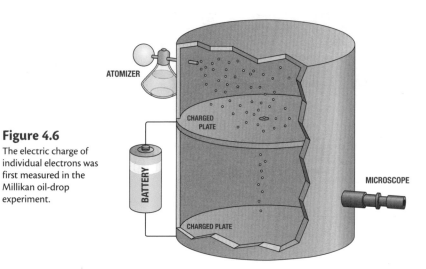

Figure 4.6
The electric charge of individual electrons was first measured in the Millikan oil-drop experiment.

♦ **Coulomb**
The unit of measure for charge. Named after Charles Augustin de Coulomb, formulator of the Electric Force Law. The amount of electric charge possessed by a single electron or a proton is 1.6×10^{-19} coulombs.

♦ **Proton**
The basic positive charge-carrying particle in an atom.

♦ **Neutron**
A neutral particle found in the nuclei of atoms.

piece to measure their motion, size, and mass. The charge on the plates was then adjusted until the electric force pushing up on the negative droplets exactly equaled the gravitational force pulling down and the drop no longer accelerated. The magnitude of this force was determined by using Newton's Law of Gravity. The charge on the plates necessary to equal this force was measured and the charge on the oil droplet was calculated from the Electric Force Law.

Millikan methodically repeated this Nobel-prize-winning experiment over several years, examining thousands of oil drops. He found that the amount of charge acquired by each oil drop was always in tiny steps of 1.6×10^{-19} **coulombs**. Because his oil drops picked up charge only in this discrete quantity, it was clear that each step represented the acquisition of an individual particle. Each particle's tiny charge value means an enormous number are required to create even a small spark.

A saying among scientists is that yesterday's Nobel Prize is today's homework assignment. Sophisticated variants of Thomson's gas discharge tubes are the familiar fluorescent bulbs that may be providing light in the room you are in right now. Detectors in modern digital cameras routinely measure the charge of individual electrons as part of the process of constructing digital photographic images. Thomson and Millikan, brilliant as they were, never envisioned these modern applications when they did their experiments. Neither could today's engineers have constructed computers, cameras, and other electronic marvels without those scientists' pioneering discoveries. Learning about the particle nature of an electron may seem mundane, but it

would have been impossible to understand and advance research in electricity without it.

Later scientists would better understand the positive aspect of the electric force and the particle that carries it, the **proton**. (See Chapter 15 for more on this subject.) Protons are identical to each other, in the same way each electron is identical to every other electron. Protons carry the exact same charge as an electron, only with the opposite sign. The protons and **neutrons** which comprise the bulk of the mass of an atom rarely migrate to a rubbed fur or rod. When an object becomes charged negatively it is because the electrons have moved *to* it. When it becomes charged positively it is because electrons have moved *from* it, leaving a net imbalance in favor of the protons.

The structure of matter is such that protons are held more rigidly in place in solids than are electrons. This is partly because of their mass. Electrons have little mass, about 1/1,836 that of protons. Newton's Third Law of Motion shows that when a collection of excess electrons, like the buildup found in a thundercloud, is attracted to a body that lacks electrons (and therefore has excess protons), like the ground, both the ground and the thundercloud will feel the same force. By the Second Law of Motion the less massive electrons will accelerate more than the protons and will therefore be the ones to break free and move, causing the visible lightning and audible thunderclaps.

This picture can be termed the **Electrical Model of Matter**. It lacks details about how

Figure 4.7
In lightning, it is the less massive electrons that move.

these charged particles are arranged and how they combine to create the myriad kinds of materials around us. But it does provide an adequate framework to help us understand basic electricity. We can summarize the model as follows:

All matter contains two kinds of electrically charged particles: positive protons and negative electrons. Electrons have little mass and can be quite mobile and transferable from one object to another. Protons are held rigidly in place in solid materials. Objects that have equal numbers of protons and electrons are electrically neutral. Objects with more electrons than protons are negatively charged. Those with fewer electrons than protons are positively charged. The amount of extra charge of either kind is called the "charge of an object."

4-3   ELECTRIC CURRENT

A rubber rod is an **insulator**, a material that does not permit electrons to move freely within it. When you rub electrons off fur and onto the end of a rubber rod, the electrons will not readily flow away, leaving that end negatively charged. But rub a copper rod with that same swatch of fur and no negative charge will build up on the rod. Why not? The fur places as many electrons onto a copper rod as it will place on a rubber rod. However, the electrons rubbed onto a copper rod will quickly flow to your hand and back to the fur or to the ground. A metal rod is a **conductor**, a material that permits electrons to freely move on its surface or through its interior.

Moving electrons create an **electric current**. They move in a wire like water flows through a pipe loosely filled with gravel. The moving water represents the mobile electrons and the stationary gravel represents the fixed atoms with their protons and neutrons. Although electrons in an electric current move through the wire, no part of it is charged because there are always equal numbers of protons and electrons in the wire at any point at any time.

An electrical current arises only when there is a source, like a battery, to push on the electrons. Batteries produce a **direct current** of electrons flowing in one direction, away from the negative terminal and toward the positive ter-

minal. They create a current only if there is a place for the electrons to flow to. Otherwise, electrons will quickly build up on the wire and push back against the electrons behind them, preventing them from entering the wire, and so the flow of electrons (the electrical current) quickly stops. And electrical current is possible only if there is a connection back to the battery or to the ground. Wall sockets into which household appliances are connected are like the battery, except that the current reverses direction 60 times per second. This type of reversing electrical flow is called **alternating current**.

4-4   MAGNETISM

Ancient Greeks living near the city of Magnesia, as well as some early Chinese, knew about "lodestones" (possibly chunks of iron ore struck by lightning) that had the strange, unexplainable power to attract iron. Steel needles stroked with such stones would become "magnetic" as well. Around 1000 BC the Chinese found that such a needle, when freely suspended, pointed north-south. This discovery led to the magnetic compass.

The magnetic compass soon spread to Europe and in 1492 Columbus used it when he first crossed the Atlantic Ocean to discover the North American continent. He noted in his journal that not only did the needle deviate slightly from exact north (which was known to mariners from the position of the Polar Star), but also that this deviation changed during the voyage. The Elizabethan physician-researcher William Gilbert proposed an explanation: Earth itself was a giant magnet, with its magnetic North Pole some distance away from true, geographic north.

Magnetism is easier to demonstrate than the electric force, because magnets retain their attractive powers when they are handled. You no doubt have used magnets to pick up paper clips or hold notes on a refrigerator. Metal that is **ferromagnetic,** such as iron and nickel, can be attracted to magnets, or can become a magnet itself. **Non-ferromagnetic** metals like silver, copper and gold cannot be attracted to magnets nor can they become magnets.

Take a bar magnet and suspend it from a string. Hold another magnet and point the end

- **Insulator**
  A material that does not permit electrons to flow through it.

- **Conductor**
  A material that allows electrons to flow through it.

- **Electric Current**
  Electric charges flowing through a conductor.

- **Direct Current**
  A steady flow of electrons in one direction through a wire.

- **Alternating Current**
  A current of electrons that changes direction of flow.

William Gilbert

Proposed that the Earth was itself a giant magnet.

- **Ferromagnetism**
  Metal alloys that are attracted to magnets or are capable of being transformed into a permanent magnet are called ferromagnetic.

Figure 4.8
Opposite poles of magnets attract each other. Similar poles repel each other.

stamped "S" (the "south pole") toward it. The suspended magnet will twist so that its north pole (stamped "N") moves toward the held magnet's south pole, while its own south pole moves away. Turn the held magnet around so that its north pole is toward the suspended magnet. Now the suspended magnet will twist as its south pole is attracted and its north pole is repelled. Unlike electrified rods, which are always entirely attracted or repelled by another charged rod, magnet ends are attracted and repelled by the ends of any other magnet.

All magnets have both north and south poles. No magnet having only one pole has ever been discovered. You can cut a magnet in half hoping to create two single-poled magnets, but if you do, the new ends immediately become oppositely polarized magnetic poles. Cut one of the pieces in half again and again as often as you want; new poles will always appear.

Either end of a magnet will attract unmagnetized ferromagnetic metal. It doesn't matter if you point a south pole or a north pole at a pile of paper clips, either end will attract paper clips equally well. A refrigerator magnet might have either the north pole or the south pole in contact with the fridge. Both will fasten and hold just as tightly.

4–5 THE ELECTROMAGNETIC INTERACTION

William Gilbert correctly hypothesized that iron magnets and electrified amber are related. However, the proof of this relationship remained undiscovered for over two centuries after Gilbert's hypothesis. In 1821 a Danish scientist, Hans Christian Oersted (1777–1851), was demonstrating to friends the flow of an electric current in a wire, when he noticed that the current caused a nearby compass needle to move (see *Figure 4.9*). This phenomenon was studied in France by Andre-Marie Ampere (1775–1836), who concluded magnetism was a force arising between electric currents. Two parallel currents flowing in the same direction attract each other. Parallel currents flowing in opposite directions repel.

Soon after this, scientists learned that a regular iron bar becomes a magnet when a current passes though a wire wrapped around it. If the current is strong enough and the bar is ferromagnetic, it will remain magnetic even after the current is turned off.

Magnetism is a manifestation of the electric force from charged particles that are moving.* The electric interaction is more properly called the electromagnetic interaction because of this relationship.

Michael Faraday (1791–1867), credited with many fundamental discoveries on electricity and magnetism, modeled magnetism by assuming the space around electric currents possessed a "field" in which the magnetic force could be felt.

The strength of a magnetic field can be mapped by using a second magnet as a probe. Imagine a compass needle freely suspended in space near a bar magnet. If we move the compass needle through space, the direction that it

---

*Unfortunately, explaining exactly *why* moving charges should create a magnetic force is beyond the scope of this book.

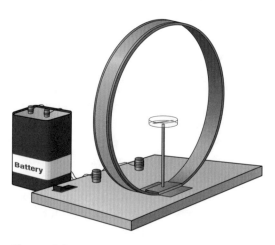

Figure 4.9
An experiment similar to Oersted's . When current flows through the coil, it generates a magnetic field that is strongest at the center where the compass sits. When current flows clockwise around the coil, the compass points to the right. When current flows counterclockwise, the compass needle points to the left.

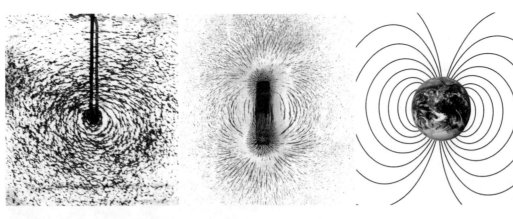

Figure 4.10
a) The field lines of a wire. Notice how the lines form a circular pattern about it.
b) The field lines of a bar magnet. The field lines arch through space connecting the north and south poles like before.
c) The field lines of Earth. Earth's magnetic field is exactly the same shape as the field of a bar magnet.

points will change as we get closer or farther from the poles. Tracing the direction that the needle points creates "**field lines**." A denser collection of the field lines indicates a stronger force at that location.

The field lines of a wire, a bar magnet, and Earth itself are presented in *Figure 4.10*. For a wire the field lines are circular loops around it. For a bar magnet the field lines arch from the South Pole to the North Pole. Arrows on the field lines indicate the direction the north end of a magnet would point if it were there. Field lines of a bar magnet can be traced by a simple experiment in which iron filings are sprinkled on a stiff sheet of paper held over the magnet. Similarly, Earth's field lines start near Earth's South Pole, curve around in space and converge again near the North Pole.

4–6   PERMANENT MAGNETS

The discovery that moving charges create magnetism raises questions. If moving charges create magnetism, how can bars of metal become permanent magnets? Is there some sort of current going around in them? Metal can stay magnetized for years or even centuries. What can cause currents to last that long?

Permanent magnets indeed have charges moving within them. The charges are the electrons orbiting around the atomic protons, turning each atom into a tiny magnet. In most materials the atoms are oriented randomly so the overall effect cancels and there is no net magnetism. In ferromagnetic materials, though, atoms align with neighboring atoms in small sections called **domains** (see *Figure 4.11*). Normally the domains themselves are oriented randomly so there is still no net magnetism. But when they

are influenced by an external magnetic field, the domains will shift and align together, producing a net magnetic force.

Suppose the north pole of a magnet is brought close to a paper clip. The domains inside the paper clip will realign until the clip becomes a magnet with its north pole facing the magnet's south pole. The magnet's north pole attracts the paper clip's south pole and they stick together. If the magnet's south pole had been brought close to the paper clip, the domains would have realigned in the other direction. Then the clip would become a magnet with its north pole facing the magnet's south pole. Again, an attraction results.

If the domains remain aligned after the external field is removed, the piece becomes a permanent magnet. Some magnets, like those found in computer hard drives, can be exceptionally strong. With time, however, the alignments break down and all permanent magnets eventually lose their strength.

Earth is not a permanent magnet. Its magnetic field is caused by charges moving in currents which are more like giant wires wrapped in a loop hundreds of miles around in the outer core. This is discussed further in Chapter 28.

- **Field Lines**

  Lines coming from an object representing the strength of the force. The denser the lines, the stronger the force.

- **Domain**

  A small section in a magnet where the magnetic force from all the atoms add together.

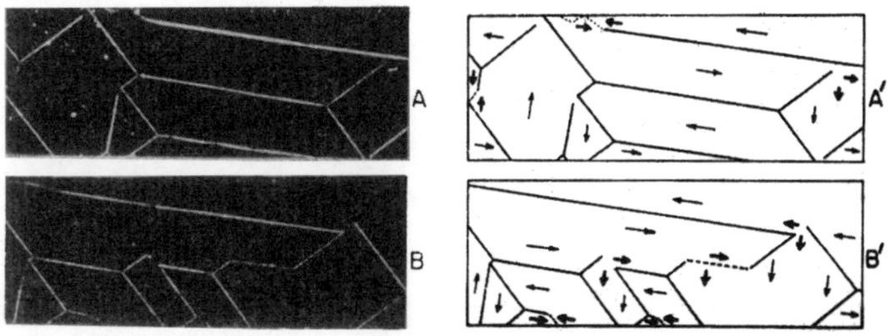

Figure 4.11
Magnetism arises when electric currents flow in tiny domains. Figures A and B are an image of the domain regions in a slice of magnetic metal. Figures A' and B' are interpretations of the images showing the direction of the magnetic fields within each domain.

4–7 THE FORCES OF CONTACT AND FRICTION

Atoms on the surface of all materials have negatively charged electrons orbiting about them. When two surfaces come together these electrons repel each other. This repulsion strengthens rapidly as the electrons get closer. When atoms are on the verge of touching, the repulsion is so great the surfaces abruptly stop getting closer. This repulsion gives a surface its hardness even though electrons themselves don't actually "touch." The force created this way is called a "**contact force**."

As a simple example consider a book on a table. A downward gravitational force pulls on the book. At the same time the electrons of the book's cover and hard table top repel one another, causing the book to be pushed upward. If you place your hand on the book and push down, the surfaces will get ever so slightly closer, and the electromagnetic repulsions will increase. If the increased upward electromagnetic force balances the total downward force, the book moves no further. If the increased upward electromagnetic force cannot increase enough to balance the downward force, the table breaks.

Sliding friction results from the same kind of interaction. Adjacent surfaces are microscopically quite uneven (*Figure 4.12*). These "bumps" and "hollows" scrape across each other when the surfaces slide. As they come into contact their

◆ **Contact Force**

The force arising between objects when they touch. Contact forces are a repulsion caused by the electromagnetic interaction.

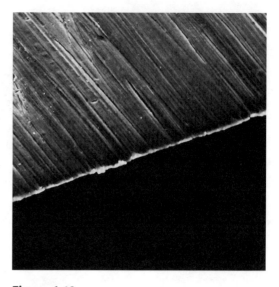

Figure 4.12

The "smooth" side of a steel surgical scalpel blade, as viewed at × 1500 magnification under a scanning electron microscope.

atoms push back against each other. This push is always *against* the direction of the motion so sliding friction always causes moving things to slow down.

Contact and frictional forces are the most common manifestations of the electromagnetic interaction in our everyday lives. Every time you touch something you are feeling the electromagnetic force. If you kick a rock, the charges in the rock repel the charges in your shoe. Charges in your shoe repel charges in your toe. These forces initiate internal electrical interactions that finally cause your brain to register pain—all due to the electromagnetic interaction.

Chapter Framework

A. Introduction
1. Electrification
2. Positive and negative charges
3. Ben Franklin
   a. *Fluid model*
   b. *The kite experiment*

B. The Electric Force Law
1. $F = kqQ/d^2$
2. Electrical force constant **k**

C. The Electrical Model of Matter
1. J. J. Thompson
   a. *Gas tube experiment*
   b. *Discovery of electrons*
2. Robert Millikan
   a. *"Oil-drop" experiment*
   b. *Electrons as particles*
3. The Electrical Model of Matter

D. Electric Current
1. Conductors
2. Insulators
3. Direct current
4. Alternating current

E. Magnetism
1. Lodestones and compasses
2. William Gilbert
3. Ferromagnetic metal
4. Magnetic poles

F. The Electromagnetic Interaction
1. Hans Christian Oersted
   a. *Magnetism and electric current*
2. Field lines
3. Permanent magnets
4. Domains

G. The Forces of Contact and Friction
1. Caused by the electromagnetic interaction

Comprehension

True/False
1. _____ Friction comes from electromagnetic forces.
2. _____ Electric force becomes stronger if the charged objects are moved farther apart.
3. _____ Neutrons have a negative charge.
4. _____ Iron and nickel are examples of ferromagnetic metals.
5. _____ Electric currents exert forces on permanent magnets.

Fill in the Blank
1. Millikan conducted experiments with oil drops that isolated and measured _____ on individual particles.
2. When Thomson conducted his experiments with tubes of gas, particles he called "corpuscles," but

which are now known as _____, moved toward the positive end of the tube.
3. When rubber is rubbed with fur, _____ move from the fur onto the rubber, leaving the rubber with a _____ charge.
4. Electrical outlets (plugs) in a wall supply _____ current.
5. _____ are regions in ferromagnetic materials where all of the atom's magnetic forces align.
6. The size and direction of electric and magnetic forces is often pictorially represented using _____.

Matching
1. _____ The basic positive charge-carrying particle in an atom.
2. _____ Metal alloys that are attracted to magnets or are capable of being transformed into a permanent magnet.
3. _____ A material that does not permit electrons to flow through it.
4. _____ The mathematical formula F=kqQ/d2, which describes the strength of the force between two objects of charge Q and q separated between their centers by the distance d.
5. _____ A current of electrons that changes direction of flow.
6. _____ The unit of measure for charge.
7. _____ Material that allows electrons to flow through it.
8. _____ The basic negative charge carrying-particle in an atom.
9. _____ A steady flow of electrons in one direction through a wire.
10. _____ A repulsive force between electrons near the surface of two different objects.
11. _____ A number relating the strength of the electric force to the charges involved and their distance apart.
12. _____ A neutral particle found in the nuclei of atoms.

a. Ferromagnetic
b. Coulomb
c. Insulator
d. Electric force constant
e. Electron
f. Proton
g. Alternating current
h. Direct current
i. Contact force
j. Neutron
k. The Electric Force Law
l. Conductor

Analysis

1. When a glass rod is rubbed with rubber, it becomes positively charged. This is because
   a) protons are transferred from rubber to glass.
   b) protons are transferred from glass to rubber.
   c) electrons are transferred from glass to rubber.
   d) electrons are transferred from rubber to glass.
   e) electrons and protons cancel out each other.

2. Who among the following did not help contribute to discoveries in electromagnetic interactions?
   a) Henry Cavendish
   b) Benjamin Franklin
   c) Thomas Edison
   d) William Gilbert

3. Contact force is cause by:

   a) Atoms randomly crashing into each other.
   b) Electrons of two atoms repelling each other.
   c) Protons of two atoms repelling each other.
   d) The force of one object pushing against the force of another object.

4. Suppose you wanted to double the electric force between two objects. How could you accomplish that?

   a) Double the charge on both objects
   b) Double the distance between the objects
   c) Cut the distance in half
   d) Double the charge on both objects while cutting the distance in half
   e) Double the charge on one of the objects

Synthesis

1. Describe an experiment that demonstrates that there are two kinds of electric charge.

2. Describe the differences between conductors and insulators.

3. Describe the important properties of a proton and an electron. What is the comparison in sizes?

4. What is electric current?

5. How do we know that there is a single electromagnetic force rather than separate electric and magnetic interactions?

6. What is makes a material ferromagnetic?

7. Explain how the contact and friction forces arise and play an important role in the following scenarios.

   a) A book placed on a table.

   b) A car tire screeches to a stop at a cross walk to avoid hitting pedestrians.

   c) A space shuttle reentering Earth's atmosphere

   d) A water skier gliding across the water

8. A rubber rod is rubbed with fur and suspended in the air. A second rubber rod that has been rubbed with fur is placed nearby.

   a) What charges are on the rubber rods?

   b) Do the rods attract or repel one another?

   c) What law explains why this occurs?

   d) As you bring the rubber rods closer together, what happens to the force between them?

   e) What could you do to decrease the force between the rods, without changing the distance?

   f) If you replaced on of the rubber rods with a glass rod that had been rubbed with silk, how would your answers to the above questions change?

9. Three spheres of metal are placed on stands that act as insulators. Spheres B and Y are neutrally charged. Sphere U holds a strong negative charge. Wire runs between sphere B and Y. Sphere U is brought close to sphere Y.

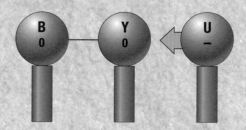

   a) Because spheres B and Y hold no net charge does that mean that no charge exists on them?

   b) What do we know about the amount of negative and positive charge in spheres B and Y?

   c) What will sphere U do to the electrons in sphere Y as it approaches?

   d) What does this do to the net charge on sphere Y?

   e) What does this do to the net charge on sphere B?

   f) How is it possible for charge to arise from two neutrally charge objects?

10. Describe two ways in which you could turn iron wire into a magnet. Only one of these two methods would work with copper wire. Which one and why?

11. If you scuff across wool carpet wearing rubber shoes, you will shock yourself when you reach for a metal doorknob, often before you even touch the knob.

    a) What type of charge will have accumulated on your body? How do you know?

    b) When you bring your finger near the doorknob, what happens to the electrons in the metal?

    c) Explain why, when the metal itself is neutral, a spark will often jump from your finger to the metal before you touch it.

Test Taking Strategies
Test Taking Tips For Specific Types of Tests

A. Multiple Choice

1. Try to answer the question before looking at the answer.
2. Look for the answer which best completes the stem.
3. Use the process of elimination.
4. When numbers are in each alternative, choose the numbers that are in the middle range, not the extremes.
5. Choose answers that are longer and more descriptive.
6. When two very similar answers appear it is likely that one of them is correct.
7. Choices containing unfamiliar terms are not likely correct.
8. Watch out for negative words in the instructions or in the main question. ie. Which one does NOT...

B. True and False

1. There is no substitute for the truth. If any part of the question is false, the whole thing is wrong!!!
2. Answer the questions as quickly as possible. Don't probe for hidden meanings, just go with your first instinct.
3. When in doubt guess true. Instructors tend to emphasize the true information.
4. Look for extreme modifiers that tend to make the question false. ie. All, Always, Never, Only etc.
5. Identify qualifiers that tend to make the question true ie. Usually, Few, Frequently, Often, Most, etc.
6. Watch out for negative words that may affect the truth. The prefixes "un", "im", "miss" will alter the meaning of the statement. Double negatives make the statement true. ex. Not uncommon, actually means common.
7. Questions that state a reason tend to be false.
8. Questions with more facts tend to be false.

C. Matching Questions

1. Examine both lists to determine the types of items and their relationships.
2. Use one list as a starting point and go through the second list to find a match.
3. Move through the entire list before selecting a match.
    - If you make a match before going through the entire list you may error because an answer later in the list may be more correct.
4. Cross off items on the second list when you are certain that you have a match.
    - It helps you stay organized.
5. Do not guess until all absolute matches have been made.
    - If you guess early in the process you may eliminate an answer that could be used correctly for a later choice.

More tips on page 163

Courtesy of the BYU Counseling and Career Center

CHAPTER 5

APPLICATIONS OF THE LAWS OF FORCE AND MOTION

Chapters 2, 3, and 4 introduced five laws that govern force and motion. The motion of all objects we encounter in our everyday lives can be understood by applying these laws to any situation of interest. This chapter offers examples designed to clearly show how the laws of motion, gravity, and electromagnetism work together. In each example you should note the relationship between the forces acting on an object and the acceleration that results. Then focus on the way the acceleration determines the subsequent motion of the object.

As you gain the ability to relate these ideas, you will be able to explain a wide range of phenomena. Don't let the examples intimidate or discourage you if their explanations are not obvious at first. With time and practice you will soon realize that all motion really does obey a few simple laws.

5–1 FINDING FORCES

When using the laws of motion, correctly identifying forces that act on a given object usually presents the most difficulty. Sometimes one or more forces go unnoticed or forces that do not influence the object may seem pertinent.

Isolating in your mind the object you are analyzing and asking the questions below will help identify the interactions in which an object participates and all the forces that act on it:

1. What role does gravity play? Is gravity unbalanced, balanced, or insignificant? If unbalanced, gravity will cause acceleration toward the attracting body's center (which in most cases will be the center of the Earth). If the gravity is balanced, you may ignore it. Gravity is only insignificant if the object being analyzed is far from Earth, the Sun, and the planets.

2. Are charged objects, current-carrying conductors, or magnets involved? If so, do they create an unbalanced or balanced net force? If unbalanced, does the force attract or repel?

3. What does the object touch? Do the contact forces from touching balance or unbalance other forces?

4. Do air or contact forces cause friction? If so, the friction will create a force that is proportional to the object's speed in a direction against the motion.

After you identify the forces, remember that all unbalanced forces cause acceleration. If an object accelerates, then an unbalanced force caused it. If an object does not accelerate, then

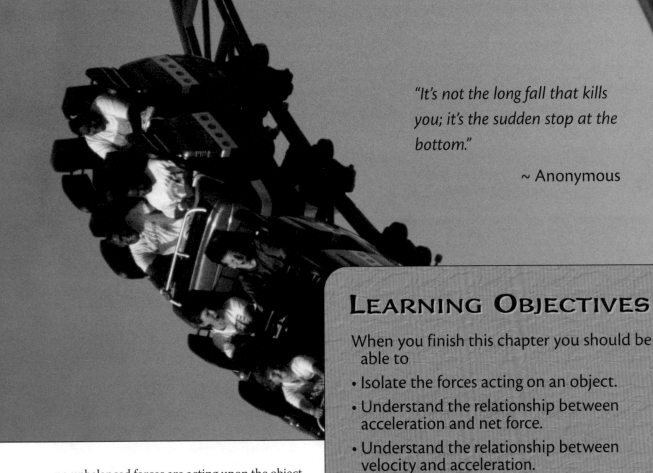

"It's not the long fall that kills you; it's the sudden stop at the bottom."

~ Anonymous

LEARNING OBJECTIVES

When you finish this chapter you should be able to

- Isolate the forces acting on an object.
- Understand the relationship between acceleration and net force.
- Understand the relationship between velocity and acceleration.
- Discuss why things in nature move the way they do.
- Apply the Laws of Motion to common everyday situations.

no unbalanced forces are acting upon the object. There are no exceptions to this rule!

5–2 STANDING ON A SCALE

We will start with a familiar situation: standing on a bathroom scale. As a health-conscious individual you eat right, exercise, and weigh yourself daily. Each morning you step on the scale, read your weight, and start your day merrily (or sadly). If the scale reading isn't what you want, you might find some comfort in know-

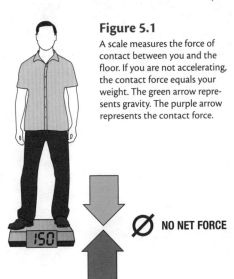

Figure 5.1

A scale measures the force of contact between you and the floor. If you are not accelerating, the contact force equals your weight. The green arrow represents gravity. The purple arrow represents the contact force.

Ø **NO NET FORCE**

ing that a bathroom scale does not really measure your weight. The scale measures the force of contact between you and the floor. But, alas, this force *is* equivalent to your weight when you are standing still and not accelerating.

How does a common bathroom scale work? When you first step on a scale you gently accelerate downward under gravity's influence. A spring in the scale, compressed by the newly added weight, pushes back with an increasingly strong force until its force balances the force of gravity.* If the spring becomes too compressed its upward force exceeds the force of gravity and pushes you back up. This is why, after you first step on the scale, you bob up and down momentarily until the forces from the scale and gravity balance and you become motionless. Now the scale reads your true weight.

---

*A spring has its own force law called Hook's Law. Hook's law says that a spring pushes back with a force that is proportional to the square of the amount of compression. The origin of this force is the electromagnetic interaction.

e.

d.

c.

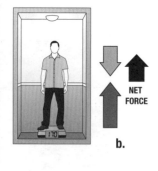

b.

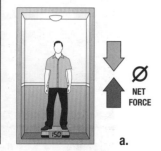

a.

MOTION

You can increase the scale's reading by pushing up against a nearby towel rack and forcing yourself downward. Now the scale registers a larger value that equals the contact force from your weight plus the additional force from the push. Let go of the towel rack and you will accelerate up until the forces again balance. The spring tension will always adjust until the forces balance and you are motionless.

An accelerating scale does not display a true weight value. Standing on a scale in a moving elevator as in *Figure 5.2* demonstrates this. When the elevator rises to a higher floor, the scale's dial will first increase in value, then go back to your actual weight. When the elevator slows as it approaches the requested floor, your scale reading will decrease in value. After the elevator comes to a full stop at the floor level, the scale's dial once again measures your actual weight. Why does the scale behave this way?

At first, as the elevator accelerates upwards, the contact force pushes upward against your feet more than the force of gravity pulls you downward. The increase in the dial reading shows this increase in the contact force. After the elevator begins moving, it glides between floors in *uniform motion.* In this stage, no *acceleration* occurs and so the scale indicates your true weight. When the elevator reaches the requested floor and begins to brake for its stop, the contact force weakens and becomes less than gravity. The unbalanced net downward force then pulls you to a stop. As you decelerate the scale shows a smaller value because the contact force is weaker. It finally returns to the true weight value after you are completely stopped and are no longer accelerating.

Figure 5.2 ⇐

The forces acting on you in a moving elevator change as the elevator's acceleration changes. The green arrow represents gravity. The purple arrow represents the contact force. Forces are balanced before starting (a), after stopping (e), and while gliding in uniform motion between floors (c). The force is unbalanced upward when you start to move (b) and unbalanced downward as you stop (d). A change in the contact force creates the imbalance in forces.

5–3   JUMPING INTO THE AIR

A professional basketball player races down the floor, leaps from the foul line, glides through the air, and jams the ball through the hoop. The crowd cheers the athlete's "hang time," and the announcer exclaims how the player defied gravity. The player didn't really defy gravity, but how exactly did he *look* like he did?

First consider this same basketball player just standing on the gymnasium floor. What forces act on him? Gravity pulls down and the contact force with the floor pushes up. Is he accelerating? No, so gravity and the contact forces balance out. Are there other forces to worry about? No.

The player then crouches down and pauses, getting ready to jump. As he crouches, his upper body moves to a lower level. In this process his upper body goes from being stationary, to moving, to being stationary again and so experiences two accelerations. The first acceleration down towards the floor begins the motion and the second acceleration up from the floor ends the downward motion. During his accelerated movements the forces are unbalanced. First there was

Figure 5.3

What forces act on a jumping basketball player?

a net downward force as the contact force weakened when the player relaxed his knees. His upper body accordingly accelerated down. Then there was a net upward force as he stiffened his knees and came to rest in a crouched position. At that time his upper body accelerated upward just enough to cancel the downward velocity. During this pause just before the jump, the forces once again balance one another.

After the slight pause he jumps. This is an acceleration upward, so the forces are unbalanced upward. The forces became unbalanced when the contact force strengthened as he suddenly pushed against the floor with his legs and—by the Third Law of Motion—the floor pushed back with equal force.*

Once the player is in the air, contact with the floor is broken and the contact force goes to zero. Now the force is unbalanced downward with the full force of gravity. The downward acceleration that results diminishes the player's upward speed. His velocity quickly reverses direction and he accelerates back to the arena floor. His legs cushion the shock and his body comes back to rest.

Let's examine how his legs "cushion the shock." If he had come down with his legs straight and unbent, he would have experienced a sudden and painful landing. Flexed knees allowed him to break his fall more gently, by spreading his stop over a longer period of time, thus decreasing his rate of acceleration. Force equals mass times acceleration. A smaller, gentler acceleration means a smaller, gentler force. A sudden, jarring stop means a greater acceleration and a greater force. Even though the greater force would be over a shorter time interval, it would still be much harder on an athlete's knees and body than the longer, gentler force.

Great basketball players and other great athletes seem to defy gravity when they are able to accelerate quickly into a large horizontal velocity as they jump. Regardless of what it may look like, they don't stay in the air any longer than they would for a standing jump with the same vertical force. They just seem to hover in the air because we don't often see people capable of

exerting that much force both horizontally and vertically at the same time.

Did you notice any similarities in this situation with that of weighing yourself in an elevator? They both are cases where the forces of gravity and contact alternate between being balanced and unbalanced because the contact force strengthens and weakens.

5–4 MOOSE PULLING A LOG

A classic example from previous incarnations of this book is a moose** pulling a log with a rope. Analyze the forces involved and explain how the moose and log move forward. We must track the forces a little more carefully than for jumping or standing on a scale, so let's go through the checklist.

1. What role does gravity play? It keeps both the moose and the log on solid ground but is balanced out by contact with the ground. It will not cause any acceleration forward or backward and so it may be ignored in this example.

2. Are charged objects involved? No.

3. What role is carried out here by contact forces? The moose's feet push against the ground. The moose pulls on the rope and the rope pulls on the log. By the Third Law, the ground (Earth) pushes back on the moose, the rope pulls back on the moose and the log pulls back on the rope.

4. Do contact forces cause friction that opposes motion? Yes. There is friction between the log and the ground.

Figure 5.4 illustrates all the forces mentioned above. *Figure 5.4a* shows the moose before starting to pull. All forces on both the moose and the log are balanced.

In *Figure 5.4b*, the moose accelerates forward. All force pairs arising from a single interaction are the same color in the diagram. Closely examine the forces on the moose. There is no vertical acceleration so we will ignore the balanced forces of gravity pulling down and contact forces pushing up. Horizontal contact with

---

*If it seems odd to think that the floor pushed back, consider what would happen if the man were pushing just as vigorously while hanging two feet off the floor on a chin-up bar. He can push all he wants but if his feet are not in contact with the floor, the floor will not push back and he will not accelerate up.

**We refer you to Animal Husbandry 101 to learn how you get a moose to do this.

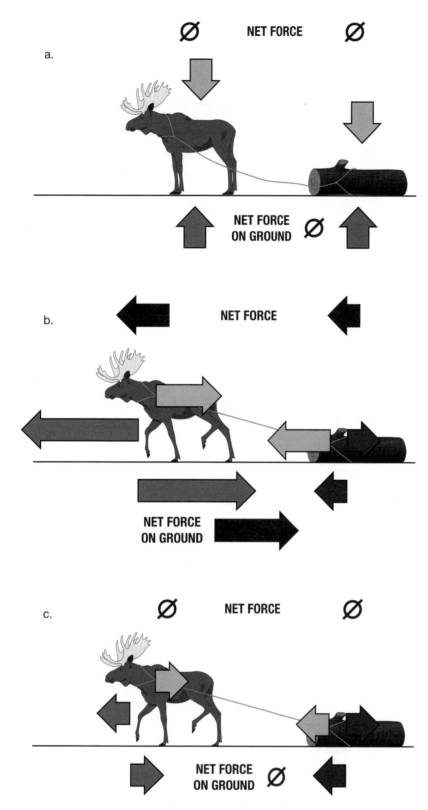

Figure 5.4

What forces are involved when a moose pulls a log?

a) Before moving, the moose and log have no force between them. Gravity and contact with the ground balance out.

b) The moose and log accelerate forward because there is a net forward force on both of them. Although the force on both is not the same, their accelerations are the same. Do you understand why?

c) The moose and log now are moving forward at uniform speed. Once again there are no unbalanced forces on them. However, the moose must continue to push forward to balance out the frictional force on the log.

the ground creates an opposite and equal force pair (shown in dark purple). Contact forces with the rope between the moose and the log create a second force pair (shown in light purple). The total horizontal force on the moose is unbalanced to the left and the moose moves forward.

Now look at the horizontal forces on the log. Contact between the moose and the log via the rope creates the light-purple force pair. Friction with the ground creates the red pair. The force of friction is less on the log than the force of the rope is on the log. The log responds to the net force and goes forward with the moose.

In the last panel the moose and log move forward at a constant speed. There are horizontal forces on them both that were not there before they started moving, but they are balanced. When the moose stops pulling, the friction force pushing backward will become unbalanced, causing the log and moose to stop.

Notice in *Figure 5.4b* that when the moose accelerates forward there is a net force on the Earth. This force, required by the Third Law, equals the force on the moose but is in the opposite direction. Hopefully from the discussions in chapters 2 and 3 you realize that this means that Earth must accelerate backwards at the same time the moose and log accelerate forward.

Of course, there is more motion on Earth than a single moose and log. There are other moose, cars, trains, winds and ocean currents, etc. all pushing in random directions. The net effect of all these random forces cancels out and Earth continues to revolve, basically unaffected by the countless forces pushing against its surface.

However, there is one acceleration on Earth's surface that is massive and directed enough to have a noticeable effect on Earth's rotation. As mentioned in chapter 3, the Moon's gravity pulls on Earth's oceans and they move in response, creating daily tides. As the ocean tides accelerate in response to the Moon's gravity, the net effect is to cause Earth's rotational speed to slow down. To compensate for this slowing, the atomic clocks that are the standard time keepers for the world are adjusted yearly to add one or two seconds at midnight on January 1. Tides have been slowing Earth's spin ever since its formation. Fossil records indicate that 400 million years ago an Earth day was only 22 hours long.

5-5 AIR FRICTION

A housefly buzzes along a train track, flying directly at an oncoming train. Both are moving in a straight line at five mph (*Figure 5.5*). As long as they are not touching there is no interaction and therefore no force between them. Then the unobservant fly slams into the oncoming train. At that moment the fly and the train both experience an opposite and equal force. The fly's motion reverses direction while the train continues on, seemingly unaffected.

The train's change in motion is different from that of the fly's because by the Second Law of Motion the resulting accelerations are not the same. Suppose the train weighs 100 tons while the fly weighs one-thousandth of an ounce, which is about 10^{-8} tons. By the Third Law of Motion:

$$\begin{array}{ccc}\textbf{force of train} & & \textbf{force of fly} \\ \textbf{on the fly} & \textbf{=} & \textbf{on the train}\end{array}$$

The Second Law allows us to substitute mass times acceleration in place of force. So we have

$$\begin{array}{cc}\textbf{fly's} \times \textbf{fly's} & = \textbf{train's} \times \textbf{train's} \\ \textbf{mass} \quad \textbf{acceleration} & \quad \textbf{mass} \quad \textbf{acceleration}\end{array}$$

Rearranging the terms we have

$$\frac{\textbf{fly's acceleration}}{\textbf{train's acceleration}} = \frac{\textbf{train's mass}}{\textbf{fly's mass}}$$

$$= \frac{\textbf{100 tons}}{\textbf{10}^{-8} \textbf{ tons}}$$

$$= \textbf{10}^{10}$$

In plain language, that formula says the fly accelerates ten billion times (10^{10}) more than the train does. The fly changes speed from five mph to the right to five mph to the left for a total change in speed of 10 mph. The train accelerates one ten-billionth of this amount so its speed slows down by only one billionth of a mile per hour. No wonder the train seems unaffected.

This example is a good way to explain air friction. As a train goes down the track, it comes into contact with a huge number of air molecules. Each molecule accelerates out of the way when the train collides with it. Each collision causes the train to accelerate backward. The change in speed caused by the collision with one air molecule is very, very small. It is much less than the change in speed caused by the fly because an air molecule has a much smaller mass than a fly does. However, there are so many air molecules that the tiny force exerted by each air molecule adds up quickly and ultimately creates a significant effect on motion.

Air friction exerts a considerable force on automobiles, airplanes, falling objects, etc. that increases rapidly with increasing speed. A car going 60 mph experiences four times the frictional force that it does when going 30 mph. To balance the increased frictional forces at faster speeds, a car engine must push harder than it has to push at slower speeds.

If air friction and friction internal to the car did not exist, a driver could get on a level freeway, accelerate up to speed, turn off the engine, and glide to their destination using no more fuel. While that is not possible, modern cars are often designed for better gas mileage through using tilted windshields and sleek, rounded fronts that minimize air friction by striking the air as indirectly as possible.

Figure 5.5

At the moment of impact, both the fly and the train experience the same force. But the fly accelerates 10^{10} times more than the train does.

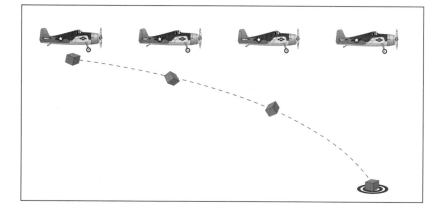

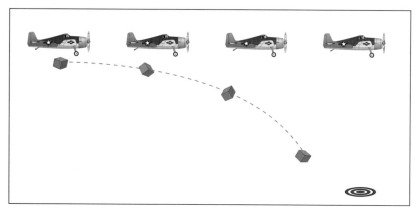

Figure 5.6

a) In the absence of air friction a package dropped from an airplane will stay directly under the airplane as it falls.

b) With air friction, the package slows in both its forward and its downward motion as it falls.

Table 5.1 – A Falling Body with Air Friction

The distance, velocity, and vertical acceleration of a free-falling skydiver, taking friction into account. Velocity is presented here in familiar units of miles per hour as well as the more standard units of meters per second. Compare with *Table 1* in Chapter 3. A terminal velocity of approximately 130 mph is reached after about 25 seconds.

Time (seconds)	Distance (meters)	Velocity (m/sec)	Velocity (miles/hr)	Acceleration (m/sec²)
0	0	0	0	9.80
1	4.9	9.8	22.0	9.52
2	19.4	19.3	43.3	8.70
3	43.1	28.0	62.9	7.50
4	74.9	35.5	79.7	6.09
5	113.4	41.6	93.4	4.72
6	157.4	46.3	103.9	3.49
7	205.5	49.8	111.8	2.51
8	256.5	52.3	117.4	1.75
9	309.7	54.1	121.4	1.19
10	364.4	55.3	124.1	0.83
20	935.9	57.6	129.5	0.01
30	1513.2	57.7	129.6	0.00

5–6 SKY DIVING

A pilot flying an airplane wants to drop an object on a target on the ground far below. To do this the pilot must release the object well before the airplane is actually over the target. While trying to figure out exactly when to release the package, the pilot remembers that in accordance with the First Law of Motion, the object will drift horizontally at the same speed as the airplane as long as there are no unbalanced horizontal forces, such as air friction, acting on it. Without friction they would just see the package descend directly below them, neither getting ahead of nor falling behind the airplane. So to hit the target, the package should be released at just the right time so as to hit the ground just as the plane flies over the target.

In reality, air friction creates an unbalanced horizontal force that pushes against the object's forward motion just as soon as the object is dropped from the plane. As a result the object's forward motion will slow down, and it will drift behind the airplane. Air friction against the bottom of the package will also push against its downward vertical motion, causing it to hit the ground at a later time as well.

The amount of air friction affecting the downward movement of the package depends on the size and shape of the package. *Table 5.1* below gives the vertical acceleration that would result if the object were an average-sized skydiver free-falling from an airplane. It is the same as *Table 3.1* except that air friction is now being taken into account.

The forces, acceleration, and velocity of a skydiver are shown in *Figure 5.7*. At zero seconds, the instant when the skydiver jumps from the airplane, the acceleration is 9.8 m/sec², the full acceleration of gravity. At this moment the skydiver has no vertical speed, experiences no vertical air friction and gravity pulls on the skydiver's body unopposed by any vertical contact forces.

As the skydiver falls faster and faster, the upward frictional force on her steadily increases. This force pushes against the downward force of gravity, decreasing the net force. After 30 seconds the speed is great enough that the forces of friction and gravity balance and the net force and acceleration go to zero. At that point the velocity remains constant. For an average-sized

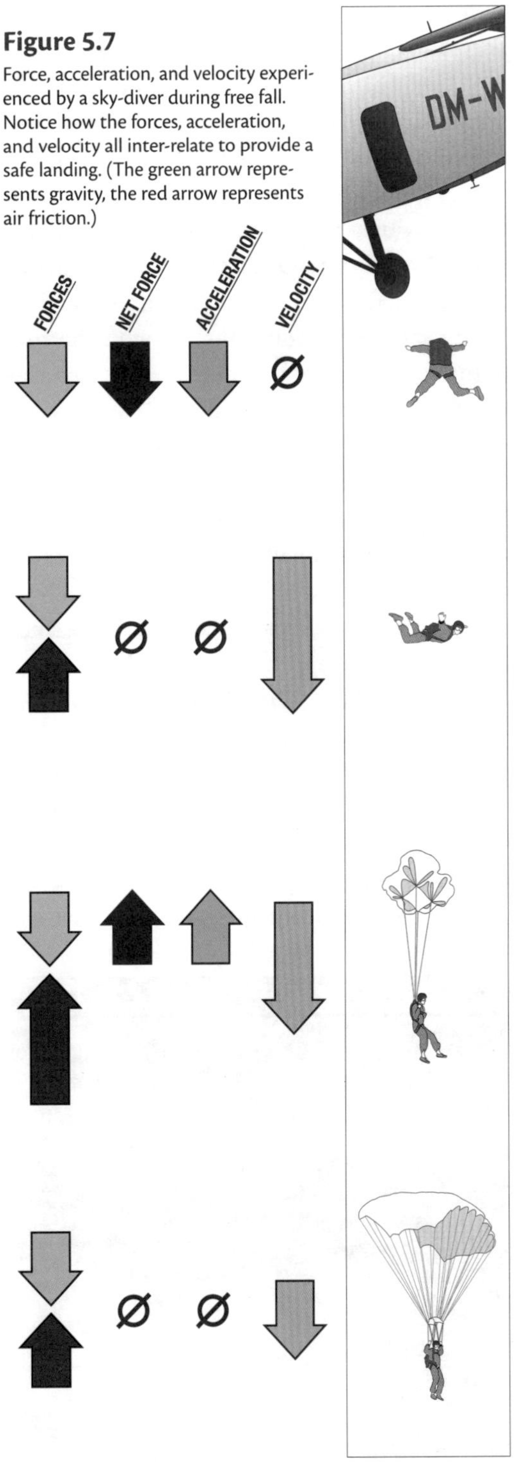

Figure 5.7
Force, acceleration, and velocity experienced by a sky-diver during free fall. Notice how the forces, acceleration, and velocity all inter-relate to provide a safe landing. (The green arrow represents gravity, the red arrow represents air friction.)

FORCES   NET FORCE   ACCELERATION   VELOCITY

anced upward force gives her an upward acceleration causing her downward speed to decrease.

As she slows down, the upward frictional force also decreases. Her speed will continue to decline until friction again balances with gravity at a speed of about 15 mph, slow enough to land safely.

5-7   THE BROKEN ELEVATOR

Suppose you enter an elevator at the top of a 10-story building. Just after you get in, the elevator cable breaks and you start to plunge to the ground far below. Is there anything you can do to save your life? Quickly you decide to try and cancel out the speed of the elevator's fall by jumping up as hard as you can just before the elevator hits the bottom.

Understandably anxious, you immediately crouch down and prepare to jump. But instead of moving down to the elevator floor, your head goes down, your feet go up, and you seem to be suspended motionless in the middle of the elevator car! "What is going on here?" you ask as you continue to plummet downward.

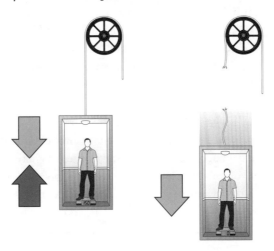

Figure 5.8
When the elevator cable breaks, the elevator no longer exerts a force on you. Your weight is unbalanced and you and the elevator accelerate downward together at the same rate.

Let's analyze the forces.

person the value of the constant velocity is about 130 mph.

The force exerted by air friction depends on surface area as well as speed. Suppose our sky-diver jumps from an airplane and reaches a speed of 130 mph. She pulls her ripcord, the parachute expands open, and the total surface area suddenly increases by a factor of 20. The force of air friction now suddenly increases by a factor of 20 as well. The total force on the sky-diver is now unbalanced upward. This unbal-

1. What role does gravity play? Gravity pulls both you and the elevator car down

2. Are charged objects involved? No.

3. What is the role of contact forces? Before the cable broke, contact between the cable and the elevator car held the car up. Contact between your feet and the elevator car floor pushed you up. When the cable broke both contact forces went away.

4. Is friction present? Yes, there will be air resistance in the elevator shaft pushing against the car as it falls. We will ignore it for now.

Recall from Chapter 3 that all objects accelerate at the same rate regardless of their mass. In the absence of air friction the elevator car will accelerate at the same rate that you accelerate. Both you and the car will fall with increasing speed until you both hit the bottom of the shaft after 2.5 seconds at a speed of over 50 mph.

Although you, inside the elevator, are speeding up as you fall, the elevator moving downward at your same rate makes you unaware of your increasing velocity. You seem to be "weightless," floating in the air, unaware of any motion. NASA uses this same effect, but in a controlled, non-life-threatening way, to train astronauts for outer-space weightlessness. A specially outfitted NASA airplane takes trainees high in the air and then dives down at the same acceleration rate as gravity. The astronauts float freely in the bay of the plane for a few minutes until the pilot pulls the aircraft out of the dive and flies back up to repeat the experience.

Going 50 mph in a falling elevator car is a significant speed. To save yourself you must somehow cancel it out before you and the faulty elevator reach solid ground. Suppose you do manage to jump up with a mighty force just before hitting the ground. In a split second you accelerate from 50 mph to zero. Does this save you? Unfortunately, the answer is "no."

It turns out that the amount of force behind such a huge acceleration would be just as hard on your body as hitting the ground. Only stopping gently with a smaller acceleration and therefore a smaller force will save you. (You might be relieved to know that all modern elevators have emergency brakes that stop them gently and safely if a cable breaks. No one has ever been killed in a falling elevator car).

5–8   GOING INTO ORBIT

NASA's space shuttle sits poised at Cape Canaveral, ready to launch on an important scientific mission into space. As the count hits zero, rockets ignite, vapors pour from the exhaust nozzles, the ship shudders and slowly lifts off.

Gaining speed, it quickly rises high and beyond spectators' views as it enters the clouds.

The Third Law explains how a shuttle launch occurs. When the engines fire up, they begin to burn fuel inside their internal chambers. This creates an expanding exhaust which pushes against the entire surface of the chamber walls. The structurally strong, rigid chamber walls in turn push back. Burning, expanding gas escapes only through nozzles at the bottom of the chambers because here nothing opposes the gas's tremendous pressure.

The exhaust nozzles allow an unbalanced force downward, as shown in *Figure 5.9*. As the burning and expanding gases push out of the nozzles, a force equal and opposite pushes up on the shuttle in accordance with the Third Law. If the gases had not escaped downward, the shuttle could not have launched upward.

Just after launch, the shuttle tilts from vertical flight to a more horizontal trajectory pointed toward the east. As with the projectile from Newton's cannon in chapter 3, the space shuttle needs to increase its *horizontal* speed as it lifts above Earth to go into orbit. By the time the engines are turned off, it will be above the

Figure 5.9
The shuttle Endeavor accelerating at about 29m/s^2. The shuttle lifts off because the upward force created when exhaust gases are ejected through the exhaust nozzles exceeds the downward force of gravity. The crew experience a force up to three times greater than gravity during liftoff.

Figure 5.10
When in orbit, the shuttle no longer needs to fire its rockets. It glides easily along in free fall under the sole influence of gravity.

atmosphere going fast enough horizontally to ensure that it never hits Earth as gravity accelerates it downward.

Half an hour after liftoff the engines are shut off and the spacecraft drifts in an orbit going west to east around Earth. While in orbit, the shuttle is in a state of **freefall** similar to the plummeting elevator in the previous example. "Freefall" describes anything that falls under the pure influence of gravity and no other forces. Unlike the broken elevator, where air friction was ignored for our convenience, a shuttle is in true freefall because it orbits high enough above the atmosphere to avoid significant frictional forces. Thus, the shuttle drifts along without additional help from the rockets.

Astronauts are pinned to their seats from the force of the engines as they accelerate into space. As soon as the shuttle engines stop, they are no longer pressed against their seats but begin to freefall as well. This state is incorrectly called "weightlessness." The astronauts have weight since gravity is still pulling on them. (Of course, being now 600 kilometers farther from Earth's center than they were before launch, their "space" weight is about 20 percent less than their "Earth" weight.) But just as a person in a broken elevator accelerates downward at the same rate as the elevator car, the astronauts are accelerating around in an orbit at the same rate as the shuttle. Being in freefall with the same acceleration as the shuttle makes the astronauts appear to be weightless.

For the shuttle to reenter Earth's atmosphere, it is first maneuvered around so that the exhaust nozzles are facing forward. The rockets are fired to decelerate the shuttle's forward motion. Downward velocity from the pull of gravity now exceeds the shuttle's slowed forward velocity. It descends back to Earth, and glides to a landing in Florida.

5-9 CENTRIPETAL ACCELERATION REVISITED

Now consider any object traveling in a circle at constant speed. The object might be the space shuttle orbiting Earth, a planet moving around our sun, a ball twirled on the end of a string, a child on a merry-go-round, or a car turning a street corner. Each of these objects' direction of motion is constantly changing. We know from the discussion in Chapter 2 that a net sideways force must exist on each of the objects. The force pulls toward the center of the circle that they move on, causing them to constantly turn towards the center.

If the direction of the force is difficult to visualize, imagine the objects' movements if there were no sideways force in action. All the objects would travel in a straight line. Only a sideways force pushing or pulling the object toward the center of the circle can change its motion from a straight line to a circular path.

Sideways forces are called **centripetal** or "center-seeking" forces. The word "centripetal"

+ **Freefall**
The act of always falling under the pure influence of gravity.

+ **Centripetal Force**
A force sideways to the motion of an object. Centripetal forces cause objects to turn toward the center of a circle.

Figure 5.11
Sideways forces cause objects to turn toward the direction of the force. The stronger the force, the tighter the turn.

does not describe the interaction from which the force arises. Instead, it describes the direction in which the force acts (sideways to the motion) and the kind of acceleration it causes (turning or changing direction). The strength of the net force required to cause an object to move with circular motion depends on the radius of the circular path and the object's speed and mass. It can be derived from the Second Law of motion and has the mathematical form:

$$\text{Force} = (\text{mass} \times \text{speed}^2)/\text{radius}$$

An object moving in a circle experiences an inward force with exactly this strength. If the force is weaker, the object turns less tightly and forms a larger circle. If the force is stronger, the object turns more tightly and forms a smaller circle.

You know from experience that you will be pressed against the left side of a car traveling around a right-hand curve at high speeds. To you it may seem that a force is propelling you out away from the circle, not in towards its center. This apparent outward force is sometimes called a "**centrifugal force**." In this case our sensations lead us astray. If an object experiences no centripetal force, it moves in a straight line and leaves the circle. It is not "thrown outward" any more than a car passenger's head is thrown forward when the car stops.

The centrifugal force is therefore not an independent force compelling objects to move outward. You press against the side of the car because your body naturally wants to continue moving in a straight line. The inside of the car pushes against you, causing you to turn, and by the Third Law you push back with equal and opposite force. The "centrifugal force" is the "Third Law's reaction" to the centripetal force turning you inward.

♦ **Centrifugal Force**
The force, required by the Third Law, of an object pushing back against the centripetal force.

5–10 Magnetic Levitation

We turn now to an example of motion created by the electromagnetic interaction. Recent advancements in engineering are making it increasingly possible that someday magnetically levitated, or **maglev**, trains will be built to connect major cities. The physical principles they are based on are a good illustration of how the electromagnetic force can be harnessed.

Electric currents passing through wires create a magnetic field. Two coils beside each other with currents going in opposite directions will create magnetic fields that repel. These fields can be quite strong if the current is large enough. The repulsion can be strong enough to cause a maglev train car to lift an inch or more above a magnetized track.

Maglev trains would not use fuel or electrically powered engines. Instead, a maglev system's cars would be fitted with large guidance magnets attached to their undercarriages. The trains would run in a guideway like that shown in *Figure 5.12*. Electric coils would line the guideway. Some of the coils would repel the large magnets on the train's undercarriage, levitating the train just above the guideway bottom. Once levitated, power would be supplied to coils within the guideway walls to create a system of changing magnetic fields that both push and pull the entire train forward. The electric current supplied to the coils in the guideway walls would alternate to change their magnetic polarity. This change in polarity would cause the magnetic field in front of the train to pull the vehicle forward, while the magnetic field behind the train would repel (push) it in the same direction.

Maglev trains now in the experimental stage in Japan, Europe, and the U.S. are of several designs, but all float on a cushion of air, eliminating friction. The lack of friction and the trains' aerodynamic designs allow them to reach speeds of more than 310 mph, about half the speed of a commercial airliner. Developers predict that maglev trains will someday link cities that are

Figure 5.12
A diagram of the track of a maglev train rail.

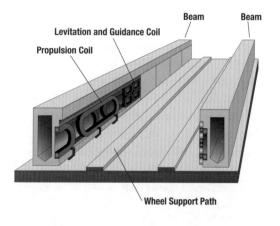

up to 1,000 miles apart. At 310 mph, you could travel from Salt Lake City to Los Angeles in just over two hours.

5–11 A FINAL PERSPECTIVE

Having waded through all these examples, it is good to stop and consider again the foundation of what we are doing when we apply Newton's Laws of Motion.

Science assumes every phenomenon in the Universe has a cause. It further assumes that the relationship between all causes and their effects is governed by laws. If this were not true we would be forced to memorize thousands of details about how different objects react under different circumstances to make sense of our world. Or, worse still, the Universe would behave in an unpredictable, whimsical way and we would have no understanding of it at all.

Newton's Laws of Motion have been tested for more than 300 years and found to be valid in an immense number of experiments and applications. As we have seen so far in this book and will see in future chapters as well, they correctly describe the motion of objects from the size of molecules to the size of galaxies. They are accurate for speeds from zero to tens of thousands of kilometers per second. Their advent changed history. Through them, mankind stopped seeing nature as being capricious and mythical. We began to understand that all of nature was obedient to certain definable, testable, and repeatable rules.

Viewed from our vantage point now, it all seems simple. The actual discovery of these laws, however, took mankind many hundreds of years. If it is so simple, why did it take so long?

When we face all the experiences and tests of life without guidance, life can be extremely bewildering. Selecting those experiences that lead to general principles is difficult when they seem at first no different from all the others. The contribution of a genius such as Newton is to separate the important from the unimportant and then combine the whole into broad laws that can explain almost everything. Only then can the rest of us stand back and exclaim, "How obvious!"

Comprehension

This chapter deals with applications of laws presented in chapters 2–4. For comprehension questions, please review the questions at the end of those chapters.

Analysis and Synthesis

1st Law

1. Provide an example of an object at rest that is experiencing no forces.

2. Provide an example of an object in uniform motion that is experiencing no forces.

3. Provide 2 examples of an object at rest that is experiencing 2 or more forces. What forces act on the objects? How do their sizes compare?

4. Provide 2 examples of an object in uniform motion that is experiencing 2 or more forces. What forces act on the objects? How do their sizes compare?

5. Why doesn't the 1st law apply to an object experiencing a single force.

6. Do the 1st and 2nd law of motion ever apply to the same object at the same time? Explain.

2nd Law

1. Provide 2 examples of an object experiencing an unbalanced force in the direction it is moving. What do these objects have in common?

2. Provide 2 examples of an object experiencing an unbalanced force opposite the direction it is moving. What do these objects have in common?

3. Provide 2 examples of an object experiencing an unbalanced force perpendicular to the direction it is moving. What do these objects have in common?

4. Give 2 examples of an object with zero velocity that is accelerating.

5. Give 2 examples of an object accelerating while moving at constant speed.

6. How many forces are acting on the moon? What is causing these forces? Why does the moon move around its orbit? Why doesn't it hit the Earth?

7. If you have 2 balls, a 1kg ball and a 2kg ball, and you push on them with the exact same force, how do the accelerations compare? Why?

8. Since all objects near the surface of the Earth experience the same gravitational acceleration when dropped, does this mean that they are experiencing the same gravitational force? Why or why not?

9. On Earth, people often exercise by playing catch with a medicine ball (an extremely heavy ball). Would the same exercise work on the space station? Why or why not?

10. In science the word "weight" means the gravitational force acting on an object. Using this definition, are objects in orbit around the Earth weightless? Explain your answer.

3rd Law

1. When a book is at rest on a table, its weight and the contact force from the table are equal and opposite. Are these forces and action-reaction pair? Explain your answer.

2. 10 year old Bobby challenges his 4 year old brother Tiny Tim to an arm wrestling match. Bobby wins without trouble. How is this possible if Tim pushes on Bobby as hard as Bobby pushes on Tim?

3. The BYU Society of Physics Students (SPS) challenges the BYU football team to a tug of war, with the one condition that the SPS get to pick the playing field. The football team accepts, and the SPS announce that the match will take place at the 7 peaks ice arena with the football team on the ice and the Physics Students standing on the concrete in the entrance to the rink. The SPS will try to pull the football players off of the ice onto the concrete, and the football players are trying to pull the SPS off of the concrete onto the ice. The first team to have a player touch the boundary between ice and concrete wins. Use Newton's 2nd and 3rd laws to explain the strategy of the SPS.

Common Misconceptions About Newton's Laws

Anyone who has been around 6 month-12month old baby for long has watched him repeatedly drop things seemingly fascinated just to watch them fall. One of the advantages students have when studying Newton's laws is that they have been experimenting with these laws from the time they first started tossing peas off of their high chair. So, they already have a reasonably good understanding of how things behave. The disadvantage is that some of their ideas are incorrect. What follows are a list of common student misconceptions about Newton's laws.

The following ideas are *incorrect*. If they sound reasonable to you, please go back and review the appropriate material. Hopefully looking at common mistakes now will help prevent them on exams.

1. Misconceptions about motion

a. An object must always accelerate in the direction it is moving. If you are moving upwards, you are accelerating upwards. If you are moving backwards, you are accelerating backwards. For example, if you throw a ball straight up, it accelerates up for the first part of its trajectory, then accelerates downward as it returns to the ground.

b. An object has no acceleration if its speed is zero. For example, a ball is not accelerating at all at the highest point of its trajectory.

If either of these sentences sounds plausible to you, you should review section 2–2 on acceleration and the examples of the elevator found in section 5–1 and jumping into the air found in section 5–2. Acceleration depends on how speed or direction is changing. It does not depend on any current value of velocity.

2. Misconceptions about Newton's 1st Law

a. An object experiencing a net force of zero has no forces acting on it. For example, an object is only at rest if there are no forces acting on it.

b. Forces can only be balanced when an object is at rest.

c. If an object is moving, there must be a net force in the direction it is moving. Once you remove this force, the object will come to rest. (Some students believe that it will come to rest immediately, others that it will stop more gradually.) This misconception is very common and very difficult to get rid of. For example, until recently the Utah state core curriculum said that there were two forces on the moon, an inward force to make it move in a circle and a nonexistent force pushing it in the direction it moves.

If any of these statements seems correct please review sections 2–1 and 5–6 where objects are moving at a constant speed with no net force. If you believe c., also review section 5–8. Be aware that many students hang on to misconception c. on the grounds that "something must have pushed on it once to get it moving in the first place." Even if a force acted on an object at some point in the past, that does not mean it is acting on the object now. As discussed in 5–8, the rocket engines don't push on the ship once they are turned off.

3. Misconceptions about Newton's 2nd Law

a. Acceleration depends only on the size of the force, not on mass. For example, because gravitational acceleration is the same for all objects, the Earth's gravity must pull on everything with the same amount of force.

b. In outer space, in the absence of gravity, all objects accelerate the same in response to the same force. Without gravity, it is as easy to push a one-ton piece of equipment as it is to push a piece of paper.

c. If there is a net force acting on an object its speed must change. For example, since the speed of the moon is constant, the forces on it are balanced: gravity balances the centripetal force.

If either a. or b. seems correct, see sections 2–4 and 2–5. Mass always matters. If you believed statement c, review section 5–9. The force on the Moon is most certainly not balanced, and the Moon accelerates. A change in direction is also an acceleration.

4. Misconceptions about Newton's 3rd Law

a. The "action" force and "reaction" force can both act on the same object. For example, when a book is sitting on a table, the book's weight and the contact force from the table form an action reaction pair.

b. An object's motion is determined by Newton's 3rd law, especially when it is a rest. In the example above, the reason that all the forces on the book are balanced is because of the 3rd law of motion.

c. The 3rd law doesn't apply to objects in motion. If you are pushing a chair across the floor at constant speed, the force you exert on the chair must be larger than the force the chair exerts backwards on you.

d. The 3rd law doesn't apply to objects in accelerated motion. If you loose an arm wrestling match, it is because your opponent pushed harder on you than you pushed on him.

e. When two things collide, the larger object exerts a larger force. For example, when a fly hits the windshield of a train, the train exerts more force on the fly.

Sections 2–6, 5–4 and 5–5 all apply Newton's 3rd law. If any of the above statements appear to be true, you should review these sections looking specifically for reasons why it is incorrect. If a careful review still leaves you wondering why the statement is wrong, please ask your teacher or a teaching assistant.

CHAPTER 6

FORCES IN FLUIDS

We have mainly used large, familiar objects to illustrate the Laws of Motion and the law of gravity. Of course, these laws apply equally well to small, microscopic objects, like molecules. In chapter 5 we discussed how friction arises from Newton's laws being obeyed by molecules as they push against objects moving through air. Let's explore this idea a little further.

Air, like all gases and liquids, is classified as a **fluid** because it flows. All fluids push with friction against the motion of objects moving through them. This friction becomes stronger when an object moves faster through the fluid since the acceleration of the molecules it strikes is greater. The amount of friction also depends on the number of molecules that contact the object. Denser fluids, like water, generate larger amounts of friction than thinner, less dense fluids like air.

Friction is only one aspect of force within fluids. There are forces from gravity and pressure as well. Mathematical formulas have been developed to describe how these forces behave. Like the formulas that describe friction, they are built upon Newton's laws, the law of gravity, and models of how the electromagnetic interaction holds molecules together.

The rules of fluid behavior are used every-where in our lives. They are the basis of well-designed home heating and air-conditioning systems. They allow engineers to plan and build massive dams and city water and sewage systems. Sportsmen fly hot-air balloons and go scuba diving in accordance with them. On a grander scale, these rules are used to explain the flow of rivers, the movement of mountains, the drift of continents, and even the behavior of the Universe itself when it was just a few minutes old. In this chapter we will consider some aspects of forces in fluids.

6–1 PRESSURE

Forces exerted by fluids are best described by **pressure**. Pressure is defined mathematically as:

Pressure = Force/Area

To illustrate what this formula means, assume you weigh 160 pounds and are standing motionless on a sidewalk. You are therefore exerting 160 pounds downward against the cement. This weight is carried by your feet, which have a surface area in contact with the ground of about 400 square centimeters. If your 160 pounds of weight is dispersed evenly on your

All the water in the world cannot sink the smallest boat— until some gets inside.

~ Anonymous

LEARNING OBJECTIVES

When you finish this chapter you should be able to

• Explain what pressure is.

• State and describe the laws governing forces in fluids.

• Describe and discuss the law of buoyancy.

• Use the law of buoyancy to explain why some objects float and why some objects sink.

• Explain convection and its cause.

feet then you are pressing down with a force of 160/400 = 0.4 pounds on every square centimeter of the area of contact. In other words, four-tenths of a pound per square centimeter is the pressure you are placing on the sidewalk.

Suppose you stand on one foot. Now your 160 pounds is distributed over half the area as before and the pressure increases to 0.8 lbs/cm². Now stand on tip-toe. The area holding your weight is now reduced to about 2 cm², so the total pressure increases to 80 lbs/cm². Quite a difference! Your toes will soon begin to hurt as they support all that weight.

Pressure is a more crucial issue in many situations than force alone. For example, a pound is a relatively small force, but if distributed over a square that is one tenth of a millimeter on a side, its pressure would be 10,000 lbs/cm². Materials unable to bear this type of pressure would break even though this same force would not cause any damage when spread over a much larger area. A 98 pound woman rocking back on spike high heels puts more pressure on the point of contact with the ground than an elephant's broad feet do. Spike heels are designed to be fashionably attractive, but because they exert so much force on such a small area, they must be built exceptionally strong or they will break when worn.

Figure 6.1
Although the ballerina's weight doesn't change, she exerts a greater pressure on the floor when on point because her weight is distributed over a smaller area.

67

6–2 PRESSURE IN BOUNDED FLUIDS

Fluids that are completely confined inside a container are called "bounded" fluids. Examples would be a balloon or bottle of water with the cap screwed on tightly. The Frenchman Blaise Pascal discovered that if a pressure is brought to bear on one side of a bounded fluid, this pressure will spread throughout the fluid, causing this same amount of pressure to be exerted on all other sides as well. This rule, called **Pascal's Law,** can be stated as follows:

> *Pressure applied to any part of a bounded fluid transmits equally to every other part with no loss. The pressure acts at right angles to any surface in contact with the fluid.*

Pascal's Law means that the fluid pressure at all points on all walls of a bounded fluid is the same and that it pushes directly against the walls.

A balloon is a good example of Pascal's Law. Balloons behave like a spring. Just as a compressed spring pushes back harder the more it is compressed, a balloon pushes back harder against the air inside it the more it expands. But even though the total pressure inside a balloon increases as it is blown up bigger, the distribution of this pressure is always even everywhere on the balloon walls. If you measure the pressure on the balloon walls at any given time, you would find the exact same value at all points on its surface.

Ordinary striped toothpaste is a great example of how pressure distributes uniformly through a bounded fluid. White toothpaste can be injected into a tube with different colored paste injected at the same time on the sides along the entire tube length, as shown in *Figure 6.2*.

• Fluid

Anything that flows. This refers to gases such as air and liquids such as water.

• Pressure

The force on an object divided by the area over which the force is applied.

Figure 6.2

Uniform distribution of pressure makes the different stripes of toothpaste emerge from the tube in the same proportions as they were inside.

When a person squeezes the tube, in the middle or at either end*, the tube pressurizes uniformly so that the white and colored paste experience the same pressure and come out together.

Hydraulic systems use Pascal's Law to harness and amplify force to lift and move heavy objects. Consider the bounded fluid in the curved cylinder in *Figure 6.3*. The piston on the right side has a total area of 100 cm², while the piston on the narrow left side has an area of just 25 cm². A force of 1 lb/cm², or 25 pounds in all, bears down on the left side. This pressure distributes throughout the fluid and emerges on the right side with the same strength of 1 lb/cm². However, the area of the right side piston is four times greater than the left. So the total force on the right side piston is also four times greater, or 100 pounds.

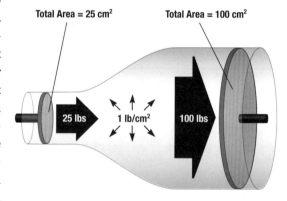

Figure 6.3

The pressure on the left side is the same as the pressure on the right side and everywhere in the container. But since the area of the right piston is four times greater that the area of the left piston, the total force on the right piston is four times greater than the force on the left piston.

6–3 PRESSURE IN UNBOUNDED FLUIDS

Fluids that lack boundaries on one or more sides, like the oceans or the atmosphere, we call "unbounded." Unbounded fluids are pulled toward the earth and held in place by gravity. If allowed to continue flowing, they will move downward until there is no lower place to go to.

---

* Whether or not a person should squeeze the tube at the end or in the middle is a question science is powerless to solve. Sorry.

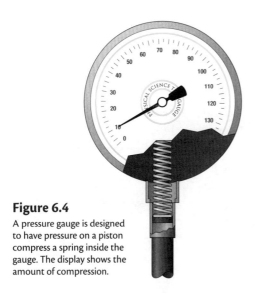

Figure 6.4

A pressure gauge is designed to have pressure on a piston compress a spring inside the gauge. The display shows the amount of compression.

You can investigate the distribution of pressure in an unbounded fluid using a pressure gauge like that shown in *Figure 6.4*. The gauge exposes a small surface area to the contact forces of the surrounding fluid. The pressure gauge measures the strength of the fluid's force by how much the fluid compresses the gauge's spring. Investigating pressure with such gauges has led to four basic rules that describe how pressure is distributed through fluids at rest. The term "at rest" refers to fluids that are not flowing along like a river nor swirling with internal eddies. The four rules are:

1. Pressure depends on depth. Greater depths have greater pressure.

Pressure at any depth equals the weight of the column of fluid directly above it. You can visualize the pressure at any level within a lake by picturing the column of fluid that rests above a square meter. If you could remove that column and measure its weight, that measurement would be the fluid pressure at that point. For example, the pressure of air at sea level is 14.7 lbs/in². Therefore the weight of all the air in the atmosphere above a square inch equals 14.7 pounds. The top of Mount Everest is above 70% of the air, so air pressure there is only 4.5 lbs/in². In contrast, the water pressure in the deepest trench of the ocean floor is over 16,000 lbs/in²!

It may seem incredible that the atmosphere exerts a pressure of almost 15 pounds per square inch over the entire surface of your body. Your body has a lot of square inches. The total resulting force is thousands of pounds, enough to crush even a hard-bodied weight lifter to a pulp.

Fortunately, we aren't crushed because the pressure inside our bodies balances the outside air pressure. We typically do not even notice air pressure.

2. Pressure is the same for all points at the same depth.

Pressure does not depend on the surface area or volume of a fluid. It only depends upon depth. As amazing at it seems, a 100 foot tall dam holding back a reservoir the size of Texas pushes against less pressure than a 300 foot tall dam holding back a one square mile lake. For that reason extremely tall dams are built only when absolutely necessary.

In times of flooding, people build containment dikes with sandbags. At the top of these temporary dikes, only a few sandbags are needed to contain the sides of a mighty river. However, as the river water rises and sandbags are added to the dike to increase its height, the sandbaggers must also build the dike broader and stronger at the base to balance the increased pressure there from the increasing water depth.

As a result of this rule, when we speak of air pressure at sea level, we do not need to make exceptions for local terrain like mountains and valleys. Pressure remains the same at sea level near a mountain in France as it does in a valley at sea level in Brazil. Pressure at sea level is the same everywhere in the world.

3. Pressure at a given depth is independent of direction.

At any given point, the pressure measured from any *direction* is the same. Imagine a tiny fish suspended motionless in the water. The fish cannot know the direction to the surface by sensing less pressure above it than below it. The pressure it feels coming from all directions is the same. If pressure were less from a given direction, the fluid would feel an unbalanced force and flow in that direction until the pressure equalized. Of course, by the first rule, a fish swimming around would notice that the amount of pressure changed as it changed depth, even though this pressure was still the same from all directions.

4. Pressure is always perpendicular to the surface of a submerged object.

When a boat floats on water, the water in contact with the bottom of it exerts a force that

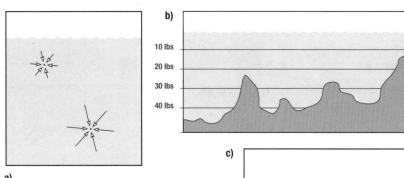

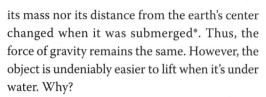

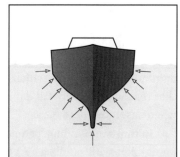

Figure 6.5

a) The pressure in a fluid is always greater the deeper you go. At any given point, the strength of the pressure, given by the length of the arrows, is the same from all directions. b) Pressure at the same depth in a fluid is the same regardless of local terrain. c) Pressure in a fluid is always perpendicular to the submerged surface. The arrows on the hull indicate the direction of the pressure.

♦ **Buoyant Force**

A force pushing upward on objects immersed in a fluid.

is always perpendicular to the surface it is in contact with (see *Figure 6.5*). With a totally submerged object, like a submarine, pressure always pushes directly inward perpendicular against the hull. If the pressure should ever push in any direction other than perpendicular, the fluid will flow until all side-ways forces balance out, leaving only a net pressure perpendicularly inward.

6–4 THE BUOYANT FORCE AND ARCHIMEDES' PRINCIPLE

Have you noticed that an object seems to weigh less when it is immersed under water than it does when it's taken out of the water? Neither

---

* The distance to the center of the Earth might change by a foot or two, but the effect this has on the force of gravity is so small it can be ignored.

its mass nor its distance from the earth's center changed when it was submerged*. Thus, the force of gravity remains the same. However, the object is undeniably easier to lift when it's under water. Why?

Consider the submerged ball in *Figure 6.6*. We know from the fourth law of pressure that a fluid pushes inward everywhere on a submerged object. From the first law we know that pressure in the fluid increases with depth. Looking at the pressure arrows in *Figure 6.6*, we see that the forces pushing horizontally on the ball balance out. However, the pressure on the bottom pushing up is greater than the pressure on the top pushing down. As a result there is a net upward contact force, called a **buoyant force**. This force balances out some of the object's weight, making it seem to weigh less.

There is a remarkably simple way to measure the buoyant force. First imagine that the space occupied by the submerged ball in *Figure 6.6* is instead filled with water (see *Figure 6.7*). Water at rest has balanced forces throughout. Therefore the forces on this ball-sized sphere of water are balanced. The only two forces present are gravity and the buoyant force. Because they are balanced, the buoyant force must equal the force of gravity which is, of course, the weight of the ball of water.

Now look again at the immersed ball in *Figure 6.6* and consider that it exactly fills the space previously occupied by the water. The surrounding water exerts a net upward force on the ball equaling the force previously exerted *on the ball of water*. This force is therefore equal to the weight of the water displaced by the object. This is the buoyant force. This rule, known as **Archimedes' Principle**, can be stated as follows:

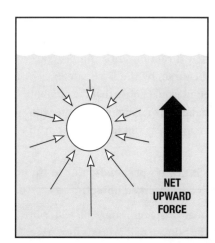

Figure 6.6 ⇨

Because forces in unbounded fluids increase with depth, all objects in a fluid feel a net upward force called a buoyant force.

NET UPWARD FORCE

Figure 6.7 ⇨

The buoyant force (orange arrow) on a ball of water exactly equals its weight (green arrow). If they were not equal, the water would flow until a balance was achieved.

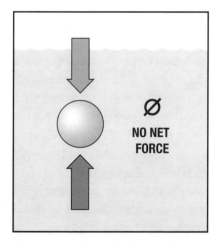

Ø NO NET FORCE

An object immersed in a fluid experiences an upward buoyant force caused by contact interactions with the surrounding fluid. The strength of this force equals the weight of the displaced fluid.

Archimedes (287–212 BC) was a brilliant man who lived in the Greek city of Syracuse in Sicily. Archimedes' Principle is so named because he used it to establish the gold content of a King's crown (See side box "Archimedes and the Crown of Gold").

6–5 FLOATING AND SINKING

An object in a fluid seems to weigh less because it experiences two forces: gravity pulling downward and the buoyant force pushing upward. The object accelerates in the direction of the net force, which is the direction of the stronger of these two forces. An object sinks if the force of gravity exceeds the buoyant force, and it rises if the buoyant force is stronger.

Consider the solid lead ball and air-filled beach ball of *Figure 6.8*. Both are the same size and have the same volume. When they are submerged they displace the same amount of water and experience the same buoyant force (shown as orange arrows). But the force of gravity is much greater on the lead ball than it is on the beach ball (shown as green arrows). Therefore the net force on each is different. The buoyant force on the beach ball exceeds the force of gravity and

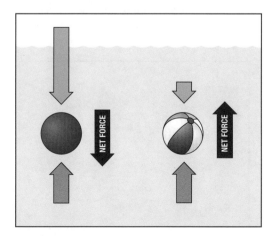

Figure 6.8

A lead ball and a beach ball, both of equal volume, are shown. Because they displace the same amount of water, the buoyant force on each is the same. But the heavier lead ball sinks while the lighter beach ball floats because their weights are so different.

ARCHIMEDES AND THE CROWN OF GOLD

Archimedes was a brilliant mathematician and inventor who lived in Syracuse on the east coast of Sicily during the second Punic War. He was the first to understand the significance and utility of the basic simple machines: the lever, the pulley, and the inclined plane. As an advisor to the King of Syracuse, he spent much of his time and talent devising ingenious ways to fend off invading Roman forces.

Deciphering which stories of antiquity are true and which are not is often difficult. This is particularly true of the tales of Archimedes because his city and its records were destroyed when Syracuse fell to Rome in 211 BC. The story of Archimedes weighing the crown of gold dates to 100 BC and likely has some truth to it, although the exact way he accomplished it is still uncertain. Whatever the truth may be, Archimedes' Principle derives its name from the following story.

The King of Syracuse asked Archimedes to determine if a crown he owned was pure gold or gold alloyed with cheaper silver. Chemical tests for purity were possible but all required that a piece of the crown be destroyed and the King wouldn't allow that. Archimedes needed to make this determination without harming the crown in any way.

Archimedes decided that he could determine the purity of the crown by making use of the fact that 1) silver is less dense than gold and 2) the buoyant force is equal to the amount of displaced water. He suspended the crown from one end of a scale and balanced it with an equal mass of pure gold suspended from the other end. He then immersed the suspended crown and the counterbalancing gold lump together into a container of water (*Figure 6.9*).

If the crown were pure gold then both the crown and the counterbalancing gold lump would be of equal density and volume. When submerged both the gold lump and the crown would displace the same amount of water, experience the same buoyant force, and the scale would remain in perfect balance. However, if the crown were partly silver it would have a greater volume than the pure gold lump, displace more water, and experience a greater buoyant force than the lump. As a result when both the crown and the lump were totally submerged, the total force down on the crown would be less than the downward force on the gold lump and the scale would tilt upward on the crown side as shown in *Figure 6.9*.

As the story goes, the crown was seen to be higher in the water than the gold lump, thus failing the purity test to the demise of the unfortunate artisan who made it. It is also said that Archimedes discovered this technique while sitting in a public bath. He became so enthused at his discovery that he went running naked into the streets shouting "Eureka! Eureka!" (I have found it! I have found it!)

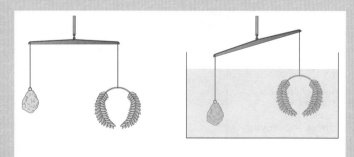

Figure 6.9

Archimedes was able to determine the purity of a crown of gold by using the buoyant force to check the crown's density.

the beach ball will rise to the surface. Gravity exceeds the buoyant force on the lead ball and it will sink to the bottom.

Now imagine two objects that have the same weight but different volumes (*Figure 6.10*). Suppose they are both made of iron but the larger ball is hollow and the smaller ball is solid. Since the hollow ball is larger, the buoyant force acting on it is larger. If the larger ball's buoyant force exceeds its weight, the net upward force will cause the ball to rise to the surface. The buoyant force on the smaller solid ball is less than that on the hollow ball. If the volume of water

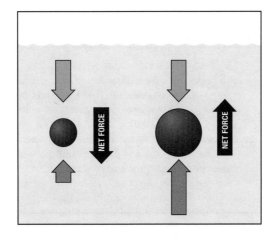

it displaces weighs less than that ball's weight, the solid ball will sink even though its weight and the weight of the hollow ball are the same.

For solid objects, the rules regarding floating and sinking relate to **density**. The definition of density is

density = mass / volume

If a solid object has a greater density (or more mass per cm³) than that of the fluid in

which it is placed, it will sink. If its density is less than the fluid's density, it will float. This is true regardless of the size of the object.

A solid object that is less dense than the fluid it is in will float at a level where the buoyant force equals the weight of the entire object. The greater the difference between the density of the object and the density of the fluid, the higher the object will float.

Icebergs illustrate this point. The density of ice is 90% of the density of fresh water. Therefore 90% of an iceberg's total volume will displace enough fresh water to equal the iceberg's total weight. An iceberg in a freshwater lake floats with 90% of its volume below the water and 10% above (*Figure 6.11*). Freshwater ice is only 70% the density of salt water. When a freshwater glacier "calves" an iceberg and currents carry it out into the open ocean, that iceberg will float higher, with 30% of its volume above the water line and only 70% of its volume beneath the surface.

Objects that are not solid may or may not float depending on their shape. Consider an aluminum sailboat on a lake. Aluminum, like iron, is denser than water, but (like the hollow iron ball in *Figure 6.10*) aluminum boats still float because they are built to obey Archimedes' Principle.

Boats have broad bottoms and empty interiors. The broad bottoms cause them to displace a large volume of water after sinking a relatively small distance. The empty interior decreases the *average* density of the boat (or in other words decreases the weight the boat would have if it were solid) so that the buoyant force balances the weight before the boat sinks down very far into the water (*Figure 6.12*).

Figure 6.10
A solid iron and a hollow iron ball, both of equal weight, are shown. Because they displace different amounts of water, the buoyant force on each is different. The larger hollow ball floats while the smaller solid ball sinks because their buoyant forces are so different.

• **Density**
An object's mass divided by its volume.

Figure 6.11
Solid objects like ice float if they are less dense than water. Freshwater ice is 90% the density of freshwater and floats 90% submerged. Freshwater ice is just 70% the density of heavier saltwater and floats 70% submerged.

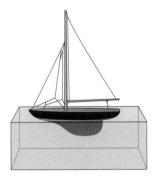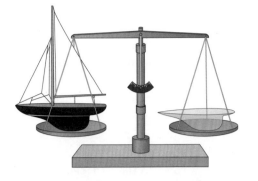

Figure 6.12
A sailboat sinks into water until its entire weight equals the weight of the water it displaces. The shape of the displaced water is the shape of just the submerged portion of the boat.

Every boat and ship, regardless of its size, its shape, or what it's made of, is designed to displace its own weight and the weight of its passengers and cargo well before it is submerged. If a boat springs a leak and takes on water then the weight of the incoming water adds to the overall weight of the boat, causing it to sink lower. If the boat sides sink below the surface and water comes pouring in, the boat—now completely incapable of displacing more than its weight in water—will sink to the bottom.

6–6 BUOYANCY IN THE ATMOSPHERE AND EARTH'S CRUST

Balloons filled with helium float in accordance with Archimedes' Principle. Helium is a gas that is much lighter than air. When the weight of the balloon plus the helium inside the balloon is less than the air it displaces, the balloon rises. A balloon of the same size filled with average temperature air could never rise because the balloon itself has weight and the density of the air inside the balloon is the same density as the air outside of it.

Hot-air balloons are able to overcome the pull of gravity and rise even though they are filled with normal air. A hot-air balloon gains buoyancy when the air inside it is caused to become less dense than the air outside. When a hot-air balloon envelope (the large colorful part) is first partially filled with air it lays on the ground, unable to lift up. The balloon operators then ignite propane burners on the basket below the envelope which heat and expand the inside air, reducing its density. When the combined weight

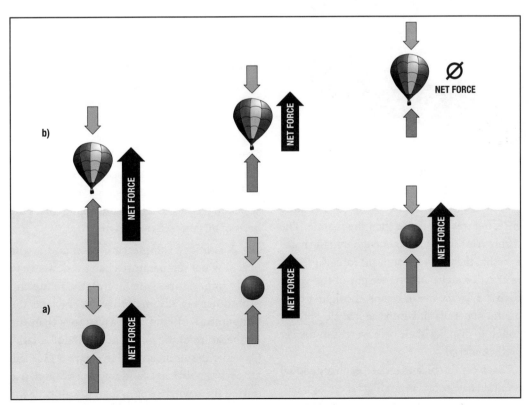

Figure 6.13
a) Solid objects in water will float or sink but not hover because water keeps the same density with depth. b) A balloon in air will hover because the buoyant force decreases with height as air density decreases.

of the cage, passengers, envelope and the hot air inside it becomes less than the weight of the air displaced by the expanding envelope, the balloon will float up into the atmosphere.

Air and water are both fluids, but there is a major difference between them. Water, like most liquids, has essentially the same density wherever it is, regardless of its depth in an ocean or lake. A ball light enough to rise through water will always come to the surface because the buoyant force does not change with depth (*Figure 6.13*).

Air, however, decreases in density with height. As a hot-air balloon rises, the buoyant force on it decreases as the density—and therefore the weight—of the surrounding air decreases. The rising hot-air balloon will eventually reach a point where the forces on it are balanced and it will hover, neither ascending nor descending. To descend, the operator reduces the buoyant force by either letting air out of the envelope or by allowing it to cool and contract.

An interesting example of buoyancy occurs between Earth's crust and mantle. The outer layer of the mantle is hot enough to have some characteristics of a fluid (see Chapter 28). The continents and ocean basins actually float in the

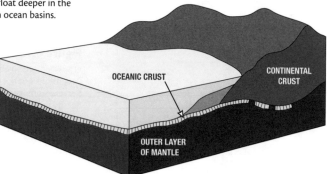

upper mantle in much the same way that ships or icebergs float in water.

The crust beneath Earth's oceans is quite dense, but it is less dense than the mantle. The oceanic crust sinks just far enough into the mantle so that the resulting buoyant force supports the crust's weight and the weight of the water above it. Like the ocean basins, the lighter continental materials sink into the mantle only far enough to displace their own weight in denser mantle material.

Each continent, and indeed each individual mountain has "roots" extending far enough into the mantle to provide the buoyant force necessary to support it. The taller a mountain or the more massive a continent is, the deeper the roots must be. Just as larger icebergs have more volume below the surface than smaller ones do, a large mountain has more volume below the surface of the land than a smaller mountain does. If the amount of material increases on a mountain or continent—for example, by the formation of a glacier or the eruption of a massive lava flow—the underlying crust sinks, over time, deeper into the mantle. If material is removed—for example, by erosion or the melting of a glacier—the underlying crust will rise. The general principle governing this fluid-like equilibrium in the Earth's crust is called **isostasy**.

6–7 CONVECTION

One final manifestation of buoyant forces that we will encounter several times in this book is convective currents, like those that create winds. If a fluid has different sections within it that are at different temperatures, those sections will also have different densities. The hotter, less dense sections will tend to rise while the denser, cooler sections will tend to sink, creating circulation currents in the fluid.

Lava lamps illustrate this. Lava lamps are containers filled with fluid and lumps of a waxy substance. When the lumps are cool they are denser than the surrounding fluid and sink to the bottom where the light is. The light heats the lumps, which expand as a result. They soon become less dense than the fluid and rise to the top of the lamp. At the top, away from the heat source, the wax cools and again becomes denser than the fluid. The wax descends to be reheated and rise again in a never-ending cycle. This cycle of heating, rising, cooling, and falling forms the basis of all convective currents.

A similar example cam be found at the beach. Water temperature changes slower than land temperature. During the day as the sun beats down equally on both water and land, the temperature of land increases more than the temperature of the ocean bordering that land. Consider the air illustrated in *Figure 6.15a*. The air over the warmer land becomes less dense during the daylight hours than the air over the

♦ Isostasy
Equilibrium in the earth's crust such that the buoyant forces elevating landmasses balance the gravitational forces that depress them.

Figure 6.14
Earth's crust floats on the outer layer of the mantle. Although the continental material is lighter than the oceanic material, it is thicker and has a greater total weight. As a result, continents float deeper in the mantle than ocean basins.

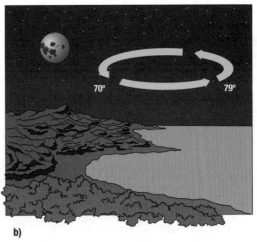

Figure 6.15

a) Daytime convection pattern near a seashore. Because the land is warmer, surface air currents blow into land as the air over it rises. b) Nighttime convection pattern near a seashore. Because now the water is warmer, surface air currents blow away from the land as the air over the ocean rises.

cooler ocean water. As a result it rises relative to the cooler air. As the warm air rises it leaves a gap. Something must take its place so the cooler ocean air flows in. The hotter air then circulates out to the ocean, cools and sinks down to replace the cooler air that moved toward the land. This motion creates a circular flow that gives rise to cool surface breezes coming in from the ocean to the land during the daytime.

At night the land loses heat faster and everything described above reverses. The air over the land becomes denser than the air over the ocean. It sinks relative to the ocean air, causing the air to circulate in the opposite direction. The surface winds now blow away from the land (*Figure 6.15b*).

Circulation in a fluid caused by differences in temperature and density is called **convection**. Convection ovens use air convection inside the oven chamber to spread heat out uniformly and quickly. Convection creates the many broad circulation patterns in the Earth's atmosphere and oceans. Convection currents exist in Earth below the crust and are related to how crustal plates drift from place to place on Earth's surface (see Chapter 30).

♦ **Convection**
Circulation in a fluid caused by temperature and density differences.

Chapter Framework

A. Introduction
1. Friction in fluids
2. Forces in fluids

B. Pressure
1. Pressure = Force/Area

C. Pressure in Bounded Fluids
1. Pascal's Law
2. Hydraulic systems

D. Pressure in Unbounded Fluids
1. Four basic rules of pressure
    a. *Pressure depends on depth*
    b. *Pressure is the same for all points at the same depth*
    c. *Pressure at a given depth is independent of direction*
    d. *Pressure is always perpendicular to the surface of submerged object*

E. The Buoyant Force and Archimedes' Principle
1. Archimedes' Principle

F. Floating and Sinking
1. A balance between gravity and buoyancy
2. Density

G. Buoyancy in the Atmosphere and Earth's Crust
1. Atmospheric density changes with height
2. Water density is constant
3. Isostasy

H. Convection
1. Temperature changes density
2. Density differences cause convection

Comprehension

True/False
1. _____ Air is considered a fluid.
2. _____ If an object floats, the buoyant force on it is larger than its weight.
3. _____ Frictional forces increase when an object moves faster through a fluid.
4. _____ A man standing in a swimming pool weighs less because water partially shields him from the full force of gravity.
5. _____ Objects that float in air, such as helium balloons, are weightless.
6. _____ If you apply a force over a larger area, the pressure decreases.

a. *Fluid*
b. *Buoyant Force*
c. *Convection*
d. *Viscosity*
e. *Isostasy*
f. *Unbounded fluids*
g. *Bounded fluids*
h. *Pressure*

Matching
1. _____ The force on an object divided by the area over which the force is applied.
2. _____ Circulation in a fluid caused by temperature and density differences.
3. _____ A measure of how easily objects travel through a fluid and how easily the fluid itself flows.
4. _____ Fluids pulled toward Earth and held in place by the force of gravity.
5. _____ General principle that governs the fluid-like equilibrium in Earth's crust.
6. _____ Equals the weight of the displaced fluid.
7. _____ Anything that flows.
8. _____ Type of fluid where pressure acts with equal force on all areas of the confining walls.

Fill in the Blank
1. Pressure in a fluid increases with _____.
2. Lava lamps provide an example of _____ currents.
3. If an object is completely submerged, the buoyant force is equal to the weight of _____. If it is floating, the buoyant force is equal to _____.
4. The total force on an object at any depth equals the _____ of the column of fluid directly above it.

Analysis

1. If a block of wood floats with half its volume submerged,

    a) the buoyant force is equal to half the weight of the block.
    b) the weight of the block is the same as that of the displaced water.
    c) the volume of the block is the same as that of the displaced water.
    d) the buoyant force is equal to twice the weight of the displaced water.
    e) the buoyant force is equal to twice the weight of the block.

2. The buoyant force on an object submerged in a fluid can be changed by

    a) changing the volume of the object, without changing the weight of the object or the weight per unit volume of the fluid.
    b) changing the weight of the object, without changing the volume of the object or the weight per unit volume of the fluid.
    c) changing the weight per unit volume of the fluid, without changing the weight of the object nor the volume of the object.
    d) Two of the above answers are correct.
    e) All of the answers (a), (b), and (c) are correct.

3. In convection currents hot air rises and cool air descends. Which of the following is correct?

    a) There is a buoyant force on a volume of hotter air, but there is not a buoyant force on a volume of cooler air.
    b) The gravitational force pulls harder on each kilogram of cooler air than it does on a kilogram of warmer air.
    c) The buoyant force on the hotter air is upward, while the buoyant force on the cooler air is downward.

d) The warmer air has a lower weight per unit volume than the cooler air which it displaces.

e) The warmer air has a higher weight per unit volume than the cooler air which it displaces.

4. The base of a dam is reinforced to accommodate for possible increases of pressure. Which of the following would cause such an increase?

   a) An increase in rainfall causing an increase in the volume of water released by the dam.

   b) A change of climatic patterns that will increase the lake's depth over the next several years.

   c) An increase in the lake's area.

   d) A large number of boats creating larger wakes that will hit the dam with greater force.

5. Which exerts the largest amount of force on the ground?

   a) A swimming pool full of water.

   b) An identical swimming pool full to the exact same level with a 200-lb log floating on top.

   c) An identical swimming pool full to the exact same level with 2 170-lb people swimming in it.

   d) An identical swimming pool full to the exact same level with a 50-lb block sitting on the bottom.

Synthesis

1. Explain why pressure can be more useful when talking about forces exerted by fluids than force alone.

2. How do convection currents form?

3. State and explain the four rules that describe how pressure distributes through a fluid at rest.

4. Identify the following as an unbounded or bounded fluid.

   a) Can of shaving cream

   b) Bowl of water

   c) Fluid in a hydraulic system

   d) Mountain lake

   e) Venus' atmosphere

5. Scuba divers can get the bends if they change pressure too rapidly. Would it be more dangerous to surface rapidly from a depth of 40 ft in the ocean, or a depth of 40 ft in a narrow pool formed in an old quarry?

6. How do contact forces and pressure give rise to the buoyant force?

7. In grade school you are told that density determines whether an object will float or sink. In this course you are told to compare buoyant and gravitational forces. Explain how the two are equivalent.

8. How does isostasy relate to the Archimedes' Principle?

9. If you drop a rock into water, the buoyant force remains virtually unchanged as it sinks, but if you release a helium balloon, the buoyant force changes as it rises. Explain why.

10. A few days after purchasing a helium balloon, it will float in mid-air with the string barely touching the floor. As long as you don't touch it, the balloon does not move.

    a) What can you conclude about the net force on the balloon?

    b) What individual forces act on the balloon?

    c) Explain how your answers in (b) and (c) relate to one another.

11. A large rubber balloon is filled with helium at ground level and released. Some balloons that suffer this fate will rise rapidly and pop. Others will drift for hours at about the same level,

    a) What forces act on the balloon after it is released?

    b) What is the direction of the net force when the balloon first begins to move?

    c) What will happen to the air pressure as the balloon rises?

    d) What will happen to the volume of the balloon as it rises?

    e) What is the buoyant force equal to?

    f) Given the possible fates of the balloon, does the buoyant force increase or decrease as the balloon rises? Why?

13. If you have two identical cups, filled as shown, can you make the cup with the most water float in the cup that contains the least water? Explain.

12. Three spheres of the exact same volume are submerged in a tub of water. After the spheres are lined up, they are released. The spheres are made of plastic with the same density as water, ice, and iron.

    a) Compare the weights of the 3 spheres.

    b) Compare the buoyant forces on the 3 spheres.

    c) What direction does the net force push on each of the spheres?

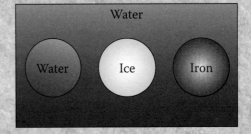

    d) What happens to each sphere after it is released?

    e) The ice sphere will rise to the top of the water then bob up and down and eventually come to a stop with part of the sphere protruding above the water's surface. Why?

MOTION AT HIGH SPEED

The most beautiful thing we can experience is the mysterious. It is the source of all true art and all science. He to whom this emotion is a stranger, who can no longer pause to wonder and stand rapt in awe, is as good as dead: his eyes are closed.

~ Albert Einstein

Scientific knowledge has grown exponentially since the closing years of the 17th century, when Sir Isaac Newton formulated his Laws of Motion.

The industrial revolution began in England a few decades after Newton's death. This was not a coincidence because his Laws of Motion helped create it. The technology that emerged from new industry also increased scientific knowledge by creating tools capable of making more precise measurements. Today in our modern world we can conduct more accurate and conclusive experiments than at any time in history. Scientists use this ability to search for new laws of nature while continuing to test and refine our knowledge of laws long since discovered.

How do we best test a law of nature? A good approach is to examine it under extreme situations. An extreme case for the Laws of Motion is high speed. In Newton's era, the fastest a person could move was about 20 m/sec (50 mph), the speed of a very fast quarter horse. Speeds rose after the automobile was invented and paved roads were built to drive on. Normal freeway speeds today are 30 m/sec (75 mph). Race cars approach speeds of 100 m/sec (225 mph).

Air travel caused another jump in speed. Commercial airplanes routinely fly faster than 240 m/sec (550 mph). A space shuttle in orbit travels at 8,000 m/sec (18,000 mph). The fastest man-made object ever, the Voyager I space probe, currently moves at 17,400 m/sec (39,000 mph) (see *Figure 7.1*). At all these speeds Newton's laws are perfect.

As impressive as some of these speeds are, we do not consider them to be "high speeds" in this chapter. We reserve that term exclusively for objects moving near the absolute limit of speed—the velocity of light traveling through space. This speed, denoted by the letter "c," is approximately 3×10^8 m/sec or 300,000 km/sec (6.70×10^8 mph).*

High speeds as defined here are never encountered in everyday life. Even the fastest rocket ships ever built, or that might ever realistically be built, travel at speeds less than one-ten-thousandth the speed of light. We examine subatomic particles in high-energy laboratories or distant astronomical objects to learn how real objects traveling at high speeds behave.

The question we ask is: "Do Newton's laws work exactly the same for speeds close to the

---

*The exact speed of light is 299,792.458 km/sec, but assuming it is 300,000 km/sec is adequate for our purposes. Light has this speed only in *the vacuum of space*. Through the atmosphere it interacts with air molecules which slow it down. Light projected through denser glass can slow down to less than 100,000 km/sec. This effect is touched upon in Chapter 11.

speed of light as they do for cars traveling 75 mph down the freeway?" In this chapter we learn to our amazement that *they don't!* At 30 percent of the speed of light, F = ma incorrectly predicts the acceleration of an object by 5 percent. At 80 percent of the speed of light, the prediction errs by more than 40 percent!

At high speeds, Newton's Laws of motion must be modified by rules that are part of the Special Theory of Relativity. This theory gives

us

LEARNING OBJECTIVES

When you finish this chapter you should be able to

- Describe how motion is defined.
- Identify the two postulates that are the foundation of the special theory of relativity.
- Discuss how those postulates lead to the conclusions of the special theory of relativity.
- Discuss what the special theory of relativity says about space and time.
- Identify and describe what we find for length, time, and simultaneity when objects moving near the speed of light are measured.
- Discuss both scientifically established and philosophical proofs of the special theory of relativity.

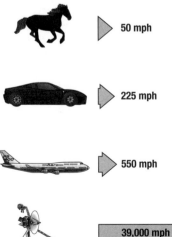

50 mph

225 mph

550 mph

39,000 mph

670,000,000 mph

Figure 7.1

A comparison of velocities. Even the fastest objects in our lives travel but a fraction of the speed of light.

The arrow for the beam of light extends 1.4 miles off the edge of the page.

unexpected and marvelous insights into time and space that have forever altered and expanded our understanding of the Universe.

7-1   MOTION AND RELATIVITY

Determining motion may seem trivial. A person standing still anywhere on the surface of the Earth is motionless, and an airplane, or a horse, or a snail moving past that person has motion. We have made this assumption tacitly in all discussions of motion thus far. But it isn't that simple. A person standing on the surface of Earth really *isn't* motionless. For starters, Earth spins around in a circle every 24 hours, creating day and night. Earth also moves around our Sun, which orbits the center of our galaxy, which moves in other ways as well. (Refer to the side-box "Your Everyday Motion.") With all of these motions taking place at the same time, our "real motion" is difficult to define.

Newton was aware of this issue. He postulated that a place existed, perhaps where God dwells, that could be considered the ultimate place of rest. He considered that God, the "Prime Mover," started the heavens in motion by pushing them from this place of rest. Mortal man's "true motion," then, could then be measured rel-

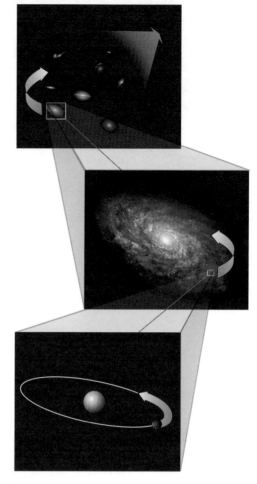

Figure 7.2

The Earth moves about the Sun, which rotates in the Milky Way galaxy. The Milky Way also has its own motion with respect to other galaxies.

YOUR EVERYDAY MOTION

Newton's First Law tells us that every state of motion feels just like any other state of motion as long as there is no acceleration. Life, therefore, feels the same whether a person is flying steadily through the air on an airplane, traveling at constant speed and direction in a car, or standing still in a classroom. This is fortunate because we undergo many different motions each day. It would be distracting to say the least if we felt them all.

We spin around with Earth, making one full revolution on a radius of 6,370 km every 24 hours. This spinning moves a person on the equator at 0.5 km/sec. Spinning in a circle is an accelerated motion which we should be able to feel. We don't notice it because the magnitude of the acceleration, only 0.000007 m/sec^2, is so small that the acceleration of gravity, 9.8 m/sec^2, easily masks it.

The Earth orbits the Sun at a velocity of 30 km/sec (*Figure 7.2*). The Sun spins around the center of the Milky Way galaxy at 220 km/sec. The Milky Way orbits about the center of a mass of nearby galaxies (called the "Local Group") at about 120 km/sec. The entire Local Group falls toward the center of a cluster of galaxies in the constellation of Virgo at a speed of about 250 km/sec. The Virgo cluster, in turn, falls toward a point called the "Great Attractor" in the constellation of Centaurus at a speed of about 570 km/sec.

The ultimate measure of our motion is with respect to a low-energy photon field left over from the "Big Bang." (See Chapter 34.) The light in this field is oriented randomly, creating a background that is uniform in all directions. Scientists have measured the Doppler shift (see Chapter 10) of this field caused by the total motion of Earth. This measurement indicates that our Sun moves at a speed of about 600 km/sec toward the constellation of Hydra. This is a large velocity but we do not feel it because our *acceleration* is very, very small.

All the velocities quoted above are measured with respect to another frame of reference. When we run out of references to compare against, we simply stop measuring!

ative to this location. However, Newton admitted that this idea could not be tested and therefore was unusable for science.

A better approach is to first note that motion is always defined with respect to something else. When we say we are standing motionless, we almost always mean with respect to the surface of Earth. When we say Earth moves in its orbit at 30 km/sec, we mean with respect to the Sun. Motion is always and only measured with respect to "reference frames," like the surface of the Earth or the Sun, which have their own state of motion as well. Because we can measure motion with respect to many different reference frames, no motion can be declared as the most correct measure of how we are moving. In other words, "absolute motion"—motion defined with respect to some place that is absolutely at rest—does not exist.

The idea that motion is only determined with respect to other objects and therefore has no absolute value is called **relativity**. Suppose you are driving an automobile down the freeway at 75 mph. If you take the car as your reference frame, you can say that you are motionless, because you are motionless within the car. You can also accurately say you are moving forward at 75 mph if you use the roadside as your reference frame. If you can ignore the looks of pity from the people you are talking to, you can also say that the roadside is moving backwards at 75 mph, if you again use the car as your reference frame. All these viewpoints are equally legitimate as far as the laws of nature are concerned.

Figure 7.3
The riders on the Octopus are in a non-inertial frame of reference, while those watching are in an inertial frame of reference.

7-2 MOTION SYMMETRY

Regardless of how we measure it, there are only two types of motion: accelerated and non-accelerated. For simplicity we call an object moving without acceleration an **inertial frame of reference**. Objects that accelerate we call **non-inertial frames of reference** (*Figure 7.3*). Inertial frames of reference do not accelerate, so no unbalanced outside forces act on them. Non-inertial frames of reference feel an unbalanced force and accelerate in response to it.

The term "frame of reference" is language from relativity. We can say we are stationary and the object moves, or the object is stationary and we move. Because we can be examined from the object's vantage point as well, a moving object also takes the role as a frame of reference.

True inertial frames of reference do not exist on Earth's surface because Earth is spinning. However, the acceleration from Earth's revolution is gentle enough to ignore for most experiments. With this caveat, we will consider a scientific laboratory, or a car or airplane or anything traveling in uniform motion to be an inertial frame of reference.

All experiments conducted in or witnessed from an inertial frame of reference must give results that do not change with the frame's location or measured velocity. If the results of your experiments changed every time you changed your velocity by defining it against a different frame of reference, the universe would be absurd and inconsistent. This idea, called **motion symmetry,** is defined as follows:

> *The laws of nature remain the same for all observers in inertial frames of reference.*

Motion symmetry is as fundamental as the related principles of position and time symmetry introduced in Chapter 1. Motion symmetry is also called the **special principle of relativity**. "Special" means it only applies to inertial frames of reference. Motion symmetry does not work when non-inertial frames of reference are being compared. The external force present in non-inertial frames can alter the results of any experiments performed in them.

To illustrate this, imagine that you wake up one morning and find yourself in a windowless room. Scattered around the room are many

Relativity

The idea that motion is only defined relative to other objects, which may have their own motion. There is no such thing as an "absolute" motion measured against objects that are absolutely at rest.

Inertial Frame of Reference

A place of being that is experiencing no acceleration. The laws of nature are the same when looking at the universe from an inertial frame of reference.

Non-inertial Frame of Reference

A place of being that is undergoing an acceleration.

Special Principle of Relativity

Another name for motion symmetry.

kinds of experimental equipment. A note on the table next to your bed says that you are either in a windowless airplane cruising at 30,000 feet on your way to London or that you are in the basement of a warehouse going nowhere. The note further explains that if you can prove which of these choices is correct by conducting an experiment, the person who played this trick on you will pay you one million dollars.

You excitedly accept the challenge but quickly realize you are doomed to fail. A steady cruising airplane and the basement of a warehouse are both inertial frames of reference. Motion symmetry tells you that no experiment can differentiate between them. So you sit back on the bed, dangling a plumb-bob in front of your face as you think. The plumb-bob reminds you that it hangs down in the same way for all inertial frames of reference on the Earth in accordance with the law of gravity. Suddenly, to your amazement, you feel a slight, steady force to one side and watch the plumb-bob drift in that direction. Excitedly, you realize that this can't happen in the basement of a warehouse but it can happen when an airplane accelerates by turning. A turning airplane becomes a non-inertial frame of reference, the experiment of hanging a plumb bob gives a different result than you would get in the basement of a warehouse, and you get the million dollars (right about the time you really wake up).

The science that studies non-inertial frames of reference is called the **General Theory of Relativity**. Only inertial frames of reference,

those considered by the special theory of relativity, will be discussed in the rest of this chapter.

7–3 GALILEAN RELATIVITY AND THE SPEED OF LIGHT

Our velocity can be quite different depending on how we choose to measure it. Suppose a lady is on board a train going north at 10 m/sec (*Figure 7.4*). She gets up and strolls to the rear of the car at 0.5 m/sec. A man seated in the same car measures her motion at 0.5 m/sec, moving south. However, a rail worker standing beside the train tracks measures her motion past him to be 9.5 m/sec, moving north. His measured value of 9.5 m/sec is the train's speed (10 m/sec) minus her speed (0.5 m/sec). A pilot flying due west high over the train at 30 m/sec, somehow also measures the lady's motion, the train's motion, and the airplane's motion together. Adding these motions as vectors, the pilot concludes that the lady's motion is 31.5 m/sec, mostly toward the east.

No paradox exists. The different measurements arise because the train moves with respect to the rail worker and the pilot moves with respect to both the train and the rail worker. Properly add or subtract these motions, take the surface of the Earth as the reference, and all three observers will agree that the lady moves north at a speed of 9.5 m/sec.

This common-sense interpretation is called **Galilean Relativity.** Galilean Relativity says that

• **Galilean Relativity**
The notion that a final speed vector can be computed by directly adding all individual velocity vectors together according to the rules of Euclidean geometry.

Figure 7.4
A lady walks on a train while a plane flies overhead. How many different speeds can be assigned to her? Are any speed values truer than the others?

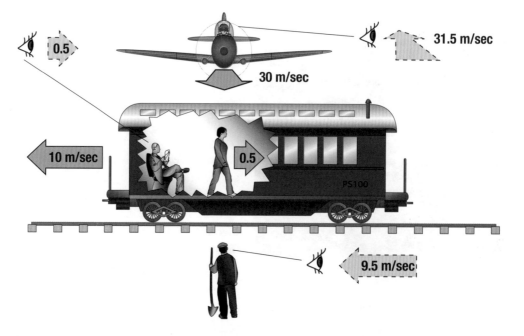

separate speed vectors combine together to form a total velocity vector according to rules laid out by standard trigonometry. Galilean Relativity holds true for all velocities encountered in everyday life. It forms the basis for many of the dreaded story problems every student has to solve in Algebra I. (e.g., Train A leaves Chicago at 11:00 a.m. bound for Detroit, traveling at 60 mph. Train B leaves at 11:30 a.m. from Detroit to Chicago, traveling 70 mph. When do the trains meet?)

In 1887, the great experimental physicist Albert Michelson and his colleague, Edward Morley, attempted to measure changes in the perceived speed of light caused by the orbital motion of the Earth. In a laboratory at Case Western Reserve University in Cleveland Ohio, they constructed a precise apparatus called an interferometer. Their interferometer was able to measure a change in the speed of light as small as 5 km/sec. They expected to find that by aiming a light beam in the same direction that the Earth orbited, the light's perceived motion would be 30 km/sec less because the Earth was traveling with the beam. When the light beam was aimed in the opposite direction, they expected to see the light beam's measured velocity to be 30 km/sec more because the Earth was now going towards the beam.

After years of trying, Michelson and Morley found that in either orientation the measured value of the light beam's speed remained unchanged! Disappointed, they proclaimed their experiment a failure. But they did not fail.

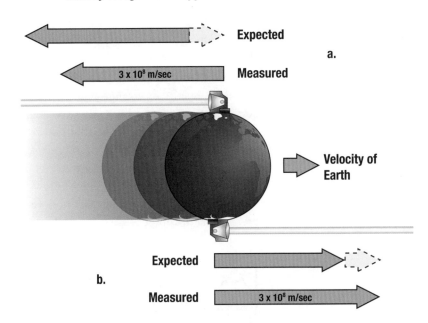

Velocity of Light Beam Opposite Direction of Earth's Motion

Expected

Measured — 3×10^8 m/sec

a.

Velocity of Earth

Expected

b.

Measured — 3×10^8 m/sec

Velocity of Light Beam in Direction of Earth's Motion

Figure 7.5
Results of the Michelson/ Morley experiment. Whether a light beam travels against the Earth's orbital motion (a) or with it (b), the measured value of its speed is the same.

Modern experiments have shown at a much higher level of precision that light indeed travels the same speed regardless of the velocity of the object emitting or receiving the light. In other words, *light does not obey Galilean Relativity.*

Return to the example of the lady on the train (*Figure 7.6*). Suppose that instead of her walking through the rail car toward the rear of the train, she shines a light toward the back of the rail car. As the light shines, she sees it travel at 300,000 km/sec. The rail worker sees the light beam and measures its speed at the same time as the lady measures it. He also measures a speed

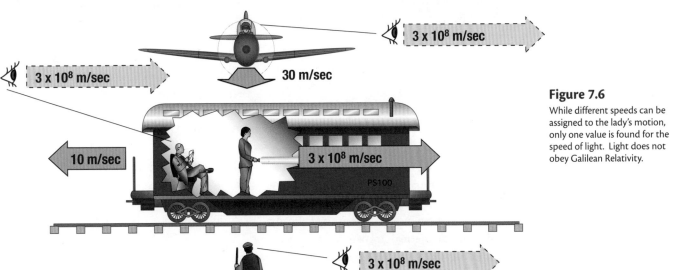

Figure 7.6
While different speeds can be assigned to the lady's motion, only one value is found for the speed of light. Light does not obey Galilean Relativity.

of 300,000 km/sec. Somehow the train's speed is irrelevant! The pilot flying overhead measures the light's speed and gets the same answer, 300,000 km/sec. The speed of light receives neither a boost nor a slowing from the motion of the receiver or of the sender.

This result is strange and makes us scramble to understand it. Only two explanations are possible. It could be that nature has rules for adding the velocity of light that differ from the rules of Galilean Relativity. Or it could be that adding the velocity of light follows the same rules as all velocity additions, and we just aren't using the proper rules!

7–4 THE SPECIAL THEORY OF RELATIVITY

Guided both by Occam's razor and by motion symmetry, Albert Einstein reasoned that it is simpler if all velocities, including that of light, added together by the same rules. The rules of addition could not be Galilean Relativity. Einstein and others, particularly the Dutch physicist Hendrick Lorentz (1853–1928), discovered a different set of rules for adding speeds. These rules, together with their predictions about time, mass, and space, are called the **Special Theory of Relativity**.

The Special Theory of Relativity rests upon two assumptions. We have already presented them, but for clarity we again offer them here:

1. All laws of nature are the same for all observers in inertial frames of reference (i.e. the principle of motion symmetry).

2. The speed of light in a vacuum has a constant value of approximately 300,000 km/sec, regardless of the speed of the device emitting or receiving the light.

Einstein actually formulated this theory before he learned of the Michelson-Morley experiment. In 1905 he was intrigued that one of the equations governing electromagnetism violated motion symmetry*. Lorentz had already found a mathematical transformation that repaired the violation but could provide no

acceptable explanation for why the transformation should be applied. Einstein showed that if the speed of light was the same for all observers, Lorentz' transformations could be derived in a simple, straightforward manner. Furthermore, his derivation indicated that Lorentz' transformations should be applied to light and *all* moving things.

Einstein's derivation was remarkably straightforward. However, it took the bold and unprecedented position that space and time are not absolute quantities. Lengths of objects change and their clocks tick at different rates when they move past at high speeds. Events that are simultaneous for you are not simultaneous when they are viewed by someone else moving past you. In other words, for Einstein's derivation to hold true, not only does absolute motion not exist, but neither do absolute space and time!

7–5 SIMULTANEITY AND LENGTH CONTRACTION

Einstein explained his theories using improbable stories he referred to as **gedanken** or "thought" experiments. Gedanken experiments are contrived situations designed to highlight certain effects. The following gedanken experiment was used by Einstein to explain how space and the simultaneity of events alter at high speeds.

A train moves along the tracks at 75% of the speed of light.[†] A woman we'll call Jane stands on the middle of one of its flatbed railcars. (See *Figure 7.7a*.) A man, Dick, stands on the side of the tracks. As Jane passes by Dick, lightning bolts strike both the front and back of Jane's flatbed car. Neither Dick nor Jane will know or can know that her car has been struck by lightning until light from the lightning bolts reaches them.

Figure 7.7 unfolds the story as seen by Dick. In *Figure 7.7c*, Jane has moved forward into the light beam coming from the forward strike. At that moment, Jane sees the light flash and knows her car was hit in the front by lightning. In *Figure 7.7d* light from both the forward and rear strikes

• **Special Theory of Relativity**
The theory of how objects in inertial frames of reference behave at high speeds.

• **Gedanken Experiment**
A situation of logic contrived to illustrate a particular effect.

*The equation is the *Lorentz Force Law*. Parts of this equation treated moving and stationary charges differently.

[†]Which is of course absurd for a train. Einstein used trains because trains were the fastest means of transportation when he published his theory. Had Einstein lived in our day he might have talked about rockets or space ships instead, even though traveling at 75% the speed of light is absurd for them as well.

has reached Dick. The beams arrive simultaneously because he was halfway between them and they hit at the same time. Then in *Figure 7.7e* the light from the rear strike catches up to Jane, who sees it happening after she has seen the forward strike.

You don't easily dismiss being hit by lightning! Dick and Jane get together later and discuss what happened. Dick exclaims, "Wow, wasn't that amazing! When you passed me on the train, two lightning bolts hit simultaneously on the front and back of your train car." Jane agrees that the lightning strikes were amazing but disagrees that they hit simultaneously. "No," she says, "The lightning hit first on the front then on the back of the car." "Well," replies Dick, "You think you were hit first on the front then on the back, but only because you moved towards the light from the forward lightning strike and moved away from the rear one."

Dick's explanation does not sit well with Jane. "If that were the case," she says, "Then the speed of the light beam coming toward me would have been greater than *c*. I would have measured its speed to be the train speed plus the speed of light or 1.75*c*. But it wasn't that value at all. It was just *c*, 300,000 km/sec. And the same is true for the rear strike. Moving away from it, my measured value would have been the speed of light minus the train speed or 0.25*c*. But that wasn't the case. Both light beams traveled at the speed of 300,000 km/sec when I measured them."

Jane then explains the situation as she saw it. Right before she passed by Dick, lightning hit the front of the car (*Figure 7.8b*). A few moments after she passed Dick, lightning hit the back of the car (*Figure 7.8d*). The spacing in time and position of the strikes was such that light from both bolts reached Dick at the same time (*Figure 7.8e*). To Jane, the car really was hit first in the front then in the rear by lightning. The strikes were not simultaneous.

Dick is puzzled. He agrees with Jane's logic, but he also measured a velocity of 300,000 km/sec for the light reaching him. He can't agree that the lightning hit the car at different times. He is halfway between the scorch marks and light from both bolts reached him at the same time.

Dick gets a brilliant idea. "I know!" he says. "The lightning strike left scorch marks on the tracks. Let's go measure the distance between

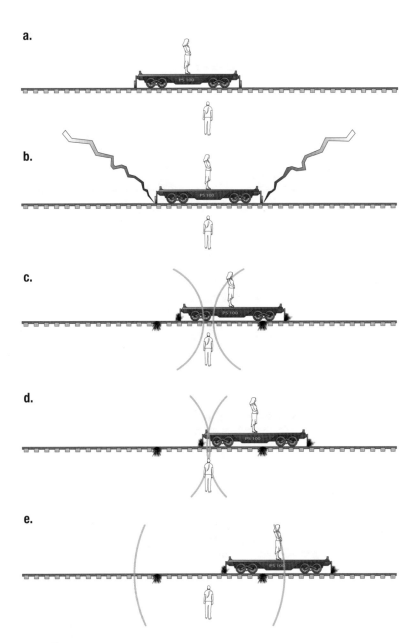

them. If I am right and lightning hit the front and rear of the car simultaneously, then the distance between the scorch marks must equal the length of the train car. But if lightning hit the car first in the front then in the rear, the distance between the scorch marks will be less than its length because the car moved forward between hits!"

They agree that this makes sense, so they hurry back to the tracks and measure the distance between the scorch marks. To Dick's astonishment, the length between marks *is* less than the length of the car! But Jane is puzzled too because the spacing between the marks is greater than she expected.

Dick and Jane are confused and seek advice from Albert Einstein. "Which one of our perspectives is correct?" they ask.

Figure 7.7

a) Jane traveling past Dick as seen from Dick's perspective. b) The train car she is riding is hit simultaneously front and back by lightning. c) Jane sees the light from the forward strike first. d) Dick sees light from both strikes simultaneously, e) Jane sees light from the rear strike last. Dick concludes Jane's train car is struck simultaneously on the front and back.

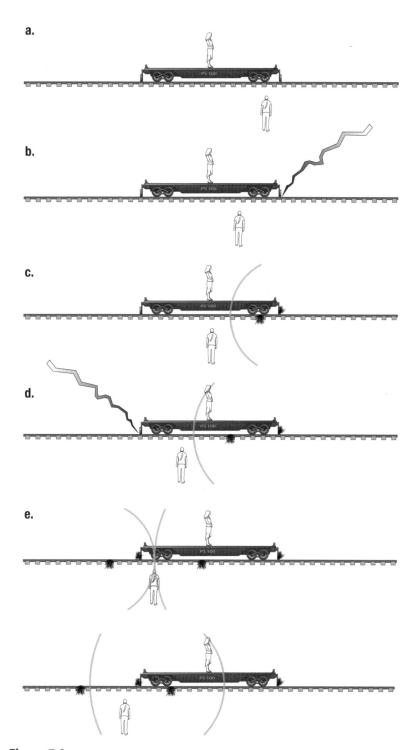

Figure 7.8

a) Jane traveling past Dick as seen from Janes's perspective. b) The train car she is riding is hit first on the front by lightning. c) Light from the front strike travels to Jane. d) Jane sees the light from the forward strike. At about this same time lightning strikes the rear of the train car. d) Dick sees light from both strikes simultaneously. e) Jane sees light from the rear strike last. Jane concludes her train car is struck first on the front and then on the back.

It is just that the length of the moving train contracted, causing the scorch marks on the tracks to be closer together than the real car length, an effect appropriately called **length contraction**. And Jane, your car was indeed hit first on the front, then the back, from your perspective. But length contraction is again an issue. The distance between scorch marks on the tracks is not as short as you expected because the tracks contracted and so a greater length than you expected was compressed in between the scorch marks."

Jane and Dick shake their heads, bewildered. "You want us to believe that moving things contract?" Jane protests. "While riding the train, I didn't feel like I had become thinner." Einstein clarifies, "You are measured to contract in the direction of motion only by someone who is not moving with you. Things that you move with always stay the same length. *Only when we measure moving things do they appear to contract. And the contraction is only in the direction of motion. Also, simultaneous events for us are not simultaneous for whoever is moving past us.*"

Dick and Jane probably still aren't entirely convinced. Admitting that times of events and measured lengths differ, depending on velocity, is certainly mind-boggling. But they must admit that Einstein's explanation does reconcile the different measurements they made.

The evidence for length contraction is not

"Both are equally correct," he replies. "By the principle of motion symmetry, Dick's point of view is not superior to Jane's point of view, nor vice-versa. Both views are equally valid."

"But how," they ask, "do we reconcile our two different sets of measurements of when the lightning struck and of the odd distance between the scorch marks on the tracks?"

"Well," Einstein replies, "as the train car went past Dick, it was indeed hit simultaneously on the front and back from Dick's perspective.

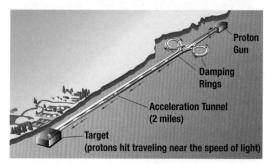

Figure 7.9

At the Stanford Linear accelerator the special theory of relativity is used in accelerating particles up to 0.99999999995c.

just from gedanken experiments. A machine at Stanford University called a linear accelerator is capable of accelerating particles up to 0.99999999995c. At these speeds, the tube that the particles travel through contracts from 2 miles to just over one inch in length, from the particle's perspective! The design and engineering of the accelerator took this length contraction into account when the machine was constructed. Otherwise the linear accelerator would not work.

7-6   TIME DILATION

A second gedanken experiment used by Einstein explains how time alters when we measure clocks moving past us. Once again Jane, the lover of open-air railroad rides, is on a rail car moving at 75% the speed of light past Dick, who once again is beside the railroad tracks. This time Dick and Jane each hold identical "light clocks." A light clock is just two mirrors facing each other with a light beam bouncing back and forth between the two mirrors. Each bounce of the light pulse is one "tick" of the clock. Dick's light clock is shown in *Figure 7.10*. The distance between mirrors, labeled "D" is four meters. The time it takes light to travel that distance is 4 ÷ (3

× 10^8) = 1.3 × 10^{-8} seconds. Dick, standing motionless beside his clock, measures 1.3 × 10^{-8} seconds between ticks. Jane also measures this amount of time between ticks on her clock.

Now Dick observes Jane passing him on a train car at a speed of 0.75c, as shown in *Figure 7.11*. From Dick's perspective, the light beam in Jane's clock travels in a diagonal path. The length the light must go between mirrors is three meters horizontally as well as four meters vertically for a distance of five meters, the hypotenuse of the triangle in the diagram.

If the speed of light increased with the train speed, Dick would see the light beam in Jane's clock take 1.3 × 10^{-8} seconds to travel the distance between mirrors, like it did when it was at rest. But, of course, it doesn't. The speed of light in Jane's clock has the same speed as the light in Dick's clock. Therefore, Dick will see a longer time between ticks in Jane's clock than in his clock because the beam in Jane's clock travels an extra meter between ticks. The prediction from this gedanken experiment is that *we measure moving clocks as running slow*. This effect is known as **time dilation**.

An experiment in which subatomic particles called mu-mesons (or just "muons") were used to test the time dilation effect showed time dilation to be real. Muons are unstable subatomic particles that can be easily created in lab-

• **Length Contraction**

The shortening of an object along its direction of motion as its speed approaches the speed of light, as measured by an observer not moving with the object.

• **Time Dilation**

The slowing of a clock as its speed approaches the speed of light as measured by an observer not moving with the clock.

STATIONARY

D = 4 meters

IN MOTION

Figure 7.10 ⇦

A stationary light clock. A pulse of light bounces back and forth between two mirrors spaced 4 meters apart. Each reflection of the light beam between the mirrors is a "tick" of the clock.

Figure 7.11 ⇗

For a light clock traveling at 0.75c, the beam travels 3 meters horizontally as well as 4 meters vertically, for a total "hypotenuse" distance of 5 meters. Since light always has the same speed, the time between ticks is greater. Therefore, moving light clocks are measured as running slow.

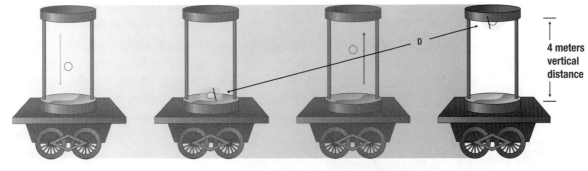

D

4 meters vertical distance

|← 3 meters horizontal distance (exaggerated) →|

oratories. Experiments show that muons exist for only 2×10^{-6} seconds, on average, after their creation. After that time, they change or "decay" into different particles. The muons' average lifetime can be used as a natural clock.

Cosmic rays naturally create muons in the Earth's upper atmosphere. When a rapidly moving proton strikes a nitrogen atom, a muon is born, often with velocities near the speed of light. Some of these cosmic-ray-created muons race down through the atmosphere toward the Earth, moving at 99 percent of the speed of light, and traveling almost 600 meters before they decay.

In 1931, scientists transported muon-detection equipment to the top of a high mountain. They measured the number of muons created by cosmic rays near the mountain top. Once they understood the number of muons being created, they moved their equipment to the bottom of the mountain. The mountain was so high that only the fastest, longest-lived muons, 5 percent of all the muons created at the mountain's top, should have made it to the bottom. Instead, more than half the muons arrived at the bottom intact. The muons could travel farther because their clocks ran slow from the scientists' perspective, allowing them to travel greater distances before decaying. From the muons' perspective, their time progressed at a normal rate and they did not live longer. However, the space they traveled through contracted so they could travel a greater distance through it in the 2×10^{-6} seconds of their intact existence.

7-7   THE TWIN PARADOX

Critics of the Special Theory of Relativity concocted a gedanken experiment of their own, called the "twin paradox," to show what many thought was a weakness in the theory. Leaving Dick and Jane and their railroad car, the critics offered the story of two identical twin babies, Jane and Sally, who are sent to visit their grandparents, who live on the planet Alderaan, 10 light years from Jane and Sally's home here on Earth. However, the rocket ship only has room for one twin, so Sally makes the trip first while Jane waits her turn.

Jane watches Sally's rocket ship lift off and fly at $0.99c$ toward Alderaan. Jane, truly a precocious baby, knows that at these speeds Sally's clock runs very slow. So Jane expects that Sally will not age at the same rate Jane ages. However, on board the rocket ship, Sally looks back as the Earth fades from view and also knows that Jane's clock runs slow. Sally thinks that Jane will not age as fast as Sally ages. A paradox! Both see the other's clock running slow. How can that be so?

The story has two frames of reference: Earth and the rocket ship. Earth can be treated as an inertial frame during the entire trip. The rocket ship is an inertial frame when gliding between planets. However, the rocket ship is a non-inertial frame of reference when it accelerates to take off and decelerates to land both on Alderaan and on Earth. Remember it is the *general* theory of relativity, not the *special* theory of relativity, that deals with non-inertial frames of reference.

Figure 7.12

a) Muons created at the top of the atmosphere by cosmic rays travel down toward Earth at speeds near the speed of light. b) Because of time dilation, they live longer when traveling than when at rest. More make it to the bottom of a tall mountain than would otherwise make it if there were no time dilation.

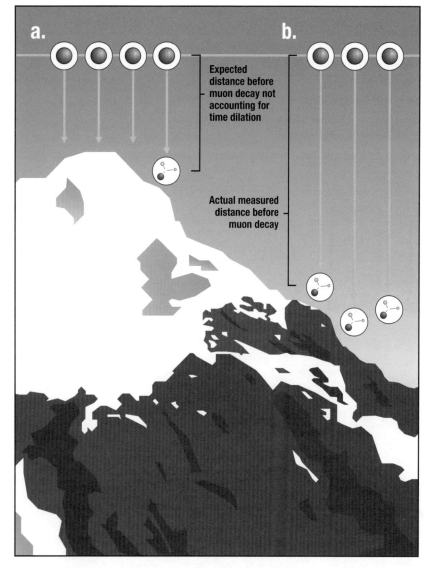

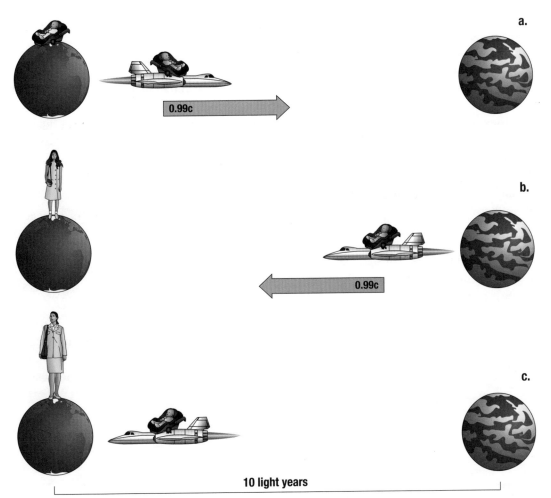

a.

b.

0.99c

c.

10 light years

Figure 7.13

a) Baby Sally takes a trip to Alderaan 10 light years away at near the speed of light while Jane stays home. b) As they travel both see the other's clock running slow. c) When Sally returns, they find that time for Sally, the twin who experienced acceleration, really did run slow. Jane has aged 20 years while Sally is still a few months old.

When the general theory of relativity is examined the paradox goes away. (Unfortunately, explaining exactly how the general theory of relativity resolves the paradox is beyond the scope of this text.)

Twenty years pass by. Sally's rocket ship makes the trip to the planet, turns around and returns to Earth. Jane, now twenty years old, anxiously awaits the reunion with her twin sister. The rocket lands and out crawls baby Sally, only a few months older than when she left! Although both saw the other's clock run slow, Sally, the twin who experienced the acceleration, was the one for whom time really slowed down.

Time dilation being made real by acceleration was confirmed by J. C. Hafele and R. E. Keating in October, 1971. Hafele and Keating flew four highly accurate atomic beam clocks on regularly scheduled commercial jet flights eastward around the world. The general theory of relativity predicted that the flying clocks, compared with reference clocks at the U. S. Naval Observatory, should have lost 40 billionths of a second during the trip. The lost time was observed just as predicted.

Surveying and navigation have been revolutionized by the global positioning system (GPS). GPS receivers calculate positions from timing signals sent from high-orbiting, fast-moving satellites. These receivers use relativity theory to compensate for the time dilation of the satellites. Without this correction they could not generate such highly accurate positions.

7-8   SPACE AND TIME

High speed objects contracting and their clocks slowing down may seem like magic. But it isn't magic at all. Rather, we have learned that time and space are not two totally different entities. Instead they are intertwined in what is called the "space-time continuum." Everything in the Universe occupies a place in space-time. As objects move past us at high speeds, we see more of their time aspect and less of their space aspect.

To explain what this means, think about the Pythagorean theorem which you studied in high school geometry. Following the symbols used in *Figure 7.14a*, the Pythagorean theorem says:

$$a^2 + b^2 = s^2$$

Now take the line segment **s** and rotate it on the grid as shown in Figure 7–14b. The ends of line segment **s** now have new values which we will label as **a'** and **b'**. Even though the values for **a'** and **b'** are different than they are for **a** and **b**, it is still true that

$$a'^2 + b'^2 = s^2$$

The value for s^2 remains unchanged. The length of **s** does not change just because we rotate it on a grid.

The same holds true for measurements in space-time. When we sit on a railcar, we can measure its spatial length, **l**, and the length of a second of its time, **t**. From these values, we can form an "hypotenuse" of sorts in space-time by writing

$$l^2 - (c\mathbf{t})^2 = s^2$$

This formula emerges from the special theory of relativity. If we measure an object moving past us, we will get different values for its length and time than when it is at rest with respect to us. Even so, length and time change together, such as to keep the value of **s** the same.

Suppose a train passes by you traveling near the speed of light. A rider on the train holds up a ruler and a clock. You take pictures of the rider's ruler and clock as they pass by a second ruler and clock that you hold up (*Figure 7.15*). The pictures show that the 12 inches on the rider's ruler corresponds to only 8 inches on your ruler because of length contraction. The pictures also show that 12 ticks on your clock correspond to only 8 ticks on the rider's clock because of

Figure 7.14

The line segments in a) and b) have the same length, s. In b) the line segment is rotated so that more of its length is measured in the vertical axis and less in the horizontal axis than in a). By analogy, when an object moves at high speed, more of its aspect is measured in time and less of its aspect is measured in space.

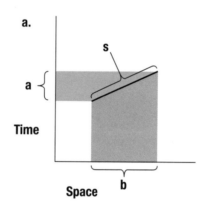

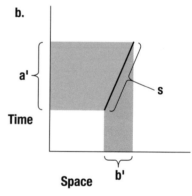

Figure 7.15

Length contraction means that moving objects are seen to shorten in length. Time dilation means that moving clocks are seen to run slow.

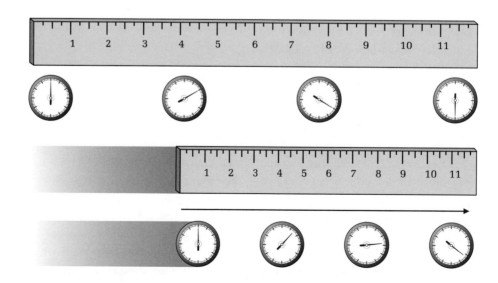

time dilation. It is as if the length of space "rotates away" from you, thus appearing shorter, while time "rotates toward" you, thus appearing longer.

This example is an analogy of how space-time behaves. Unfortunately, a more exact treatment of space-time is beyond the scope of this book. But a person does not need to know the exact mathematics of the Special Theory of Relativity to appreciate the discovery that time and space are not unchanging, rigid entities. We will see this interconnection again in Chapters 33 and 34 when we learn about black holes and cosmology.

ALBERT EINSTEIN

Albert Einstein is arguably the greatest scientist who ever lived. He was born in Ulm, Germany, but received his early schooling in Munich. He did not show much proficiency at school work and rebelled against the regimentation of German education. One of his teachers suggested he drop out of class because he was so disruptive. One of his uncles tried to help him by giving him private instruction in the rudiments of algebra, which seemed to arouse his interest in mathematics.

Einstein's family was Jewish, but did not practice their religion. The young Einstein went through a period of intense interest in Judaism, but became disillusioned with organized religion. He later wrote:

> Suspicion against every kind of authority grew out of this experience . . . an attitude which has never again left me, even though later on, because of a better insight into the causal connections, it lost some of its original poignancy. (Albert Einstein, *Philosopher-Scientist*, New York: Harper, 1945, p. 5)

But Einstein was not necessarily atheistic. Many of his later statements would be sprinkled with references to God: "God does not play dice!" "God is subtle, but He is not malicious!" In fact, a colleague, Niels Bohr, once asked Einstein to "Stop telling God what to do!" Einstein's God is best described as a pantheistic awe for the harmony and order he found in nature.

At the age of sixteen, Einstein decided to study electrical engineering at the Swiss Federal Polytechnic University in Zurich, but he failed the entrance examination. To prepare for a second try, he enrolled at the high school at Aarau. When the university finally admitted him, his interest had shifted to theoretical physics. He skipped class to study on his own the writings of Ludwig Boltzman, James Clerk Maxwell, Herman Helmholtz, and others. He relied on the meticulous notes of his friend and fellow student, Marcel Grossmann, to prepare for examinations.

He received his Ph.D. in 1905 from the University of Zurich and intended to teach, but he could not find an academic position. He then took a job with the patent office in Berne where he made preliminary evaluations of patent applications.

The work was not taxing, so Einstein had time to think and to write about subjects far removed from his bureaucratic job responsibilities. In 1905, which may be the most remarkable year in the history of science, the recently graduated, completely unknown patent clerk published four papers. Each contained a great discovery Einstein had made in the field of physics: the creation of the Special Theory of Relativity, the establishment of the equivalence between mass and energy, the explanation of Brownian motion, and the photon theory of light.

Einstein was a major force in the development of theories of the atom and how captured electrons behaved. Although he never was in complete agreement with the scientists of his day on all aspects of atomic theory, his questions developed and refined atomic theory as it is now generally accepted. His greatest intellectual triumph probably came with his publication of the General Theory of Relativity, which first appeared in print in 1916. As a theory of gravity, it boldly and accurately predicted that gravity was the manifestation of a curvature of space and time.

Chapter Framework

A. Introduction
1. Newtons Laws of Motion break down at high speeds

B. Motion and Relativity
1. Motion is only defined with respect to a reference frame
2. No such thing as absolute motion

C. Motion Symmetry
1. Inertial frames of reference
2. Non-inertial frames of reference
3. Special principle of relativity

D. Galilean Relativity and the Speed of Light
1. Michelson/Morley experiment
2. Light does not obey Galilean Relativity

E. The Special Theory of Relativity
1. Based upon two assumptions
2. Neither motion, space, nor time are absolute

F. Simultaneity and Length Contraction
1. Moving lengths contract
2. Simultaneity is relative to motion

G. Time Dilation
1. Moving clocks run slow

H. The Twin Paradox
1. Time really slows down for the twin that accelerated

I. Space and Time
1. Intertwined into space-time

Comprehension

Matching

a. Relativity
b. Non-inertial frame of reference
c. Inertial frame of reference
d. Special principle of relativity
e. Gedanken experiment
f. Motion symmetry
g. General Theory of Relativity
h. Special Theory of Relativity
i. Galilean Relativity

1. __c__ An object or location that is experiencing no acceleration.
2. __b__ An object or location that is undergoing an acceleration.
3. __f__ The observation that the laws of nature are the same for all inertial frames of reference.
4. __d__ Another name for motion symmetry.
5. __g__ The theory that considers non-inertial frames of reference.
6. __i__ The notion that separate speed vectors can be added together in a "straight-forward" way to form a total velocity vector.
7. __a__ The idea that motion is only defined relative to other objects, which may have their own motion.
8. __h__ The theory that describes how nature behaves when encountering high speeds.
9. __e__ A situation of logic contrived to illustrate a particular effect.

True/False

1. _____ The laws of nature remain the same for any inertial frame of reference.
2. _____ We call any object moving without acceleration an inertial frame of reference.
3. _____ A laboratory on Earth's surface is a true inertial frame of reference.
4. _____ Motion symmetry only works for inertial frames of reference.
5. _____ "Absolute motion" only exists in outer space.
6. _____ According to Einstein, absolute space and time don't exist.
7. _____ Light does not obey Galilean Relativity.
8. _____ The speed of light in a vacuum has a constant value.
9. _____ The faster a clock moves, the faster its time runs.
10. _____ An astronaut in a spaceship moving near the speed of light will observe all of the objects within the spaceship to be shorter than they were before the spaceship took off.

Fill in the Blank

1. When traveling near the speed of light, length _____ and time _____.
2. Time and space are intertwined into what is called the _____.
3. Newton's laws are insufficient for objects traveling at _____ speeds.
4. The two types of motion are _____ and _____.
5. True inertial frames of reference do not exist on Earth's surface because Earth is _____.
6. As objects move past us at high speeds, we see more of their _____ aspect and less of their _____ aspect.

Analysis

1. Non-inertial frames of reference
   a) have no unbalanced forces acting on them.
   b) feel an unbalanced force.
   c) accelerate.
   d) both (b) and (c).

2. Which of the following is in accelerated motion?
   a) A spaceship that isn't experiencing a net force.
   b) A merry-go-round that is spinning at a constant rate.
   c) A hippopotamus sliding straight across a frictionless surface.
   d) None of the above.

3. You are traveling in a straight line down the freeway with your cruise control set at 55 mph. Assuming you can choose any reference point you please, which of the following viewpoint(s) would be scientifically legitimate?
   a) You are at rest.
   b) You are moving forward at 55 mph.
   c) The freeway is moving backward at 55 mph.
   d) You are speeding up from 0 to 55.
   e) All of the above.

f) Only (a), (b), and (c).

4. How does the chapter define "high speed"?

   a) Faster than the speed of sound.
   b) Faster than a speeding bullet.
   c) Faster than the speed of light.
   d) Slightly slower than the speed of light.

5. In what direction do moving objects contract?

   a) In all directions.
   b) In the direction perpendicular to the direction of motion.
   c) In the direction of motion.
   d) Moving objects expand, not contract.

6. From the scientists' reference frame, the muon experiment demonstrated

   a) time dilation.
   b) length contraction.
   c) mass increase.
   d) simultaneity.

Synthesis

1. What are the two assumptions of the special theory of relativity?

2. What are some of the predictions of the special theory of relativity?

3. What is the difference between the Special and the General Theories of Relativity?

4. What is a "light clock"?

5. You are enjoying an enthralling Physical Science lecture in a windowless room when your professor insists that the entire classroom is moving straight toward the Pacific coast at 350 mph.

   a) Is there any experiment you could perform to prove your professor wrong? Why?

   b) Now the professor says the classroom is spinning at 60 rpm. Can you prove your professor wrong? Why?

   c) Name and state the scientific principle on which you based your answers.

6. A railcar travels at 3/4 the speed of light, and your friend happens to be on it. As you stand on the ground watching your friend pass by, lightning bolts strike both the front and the back of your friend's railcar.

   a) If he saw the lightning bolts strike the front and the back of the railcar simultaneously, you will disagree. What do you say happened? Why? *Note: this is different from the situation in the book.*

   b) To find out who is right, you decide to measure the distance between the scorch marks. Is the distance what you expected it to be? Is it what your friend expected it to be?

   c) What does the distance between the scorch marks illustrate about the lengths of moving objects?

   d) Who was right about the timing of the lightning strikes? What can you conclude about events that are simultaneous in one reference frame?

7. Your friend is on the railcar again traveling past you at 3/4 the speed of light. You are both holding identical light clocks.

   a) From your perspective, how does the distance between the mirrors of your friend's light clock compare to the distance between the mirrors of your own?

   b) How fast is the light traveling between your mirrors? How fast is the light traveling between your friend's mirrors?

   c) Based on the distance between the mirrors and the speed at which the light is traveling, what can you conclude about your friend's light clock?

   d) From your friend's perspective, does the distance between the mirrors of your friend's light clock appear to be any different than normal? Does time seem to be passing at a different pace than it normally does?

8. A disgruntled co-worker impatiently orders you to "get moving." Kindly respond that you are already moving, and support your argument by explaining the relativity of motion.

9. If the idea of motion symmetry is true, why do some people experience motion sickness? Why is it more common to get sea sick than car sick?

10. Suppose you're in a bus traveling at 60 mph. You throw an orange toward the front of the bus at 20 mph. Then you send a light beam toward the front of the bus at the speed of light.

   a) From the perspective of a pedestrian observing the bus from the sidewalk, how fast was the orange traveling?

   b) From the perspective of the same pedestrian, how fast is the light beam moving?

   c) What can you conclude about the applicability of Galilean relativity?

CONSERVATION LAWS

CHAPTER 8

If you set out to make cookies, it is helpful to know what type of ingredients you'll need. However, just knowing that cookies are made of flour, butter, sugar, and eggs, etc., isn't enough. As a cook, you also need to know how much of each ingredient to add into the mixture to get the amount of cookies you desire. You know how many cookies you'll get each time because you now have an equation that allows you to predict exact quantities.

Similarly, one of the ultimate goals of science is to be able to quantitatively predict outcomes. In order to do this, the scientist needs the ability to write equations (e.g., cookie recipes). This means that it is important to be able to identify measurable properties of matter, such as mass, charge, etc., that stay the same. Doing so allows you to write an equation showing that these properties are equal before and after a physical process. Any quantity that remains constant is called a **conserved quantity**.

Some conserved quantities are more interesting than others. The equation "2 = 2," while true and easy to prove, isn't very interesting, but the equation "1 can of juice concentrate + 3 cans water = 1 quart juice" has numerous applications. In general, conserved quantities are par-

ticularly useful when the property in question can be transformed or transferred without changing the total. This allows the scientist to write an equation where the two sides aren't identical.

In this chapter we are going to define several important conserved quantities, explain ways in which they can change without varying the total, and discuss why they are important in science.

8–1 CONSERVATION OF MASS

One basic conservation law has already been hinted at in the paragraphs above. Every time a cook combines 2 cups of flour, 1 cup of butter, 1 cup of sugar, and 1 large egg,* about the same amount of cookie dough will be produced, and about the same number of cookies (3 dozen) can be made. If the cook accurately weighs the ingredients and then weighs the dough, it will be found that the dough weighs exactly the same

---

*For better sugar cookies, we suggest adding 1 tsp vanilla and 1/2 tsp almond extract. If you're using unsalted butter, add 1/4 tsp of salt.

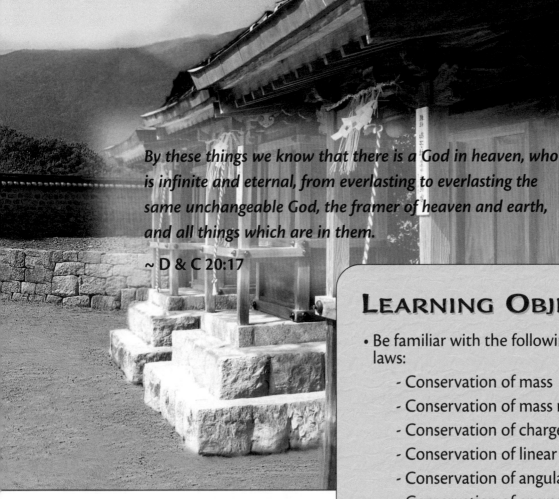

By these things we know that there is a God in heaven, who is infinite and eternal, from everlasting to everlasting the same unchangeable God, the framer of heaven and earth, and all things which are in them.

~ D & C 20:17

LEARNING OBJECTIVES

• Be familiar with the following conservation laws:

  - Conservation of mass
  - Conservation of mass number
  - Conservation of charge
  - Conservation of linear momentum
  - Conservation of angular momentum
  - Conservation of energy

• Be able to identify which of the above quantities are conserved in a given situation.

• Be able to apply the appropriate laws to predict the outcomes of simple situations.

amount as the combined weight of the ingredients before they were mixed together. Weigh the finished cookies, however, and their combined weight will be found to be slightly less than the total weight of the dough, even when every visible smear of mix has been scraped from the bowl and added to the cookie dough.

Careful observation of cookies fresh from the oven will show some steam rising from them. If the cook could carefully gather all of the steam together and add its weight to the weight of the cookies, the total weight would once again be the same as the weight of the original ingredi-

Figure 8.1

The steam rising from the cookies consists of water molecules that were originally part of the cookie dough.

ents. Conduct the same experiment with a recipe for peanut-butter cookies or macaroons or peach upside-down cake for the same result: The total weight of the ingredients in each recipe will be equal to the total weight of the resulting cookies or cake, plus a small amount of steam. The cook has discovered an important law of conservation of weight of cookie and cake ingredients.

This basic principle extends far beyond the admittedly fascinating study and practical use of cookies. It turns out that in most* physical processes, regardless of the materials or the heat or time involved, if a careful accounting is made for all the material the process started with, the total mass doesn't change. While mass can

*Note that we said most, not all. This means that there are some situations where mass changes. We will discuss these more in the next chapter.

◆ **Conserved Quantity**

Unchanging in time. A quantity is "conserved" if the amount of that quantity does not change in time, even though processes may be changing its form.

change in form, or transfer from one object to another, the total mass remains exactly the same. This means that all things physical must obey a general law of *conservation of mass*.

The applications of this law extend far beyond baking. On a macroscopic level, people use the principle each time they water their garden. Suppose the gardener has a stream of water coming from the hose, amounting to about one cupful (1/4 liter) each second. By putting his thumb over the end of a hose, the gardener can spray the water rather than having it stream out. That thumb can't create or destroy water; the same 1/4 liter is coming out the smaller opening each second. To move the same mass through a smaller hole in the same amount of time, the water must move faster, and so it sprays farther.

Conservation of mass is used regularly to understand chemical processes. The *Carbon Cycle* is a prime example. Animals release carbon dioxide into the air when they exhale, and decaying plant and animal material release more

Figure 8.2

The Carbon Cycle is an example of conservation of mass. Trees do not create wood out of nothing, but convert CO_2 and water into new wood.

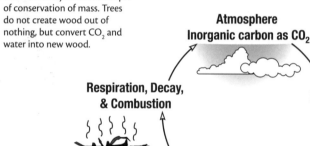

carbon into the atmosphere. Plants use and store carbon dioxide from the air as part of their metabolism. A growing tree is not creating its mass. It is taking carbon dioxide from the air (through its leaves) and water from the ground (through its root system) and recombining these raw materials to make new wood. Ideally, the amount of carbon dioxide released into the air will be equal to the amount being stored by plants, and the level of carbon dioxide in the atmosphere will remain constant. However, there is now concern in the scientific community about the combined impact of burning fossil fuels, which increases the amount of carbon dioxide released into the atmosphere, while at the same time deforestation is decreasing the

number of plants available to remove and store all that increase in atmospheric carbon.

This brings us to another interesting point. It isn't just the total mass that is conserved in the carbon cycle. The total amount of carbon also stays the same. Whether the carbon is contained in carbon dioxide molecules, wood molecules, or transformed into nearly pure carbon (charcoal) the total amount of carbon doesn't change. This suggests that there is another conservation rule dealing with the building blocks that make up matter.

8–2 CONSERVATION OF FUNDAMENTAL PARTICLES

In Chapter 1 the fundamental building blocks of matter were introduced and briefly discussed. One of the primary aims of science has always been to discover the smallest pieces of matter.

The standard tools used in this quest have been increasingly high-tech hammers, which are used to smash matter into tiny pieces (see *Figure 8.3*). The underlying assumption is that, as the hammers get bigger, at some point the material being smashed won't get any smaller. At this point, scientists picking through the debris and finding that smallest, unbreakable particle will know that particle is the fundamental building block of all matter. Once these smallest constituent parts are identified, the total number of these fundamental particles should always stay

Figure 8.3

The current hammer of choice is known as a particle accelerator. Electric forces are used to accelerate groups of atoms up to speeds very close to the speed of light. Two or more groups are then sent slamming into each other head on. This is a diagram of the Large Hadron Collider at CERN. (Courtesy CERN)

the same. This means that the number of fundamental particles should be a conserved quantity.

The fact that the total mass of carbon doesn't change in chemical processes is significant because carbon is a substance made entirely of only one type of atom. Historically, atoms were considered to be fundamental particles. Experiments showed that there are approximately 100 different types of atoms. As long as the "hammer" used to break matter up is a chemical process the total number of atoms of any given type does not change. This means that the number of atoms of each element in a chemical reaction must stay the same. Thus, it is a cornerstone rule of chemistry that there must always be the same number of atoms of each element at the beginning and end of a chemical reaction.

However, there is no law of conservation of atoms, because when the forces are large enough, in atomic bombs for example, atoms can be separated into protons, neutrons, and electrons. For a short time, scientists thought that protons, neutrons, and electrons might be the fundamental particles. With electrons, at least, this appears to be true. No matter how hard our highest-tech scientific hammer hits an electron, it resolutely remains an electron. However, extreme force does do odd things to protons and neutrons.

Our current understanding of matter is that there are two types of fundamental particles.

The first class of fundamental particles is the electron-like particles*. These include the familiar *electrons*, the *muons* (also called mu mesons) mentioned in the previous chapter, a particle called a *neutrino*, which is essentially an electron that has no charge, and some other particles of great interest to particle physicists and

*The technical name for electron-like particles is *lepton*.

of little if any importance to students simply trying to get a basic grasp on the physical sciences.** There is a conservation law called the *conservation of lepton number* that says the total number of these electron-like particles is constant. In other words, one type can be changed into another, but the total number always stays the same.

The second class of fundamental particles is the *quarks*. While it has never been possible to separate a quark completely from a proton or neutron, there is strong evidence that every proton is composed of three quarks, and each neutron is also composed of three quarks. Additionally, under the right conditions, neutrons can turn into protons and vice-versa. However, the total number of quarks doesn't change. Because we can't pull or pry quarks from out of their protons and neutrons, this has the added effect that the number of protons added to the number of neutrons, also known as the **atomic mass number,** doesn't change. This conservation law is known as *conservation of atomic mass number.*

There is one more catch to the rules governing conservation of fundamental particles. For each fundamental particle, there is also a corresponding anti-matter particle. An anti-matter particle cancels out the normal particle. When we count these particles, they count as negative numbers. We subtract them rather than add them. This means that, as long as you can find the necessary mass somewhere, you can create a fundamental particle, but only if you create the

**For those students who find it interesting enough to pursue regardless of whether or not it is within the scope of the course, please see http://www.fnal.gov/pub/inquiring/matter/madeof/ for a fine discussion of the standard model of matter written by scientists at Fermi National Lab and geared toward the general public.

• **Atomic Mass Number**

The total number of protons + neutrons in the nucleus of an atom.

ATOMIC HISTORY

The word 'atom' comes from Greek for 'cannot be divided.' While ancient Greek philosophers came up with the idea of a smallest particle and coined the term, they had very little idea what this smallest particle was. Over several thousand years alchemists made a diligent effort to transform lead into gold, assuming that since the two metals had similar properties they had to be made up of the same stuff. With the renaissance and its accompanying systematic approach to observation, early scientists found that certain materials could not be changed. These materials that couldn't be broken down any further were called elements. It was assumed that each element had to be made of a different fundamental particle, and the word atom was taken to describe these particles.

Figure 8.4
Rubbing a balloon on your head does not create charge, but simply redistributes existing charge.

♦ **Linear Momentum**
An object's mass times its velocity. Measures the amount of motion in a straight line.

Figure 8.5
When a firecracker explodes in midair, the path of the center of the explosion is exactly the same as the path the firecracker would have followed if it had never exploded. Since there are no horizontal forces, the central point of the remnant pieces keeps moving at a constant horizontal speed.

corresponding anti-particle. For example, if you had three electrons and a friend gave you some extra mass, you could make a fourth electron and an anti-matter electron, because "four minus one" is still equal to "three." We'll discuss other places where you might get this extra mass in the next chapter.

8–3 CONSERVATION OF CHARGES

Just as mass is the property of matter that governs one fundamental force (gravity), charge is the property of matter associated with electro-magnetic forces. And, just like mass, total charge is conserved. If you add up the total amount of positive charge and subtract the total amount of negative charge, that number will remain the same before and after any physical process.

This shouldn't come as a big surprise after reading Chapter 4, but when you scuff across the carpet in your tennis shoes, you're not really creating charge but just moving existing charge around, sometimes with mildly shocking results. This is because all matter, including the tennis shoes and carpet, is made of protons, neutrons, and electrons. The neutrons have no charge, but both protons and electrons are charged parti-cles. Electrons are found around the outside of atoms and are transferred fairly easy from one object to another.

So as tennis shoes get scuffed across carpet, that action is not creating an electrical charge. The rubber on the bottom of the shoes is stealing electrons from the wool or nylon in the carpet.

The shoes and the person wearing them are left with a negative charge from the extra electrons taken up during the scuffing, while the carpet has a positive charge. The total number of electrons doesn't change (conservation of electron-like par-ticles), the total number of protons + neutrons doesn't change (conservation of mass number), and the total charge is still the same.

8–4 CONSERVATION OF LINEAR MOMENTUM

We've already encountered one other con-served quantity. Newton's first law states that when there are no net forces on an object, its motion will not change. If it is at rest, it stays that way. If it is moving, it keeps moving in a straight line at a constant speed. This means that the motion of a single object subject to no net force is a conserved quantity, although a boring one.

However, we can make life more interesting by having our chosen object explode. In an explosion, the forces all come from within the object, specifically, the different pieces push-ing against each other. Newton's third law says the pieces push against each other with equal and opposite forces, so the total force on all the pieces together is still zero. This means that Newton's first law still applies and the total "motion" of all of the pieces added together can-not change.

While it doesn't seem necessary to define what we mean by the "motion" of a single object, it's a little more important to define what we mean when we talk about the motion of a group of fragments of different masses moving in dif-ferent directions at different speeds. In this sit-uation the quantity that stays the same is the mass times velocity. If the mass of each fragment is multiplied by the fragment's velocity and then added together, taking into account the direc-tion, that sum will be exactly equal to the mass of the original object times its velocity.

This quantity is called an object's **linear momentum**. As long as there are no net forces, the total momentum on an object or set of objects that interact with each other is conserved.

Conservation of momentum is often used to determine the speed and direction two objects were traveling before a collision or to predict the

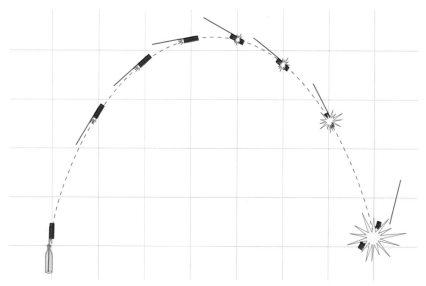

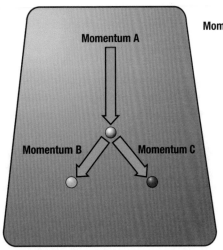

Momentum A = Momentum B + Momentum C

Figure 8.6
The momentum of the cue ball before it collides with the other balls is exactly the same as the total momentum of the balls after the collision.

speed and direction of objects after a collision. In the instance of a car crash, the vehicles skid to a stop after the collision. By measuring the skid marks, police can determine the speed and direction the cars were going immediately after they hit. Conservation of momentum then allows them to reconstruct how fast and what direction the cars were moving before the crash.

Pool sharks use the same principles in reverse. They have direct control of the speed and direction of their cue ball before a collision, and because of conservation of momentum, this means that with practice they are able to predict the motion of the ball or balls that they hit after the collision. However, few pool sharks learned about conservation of momentum in school.

8–5   CONSERVATION OF LINEAR MOMENTUM AT VERY HIGH SPEEDS

It has already been pointed out that Newton's second law, F=ma, doesn't seem to work properly at high speeds. Therefore, it makes sense to take a good look at what happens to conservation of momentum when objects are moving at speeds close to the speed of light.

Suppose two bored astronauts decide to pass the time by blowing things up. One of their explosions succeeds in sending two equal fragments off in exactly opposite directions at ¾ the speed of light, one heading towards the front and the other towards the back of their ship (see *Figure 8.7*). Since the total momentum to start with was zero, and the ending momentums cancel out, momentum is clearly conserved, according to the astronauts.

Now, to see how motion near the speed of light affects things, we need to look at what happens from the point of view of that space capsule's ground control crew down on the Earth. Let's say that the astronauts' ship is traveling away from Earth at ¾ the speed of light. The total object was moving ¾ the speed of light before the explosion. After the explosion, ½ of it isn't moving at all in Earth's frame of reference (¾ the speed of light forwards + ¾ backwards is zero).

Figure 8.7
From the point of view of the astronauts there is no momentum before the explosion, and equal and opposite momentum after. From the point of view of Ground Control, the explosion stops 1/2 of the object but the other half is ***not*** moving twice as fast.

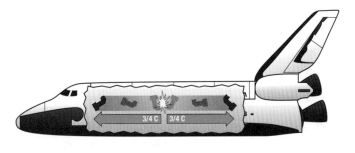

• **Angular Momentum**

Angular momentum is a quantity that measures the amount of rotation motion an object has.

Emmy Noether

Emmy Noether was born in Germany in 1882, the daughter of a math professor. She wanted to follow in her father's footsteps, but none of the universities of her day would allow a woman to enroll as a student.

After auditing courses for 2 years, she took and passed the entrance exams for the doctoral program. A year later, the university where her father taught agreed to accept her as a student in good standing. In 1907 she received her doctorate in mathematics.

She then taught classes for free under her father's and other professor's names for several years, and finally was granted official status in 1919. In 1933 she fled Germany when the Nazis came to power and came to the United States where she taught at Bryn Mawr and Princeton.

That means if there were no changes to the law, in order to conserve momentum, the remaining piece needs to be moving forwards at 1½ times the speed of light.

There is just one problem with this answer: nothing can travel faster than the speed of light. So, the second-half of the exploded material can't be moving faster than the speed of light. If the astronauts were to shine a flashlight at the speed of light both they and ground control would measure the light to travel at the speed of light. The second half of the hurtling object is clearly moving slower than the light, according to the astronauts, so it must be moving slower than the speed of light, according to ground control, too. In fact, if Ground Control measured the speed of the exploded object before it crashed into some vital part of the astronauts' equipment, you'd find that it was only going 96% of the speed of light.

There are two possible solutions to this problem. Momentum depends on mass and speed. The speeds don't add up, so either momentum isn't conserved or mass changes with speed. In other words, in order to have the momentum of the two halves be equal when the second half isn't moving as fast as it should, it has to have more mass to make up for the reduced speed. But if dividing an object into two equal halves results in the faster moving half having greater mass, there is a problem with our first conservation law. You need to be able to explain where the mass comes from; you're not supposed to be able to create it from nothing.

In order for momentum to be conserved, mass would need to change by exactly the same factor as time and length, so the idea of relativistic changes in mass was given preference early on. A mathematician-contemporary of Einstein named Emmy Noether showed that conservation of momentum was a direct result of position symmetry, which is one of the underlying assumptions of all science. If momentum wasn't conserved, position symmetry didn't hold true, and scientific laws wouldn't stay the same from place to place. This made physicists even more willing to accept the idea that conservation of momentum, not mass, held at high speeds.

Subsequent experiments in devices called cyclotrons, which can accelerate charged particles up to speeds very close to the speed of light, verified this. The faster the particles moved, the more force was required to accelerate them. Since mass is the ratio of force to acceleration, this meant that the mass had to be increasing. The relativistic increase in mass not only solved the problems with conservation of momentum at high speeds, but also explained the apparent breakdown of Newton's 2nd law. We will discuss how the mass increases in the next chapter.

8–6 CONSERVATION OF ANGULAR MOMENTUM

Most small children have determined that linear motion is not the only type of motion that is conserved. When you ride a bicycle, the faster your tires are turning, the easier it is to keep it upright. Tops will stay balanced on a point just to keep spinning, and our Moon has remained in orbit around Earth for several billion years. There is a quantity associated with angular motion that also is conserved.

This quantity is called **angular momentum**. For a single object orbiting about a point, like the Moon about Earth, the angular momentum depends on the mass of the object, how fast it is moving, and how far it is from the center of its orbit. The equation is

Angular momentum = mass × speed × radius

The same relationship works for spinning tires where most of the mass is at the same distance from the center of the circle. With more complicated objects, like tops, where different parts of the objects are at different distances from the center of rotation, in order to figure out the angular momentum, it is necessary to add up the angular momentum due to the mass at each distance separately.

As long as there are no forces acting to speed up or slow down the rotation, a spinning object will keep the same angular momentum. One consequence of this is that anything that is spinning will tend to keep spinning in the same direction. This is why a moving bicycle is so much easier to keep upright. For the bicycle to fall over, the direction the tire is spinning would have to change from spinning in a vertical plane to spinning in a horizontal plane. Just as it is harder to turn a corner in a car with more linear momentum, it is harder for a bicycle wheel with larger angular momentum to tilt downward.

Balancing on a moving bike, therefore, is not that hard, but balancing on a stationary bicycle is quite a trick.

Another consequence of conservation of angular momentum comes from the way both speed and distance play into the equation. Imagine a ball on a string spinning on a circle (a tether ball is close enough.) What happens if the string is pulled in to make it shorter? In terms of conservation of angular momentum, mass × speed × radius of the circle must stay constant. If the radius of the circle gets smaller, either the mass must become greater or the speed must increase to compensate. Changing mass is typically off limits, so the ball will have to speed up. Also, the distance the ball must travel to make each complete revolution is now smaller. The net effect is that as the string gets shorter, the ball will spin around much faster.

This effect is particularly useful for ice skaters, gymnasts, divers, and participants in any other sport in which there is a lot of spinning or flipping. If a diver needs to speed up her rotation in order to enter the water properly, she can pull her arms and legs into a tuck position to bring them closer to the center of rotation. In order to slow rotation down, she will push her arms and legs out into a layout position. The change in speed can be even more dramatic in figure skating. Skaters often enter a spin with their arms and legs extended out away from their body. They then pull their legs close together and their arms in tight against their torsos and spin at a much faster speed.

8-7 CONSERVATION OF ENERGY

We have talked about how momentum is conserved when there are no external forces acting on an object, but that is a very special circumstance. There is one last conservation law that applies even when there are forces present.

Every child knows that when a rubber ball

Figure 8.8
Because angular momentum is conserved, divers can control their rotational velocity by tucking their limbs. The frames are taken at equal intervals. Note that in the first four frames the diver is in a "pike" and completes 1/2 revolution between frames. When he stretches out, he only makes 1/3 revolution in the same amount of time.

is thrown hard enough at a wall, the ball will bounce back in the opposite direction. The ball's forward momentum is clearly not conserved because a force from the wall acts on the ball and changes its direction. However, the ball bounces off at very nearly the same speed it was going before it hit, so something stayed the same. Similarly, if a rubber ball is dropped on a hard surface, it will bounce back to almost the same height from which it was dropped. Its speed and direction both changed during this bounce, but something stayed almost the same for it to return to almost the same point from which it was dropped. This "something" quantity that is conserved in both of these examples (and in all test situations we've yet been able to devise) is called the "total energy."

Because energy is conserved in almost all interactions, this conservation law is used extensively in all of the science disciplines and throughout the rest of this book. Rules about what energy is and how it is transferred are important enough that we've devoted the entire next chapter to them.

Chapter Framework

A. Introduction
   1. Conserved quantity
B. Conservation of Mass
   1. Cookies and the Carbon Cycle
C. Conservations of Fundamental Particles
   1. Leptons
   2. Quarks
   3. Atomic mass number
D. Conservation of Charges
E. Conservation of Linear Momentum
F. Conservation of Linear Momentum at Very High Speeds
   1. Momentum or mass
   2. Emmy Noether
G. Conservation of Angular Momentum
   1. Angular momentum = mass × speed × radius
H. Conservation of Energy

Comprehension

True/False

1. _____ All physical objects must obey a general law of conservation of mass.
2. _____ There is no law of conservation of atoms.
3. _____ Protons and neutrons are fundamental particles.
4. _____ Electron-like particles are considered to be fundamental particles.
5. _____ Atomic mass number is always conserved.
6. _____ Neutrons, protons, and electrons are all charged particles.
7. _____ Electrons can easily be transferred from one object to another.
8. _____ Scuffing across the carpet with your tennis shoes creates charge that didn't previously exist.
9. _____ The motion of a single object subject to no net forces is conserved.
10. ___ Particles moving at high speeds require less force to accelerate than slower particles.

Matching

a. Atomic mass number
b. Angular momentum
c. Conserved quantity
d. Carbon Cycle
e. Fundamental particles
f. Linear momentum

1. _____ Any quantity that remains constant.
2. _____ The process by which carbon is transferred through the atmosphere to living organisms and back to the atmosphere.
3. _____ Obtained by adding the number of protons to the number of neutrons.
4. _____ An object's mass times its velocity.
5. _____ An object's mass times its speed times its distance from the center of its orbit.
6. _____ Small, unbreakable constituents of matter.

Fill in the Blank

1. Any quantity that is equal before and after a phys-ical process is called a _____ quantity.
2. _____ is the property of matter associated with electromagnetic forces.
3. A spinning ice skater is applying conservation of _____.
4. There is evidence that every proton and neutron is composed of three _____.
5. At high speeds, conservation of _____ holds, not conservation of mass.
6. Linear momentum depends on _____ and _____.
7. Anything that is spinning will tend to keep spinning in the same _____.
8. The forces in an explosion come from _____ the object.
9. According to Newton's 3rd Law, in an explosion, the different pieces push against each other with _____ and _____ forces.

Analysis

1. At low speeds, mass can
   a) change in form.
   b) transfer from one object to another.
   c) change its total amount.
   d) both (a) and (b).

2. Which of the following quantities remain(s) constant in the Carbon Cycle?
   a) Total amount of carbon dioxide.
   b) Total amount of carbon.
   c) Total mass.
   d) All of the above.
   e) (b) and (c) only.

3. Angular momentum depends on which of the following?
   a) The mass of the object.
   b) How fast it's moving.
   c) How far it is from the center of its orbit.
   d) All of the above.

Synthesis

1. What does it mean for a quantity to be conserved?

2. Names the six conservation principles discussed in this chapter.

3. What are the two classes of fundamental particles?

4. If you weigh all of the ingredients before making a cake, and then you weigh the finished cake, what will you find? What accounts for the missing weight?

5. You are spinning in a swivel chair with your arms and legs straight out. What happens if you pull

your limbs in toward you? What conservation principle explains this?

6. You scuff across nylon carpet while wearing tennis shoes.

   a) What happens to the electrons in the carpet?

   b) Does the carpet become positively or negatively charged? How about you and your shoes?

   c) What has happened to the total charge of the system? What has happened to the total number of electrons? What has happened to the sum of the protons and the neutrons of the system?

   d) What three conservation principles account for this?

7. Your friend is trying to learn to ride a unicycle without much success. Your friend first wants to learn to balance while the cycle is stationary before attempting to pedal. Using conservation of angular momentum, explain why your friend may be having difficulties.

8. In terms of the Carbon Cycle, explain why a growing plant doesn't violate conservation of mass. What conservation principle accounts for this?

9. Explain how it is possible for police to determine the speed and direction of two vehicles before a crash by measuring the skid marks. What conservation principle allows them to do this?

10. Explain how pool sharks take advantage of conservation of momentum to improve their game?

11. Explain how the speed of light being a constant for everyone leads to the conclusion that mass increases with speed.

ENERGY

Work is of two kinds: first, altering the position of matter at or near the earth's surface relatively to other such matter; second, telling other people to do so. The first kind is unpleasant and ill paid; the second is pleasant and highly paid.

~ Bertrand Russell

The process of learning usually requires us to define and understand new terms. Whether a term represents a material object or a scientific principle, the more we understand a term's meaning, the more we are able to appropriately use it. In science, we sometimes have trouble defining the exact meaning of a term because observation and experiment frequently lead us more to an understanding of what something does rather than what something is. As a result "mass" is defined as "a resistance to acceleration," or "a factor in determining gravitational pull," even though these definitions do not say what causes mass. Similarly, scientific definitions of energy concentrate more on what energy does than what energy actually is.

9–1 WHAT IS ENERGY?

One such incomplete definition of energy is that "energy is a measurement of an object's destructive capacity." A more traditional definition is that "energy is the ability to exert a force on an object while it moves through some distance in the direction of the applied force." Thus, energy is a property associated with an object's physical state, position, or motion that is often transformed but always conserved.

There are several different types of energy, and to help keep track of them they are classified as depending either on position or on motion. Any energy that depends on the position of an object or on the positions of an object's constituent parts is known as **potential energy**. An energy that depends on an object's motion is known as **kinetic energy**.

Types of energy are further broken down into mechanical (macroscopic) and internal (microscopic) energies, based on whether the energy depends on the position/motion of the whole object or on the atoms and molecules that make up the object.

Figure 9.1
The faster a car moves, the more kinetic energy it has.

LEARNING OBJECTIVES

When you have studied this chapter, you
should know

• What energy is
• The different forms of energy
  -kinetic energy
  -gravitation potential energy
  -other forms of energy
• Energy transfer process
  -Conduction convection and radiation
• Mass energy equivalence

<table>
<tr><td>

9–2   TYPES OF MECHANICAL
ENERGY

</td></tr>
</table>

Kinetic Energy

Since we've defined energy as a measure of
destructive capacity, we could calculate how
much damage a moving vehicle could cause in
a specific scenario if we had a formula for kinetic
energy. Obviously, the faster a car moves the
more damage it could cause, so kinetic energy
must depend on speed (*see Figure 9.1*). The more
massive a vehicle is, the more destruction it
could cause, (hence the army's tendency to use
extremely heavy vehicles), so kinetic energy must
also depend on mass (*see Figure 9.2*).

The formula for kinetic energy at low speeds
is:

$$\text{Energy} = \tfrac{1}{2}\,\text{mass} \times \text{speed}^2$$

Figure 9.2

The more massive a vehicle
is, the more kinetic energy
it has.

105

- **Potential Energy**

Energy that depends on the position of an object or on the positions of an object's constituent parts.

- **Kinetic Energy**

The form of energy associated with motion. The kinetic energy of an object in motion is given by KE = ¹/₂mass × speed²

- **Gravitational Potential Energy**

The energy stored in an object that has the potential to fall. Near the surface of the earth, the increase of gravitational potential energy of an object that is lifted is given by GPE = weight × height.

Figure 9.3
The bowling ball's gravitational potential energy depends on its weight and the height from which it was dropped.

Why is speed squared in this basic formula? Ask yourself if you would rather try to catch a 20-gram bullet coming at you at 300 mph or a 300-gram baseball traveling at 20 mph. Speed plays a more important role than mass in determining the destructive potential of an object.

For instance, a car hitting a wall while traveling 50 mph is more than twice as likely to kill the driver than a car hitting that same wall while traveling at 35 mph. The reason for this is because of the kinetic energy involved at the two speeds. The car going 50 mph has twice as much kinetic energy as one going 35 mph.

Gravitational Potential Energy

A student who has dropped a 15-pound bowling ball on their foot learns quickly that a falling object can be destructive. This destruction results from gravity pulling the bowling ball toward Earth. This type of energy is called **gravitational potential energy**, and it depends on the object's height (position) and its weight. The higher the bowling ball (or any object) is from the Earth's center (or the student's foot), and the heavier the object is, the more memorable this brief experience with gravitational potential energy becomes.

The formula for gravitational potential energy is:

$$\textbf{Energy} = \textbf{weight} \times \textbf{height}$$

It is customary to pick a convenient reference point for test objects on or near Earth and measure all heights from that fixed point. For most situations, the floor of a room or a nearby lawn or sidewalk makes a convenient reference point. However, if the change in energy of an airplane flying from Denver to Los Angeles were to be measured, sea level would probably be a more convenient reference point to use in calculating the airplane's actual height.

Calculations of the gravitational potential energy of meteorites or other objects located far from Earth become more complicated than the Energy = weight × height formula above because the object's weight decreases appreciably at those distances from Earth. However, even for astronomical objects, the gravitational potential energy depends on the distance (e.g., height) between the two objects and the size of the gravitational force they exert on each other (weight = force of gravity from Earth). Gravitational potential energy depends on the *distance* between an object and the Earth, and the resulting amount of the gravitational *force* they exert on each other. The farther apart they are, the weaker the gravitational force is between them. However, gravitational *energy* potential increases with distance. A can of tuna on the space station has more gravitational potential energy than one on the kitchen counter even though it weighs 10% less than it would on the surface of the Earth.

This helps explain why a chunk of solid rock the size of a garbage truck falling 100 feet onto a concrete parking lot will probably destroy several cars and break up the concrete right where it landed, while a chunk of solid rock the size of a mere garbage can, falling from 100 miles up, will probably vaporize on impact, create an enormous crater where the parking lot used to be, and kill any nearby dinosaurs. Asteroid and comet impacts on Earth are considered dangerous because of their great mass, high speeds, and long distances to fall. This means that they possess huge amounts of kinetic and gravitational potential energy, or in other words they have large destructive capability.

Electrical Potential Energy

Children in modern societies are taught at an early age not to stick their fingers or any objects into electrical outlets for obvious reasons. There is some destructive capacity, and therefore energy, associated with electricity.

Electric-power generating plants create a force that keeps positive and negative charges separate from each other (think of the positive and negative ends of a 9 volt battery). A natural, attractive force tries to pull positive and negative forces back together.

A really inquisitive student might test that statement by sticking a 9 volt battery in his or her mouth (despite childhood lessons to the contrary). Touching both positive and negative contact points provides a path for positive and negative electric charges to reunite, and may also generate more respect in the student for accepting, without question, authority as a legitimate source of knowledge.

This example of electrical potential energy is similar to our description of gravitational forces. A heavy object in a high place experiences a force attracting it to the ground and will cause damage to anything in its path if an opportunity is provided for the object to travel towards the ground.

Just like gravity operating on solid objects, the electric potential energy for particles that have *opposite* charges *increases* as the distance *increases* between the charges. The farther apart the oppositely charged particles are, the farther they have to move to obey that natural law of electrical attraction, and the more damage they can do along the way. The amount of energy will also depend on the size of the force between the two charges, and so the energy will be *larger* if the charge is larger (see *Figure 9.4*).

Because electricity is composed of positive charges and negative charges, it is possible to have two charges that are both positive, or two that are both negative. Opposites (positive and negative) attract, but like charges (positive and positive, or negative and negative) repel. In this case, if two same-type charges are placed close to each other, the charges will want to move apart. The closer the charges are, the stronger their repelling force, and the farther they want to go to get away from each other. Electrical potential energy for like-charges is *greatest* when the two charges are *closest*.

9–3 TRANSFORMING AND TRANSFERRING MECHANICAL ENERGY: WORK

In all the examples of energy we've studied so far, energy has been transformed. In order to make energy work for us, it must be changed from one form to another. However, we know that energy is conserved, meaning it is neither destroyed nor created.

How does the form of energy change when—say—a rubber ball is dropped towards the floor? Let's suppose it is being held at shoulder level. This means the ball has gravitational potential energy. When the ball is released it starts to move in the direction of the gravitational force. As it does so, its distance from the Earth decreases, so it starts to lose its gravitational potential energy. However, at the same time the ball's speed is increasing. This means that it is gaining kinetic energy (see *Figure 9.5*).

As the ball falls, it loses potential energy and gains kinetic energy until just before it reaches the ground, where its potential energy is zero and its kinetic energy is the same as the potential energy it had when it was dropped. The total energy, potential plus kinetic, never changed. The energy has changed form from potential to kinetic, but the sum of the two is exactly the same at all points. Therefore, total energy is *conserved*. The gravitational potential energy isn't lost as the force of gravity pulls the ball down. It is turned into kinetic energy.

At the moment the ball actually hits the floor, all of the ball's energy is now in the form of kinetic energy. After impact, the ball's kinetic energy gradually transforms back into gravitational potential energy as it rises against the force of gravity. Once the ball has returned to its original position, it again has the same amount of gravitational potential energy it had at the beginning of our experiment.

When we allowed the ball to move in the direction of the gravitational force, energy changed forms. Mechanical energy is trans-

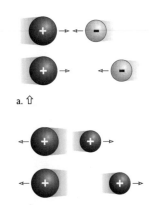

Figure 9.4

When is the energy the largest for each set of charges?

Figure 9.5

The total energy stays the same while the way it is divided between kinetic energy (purple) and gravitational potential energy (orange) changes.

● **Electrical Potential Energy**

The form of energy associated with the relative positions of charged objects. Objects with opposite charges have maximum electrical potential energy when they are separated by greatest distance, but objects with the same charge have maximum electrical potential energy when they are separated by the least distance. The type of energy stored in a lightning cloud.

• **Work**

The technical name given to the process by which energy is transferred to or from an object by an agent that exerts force on the object and the object moves along the direction of the force.

• **Internal Energy**

A name given to energy hidden within matter but manifest by the temperature of the matter, the shape of the matter, the physical state of the matter (solid, liquid, gas), the chemical composition of the matter (i.e., the kind of energy that might be released by burning or explosion of a substance), etc.

Figure 9.6
a) No matter how heavy the backpack is, the student is doing no work on it by simply lugging it around campus at a constant speed. It's gravitational potential energy and kinetic energy remain the same.
b) Work is done on the backpack only by changing its height (gravitational potential energy) or its velocity (kinetic energy).

formed or transferred when a force acts on an object while it moves along the direction of that force. The word that has been commandeered by scientists to describe these energy transformations is **work**. (You are now being officially warned; the term "work" in a physical science class means something quite different from the standard English definition.) *Work*, as a science term, means what is done to move an object in the direction of an applied force. The formula is:

Work = force × distance parallel to the direction of the force

This means that a person sitting at a desk typing on a computer is doing very little actual "work," as defined in science. Pushing down on the keys moves them a small distance in the direction in which they were pushed, but the size of the force and distance is almost insignificant.

Additionally, a student carrying a 70-lb backpack and moving along at a fairly constant speed across level ground is not doing any work on the backpack. The student is exerting a force on the backpack (70 lbs upward), and is moving it through a distance along the ground. However, the force is up and the distance is sideways. The backpack wasn't moved in the direction of the applied force, so the student is doing absolutely no work at all on the backpack. The backpack has the same gravitational potential energy and the same kinetic energy. No energy transformations have taken place (see *Figure 9.6*).*

Doing work on an object (i.e., moving the object in the direction of an applied force) is nec-

essary in order to change the mechanical energy of that object. To change the backpack's energy, the student can do one of two things: Change its speed or change its height. The student can apply a forward force to the backpack to speed it up. A forward force is a force in the direction that the student is moving, so that the student is doing work on the backpack and changing its kinetic energy. To change height, the student could veer off the level and beaten track to climb some stairs. That way a displacement would be created along the direction of the upward force the student was exerting on the backpack. Thus, the student would again be doing work on the backpack and changing its gravitational potential energy.

Work is not a form of energy; it is a way of transferring or transforming energy. Doing work can change the amount of mechanical energy, but the total energy is still the same. It is still important in science and industry to be able to identify where lost energy went or gained mechanical energy came from.

9–4   TYPES OF INTERNAL ENERGY

It is fairly easy to account for the energy in some situations, like the bouncing ball experiment, for instance. You can see the ball dropping and speeding up as it heads toward the floor. We have studied how the energy is transformed. In other situations, like the student hiking up stairs wearing a backpack, one can easily see that the gravitational potential energy is increasing, but it is more difficult to identify where the energy is coming from. There are many types of energy that depend on the positions and motions of the atoms and molecules that make objects up rather than the position or motion of the entire object. These energies are collectively labeled as **internal energies**.

An internal energy, because it deals with positions and motions of objects on an atomic scale, can be difficult to track. Historically, when-

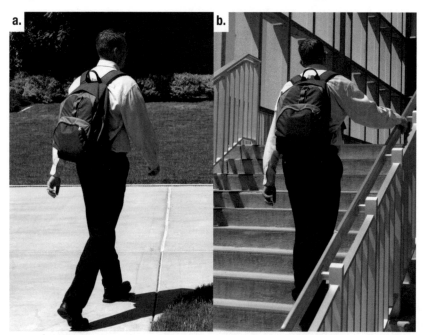

a.   b.

---

* You may wonder why your back aches if you're not doing any work. The muscles in your back are contracting through a distance every time a muscle fiber "fires," so you are doing work on your back muscles. You are just not doing any work on the backpack.

ever mechanical energy has seemed to appear or vanish, a more careful look has shown that it was actually transformed from or into some type of internal energy. Internal energies will be discussed in detail in later chapters, but a few important categories will be touched on here.

Thermal Energy

One of the more blatant examples of seemingly disappearing energy happens every time a driver brakes her car to stop at a red light. The car initially had a great deal of kinetic energy. When the driver pushed on the brakes, the kinetic energy decreased until it was gone. Where that kinetic energy went isn't immediately obvious. When the car's brakes are first depressed by the driver's foot, the brakes pads exert a force on the tires as they rotate through a distance. The energy is transferred because of work done by the brake pads, so the first place to look for the lost energy is in the brake pads. The pads would be hot, and that heat is the car's kinetic energy.

When energy seems to vanish, it tends to end up as heat. (The reasons for this will be discussed in Chapter 18). The bouncing ball discussed at the beginning of this chapter doesn't quite go back to the same height it started from, but the ball (if it could be examined in midair with a very sensitive thermometer) would be found to be slightly warmer than it was before it was dropped. Friction with the air and ground transformed some of the energy into heat.

The same is true of most processes. A little energy gets transformed into heat even in a process in which the frictional forces are very small, such as a pendulum swinging. The law of conservation of total energy is the reason why there are no **perpetual motion machines**. Hopeful inventors through the years have tried every possible—and some impossible—designs to circumvent that law. As a "perpetual motion" machine goes through its cycle, a tiny bit of energy is lost as heat on each cycle. That loss (i.e., transformation of kinetic energy into thermal energy) eventually leaves the machine with no mechanical energy and no further movement.

While losing energy to heat is ubiquitous, the connection between energy and heat was one of the last pieces to fit into the law of conservation of energy. It wasn't until the mid-1800s that scientists carefully measured the size of frictional forces and the distance through which they were applied and showed that the work done was directly proportional to changes in temperature.

Figure 9.7
If he doesn't keep pumping, the swing will eventually stop. What happens to the mechanical energy?

Heat transfer process

One reason it took so long to identify heat as a type of energy is because of the way heat transfers from one object to another. It behaves in a way that is analogous to the way fluids behave, and so for many years, heat was thought to be some sort of flowing physical fluid.* Moving water from one place to another, from a well to a fire for instance, can be done one of three ways (see *Figure 9.8*): a) Line up a bucket brigade where people who are not moving pass buckets of water from one person to the next, b) give each person their own bucket that they run to fill up at the well and then run with to the fire, or c) use a pump to lift the well water to a hose that can be used to spray water directly from the well onto the fire. The manner in which heat is transferred can be classified as one of three analogous types: by conduction, by convection, or by radiation.

Conduction—Conduction takes place when objects having different temperatures are placed in direct contact with each other. The heat moves from the hotter object to the cooler one. Just like the stationary people in the bucket brigade, matter acts as a stationary conduit through which the heat moves, and no matter is exchanged, just energy.

Examples of conduction include burning

● **Perpetual Motion Machine**
A perpetual motion machine is something that keeps moving forever without any energy being added.

● **Conduction**
The transmission of an electric charge or heat through a conducting medium without perceptible motion of the medium itself.

---

* The idea that heat was a fluid was taken pretty much for granted through the 18th and most of the 19th centuries. This fluid was called "caloric." The word calorie is a vestige of this idea.

Figure 9.8

a. Passing buckets of water from one stationary person to the next is analogous to the way heat is transferred through conduction.

b. People running back and forth with buckets of water is analogous to the way moving material transports heat in convection.

c. Spraying water directly from a well is analogous to transferring heat directly through radiation.

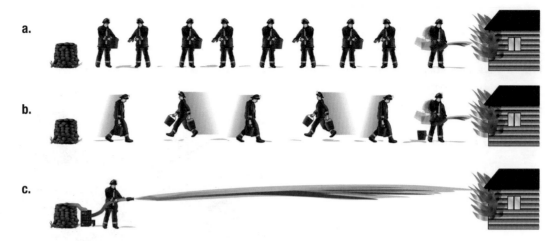

- **Convection**

The process by which energy is moved from one place to another by being stored in matter as internal energy, then moving the matter from one place to another.

- **Radiation**

The process by which energy is moved from one place to another in the form of light or related forms such as X-rays, gamma rays, microwaves, etc.

- **Chemical Potential Energy**

The form of internal energy associated with the physical and chemical states of matter. The type of energy stored in a car battery.

- **Elastic Potential Energy**

The form of internal energy associated with stretching or compressing material.

one's hand when a roommate says that the pan left on the stove has cooled down, cooking eggs by submerging them in boiling water, or cooling down a can of soda by surrounding the can with ice. No material is being exchanged between the two objects, but energy is moving through direct contact.

Convection—Convection takes place when hot material moves around and transfers heat. Heat carried by hot material is just like people running with buckets of water. As hot and cold material mix, the overall temperature changes. Convection can either occur naturally or be forced.

Baseboard heaters raise the temperature of the air around them. The less dense warm air rises and is replaced by cooler, denser air near the floor. As the warm air mixes with the cool air, the temperature in the room as a whole goes up. This is natural convection.

A standard furnace uses fans to help the process along. Air is heated inside the furnace and then blown through ducts to all the rooms in the house. The air mixes and the temperature inside the house increases.

Radiation—This last process is a direct transfer of heat from one place to another without any need for intervening matter. The Sun is nearly 100,000,000 miles from Earth, with mostly empty space between, yet the Sun is able to adequately heat Earth. The energy is transferred in the form of electromagnetic radiation (sunlight). In an example closer to home, the heat of a campfire on a cold night can be felt by a person sitting near the fire even though the surrounding air is cold. The reason the camper's side facing the fire feels so much warmer than the side facing away is because of the radiative heat transfer from the fire.

Chemical Potential Energy

As that campfire radiates its energy towards its grateful campers, one might logically ask where that burning-log energy came from in the first place. The logs are not falling, slowing down, losing charge, or doing anything else that decreases their mechanical energy. They are, however, turning from wood into chunks of carbon, carbon dioxide gas, and water vapor.

One type of internal energy has to do with the way atoms are organized to make molecules. Atoms have differing amounts of energy, depending on how they are bonded together to form various kinds of molecules. Air and dynamite both contain hydrogen, nitrogen, carbon, and oxygen. However, dynamite has quite a bit more destructive capacity than air because the atoms are bonded together differently, resulting in molecules with very different structures and properties. Energy associated with chemical bonds is known as **chemical potential energy**.

Elastic Potential Energy

Another type of energy, **elastic potential energy**, also depends on the position of atoms and molecules. When a material is in equilibrium, all the forces on any point in the material balance out. In many substances, if molecules in the material are displaced from this equilibrium position, the resulting unbalanced forces will push them back toward the point where the forces balance.

Springs and rubber bands provide the most familiar examples of this type of energy. A rubber band has a relaxed position. If you stretch a rubber band, you have to exert a force through the distance you stretch it. You are storing energy

Figure 9.9
When you jump on a trampoline, the kinetic energy you have when you first hit the trampoline is converted into elastic potential energy when you stretch the springs and fabric. As they return to their equilibrium position, the trampoline exerts an upward force on you through the distance the trampoline stretched. The work done on you transforms this elastic energy back into kinetic energy, which in turn becomes gravitational potential energy.

by moving the molecules farther apart than they were in their equilibrium position. If you let go of the rubber band, the force pulling the molecules back to their equilibrium position converts this stored energy into kinetic energy (see *Figure 9.9*).

This type of energy is also present in carbon dioxide when it is compressed and used to propel everything from clothesline model rockets to whipped cream from a can. The process of compressing the carbon dioxide forces carbon dioxide molecules closer together inside a strong can or cartridge, thereby changing the molecules' natural equilibrium. The pressure of the compressed gas inside the cartridge is higher than the pressure outside, so when the cartridge is punctured or the nozzle is opened there is an unbalanced force pushing the carbon dioxide out of the can and an equal and opposite force on the container. This stored elastic energy is converted into kinetic energy of the gas, and possibly the can.

In some situations, the stored elastic energy is not converted into mechanical energy but is just transferred to neighboring molecules. Molecules that are pushed together move back to their equilibrium position, but push their neighbors closer to the molecules a bit further away in the process (see *Figure 9.10*). The energy doesn't change form but moves from one group of atoms to the next through the material. Methods of transferring elastic energy will be discussed in greater detail in Chapter 10.

Nuclear Potential Energy

The nucleus of an atom has two competing forces acting inside it. A strong nuclear force in each atom holds its protons and neutrons together and an electromagnetic force pushes its protons apart.

The atom's nucleus is made up of positively charged particles held close to each other, so a large electrical potential energy is associated with the nucleus. The strong force is attractive, so it makes sense that just as with opposite charges, the closer the protons and neutrons are, the lower the associated potential energy will be. Details on how the total nuclear energy changes as protons and neutrons are combined and separated are discussed in Chapter 25.

There is some basic information about nuclear energy that is appropriate to mention at this point in our overview of the various types of energies. Ever since the first nuclear bombs ended World War II in a spectacular and devastating show of energy, everything we know about nuclear energy has been closely associated with Albert Einstein, relativity, and probably the most famous equation of our day, $E = mc^2$. Most American high school students have heard and probably memorized the $E = mc^2$ equation in the context of nuclear energy studies, without having any idea of what the equation means. Now, of course, you know that Einstein's theory of relativity is about what happens when objects travel close to the speed of light. **Nuclear poten-**

Figure 9.10
When someone standing in a group of people invades the personal space of another, that person instinctively moves to reach their "equilibrium" position, resulting in a chain reaction as the person who moved invades the space of another person, who then moves in to a new equilibrium position. This situation is analogous to how molecules behave in ways that return them to their equilibrium position.

tial energy is about the positions of protons and neutrons in a nucleus. The connection between a relativity-related equation and the energy released by nuclear explosions isn't exactly obvious. But we are about to look at what happens to energy at high—really high—speeds.

9–5 RELATIVISTIC ENERGY AND MASS-ENERGY EQUIVALENCE

Kinetic energy depends on mass and speed, both of which are impacted by special relativity. Maximum speed is limited by special relativity. The speed of light is the same for all observers, and despite the hopes of entire generations of science fiction authors and readers, nothing can travel faster than the speed of light*. Additionally, in the previous chapter the law of conservation of momentum showed that a moving object has more mass than an otherwise identical stationary object. This means that at a minimum, when we discuss energies of objects moving at high speeds, we must take into account the relativistic changes in mass and speed.

Readers studying the previous chapter may have finished that chapter wondering exactly where the additional mass came from and where it would go. Einstein, in a remarkable leap of intuition supported by elegant, if complex, math formulas that have weathered almost a century of testing, showed that *mass is related to energy*. He used conservation of momentum and known equations for the momentum of light to show how the energy of an object and its mass are related. He determined that an object that emitted light (light has no mass) would lose mass proportional to the energy it radiated away. The equation he derived was the now classic, deceptively simple $E = mc^2$. 'E' stands for energy, 'm'

◆ **Nuclear Potential Energy**

The energy stored in the nucleus of an atom.

Figure 9.11

A collision in two frames of reference.

stands for mass and 'c' stands for the speed of light, 300,000,000 m/s.

This equation solves the mystery left from Chapter 8 of how mass changes with speed. If the equation really works, then it isn't the speed that causes mass to change, it is the energy. If something is moving fast, it has more energy, so it has more mass. If you slow something down by exerting a force on it, you are doing work and transferring energy away from the object. Less energy means less mass. But as long as the energy is still there, so is the mass, regardless of what form the energy takes. Let's take a look at a thought experiment which shows that mass depends on energy rather than speed.

In *Figure 9.11*, two identical objects move toward each other at the same high speed (near the speed of light). To simplify this explanation, no forces act on either object. As a result, no work will be done on them and consequently no change in their energy. From both reference frames the moving objects have the same size mass, which is larger than the mass they would have if they weren't moving. If these two same-sized objects collide and stick together, the energy will all be converted to some form of internal energy, most likely heat. Because momentum is conserved, the total speed after the impact will be zero. Because the objects are no longer moving, if mass depends on speed then the objects will return to their "normal" mass. If mass depends on energy, they keep their larger mass. So, what happens to the mass?

In the first frame of reference (Figure 19.11a), it is going to be hard to tell. The speed is zero, and any mass times zero speed is still zero momentum. We need to look at the momentum from the point of view of someone walking by at a low speed perpendicular to the direction our objects were moving, so we don't multiply by zero (Figure 19.11b).

a.

In a frame of reference where the two balls are moving horizontally, the total momentum is zero. The combined mass will not be moving if they hit and stick together.

b.

In a frame of reference moving slowly towards the bottom of the page with respect to the first frame, the balls will appear to be moving slowly towards the top of the page. They will have a small vertical momentum. When they hit and stick, the combined mass will continue to move towards the top of the page at the same speed.

---

* This can be demonstrated with a thought experiment. Suppose I am in a spaceship moving 50% faster than the speed of light, 450 million meters each second, as measured by you. For some reason I decide to turn on a flashlight and point it forward. In my reference frame light travels 300 million meters each second, so the light would be 300 million meters in front of the spaceship after one second. In your frame the light also travels 300 million meters each second, while the space ship has traveled 450 million miles in the same second. So you conclude that the light is 150 million miles behind the spaceship. While it is possible to explain differences in distance, a single beam of light can't be both in front of and behind the space ship at the same time. The principle of non-contradiction doesn't bend that far. This means it is impossible to travel faster than light.

When we do so, we start out with a small momentum along the perpendicular direction that is equal to the relativistic mass of both objects times the perpendicular speed. After the collision momentum must be conserved. The combined mass times speed has to be the same as it was before and the speed of the observer hasn't changed. So after the collision, the combined mass must still be equal to the mass of both objects when they were moving.

In a real situation like this the energy would most likely end up as heat, but it doesn't matter what type of energy the kinetic energy has transformed into. As long as the energy is present, so is the extra mass.

This means that rather than conserving mass or energy individually, there is a new conservation rule. **Mass is equivalent to energy**. Mass and energy are really two ways of measuring the same thing. **The total of mass and energy is conserved, but neither mass nor energy is *individually* conserved**.

The first and most obvious consequence of this is that mass can be created out of energy and vice versa, as long as none of the other conservation rules are broken. This may seem like an impossibility, but it happens all the time in our atmosphere. Remember the muons back in Chapter 6? They are the result of this process called "pair production." Scientists have replicated this process by using controlled high-energy light beams. These high energy beams of light will produce electrons and *anti-matter electrons* when the energy of the light is greater than the combined mass of the two particles times the speed of light squared. The anti-matter electron exists only a short time before it collides with a matter electron. The result is that the collision annihilates both matter electron and anti-matter electron, and their combined mass is turned back into energy.

The second consequence is that any time an object releases a large amount of energy, there will be a corresponding drop in the object's mass. In nuclear energy, where the forces involved aren't understood well enough to allow scientists to calculate the energy directly, we can still accurately predict how much energy will be released simply by measuring the change in the mass caused by the nuclear reaction. Einstein's equation is associated with nuclear power because it is the easiest way to determine how much energy a nucleus will give up.

So exactly what do we mean by a "large amount of energy"? The energy released by burning 1 kg of gasoline (1/4 gallon) would change the mass of the gas 0.0000000005 kg. We cannot measure changes in mass that small. Even in nuclear reactions which have the largest changes of energy known in nature, the mass changes, while measurable, are less than 0.1% of the total mass.

The changes in mass are so small that unless we are dealing with a nuclear reaction or an object with the extraordinarily large kinetic energies of something moving at close to the speed of light, the change will be insignificant. For most objects, mass and energy are conserved independently. Only in these extreme cases do we need to combine the laws into a law of conservation of mass-energy.

9–6   CONCLUSION

The different types of energy discussed in the chapter are summarized in *Table 9.1*. Conservation of energy and energy transformations are the most widely used physics concepts, and will prove very important in subsequent chapters. Some of the missing details (like why thermal energy is a microscopic kinetic energy) will be covered later.

Table 9.1

The total energy of an object can be changed only by moving energy to or from somewhere else through one or more of the energy transfer processes.

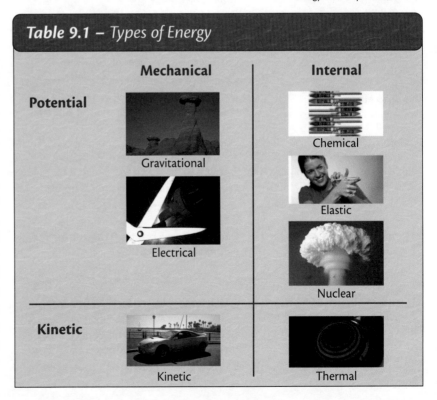
Table 9.1 – Types of Energy

Chapter Framework

A. What Is Energy?
1. Exerting force
2. Destructive capacity

B. Types of Mechanical Energy
1. Kinetic energy
2. Gravitational potential energy
3. Electrical potential energy

C. Transforming and Transferring Mechanical Energy: Work
1. Total energy
2. Work = force × distance parallel to direction of force

D. Types of Internal Energy
1. Thermal energy
   a. *perpetual motion machines*
   b. *Heat transfer processes—Conduction, convection, radiation*
2. Chemical potential energy
3. Elastic potential energy
4. Nuclear potential energy

E. Relativistic Energy and Mass-Energy Equivalence

Comprehension

Matching

a. *Potential energy*
b. *Mechanical energy*
c. *Internal energy*
d. *Gravitational potential energy*
e. *Perpetual motion machine*
f. *Kinetic energy*
g. *Work*
h. *Conduction*
i. *Nuclear potential energy*
j. *Convection*
k. *Chemical potential energy*
l. *Elastic potential energy*
m. *Radiation*

1. ____ Depends on an object's position.
2. ____ Depends on the position and motion of the object on the atomic scale.
3. ____ Weight times height.
4. ____ Depends on the position and motion of the whole object.
5. ____ Done to move an object in the direction of an applied force.
6. ____ Something that keeps moving forever without any energy being added
7. ____ Depends on an object's motion.
8. ____ Energy moves through direct contact.
9. ____ Heat is transferred when the hot material moves around.
10. ____ Direct transfer of heat from one place to another without any need for intervening matter.
11. ____ Energy associated with chemical bonds.
12. ____ Depends on the position of atoms and molecules.
13. ____ Depends on the positions of protons and neutrons in a nucleus.

True/False

1. ____ Speed plays a more significant role than mass in determining an object's kinetic energy.
2. ____ Gravitational potential energy decreases as the distance between two objects increases.
3. ____ If an object remains stationary, then no work is being done on it.
4. ____ In the process of conduction, both matter and energy are exchanged.
5. ____ The closer the protons and neutrons are to each other, the lower the nuclear potential energy will be.
6. ____ Mass and energy are really two ways of measuring the same thing.
7. ____ The heat you feel on your face from a campfire when the surrounding air is cold is an example of radiation.

Fill in the Blank

1. Kinetic energy depends on _____ and _____.
2. When traveling near the speed of light, mass _____.
3. When a cold object and a hot object are placed in direct contact with each other, energy moves from the _____ object to the _____ object.
4. The transfer of heat from the Sun to Earth is an example of _____.
5. Besides stupidity, sitting on a hot stove is an example of _____.
6. Baseboard heaters and standard furnaces heat the house by _____.
7. In the equation $E = mc^2$, 'E' stands for _____, 'm' stands for _____ and 'c' stands for _____.

Analysis

1. Energy can be defined as
   a) a measure of destructive capacity.
   b) the ability to exert a force on an object while it moves through some distance in the direction of the applied force.
   c) both (a) and (b).

2. If you move two positively charged objects closer together, then electrical potential energy
   a) increases.
   b) decreases.
   c) stays the same.

3. Two objects with opposite charges are brought closer together. Electrical potential energy
   a) increases.
   b) decreases.
   c) stays the same.

4. As you dribble a basketball, which of the following quantities is/are conserved?
   a) Gravitational potential energy.
   b) Kinetic energy.
   c) Internal energy.
   d) Total energy.
   e) More than one of the above.

5. If an object has kinetic energy, then it must

   a) be electrically charged.
   b) be moving.
   c) be in an elevated position.
   d) be at rest.

6. Work is always done on an object when

   a) more than one force is applied to the object.
   b) the object moves at a constant speed in a straight line.
   c) a force moves the object through a distance in the direction of the force.
   d) all of the above.

7. If you're skiing downhill, which of the follow must be true?

   a) Your internal energy decreases.
   b) Your kinetic energy increases.
   c) Your gravitational potential energy decreases.
   d) You fall.

8. "Pair production" demonstrates which of the following?

   a) Conservation of electric charge.
   b) Conservation of energy.
   c) Conservation of mass.
   d) Conservation of mass-energy.

Synthesis

1. Name two examples of objects with elastic potential energy.

2. What is the speed limit of the universe?

3. What is meant by the conservation of mass-energy?

4. What are two consequences of mass-energy equivalence?

5. Describe the important energy transfer and transformation mechanisms (work, conduction, radiation, and convection).

6. Air and dynamite contain many of the same elements. What makes dynamite so much more destructive than air?

7. Describe the energy changes that occur when an athlete pole-vaults, beginning with the athlete eating breakfast and ending after the athlete hits the mat.

8. You walk into a computer lab and see many students doing homework. However, based on what you learned in Physical Science, you conclude that no one is really doing much "work" at all. What leads you to this conclusion?

9. You accidentally drop your cell phone off of a balcony. You know that the only thing that could possibly console you would be to apply Physical Science to the tragedy.

   a) What kind(s) of energy does it have before it falls?

   b) What kind(s) of energy does it lose as it falls?

   c) What kind(s) of energy does it gain as it falls?

   d) What kind(s) of energy does it have just after it hits the ground and stops?

   e) How does the total amount of energy in (d) compare with that in (a)? How do you know?

10. A frictionless pendulum is set in motion.

    a) What kind of energy does it have at the highest point of its swing?

    b) What kind of energy does it gain as it swings downward?

    c) As it swings upward again, what kind of energy does it lose? What kind does it gain?

    d) How does the conservation of energy apply to this situation?

11. Now consider a real pendulum (with friction).

    a) What kind of energy does it have at the highest point of its swing?

    b) What kind of energy does it gain as it swings downward?

    c) As time passes, what happens to the maximum height of each swing? If you attached a sensitive thermometer to the pendulum, what would happen to its temperature as it continued to swing?

    d) What will be the fate of the pendulum? What kind of energy will it have at that time?

    e) How does the conservation of energy apply to this situation?

12. A constant force propels a rocket ship through space.

    a) Describe the resulting speed and acceleration of the rocket ship.

    b) Is there a limit to how fast the rocket ship can go? If so, what is it?

    c) What is the relationship between mass and energy? What happens to the energy transferred to the rocket ship at high speeds?

    d) What effect does this have on the rocket ship's acceleration?

13. Explain how pressing on the nozzle of a Ready Whip container releases the whipped cream. What type of energy does the compressed carbon dioxide have?

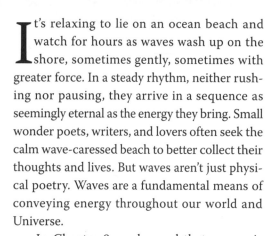

WAVES

CHAPTER 10

It's relaxing to lie on an ocean beach and watch for hours as waves wash up on the shore, sometimes gently, sometimes with greater force. In a steady rhythm, neither rushing nor pausing, they arrive in a sequence as seemingly eternal as the energy they bring. Small wonder poets, writers, and lovers often seek the calm wave-caressed beach to better collect their thoughts and lives. But waves aren't just physical poetry. Waves are a fundamental means of conveying energy throughout our world and Universe.

In Chapter 9, we learned that energy is transported by conduction, convection, and radiation. Conduction transports heat energy through materials that touch. Convection transfers heat and kinetic energy through material that moves. Radiation transmits energy through the emptiness of space without any assistance from matter at all. In addition to these three mechanisms, energy is also conveyed through a medium when **mechanical waves** propagate through it.

Energy is conveyed by mechanical waves when material vibrates in place. The vibrational energy travels through the material but the material itself stays in the same location. One way this

energy—call it a "disturbance"—can pass through the material is illustrated by the waving rope in *Figure 10.1*. In the figure, two people have stretched a rope tightly between them. One person then rapidly moves their rope end up and down, causing a disturbance in the form of a few "ripples." The ripples travel the length of rope to the other person, bringing the disturbance energy with them. As the disturbance travels down the rope, individual parts of the rope move up and down and then return to their starting points after the wave has passed by.

Water waves behave in the same manner. Throw a rock into a pond and the energy of the

Figure 10.1

It is the disturbance that is propagated from one place to another, not parts of the medium itself.

LEARNING OBJECTIVES

When you finished with this chapter you should be able to

- Define what a wave is.
- State the similarities and differences between transverse and longitudinal waves.
- Describe the four properties every wave possesses.
- Describe the four different types of wave behavior and give examples of each.
- Explain what standing waves are and how they are created.
- Explain the Doppler effect and how it changes wavelength and frequency.

splash spreads out as a circular wave from the place where the rock hit. Sticks and leaves floating on the surface of the pond bob in a vertical circle as the wave passes by. Like the parts of the rope, the sticks and leaves and the water they float on return to their original position after the wave has gone by (*Figure 10.2*).

A good example of how a wave works is "doing the wave" at a football game. The wave starts when cheerleaders coax a section of fans into standing up and sitting down. Then their neighbors to one side do the same. If everyone feels the spirit of the moment, the act of standing up and sitting down circles the stadium. This

Figure 10.2

Water moves in a circular pattern as a surface wave passes through it. Notice that the red water particle on the surface will return to its orginal position after the wave passes.

"disturbance" goes around the arena while the people themselves, "the material," stay at their seats standing up and sitting down in sequence with their neighbors.

Water waves, waves along a rope, and waves in a football stadium have several features in common. Each travels through something tangible, a "medium" which supports the wave's motion. Each medium has an equilibrium shape. For water the shape is a level surface, for the rope it is a straight line, and for the football stadium it is people sitting in their seats. Each of these waves cause a deviation from the equilibrium shape.

Materials that propagate waves always contain some mechanism for restoring their shape. Internal forces within the rope cause it to return to a straight line. Gravity causes the surface of water to return to being flat. Forces attempting to restore the medium to its equilibrium position cause the wave to be propagated.

117

- **Mechanical Wave**

A vibration in material that transports energy.

- **Equilibrium Position**

The place where a molecule will reside when no unbalanced forces are acting upon it.

- **Longitudinal Wave**

A wave in which the molecules of the medium vibrate in the same direction as the wave propagates.

- **Transverse Wave**

A wave in which the molecules of the medium vibrate at right angles to the direction the wave propagates.

- **Surface Wave**

A wave that travels along the surface of a medium. In this wave particles travel in a circular motion.

Without restoring forces, no wave would be generated.

10–1 WAVE TYPES

Molecules make up all physical matter (as explained in more detail in Chapter 13). Each molecule inside a medium has a place where it naturally resides called its **equilibrium position**. A wave passing through the medium applies an alternating unbalanced force to each molecule, causing it to vibrate around its equilibrium position.

Mechanical waves are of two different types, depending on how the medium's molecules vibrate when the wave passes by. If the material vibrates in the same direction that the wave moves, the disturbance is a **longitudinal** or **compression wave** (see *Figure 10.3*). If the material vibrates at right angles to the direction the wave moves, the disturbance is a **transverse** or **shear** wave (see *Figure 10.4*). Both of these types

of waves travel through the interiors of materials.

Surface waves, such as water waves, travel along the surface of a medium and usually contain both longitudinal and transverse motions. This results in a net circular motion for the molecules on the surface (refer back to Figure 10.2). Since surface waves are a combination of longitudinal and transverse waves, they will not be treated separately in this chapter.

Transverse Waves

The forces in a transverse wave stretch the bonds between molecules up and down in a direction that is sideways or perpendicular to the direction the wave propagates (*Figure 10.5a*). These sideways forces are called "shear" forces, so transverse waves are also called shear waves. As previously mentioned, when a shear wave passes by a point, the molecules at that point vibrate back and forth at right angles to the direction in which the wave is moving.

Shear forces can be exerted on all states of materials; solids, liquids, gases, and plasmas. (See Chapter 12 for more details on states of materials.) The molecules in liquids, gases, and plasmas are not rigidly bound to one another and drift away in the direction the force pushes them. Only in solids do binding forces pull the molecules back to their equilibrium positions. As a result shear waves only propagate through solids.*

A person slamming his fist on a table creates a shear wave. The sudden force of fist hitting table causes a wave of vibrational energy to travel in all directions through the table, making, say, a book on anger management on the far end of the table jump. "The wave" of fans is a shear wave because the people stand up and down while the wave travels at right angles to their motion. Light is another example of a shear wave. Light's properties are sufficiently different from standard mechanical waves, though, that we describe them separately in Chapter 11.

Longitudinal Waves

The forces in a longitudinal wave stretch and

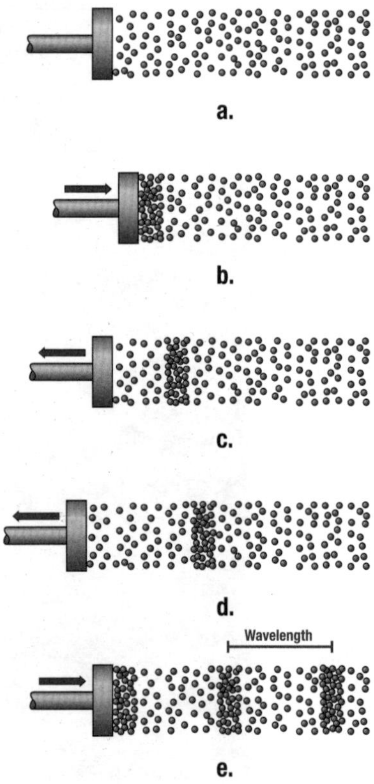

Figure 10.3

In a longitudinal or compression wave the material vibrates back and forth in the same direction the wave propagates.

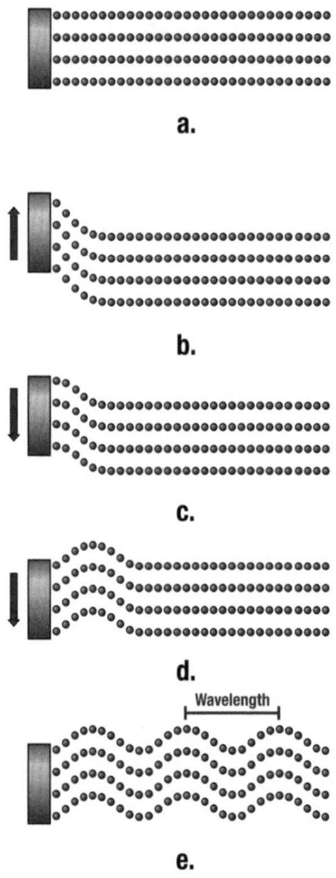

Figure 10.4

In a transverse or shear wave the material vibrates up and down at right angles to the direction the wave propagates.

Surface waves on a pond or lake do have a shearing motion in them. This is because at the surface of a liquid, gravity acts as a restoring force pulling the molecules back down to their original positions. *Inside* fluids this effect doesn't work, so shear waves do not travel inside fluids.

compress the bonds between molecules back and forth in the same direction that the wave propagates (*Figure 10.5b*). These forces are called "compression" forces, so longitudinal waves are also called compression or pressure waves. A compression wave passing a point causes the molecules at that point to vibrate back and forth in the direction the wave is moving.

Compression waves travel through all states of matter because molecules can be compressed regardless of their state. In liquids, gases, and plasmas, the molecules are not rigidly bound to each other yet they still resist being compressed or pulled too far apart. This resistance provides the restoring force necessary to propagate the wave.

As an example, imagine a person standing in a line of people who are all holding hands and singing. For some reason, the person starts swaying side-to-side with the music. This makes those on either side also start moving side-to-side. This movement creates a wave where the swaying disturbance moves along the line of people.

Sound is a compression wave. A vibrating object in contact with the air causes a series of compressions and decompressions in the surrounding air that travel outward in all directions. These compressions in turn cause a series of oscillating forces on any object they strike, such as a human eardrum. The energy from the wave is transmitted to the eardrum and the hearer understands it as sound.

Whether a wave is longitudinal or transverse, its energy thins as the wave front spreads out through the medium. Eventually the coherence in the wave movement is lost and turns into

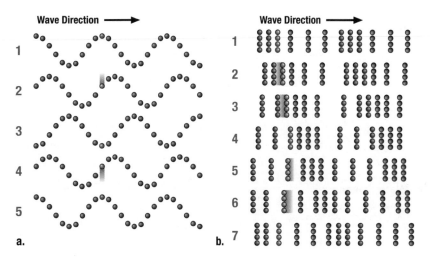

chaotic random molecular motion. At this point the wave has disappeared and its energy has become part of the overall thermal energy of the medium it was in.

10–2 WAVE PROPERTIES

Figure 10.6 is an illustration of both a compression and a shear wave "frozen" in space to show how particle displacement changes with location. The places of maximum upward or forward displacement are called "**crests**." The points of maximum downward or backward displacement are called "**troughs**." Half-way in between the particles are at their equilibrium position. How particles vibrate when a wave passes through them can be completely described by four properties: *amplitude, wavelength, frequency, and speed.*

Amplitude, labeled in Figures 10.6a and 10.6b, is the maximum distance a particle moves from its natural resting place when a wave passes

Figure 10.5
These two figures illustrate the motion a particle undergoes when a) a shear wave passes by and b) a compression wave passes by.

♦ **Crest**
The part of a wave where the particles are displaced a maximum amount above or in front of their equilibrium position.

♦ **Trough**
The part of a wave where the particles are displaced a maximum amount below or behind their equilibrium position.

♦ **Amplitude**
The maximum amount that a particle will displace from its normal, undisturbed position when a wave passes through it.

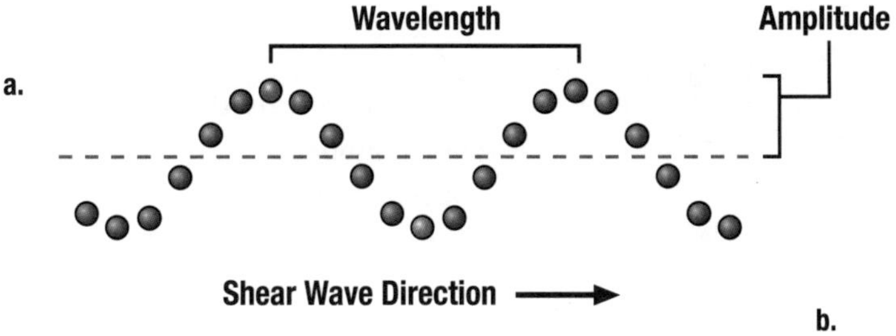

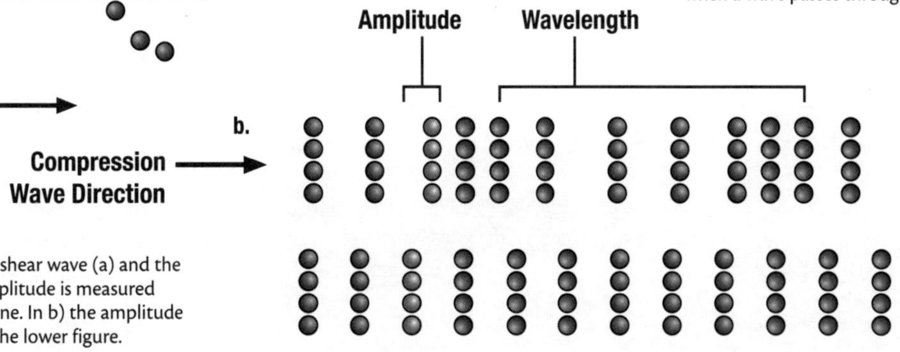

Figure 10.6
An illustration of amplitude and wavelength for the shear wave (a) and the compression wave (b) from Figure 10.5. In a) the amplitude is measured from the equilibrium position given as the straight line. In b) the amplitude is measured from the equilibrium position given in the lower figure.

• **Wavelength**
The distance between successive similar parts in a repeating wave.

• **Frequency**
The number of wave amplitude crests that pass a particular point in space every second.

• **Wave Speed**
The rate at which a specific wave disturbance travels from point to point.

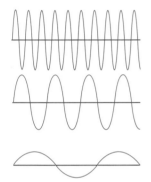

Figure 10.7
Three waves showing a progression from high frequency and long wavelength to low frequency and large wavelength.

Table 10.1
The relationship between wavelength and frequency for sound. As frequency increases wavelength decreases. The speed remains the same.

through it. In other words, amplitude is the distance a particle travels when going from its equilibrium position to a crest or to a trough. With mechanical waves, amplitude correlates with the amount of energy transmitted; greater energy means greater displacement. For sound waves, amplitude is loudness. A strong sound wave, like the sound from a police siren or a really unhappy baby, has large amplitude. A weak wave, such as a whisper ("Wake up, dear. It's your turn to feed the baby.") has small amplitude.

Wavelength, as shown in Figure 10.6a and b, is the distance between successive "like-parts" in a repeating wave. Wavelength is most easily measured between successive crests. However, the distance between any similar parts in succession, such as adjacent troughs, or ascending nodes, will also be equal to the wavelength. Sound waves have wavelengths ranging from a few centimeters to several meters long. Longer waves have lower tones while shorter waves have higher tones. Light wavelengths are on the order of a few millionths of a meter in length.

Frequency measures the number of wave crests passing a particular point every second. If the waves of Figure 10.6 were "unfrozen" and allowed to fly through space in a natural manner, a succession of crests and troughs would be seen going by. Frequency is a count of the number of crests that pass by a fixed point in one second. The unit used to measure frequency is "oscillations per second," or *hertz* in honor of Heinrich Hertz, a German physicist who studied the production and reception of radio waves in the late 19th century. Frequency in sound waves also relates to pitch. Higher frequencies produce higher tones while lower frequencies produce lower tones.

Our ears are sensitive to frequencies of sound waves from 20 to 20,000 hertz. Waves from earthquakes have frequencies from 10 to 1000 hertz, explaining why they often create a low rumbling sound. Frequencies of radio waves (the values listed numerically on the dials of AM and FM receivers) range from a few thousand hertz to several million hertz.

Wave Speed is the rate that the disturbance energy travels through the medium. Wave speed depends on the medium's elastic properties, its density and the type of wave going through it. In general speeds are higher when the material is stiffer and lower when it is denser. In a given medium, compression waves travel faster than shear waves. For either type of wave the speed is the same regardless of the amplitude, wavelength, or frequency.

Speeds vary greatly between different materials. The speed of sound in air at sea level at 20° C is about 340 m/sec (760 mph). Sound travels slower than this when the air is cooler and denser. Compression waves, traveling through stiff rock layers like those created by earthquakes, travel at 5,500 m/sec (12,000 mph) or more.

Frequency, wavelength, and speed are related by the formula:

wave speed = frequency x wavelength

This important relation is illustrated by watching the waves of Figure 10.6 go by. In one second, a single wave crest travels a distance equal to the length of a wavelength multiplied by the number of wavelengths going past, which is the frequency.

Because wave speed in a medium remains constant for all wavelengths and frequencies, the wavelength times the frequency is also constant. Therefore, *high frequency corresponds to short wavelengths and low frequency corresponds to long wavelengths* (see *Figure 10.7*).

For example, suppose a sound wave has a wavelength of 10 meters and a frequency of 34 oscillations per second. That means 34 wave crests, each separated by 10 meters, pass any point in the medium in one second. Therefore, the wave must move a distance of 34 times 10 meters, or 340 meters, each second. If the wavelength were half this amount, then the frequency must be twice as great because the speed of 340 m/sec must always equal frequency times wave-

Table 10.1 – *Wavelength and Frequency*		
Wavelength (meters)	**Frequency** (Hertz)	**Speed** (m/sec)
3.4	100	340
10	34	340
20	1.7	340
1000	.34	340

length. *Table 10.1* shows this relationship for several different sound frequencies.

10-3 WAVE PHENOMENA

All waves, regardless of their type, exhibit four characteristic behaviors: *reflection, refraction, diffraction, and interference.* Conversely, any phenomenon that displays all four of these characteristics has to be a wave. An unknown energy transfer process can be tested to see if it is a wave or not by seeing if it has all four of these properties.

Reflection

Waves "bounce," or **reflect** when they encounter abrupt changes in the nature or density of the medium they travel through. Water waves in a bathtub reflect when they encounter the denser, solid tub walls. Sound waves traveling through air reflect when they strike a solid wall. Reflected sound waves are the echoes you hear in a canyon. Reflection determines the acoustical properties of rooms and auditoriums (*Figure 10.8*).

We are all familiar with the reflection of light from mirrors, but we may not realize that

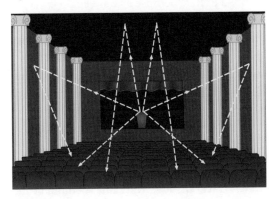

Figure 10.8
Much of the sound you hear in a room is from reflections off the walls and ceiling.

light reflects to some degree off nearly all other surfaces as well. Light illuminating a room reflects and bounces rapidly around until virtually every surface is sending some light off in every direction. The reflections are so pervasive that wherever we stand, reflected light reaches our eyes, allowing us to see. Without reflection, we would be able to see almost nothing.

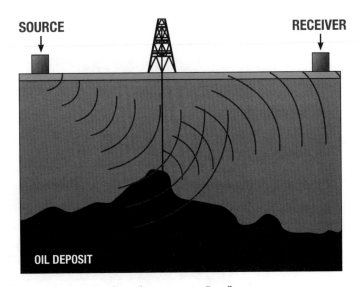

SOURCE   **RECEIVER**

OIL DEPOSIT

Geologists use earthquake waves to "see" inside Earth in much the same way we use light to see objects around us (*Figure 10.9*). The upper layer of Earth is not homogeneous but is composed of a variety of non-uniform structures, as explained in greater detail in Chapter 28. Waves created by explosions or other means travel into Earth's crust and reflect back upward from the boundaries between these structures. The reflected waves reach the surface where sensitive instruments detect and measure them. The analysis of these signals provides information about rock and mineral layers, oil deposits, ore deposits, and even the materials below Earth's crust.

Refraction

Waves penetrate boundaries as well as reflect from them. When traveling from one medium to another, the wave speed often changes. An alteration in wave speed causes the wave's direction to change as well (*Figure 10.10*). This phenomenon is called **refraction**.

Light travels more slowly through glass and other transparent materials than it does through air. When light enters glass and slows down, the wave crests "bunch up." The slowing and bunching occurs first on the side of the wave that first strikes the glass surface, causing the wave to bend in that direction. This effect is similar to what hap-

Figure 10.9
Reflecting waves are used to probe the interior of Earth to find layers of different material and structure.

● **Reflection**
The act of bouncing off a surface.

● **Refraction**
The act of changing direction when passing from one medium to another.

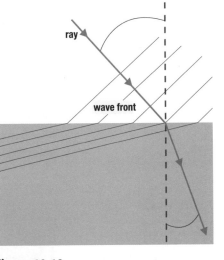

ray

wave front

Figure 10.10
When a wave penetrates into material of greater density, the slower speed causes the wave direction to change.

♦ **Diffraction**
The changing of direction of waves to bend around corners and spread as they encounter obstacles.

♦ **Interference**
The canceling and enhancing effect that occurs when two waves move through the same space at the same time.

pens to an automobile when its left-side and right-side brakes work unevenly. If one side of a car slows down first when applying the brakes, the car will veer in that direction.

Because of refraction, objects inside denser material appear to be at different positions than they really are. A fish will appear to be higher in the water than it is. A stick in water will appear to be bent (*Figure 10.11*).

When the light wave exits the glass it reverts to the speed it had before entering. This speed-up causes it to refract in the opposite direction as before. So for example, light exiting a plane glass window bends back to its original direction, making objects seen through the window appear normal.

The refraction of light passing through glass can be manipulated and preserved by shaping the glass surface into a curve. The lenses of eyeglasses, telescopes, microscopes and other optical instruments use refraction by curved glass to focus light as needed.

Sound travels faster in warm air than in cool air, causing sound waves to refract when moving through air layers of differing temperatures. This causes sound waves to always bend toward denser, cooler air. Refraction can also be observed in ocean waves washing up on gently

sloping beaches. An ocean's wave speed depends on the depth of the water. Waves moving from deep to shallow water become slower as they approach the beach. This slowing causes refraction which always steers the wave more directly into the beach.

Diffraction

Diffraction is when a wave bends around corners or obstacles or spreads out through a small opening (*Figure 10.12*). Diffraction allows sound to be heard around a corner, even when the hearer is not in a direct line of sight with the source. Water waves spread after they pass through a narrow opening in a breakwater, disturbing an area behind the opening that is much broader than the opening itself. The spreading becomes more pronounced as the opening becomes smaller (Figures 10.12b and c).

The amount of diffraction depends on the size of the wavelength relative to the size of the opening the wave passes through, or to the size of the obstacle it passes by. If the hole or obstacle is large compared to the wavelength, little diffraction occurs. Diffraction increases as the opening's size decreases in comparison with the wavelength's size.

Although light is a wave, we typically do not notice it diffract because its wavelength is microscopically short and we rarely view anything through holes that small. If we cause light to pass through a small opening, perhaps by closing our eyelids until only a tiny slit is left through which light may pass, diffraction blurs the images we see.

Interference

Interference occurs when two or more waves travel through the same medium at the same time. At some locations these waves will work together to create a greater disturbance. In other locations the waves will work against each other, creating little or no disturbance.

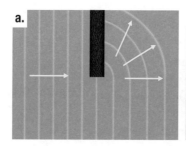
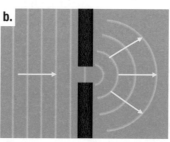
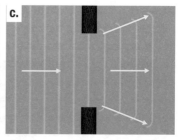

--- **constructive interference**   --- **destructive interference**

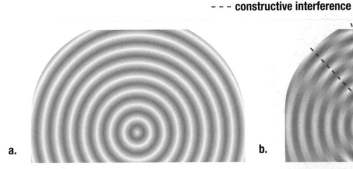

a.

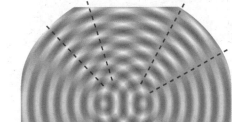

b.

Figure 10.13
a) Dropping a rock in a pond will create circular waves. Here color signals depth; the darker blue represents wave troughs, and the white represents wave crests. b) Dropping two rocks close to each other will create waves that cause constructive and destructive interference. Notice that constructive interference causes lines of higher contrast or amplitude between troughs and crests (blue and white) while destructive interference creates muddy purple lines with low amplitude.

Imagine two rocks dropped near each other in an otherwise smooth pond (*Figure 10.13*). Each rock creates a set of circular waves that radiate out across the surface. Both sets of waves pass through some points on the surface at the same time. At points where the waves are in synchronization, the crests and troughs from both waves arrive together, causing the amplitude to be greater than it would be for either wave alone. Here the two waves enhance each other in **constructive interference**.

Between regions of constructive interference, the waves will be out of synchronization. Crests from one wave will try to cause the water to rise while troughs from the other wave will try to make the same water fall. Here the two waves cancel each other in **destructive interference**.

Interesting acoustical effects occur when sound waves interfere. Sound coming from a single musical instrument being played in a room reflects from the walls and diffracts around obstacles. As reflected waves overlap, areas of constructive and destructive interference can occur, making the instrument sound louder or softer depending on where you sit. Auditoriums often have panels or curtains to absorb sound and minimize interference from reflected waves.

Interference can take place between sounds from two different instruments, or between an instrument and a frequency "standard" like a tuning fork. Musicians use interference to tune their instruments by listening for "beats." A beat is a slowly changing amplitude caused by alternating constructive and destructive interference. Unlike the spatial interference described above, beats are heard by all listeners, regardless of where they are, when the instrument frequency is close to, but not identical with, the standard.

The beat frequency becomes slower as the instrument becomes more in tune.

Other forms of energy transportation besides waves, such as convection, will reflect and refract. However, diffraction and interference are unique to waves. In the example where two rocks were tossed into a pond, the waves from a single rock would, by themselves, cause a disturbance at all points on the water surface. But add *more* disturbance energy to the pond by tossing in a second rock and some points experience *less* disturbance than before. Waves are the only energy process we know of that exhibits this kind of cancellation.

Standing Waves

Reflection and interference can come together under the right circumstances to create a phenomenon called a **standing wave**. Imagine a rope with one end attached to a wall while the other end is grasped and shaken up and down. The wave generated by the shaking travels down the rope, reflects from the wall and travels back to the end where in the shaking had started (*Figure 10.14*). If the wavelength, frequency, and speed of the wave are such that the reflected wave arrives in synchronization with the shaking, the new energy adds to the previous energy and the total energy in the wave grows. By keeping the wave energy confined

• **Constructive Interference**
When two or more waves passing through the same space at the same time both disturb the medium in the same way so that the resultant amplitude is larger than the amplitude of each individual wave separately.

• **Destructive Interference**
When two or more waves passing through the same space at the same time both disturb the medium in opposite ways so that the resultant amplitude is smaller than the amplitude of each individual wave separately.

• **Standing Wave**
A wave characterized by lack of vibration at certain points, between which areas of maximum vibration occur.

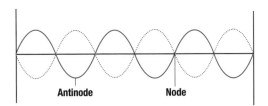

Antinode   Node

Figure 10.14
Standing waves created when waves of the same wavelength move through a string from opposite ends. The solid and dashed curves show the string at two different times.

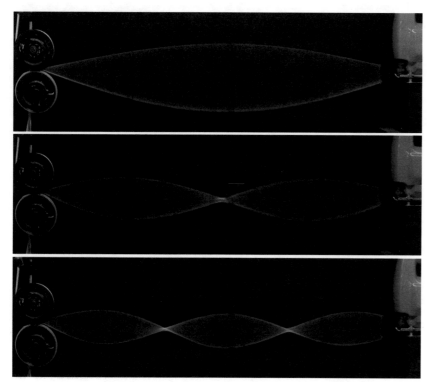

⇦ **Figure 10.15**
Images of one, two and three standing waves in a vibrating string. The places of no vibration (nodes) and maximum vibration (antinodes) are clearly visible. The number of antinodes equals the number of standing waves.

⇩ **Figure 10.17**
Standing wave patterns on a square metal plate. The rich variety in patterns comes from interference between waves of different wavelength set up in each of the two dimensions.

♦ **Resonance**

The creation of an amplitude of oscillation in a system exposed to a periodic infusion of energy.

♦ **Node**

A location of no vibration in a standing wave.

♦ **Antinode**

A location of maximum vibration in a standing wave.

between the reflecting ends, standing waves capture and hold energy in place. Energy confined this way is called a **resonance**.

Standing waves create places of constructive and destructive interference along the entire length of the rope. *Figure 10.15* shows one, two, and three standing waves. The points of no motion are places of destructive interference called **nodes**. The points of maximum motion are places of constructive interference called **antinodes**.

Only waves with wavelengths that are divisible into the rope length with no remainder will create standing waves as illustrated in *Figure 10.16*. If the waves are not exactly divisible into the length, the reflected wave will not synchronize with the shaking. Places of constructive and destructive interference will drift on the rope and neither nodes nor antinodes will be established (Figure 10.16d).

Standing waves can also occur in two-dimensional media, such as a drumhead. In these cases, the nodes are lines rather than points, but the idea is the same. Two dimensional surfaces can sustain resonances in two

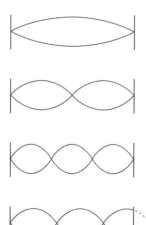

Figure 10.16
To get standing waves between two stationary points at the ends of a string, the wavelengths must just fit the space between the points. The upper and middle waves are allowed; the lower wave is not allowed.

directions at once. This gives them a greater variety of standing wave patterns than is possible for a one-dimensional rope. A few standing wave patterns in a square metal plate are shown in *Figure 10.17*.

Standing waves also exist in three-dimensional objects such as the volume of air inside the resonance chamber of a guitar or violin. Wind instruments create musical notes by setting up standing waves inside them. Energy from the standing wave escapes at the instrument's ends, filling the air with regular waves of music of the same wavelength and frequency. The varying shapes, sizes, and reflective properties of each musical instrument create the particular set of standing waves that gives each musical instrument its own unique sound. The performance of a beautiful symphonic orchestral piece, where waves of all different lengths and frequencies blend harmoniously together, is perhaps the greatest use of constructive interference ever created by mankind.

Doppler Effect

The last topic to present in this chapter is how the motion of whatever is generating or receiving waves can alter wavelength and frequency. This change is called the **Doppler effect** or **Doppler shift** after Christian Doppler (1803–1853) an Austrian mathematician who first discovered it. It plays an important role in sensing and measuring motion.

Consider the waves generated by the boat in *Figure 10.18*. When the boat moves forward, it shortens the distance between crests in that direction. At the same time, it lengthens out the distance between crests behind it. This makes the wavelength in front of the boat smaller and the wavelength behind the boat larger. Since frequency and wavelength are inversely related to each other, the wave's frequency in front of the boat is higher and the wave's frequency behind the boat is lower as well. So a wave's frequency is higher if the source moves toward the receiver and lower if the source moves away from the receiver.

The same effect occurs if the receiver moves toward or away from the source of the waves. Consider a boat that cruises through a lake and runs into the on-coming wake of another boat.

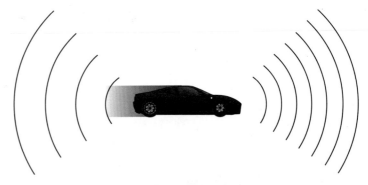

The moving boat encounters the wake's wave crests more rapidly than it would if sitting stationary in the water. So the frequency the boat measures is higher. If the boat were moving away from the wake, it would encounter the crests less rapidly and measure a lower frequency.

The same amount of Doppler shifting takes place regardless of whether the sender or receiver moves. Therefore the Doppler shift only measures the relative speed between the sender and receiver and not any sort of absolute motion of either one. This is as expected by the principle of relativity (Chapter 7).

The Doppler effect can be detected in sounds we all hear on a normal basis. Most of us have been on a street when a police car, its siren blaring, drives towards us on its way to some emergency. The siren, because it is moving toward us, has a higher frequency, and therefore a higher pitch, than if the police car were parked (*Figure 10.19*). When the police car passes, the sound we hear immediately drops to a lower frequency and pitch. The amount of this frequency change depends solely on the speed of the car, not its distance or any other factor.

Doppler radar is used by weather stations to better predict storm movements. A Doppler radar bounces a radio signal off a distant storm cloud and receives it back again. The amount of Doppler shifting in the received signal tells the weatherman the speed that the cloud is moving towards or away from the station, allowing a more accurate prediction of when the storm will arrive.

Figure 10.19

Sound waves from a moving car are closer together in front of the car in the same way that water waves are closer in front of a moving boat. Waves behind the car are father apart than those in front. Where would the pitch be higher?

◆ Doppler Effect

A change in the observed frequency of a wave occurring when the source and observer are in motion relative to each other.

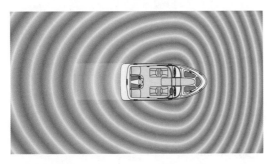

Figure 10.18

Wave crests are closer in front of the boat than behind it because of the motion of the boat.

Chapter Framework

A. Waves
1. Transport energy
2. Travel through a medium needs restoring force

B. Wave Types
1. Longitudinal
2. Transverse
2. Surface

C. Wave Properties
1. Amplitude
2. Wavelength
3. Frequency
4. Wave Speed
5. Characteristics
   a. Crests and troughs

D. Wave Phenomena
1. Reflection
2. Refraction
3. Diffraction
4. Interference
   a. Constructive
   b. Destructive
5. Standing Waves
   a. Nodes and antinodes
6. Doppler Effect

Comprehension

Matching

1. _____ A wave where the medium is displaced parallel to the direction the wave travels.
2. _____ The maximum distance that a particle moves from its resting position when a traveling wave passes through it.
3. _____ The rate that a single wave peak travels in a medium.
4. _____ A wave's ability to bend around corners and spread behind holes.
5. _____ A place in a medium where a molecule naturally resides.
6. _____ The change in speed and direction as a wave moves from one medium into another.
7. _____ The result of confined waves interfering in such a way that destructive and constructive interference always occur in a fixed location.
8. _____ Occurs when two or more waves travel through the same medium at the same time.
9. _____ The distance between successive similar parts in repeating waves.
10. _____ The act of bouncing off the boundary between two different mediums.
11. _____ A fixed position of destructive interference in a standing wave.
12. _____ Wave where the forces stretch the bonds between molecules in a direction that is per-

a. Reflection
b. Transverse wave
c. Wavelength
d. Standing wave
e. Antinode
f. Equilibrium position
g. Frequency
h. Refraction
i. Interference
j. Wave speed
k. Longitudinal wave
l. Amplitude
m. Node
n. Diffraction

pendicular to the direction the wave travels.
13. _____ The number of wave crests passing a particular point every second.
14. _____ A fixed position of constructive interference in a standing wave.

True/ False

1. _____ Compression waves travel through all different states of matter.
2. _____ Musical instruments use standing waves to produce sound.
3. _____ Waves cause the medium they travel through to change from its equilibrium shape.
4. _____ Doppler shift measures the absolute speed of the sender.
5. _____ The major determinants in wave speed are the wave's frequency and amplitude.
6. _____ Standing waves occur any time two waves interfere with each other.

Fill in the Blank

1. Mechanical waves travel through a _____ which supports the waves' motion.
2. Shear waves only travel through _____.
3. Geologists use _____ waves to "see" inside Earth.
4. The amount of diffraction depends on the size of the _____ relative to the size of the opening the wave passes through.
5. _____ equals frequency x wavelength.
6. Another name for a compression wave is a _____ wave.

Analysis

1. Which of the following is an example of refraction?
   a) An echo that bounces off a nearby wall.
   b) Constructive interference occurring between waves in a lake.
   c) Sound from a T.V. in a nearby room that passes through the walls.
   d) Eyeglasses correcting a person's vision.

2. Which of the following is a shear wave?
   a) light
   b) human speech
   c) car horn
   d) a wave traveling towards the shore of a lake
   e) none of the above

3. What necessarily decreases if you increase wavelength of a sound wave?
   a) amplitude
   b) frequency
   c) speed
   d) volume

4. What would happen to the wavelength of sound emitted from a radio that began moving away from you?

   a) Wavelength would decrease.
   b) Everything would remain the same.
   c) Wavelength would increase.
   d) Amplitude would increase.
   e) Frequency would increase.

5. Locations in an auditorium where sound becomes soft or muffled could be places of

   a) constructive interference
   b) antinodes
   c) diffraction
   d) refraction
   e) destructive interference

6. In which of the following situations would a compression wave travel the fastest?

   a) the upper bounds of the atmosphere
   b) the atmosphere at sea level
   c) bottom of the ocean
   d) doesn't make a difference

7. The amplitude of a sound wave is a physical quantity that determines the

   a) pitch
   b) loudness
   c) quality
   d) wavelength
   e) velocity

8. If the spectrum of a star is studied, and the frequencies are shifted towards the blue, what can you conclude about that star?

   a) It is far away.
   b) It is moving away from the earth.
   c) It is close to the Earth.
   d) It is moving towards the Earth.

Synthesis

1. What is a mechanical wave.

2. How do glass lenses prevent refraction from reversing itself when leaving the glass?

3. Why don't shear waves travel through liquids?

4. Explain how reflection of waves in a standing wave might create constructive and destructive interference?

5. Why doesn't changing frequency and wavelength affect wave speed?

6. What conditions need to be met in order to produce a standing wave?

7. Why can you hear someone talking around a corner when you can't see them?

8. What is the difference between diffraction and refraction? Give and explain an example of each.

9. How do panels and curtains in an auditorium minimize wave interference?

10. Why do waves travel through dense material faster than materials that are not as dense?

11. Tools like ultrasound, sonar, and seismology give us information about things we cannot see or touch. What properties of waves allow this?

12. Instructions on stereo speakers tell you to install them certain distances away from walls or other hard surfaces. Why would this be important?

THE PROPERTIES OF LIGHT

CHAPTER 11

And God said, Let there be light: and there was light.

~ Genesis 1:3

Light, like matter and energy, is a fundamental part of the Universe. The warmth and energy light brings from our Sun makes life possible. Light illuminates our surroundings, allowing us to see, move, learn, and function as a society. Light is such a large part of our lives that we usually take it for granted.

Our familiarity with light does not mean that we completely understand it. Some evidence tells us light is a wave transporting energy like the waves discussed in Chapter 10. Other evidence supports light being a stream of particles, transporting energy more like convection does. Other than those two choices, we know of nothing else that light could be.

In this chapter we will explore some facts about light and the scientific models created to explain them. We will find that light is modeled in two different ways, as a wave and as a stream of particles. The wave model and particle model are each superior to the other in some situations but inferior in others. Amazingly, the models are not yet fully reconciled with each other. We are certain someday they will be and anticipate that this reconciliation will teach us something new and wonderful about the Universe, while likely presenting us with many more questions as well.

11–1 THE SPEED OF LIGHT

In Chapter 7, we learned that light travels faster than any other known entity. It moves so rapidly that the renowned 17th century mathematician and philosopher René Descartes believed it traveled instantaneously with infinite speed. Galileo Galilei knew that light moved very fast but thought that its speed was finite. To test this hypothesis he and a colleague each took covered lanterns and stood on adjacent hill tops. Galileo uncovered his lantern and the colleague in turn uncovered his own lantern as soon as he saw light from Galileo's lantern. By measuring the time between when he uncovered his lantern and when he saw light from his colleagues' lamp, Galileo inferred a speed for light of at least 500 km/sec. As you might imagine from simply knowing how slowly one's reflexes work, this value was nowhere near light's actual speed.

In 1676, Danish astronomer Olaus Roemer obtained the first accurate measurement of the speed of light from observing Jupiter's moons. Every week these moons are eclipsed several dozen times as they orbit behind Jupiter. When Jupiter was farthest from Earth, these eclipses came fifteen minutes later than they did when

LEARNING OBJECTIVES

When you finish this chapter you should be able to

- Discuss the original experiments that determined the speed of light.
- Explain why we believe light to be a wave.
- Recite the different types of electromagnetic radiation.
- Explain what a "field" is and how it relates to electromagnetic radiation.
- Explain why we believe light to also be a stream of particles.
- Discuss the evidence for and ideas behind the theory of wave-particle duality.

Jupiter was nearest. Roemer correctly concluded that the later eclipse times were an illusion arising from light taking fifteen minutes longer to travel from Jupiter to Earth when Jupiter was most distant (*Figure 11.1*). The speed of light was then calculated by dividing the difference in the distance to Jupiter by 15 minutes.

Armand Fizeau (1819–1896) devised a rotating toothed wheel like the one shown in *Figure 11.2* to more precisely measure the speed of light. In the earliest versions of his experi-

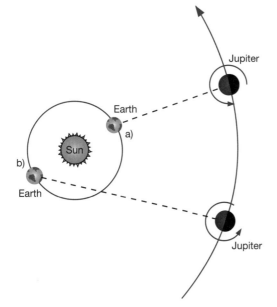

⇧ **Figure 11.2**

A method by which the speed of light can be measured. The wheel advances one tooth while a light pulse travels to the mirror and back.

⇦ **Figure 11.1**

Roemer found that light from Jupiter took 15 minutes longer to reach Earth in position b) than in position a). From this he was able to estimate the speed of light.

129

ment, a beam of light passed through a gap in the wheel's teeth, traveled 8.63 kilometers to a mirror and was reflected back towards the device, where it was blocked by a tooth which had rotated into its path. Knowing the wheel's rotation speed, the gap sizes between the teeth, and the distance to the mirror, Fizeau was able to calculate the speed of light.

Today we can use high-speed electronic sensors to easily measure time intervals shorter than one-billionth of a second, the time that it takes light to travel one foot. Using these sensors to time light racing to a mirror and back we have found light's speed to be 299,792.458 km/sec. At this speed, light can travel around Earth in 0.13 seconds, from Earth to the Moon and back again in 2.6 seconds, from the Sun to Earth in 8.3 minutes, and across the entire solar system in about 11 hours. The speed of light through air moves about 900,000 times the speed of sound. That's the equivalent of 30,000 times the speed of our fastest rockets and 10,000 times the speed of Earth in its orbit around the Sun.

The distance light travels in a given amount of time is a convenient way of expressing distances in space. For example, the average Earth-to-Sun distance of 93 million miles is often expressed in its light-travel time of 8.3 light-minutes. The diameter of the solar system is 11 light-hours, the distance from Earth to the nearest star, Alpha Centauri, is 4.3 light-years, and the distance to the farthest galaxies we know of is more than 10 billion light years.

11–2 THE WAVE NATURE OF LIGHT

So exactly what is light? In the introduction we pointed out that it could be either a stream of particles or a wave. If light is a wave it will reflect, refract, diffract, and interfere. In Chapter 10 we noted how light reflects as shown by your image in a mirror. The way a stick half-submerged in water looks bent proves that light also refracts (refer back to Figure 10.11).

Proving diffraction and interference requires more careful experimentation. Recall that diffraction of a wave is noticeable only when the wavelength is comparable to the size of the opening that the wave goes through. Light has wavelengths between 4 and 8 x 10⁻⁶ meters. Light's diffraction is measurable only when it is projected through holes or around objects of a similar size.

Sir Isaac Newton didn't know that the wavelength of light was so small. So when he observed that objects placed in a strong beam of light cast very sharp shadows, he incorrectly reasoned that no diffraction was taking place at all. If it were, he thought, the shadow edges would be blurred, causing the shadow to look fuzzy. The sharpness of the shadows was taken to be evidence that light was a stream of particles.

Newton knew that a particle model of light was as consistent with reflection and refraction as a wave model was. Particles striking a mirror reflect like balls bouncing off a wall. In the interface between two media (like air and water) these particles would be like tennis balls striking and passing through a piece of tissue paper. The tissue paper would rupture, but the speed of the balls would be slowed as they passed through in just such a way to account for the refraction. With no evidence for diffraction, Newton's particle hypothesis was accepted as being correct until the 1800s.

Today, using lasers and tiny holes etched through thin sheets of metal, the effect of diffraction can easily be demonstrated. *Figure 11.3* illustrates diffraction of a light beam sent through a series of very small holes. Hole "a" is

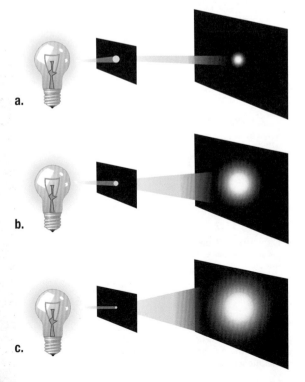

Figure 11.3
The diffraction of light. The light spot emerging from the smallest hole diffracts the most, proving that light is a wave.

a.

b.

c.

the largest and hole "c" is the smallest. If light were a stream of particles, the light spot behind the smallest hole should be the smallest one. Instead, as the holes get smaller the light fans out over a larger area, resulting in a larger light spot, which would be expected for a wave.

Interference was the most difficult of the four wave qualities to discover. The first definitive demonstration of interference was in 1801 by Thomas Young, a London physician and distinguished scholar in many subjects. Young announced his success to the world with this preamble:

Much as I venerate the name of Newton, I am not therefore obliged to believe that he was infallible. I see . . . with regret that he was liable to err, and that this authority has, perhaps, sometimes even retarded the progress of science.

Young showed interference by inventing a simple yet profound test called the "double-slit experiment." To understand how it works, consider a thin sheet of metal with a small narrow slit in it. Light of a single wavelength passing through the slit diffracts out in a fan-like pattern as shown in *Figure 11.4a*.

Now suppose we create a second slit of equal size next to the first slit. When light passes through this second slit it also diffracts. Diffraction from both slits causes the emerging light to overlap, giving rise to places of constructive and destructive interference. As a result, the pattern of light striking the screen behind the slits alternates between bright and dark lines. At the location of the bright lines, the two waves combine constructively, creating a stronger wave than before. Between the bright lines, the two waves combine destructively, so that no light arrives at the screen. *Figure 11.4b* shows the resulting pattern of bright and dark lines. *Figure 11.5* is a photograph of an actual

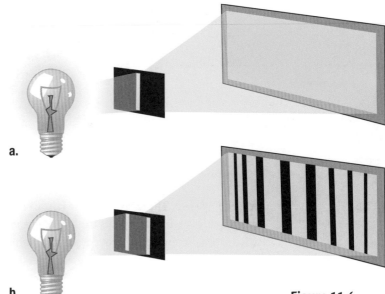

a.

b.

pattern created by a laser beam passing though a double slit.

Young's double-slit interference pattern proved undeniably that light travels through space as a wave. The demonstration is most dramatic at any one of the dark lines. When only one slit is open, light illuminates and brightens the entire area behind the slit. However, when *additional* light passes through the other slit, areas behind the first slit now become *dark.* Such is the nature of interference. Waves are the only phenomenon we know of that will do this.

When Thomas Young proved light's wave nature with the double-slit experiment, he also discovered that the spacing between bright lines for red light exceeded the spacing between bright lines for blue light. This was proof that different colors have different wavelengths. Blue light has a smaller wavelength than red light and does not diffract as much. As a result, the pattern of bright and dark lines in blue light is more compressed.

Diffraction and interference can be seen by viewing a distant light source, such as a streetlamp or car light, through a handkerchief or

Figure 11.4

a) Light passing through a single slit diffracts to either side of it.

b) Light passing through two slits diffracts and interferes as well, creating a series of bright lines (constructive interference) and dark lines (destructive interference).

Thomas Young

An exceptional scholar. In addition to discovering light interference, he made breakthrough discoveries in anatomy, linguistics, and astronomy.

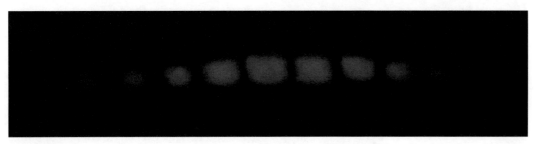

Figure 11.5

A photograph of the interference pattern found when red laser light passes through a double slit.

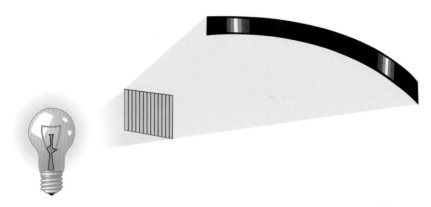

Figure 11.6

A diffraction grating separates light into its component colors by means of interference.

James Clerk Maxwell

The Scottish physicist James Clerk Maxwell (1831–1879) did revolutionary work in electromagnetism and the kinetic theory of gases. After graduating (1854) with a degree in mathematics from Trinity College, Cambridge, he held professorships at Marischal College in Aberdeen (1856) and King's College in London (1860) and became the first Cavendish Professor of Physics at Cambridge in 1871.

♦ **Maxwell's Equations**

A set of four fundamental laws, expressed in mathematical form, than govern electricity and magnetism and their interrelationship. The Electrical Force Law is included in Maxwell's Equations.

other thin fabric. The weaving in the fabric creates a checkerboard of tiny slits the size of light's wavelength. Viewing the source of the light through the cloth replicates the double-slit experiment with the slits being both horizontal and vertical. Viewed through the material, the light source appears broadened because of diffraction. The light also appears interlaced top to bottom and side to side with alternating light and dark spots from constructive and destructive interference. Separate colors may even be noticed in the interference pattern because, as mentioned above, the locations of constructive interference depend on wavelength.

Diffraction gratings use the dependence of interference on wavelength to create colorful rainbows as shown in *Figure 11.6*. Diffraction gratings are a piece of glass or plastic upon which a large number of long parallel scratches are placed close together. The undisturbed glass between the scratches acts as a set of narrowly-spaced slits. When a ray of white light passes through a grating, constructive interference breaks it into a series of rays separated by broad, dark regions. The direction of the rays depends on wavelength, with the redder light bent further out than the blue light. As a result, a bright image viewed through a diffraction grating has a rainbow image of it visible on either side.

11–3 THE MEDIUM OF LIGHT WAVES

Light comes to Earth from stars and the Sun through the emptiness of space. Yet we learned in the previous chapter that waves need a medium to travel through. If light is a wave, what is the medium in space that carries it?

Early researchers working with light con-

sidered it to be inconceivable that a wave could travel through nothing and postulated in the 1800s that empty space wasn't so "empty," after all. They hypothesized that a fine light-carrying substance called "luminiferous ether" or just "ether" filled space. The ether had to be very stiff to explain light's rapid speed. But it also had to be supple enough to allow planets to orbit through it without losing forward motion. Can such a thing really exist? The Michelson–Morley experiment talked about in Chapter 7 was designed to probe the nature of the luminiferous ether as well as measure the boost to the speed of light from Earth's orbital motion. When no boost was found, the idea of a luminiferous ether was abandoned in favor of the idea of a "field." We talked about fields in Chapter 4 when learning about magnetism, but more detail about them is necessary here.

Strictly speaking, fields are mathematical equations that map an attribute, like force, to every point in the space where the field is present. An example of a simple field is temperature. Every room has an average temperature, but the area near a heater will be hotter than average, while the area near a window may be colder. A formula that describes how room temperature differs with location is a description of the "temperature field" of that room.

In Chapter 4, the electromagnetic field was introduced as being the "medium" that transmitted the electromagnetic force. We learned in that chapter that iron filings can trace the magnetic aspect of this field around a magnet, revealing its strength and direction. We also learned that the electric force law describes how the electric force in this field diminishes with distance from a charged object.

In the late 1800s James Clerk Maxwell (1831–1879) found that the electric force law and the laws of magnetism could be combined into a more general set of four equations that completely describe the nature of any electromagnetic field. This set of laws, known as **Maxwell's Equations,** flawlessly predict the strength and direction of the electromagnetic force at any location in space.

Although Maxwell's Equations were a great advancement in understanding the laws of nature, they do not explain exactly *how* this force is physically transmitted. That understanding will probably require a greater knowledge of the nature of space itself than we currently have. But regardless of how the force from electromagnetic fields penetrates through space, Maxwell's Equations still give us an understanding of the shapes of fields, the strengths of forces within fields, and how fields change when charges move.

Maxwell found his equations predicted that a charge vibrating up and down will create an electromagnetic field that propagates outward as a transverse wave. Unlike the mechanical waves explained in Chapter 10, these electromagnetic waves travel through empty space and are not a vibration of matter. They are varying electric and magnetic forces radiating outward from the source. They are transverse waves because the direction of the electric and magnetic force vectors of the wave are perpendicular to the direction the wave travels (*Figure 11.7*). The electric and magnetic force vectors are also at right angles to each other.

Maxwell quickly worked out from his equations how fast these waves would travel through space. He found that their speed was exactly the speed of light as measured by Fizeau. This remarkable agreement could not be a coincidence and on December 8, 1864, he told the scientists of the British Royal Society:

> *The agreement of the results seems to show that light . . . is an electromagnetic disturbance propagated through the field according to electromagnetic laws.*

The correspondence between the theoretically predicted speed and the actual measured speed of light strikingly confirmed the accuracy of Maxwell's formulas and the connection between electric charge and light itself. Perhaps even more significantly, Maxwell's Equations predicted that other waves existed in addition to light. These other waves had the same speed but different frequencies and wavelengths that ranged from zero to infinity. These waves were soon created in laboratories and harnessed to create radio, television, radar, and other devices.

11-4 THE ELECTROMAGNETIC FAMILY

The family of waves predicted by Maxwell's equations is collectively called **electromagnetic radiation**. Grouped in order from low frequency

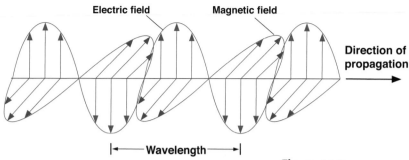

Figure 11.7

The force vectors from an electromagnetic wave are perpendicular to the direction the wave travels. The electric and magnetic force vectors are also perpendicular to each other.

to high frequency, they are: radio waves (AM, FM, VHF, UHF), microwaves, infrared radiation, visible light (red to blue), ultraviolet radiation, x-rays, and gamma rays (*Figure 11.8*).

Visible light is just the relatively small range of frequencies that our eyes see. Wavelength determines the color of light, with red corresponding to the longer wavelengths (lower frequencies), and blue and violet to the shorter wavelengths (higher frequencies) as previously mentioned.

Electromagnetic waves radiate out when-

◆ **Electromagnetic Radiation**

Radiation originating in a varying electromagnetic field, such as visible light, radio waves, x-rays, and gamma rays.

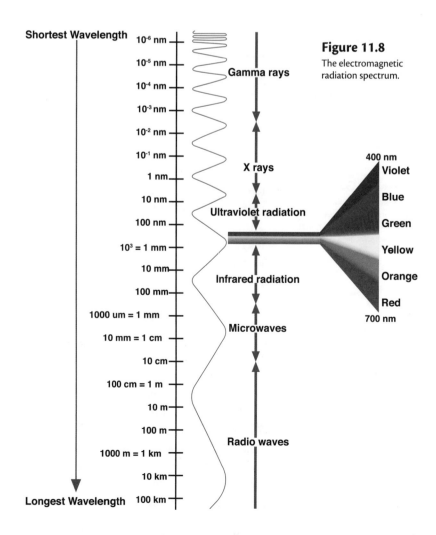

Figure 11.8

The electromagnetic radiation spectrum.

ever electric charge *accelerates*. Radio, television, and cell phone signals come from electrons accelerating in antennas. Electrons accelerating in the hot outer layers of our Sun or in the hot filament of an electric light bulb create visible light. X-rays form when fast electrons suddenly decelerate to a stop in an x-ray tube.

Radio and television signals travel from broadcast antennas through space to radios and television sets. When they arrive they exert forces on the electrons in a receiving antenna which cause the electrons to move in the same pattern that created the wave. This motion can be detected by sensitive electronics in the radio and television set and converted into sound or pictures. Visible light interacts with electrons in the retina of the eye or on a piece of photographic film, causing reactions that relay visual information to the brain or preserve it on paper.

11–5 THE PARTICLE NATURE OF LIGHT

Thomas Young's double-slit experiment settled the debate over the nature of light for nearly a century. Then in 1887 Heinrich Hertz discovered a curious property of light that triggered a revolution of thought, culminating 30 years later in a second model of light.

Hertz discovered that shining light on some types of metals caused the metals to release electrons. The ejected electrons possessed more energy if the light had a shorter wavelength, like ultraviolet light, than if its wavelength were longer. This attribute, called the **photoelectric effect**, was an unexpected phenomenon that puzzled experimenters.

In the wave model of light, a wave striking the surface of a metal imparts equal energy to all electrons along the wave front. According to this model energy may build up in the metal until even low-amplitude waves eventually will eject electrons. As we learned in Chapter 10, amplitude defines the amount of wave energy. Since greater brightness equals greater amplitude, brighter light should cause metals to eject electrons with greater energy. Yet experiments showed that a dim ultraviolet light ejects electrons with high energy from metals for which a blindingly bright red light ejects no electrons at all.

Photoelectric experiments led to the clear conclusion that light energy associates with *frequency*. Ultraviolet light with its higher frequency possesses greater energy than lower frequency red light. Theories attempting to explain why higher light frequencies had higher energy all failed. Soon it became obvious that the wave model of light was unable to explain this.

In 1905 Albert Einstein introduced a new model of light that explained the photoelectric effect simply and perfectly. This bold model assumed that light was composed of particles called **photons** that were pure energy with no mass or charge. The energy of a photon is given by Planck's equation, which is:

$$\text{Energy} = h \times \text{frequency}$$

where h is a previously known value called **Planck's constant**, a small number equal to 6.63×10^{-34} in the metric system of units. The formula says that each photon of light carries an amount of energy proportional to its frequency. Doubling the frequency doubles the energy. Under this model a beam of light is brighter when it has more photons, not because each photon has more energy.

It is useful to think of photons as being like bullets that pack a greater wallop when their frequencies are greater. Fire bullets at marbles and a marble will go flying if a bullet of sufficient energy hits it. In the same way, an electron in a metal flies off the metal when a photon of sufficient energy hits it. Ultraviolet photons hold enough energy to eject electrons in cases where red photons do not. Making the red light brighter increases the number of photons. But since each photon still cannot eject an electron, no increase in brightness will cause electrons to be emitted.

A simple experiment that reveals the particle nature of light is done by creating a print from a black and white negative using high frequency, low intensity light. Photographic prints are normally made by shining moderately bright yellow light through a film negative onto light-sensitive print paper. This creates various shades of gray on the paper that are smooth and continuous. Instead of doing this, replace the yellow light with a very low-intensity ultraviolet

- **Photoelectric Effect**

The ejection of electrons from metals when light is shined on the metal's surface.

- **Photon**

A particle of light. It possesses energy, frequency, and wavelength but neither mass nor charge.

- **Planck's Constant**

A value when multiplied by the frequency of light, gives the energy of the photon of light at that frequency.

PHYSICS OF BROADCASTING

Broadcast technology is everywhere. We watch TV, listen to radio, retrieve information over the Internet, and talk on cell phones. All of these systems use electromagnetic waves to transport their information. How do they do it? How can an electromagnetic wave carry a voice or music or picture? Each system has its own technology, but a few basic ideas remain common to them all.

First, a transmitter generates a simple sine wave called a "carrier wave." The carrier-wave frequency is the value a radio or TV dial is tuned to when different stations or channels are being selected. Cell phones automatically choose a unique carrier-wave frequency for the area or "cell" they are in each time a phone call is placed. The purpose

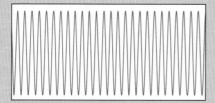

Figure 11.9
The carrier frequency.

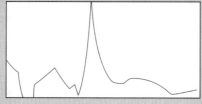

Figure 11.10
The modulating signal.

Figure 11.11
The carrier signal with amplitude modulation.

Figure 11.12
The carrier signal with frequency modulation.

of the carrier wave is to transport an encoded signal.

Sound or picture information is encoded onto a carrier wave through a process called "modulation." Carrier waves are modulated by changing either their amplitude or frequency or both. AM radios use amplitude modulation (AM) while FM radio, television, and cell phones use frequency modulation (FM).

A simple early means of AM communication was Morse Code. In Morse Code, the code key turned the transmitter on and off, causing the amplitude of the carrier wave to go from nothing to full power whenever the key was pressed. The information sent was a series of long and short signals encoded to represent the alphabet. A person on the receiving end translated the resultant "dots and dashes" first into letters and then into words.

A modern AM radio transmitter modulates the carrier signal amplitude smoothly in direct proportion to the energy of the sound as shown in *Figures 11.9–11.11*. The carrier wave transports this modulated signal through space where a radio antenna picks it up. The radio generates its own signal at the frequency of the carrier wave and subtracts it off the received signal, leaving only the modulated signal. The speakers amplify that signal and reproduce it as a voice or music.

AM radio has a few technical weaknesses. Most natural and man-made radio noise is AM in nature. AM receivers have no means of rejecting that noise, causing the reception clarity to degrade rapidly with distance from the source. Also, quiet sounds generate a weaker signal than loud sounds because the amplitude is modulated down. This requires all AM receivers to have circuits to compensate for the signal level differences.

These problems are overcome when the frequency instead of the amplitude is modulated (*Figure 11.12*). In FM signals, a positive peak in the modulating signal pushes the carrier frequency slightly higher while a negative peak pushes it lower. At the receiving end, a discriminator circuit subtracts the carrier wave off and converts the remaining frequency variations to the original signal. Since the recovered audio is dependent only

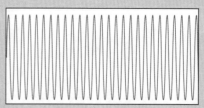

Figure 11.13
The carrier signal.

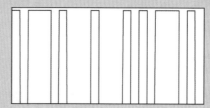

Figure 11.14
A digital modulation.

Figure 11.15
The carrier signal with digital modulation.

on the frequency and not amplitude, no compensation for different signal levels is required and the noise picked up during transmission is much less than with AM signals.

There are other types of modulation, but all are variations of AM or FM. Digital radio or cell phones modulate the frequency in a stream of "ones" and "zeros" creating a signal that is analogous to a rapid FM Morse code (*Figures 11.13–11.15*). The digital signal is constructed by computer chips that are programmed to turn sound or picture information into a stream of ones and zeros. Receiving cell phones take the encoded stream and reconstruct it as the original signal according to the code scheme. Because coding schemes can be as varied as our imaginations allow, digital signals are virtually limitless in the type of information they can convey. And since they only communicate an "on" and "off" state like a Morse Code transmitter, they are not as susceptible to noise as either standard "analog" FM or AM encoding.

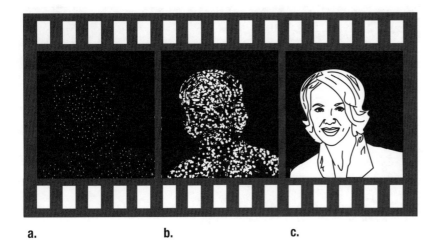

a.   b.   c.

Figure 11.16

The appearance of a photograph if the light level is increased slowly.

♦ **Wave-Particle Duality**

The state of possessing both wave and particle properties.

Figure 11.17

The appearance of the two-slit interference pattern as the amount of light is gradually increased.

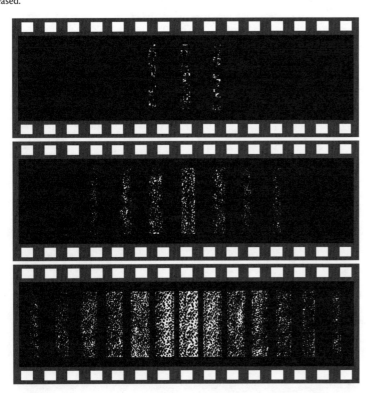

light. The ultraviolet light will produce a weak stream of high energy photons. *Figure 11.16* represents a series of images developed this way after exposure for different amounts of time.

In Figure 11.16a the exposure was so short only a few photons struck the paper and there is not much of an image. Expose for a longer period of time and the image being projected onto the paper will appear as a collection of bright dots, all of which have about the same intensity as shown in Figure 11.16b. Although the image is spotty, you can still tell that it is a woman's face. For longer exposures still, the number of dots increases until the entire range of light and dark imagery captured in the film negative gradually fills in, creating the original picture as shown

in Figure 11.16c. The difference between the bright and dark places in a real photographic exposure arises not because the dots have different shades of gray, but because more dots have hit the bright areas than have hit the dimmer areas. The wave model of light cannot explain this result. Only if light arrives as a stream of particles does the developing picture make sense.

Thousands of experiments have verified the existence of photons of light. The particle model of light was used in creating digital cameras, which work by detecting individual photons. We normally do not notice photons with our eyes only because even the dimmest light beam contains so many photons that the signal appears continuous and smooth.

11–6 WAVE-PARTICLE DUALITY

Can light be both a particle and a wave? After considering the available facts we still do not have a definitive answer. We have found that every time we devise an experiment to measure light's wave properties, such as wavelength, frequency, and interference, it works. And every time we devise an experiment to measure light's particle properties, such as photon position and energy, it also works. An experiment has not yet been devised that simultaneously measures the particle and wave properties of light to see which emerges as superior. Currently accepted theories suggest that such an experiment is impossible.

Macroscopic particles and waves have complementary natures. Particles are localized lumps. Waves are spread-out disturbances. The principle of non-contradiction says that when two contrary propositions are offered, both cannot be true. This principle is telling us that our separate wave and particle models as currently understood cannot both be fully correct.

We can avoid conflict with the Principle of Non-contradiction by assuming light is neither a particle nor a wave. Light is light. It has both characteristics of waves and of particles, but must be something more than either of these. We say it possesses **wave-particle duality**.

The double-slit experiment exemplifies wave-particle duality. Imagine repeating this experiment with low-intensity light—so low it takes several hours or days to completely expose the film. This slow exposure allows us to examine how the image of the interference pattern is built up as more and more light reaches the film. As shown in *Figure 11.17,* an interference pattern emerges even when light levels are so low that photons arrive one at a time. This interference pattern can occur only if light is a wave because particles don't interfere. However, the interference image on the photographic paper is being constructed one dot at a time. This can occur only if light is a stream of photons arriving one after another.

As puzzling as this is, there is a clue to reconciling these two natures: the photons do not strike the paper at random places. They have a greater probability of striking the locations where the image is brightest and a lower probability of arriving at the darker locations. In other words, the image of an interference pattern in Figure 11.17 builds up because regions where constructive wave interference occurs have a high probability of being struck by a photon and regions where destructive interference occurs have a low probability of being struck by a photon.

Scientists approach understanding wave-particle duality by treating light as a stream of particles arriving at locations predicted in a probabilistic fashion from the wave model. The particle part of wave-particle duality tells us how the light is detected and the wave part tells us how the photons travel and where they will be detected. This will be discussed further in Chapter 15, where you will learn that particles of matter also possess wave-particle duality.

References

1. Mason, *A History of the Sciences*, p. 468.

Chapter Framework

A. The Speed of Light
1. Galileo, Olaus Roemer, Armand Fizeau

B. The Wave Nature of Light
1. Shows All Four Wave Properties
2. Thomas Young
3. Double Slit Experiment

C. The Medium of Light Waves
1. Field
2. James Clerk Maxwell
3. Maxwell's Equations

D. The Electromagnetic Family
1. Electromagnetic Radiation
   a. Radio to gamma rays
   b. Acceleration of charged particles
2. Broadcasting
   a. Amplitude modulation
   b. Frequency modulation

E. The Particle Nature of Light
1. Photoelectric Effect
2. Light Energy Associates with Frequency
3. Photons

F. Wave-Particle Duality

Comprehension

Matching

Match the experiment with what it proved about light.

1. _____ Handkerchief held up to light.
2. _____ Interference pattern created by the double-slit experiment.
3. _____ Photoelectric effect.
4. _____ Picture formed by low intensity light.
5. _____ The way a digital cameras operate.
6. _____ Single spot of light after passing through double-slit experiment.

a. Particle
b. Wave

Match the word to its corresponding definition.

1. _____ Carrier wave modulated by changing the frequency.
2. _____ The ejection of electrons from metals when light is shined on the metal's surface.
3. _____ Possessing both wave and particle properties.
4. _____ A particle of light. It possesses energy, frequency, and wavelength but neither mass nor charge.
5. _____ A series of bright lines separated by dark areas.
6. _____ Carrier wave modulated by changing the amplitude.
7. _____ Radiation originating in a varying electromagnetic field, such as visible light, radio waves, x-rays, and gamma rays.

a. Interference pattern
b. Photon
c. Electromagnetic radiation
d. Photoelectric effect
e. Wave-particle duality
f. AM
g. FM

True/ False

1. _____ Sharp shadows ultimately prove that light doesn't diffract and is therefore a particle.
2. _____ Light is an electromagnetic disturbance spread throughout space according to electromagnetic laws.
3. _____ Galileo accurately predicted the speed of light using two lanterns.
4. _____ The photoelectric effect shows that frequency of light determines whether or not an electron will be discharged.

Fill in the Blank

1. The _____ experiment first proved that light created interference patterns.
2. Roemer measured the _____ by using Jupiter's moons.
3. Maxwell's equations predict the strength and direction of the _____.
4. The particle nature of light becomes evident when light is _____.
5. The wave nature tells us how light _____.
6. Electromagnetic radiation is given off when charged particles _____ .

Analysis

1. Traveling at the speed of light, Diana and Anna go on a trip that takes them 10 light seconds. How far did they travel?

   a) 350,000 km
   b) 2,997,925 km
   c) 6,230,543 km
   d) 1,876,232 km

2. The difference between blue light and red light is that

   a) red light has more energy per photon
   b) red light has a higher speed
   c) blue light has a higher speed
   d) red light has a longer wavelength
   e) blue light has a longer wavelength

3. One night Sam looks at a street light through the screen of a window or door. He carefully observes the apparent image. The image reveals light streaks extend outward from a central bright spot. The outward streaks are also seen to consist of a series of light and dark spaces. When the same light is viewed without looking through a screen no streaks are seen. The presence and pattern of the streaks are due to

   a) diffraction and interference
   b) refraction and interference
   c) diffraction and refraction
   d) reflection and refraction
   e) reflection and diffraction

4. Of the following, the one with the least energy per photon is

    a) infrared light
    b) x-rays
    c) blue light
    d) red light
    e) ultraviolet light

5. The wavelength of red light (700 nanometers) is longer than the wavelength of violet light (400 nanometers). Which of the following statements is true?

    a) The photon energy of red light is highest because the wavelength is longest.
    b) The photon energy of both colors is the same because light travels with a constant velocity.
    c) The photon energy of violet light is highest because the frequency is highest.
    d) The photon energy of the light waves depends on the wave amplitudes which are not given.
    e) The photon energies of both colors are small, which make it difficult for the eye to see.

Synthesis

1. How does the double-slit experiment show that light has interference properties?

2. List the different types of electromagnetic radiation in order from the lowest frequency to the highest frequency.

3. What four characteristics does light exhibit that shows its wave nature?

4. Using the principle of non-contradiction, explain and justify what the chapter concludes about the nature of light?

5. How do scientists think that light travels through space?

6. Why do scientists use light as a unit of measurement when speaking of large distances in space?

7. If a door between a brightly lit room and a dark one is left slightly ajar, there will be a band of light on the floor. If the door is slowly closed, what happens to this band of light? Why?

8. When very dim light is used to make a photograph, what happens to the image? If very dim light was used in a double slit experiment, what would happen to the image? How does a double slit experiment done with dim light show the dual nature of photons?

9. How did luminiferous ether filling space allow scientists to continue considering light as a wave?

10. Why does a diffraction grating cause colors in light to separate? In what order should colors appear?

11. Upon seeing the sharp image of shadow, Newton concluded that light was not a wave. He did not know the wavelength of light. Why might this knowledge have changed his conclusion?

12. In a photoelectric effect experiment using visible light, what happens when you change the brightness of the light source? What happens when you change the frequency of the light source? How does the photoelectric effect prove that light behaves as a particle? What would have happened if light were just a wave?

PHYSICAL PROPERTIES OF MATTER AND THE CONTINUOUS MODEL

Although nature commences with reason and ends in experience it is necessary for us to do the opposite, that is to commence with experience and from this to procede to investigate the reason.

~ Leonardo da Vinci

Back in Chapter 1, you learned about the existence of protons and electrons, atoms and molecules. You were also briefly introduced to the "scientific method." You now have a set of basic facts about science to refer to and work with as we consider the fundamental building blocks of all matter in more detail.

In future chapters you will learn what matter is made of, and why matter behaves the way it does. You will also learn the importance of careful scientific research and how scientific processes work, and you will have the opportunity to experience vicariously the way scientists have reached their current answers to questions about matter. Scientific understanding evolves through experiments, development of models to explain the experiments, followed by new experiments to test the models.

You will read in these chapters, in roughly chronological order, about the key experiments and models. You should study the material in these chapters as if you were making the observations and formulating the models. Think carefully about the questions that are posed along the way. This way you will understand not only the "what?" and "why?" of all scientific inquiry, but also the "how do we know what we know?" question that every researcher asks.

The scientific process begins by comparing and contrasting different kinds of materials with respect to a few of their **physical properties**. Aristotle, the famous Greek philosopher, set this precedent many centuries ago. Comparison allows us to classify substances into different groups according to their physical behavior.

Imagine that you are a scientist looking into a box full of unrecognizable material. Your assignment is to determine what this material is, and how it compares with other matter that you are familiar with. Unless you already have some sense of how all matter behaves under basic scientific testing, you will be unable to complete your assignment, much less try to answer any questions about "why" the unrecognizable material in the box behaves the way it does.

However, because we are already pretending that you are a scientist, we can also imagine that you already know that comparison—comparing an unknown substance against a known substance—is an important first step in the scientific study of any kind of matter. The following list of physical properties will serve as the basis for our comparisons:

- The physical state of the unknown matter
- The temperatures at which this matter changes its physical state
- The density of the matter in its various states

LEARNING OBJECTIVES

- Identify the four states of matter and key physical properties associated with them:

  density, temperatures at which matter changes state, response to forces, and electrical conductivity

- Distinguish between compression, tension, and shear forces, and be able to associate the forces with states of matter

- Characterize materials as being ionic or metallic conductors or insulators

- How the different states of matter respond to different types of forces
- The color of the matter
- Whether this matter conducts electricity

Other physical properties could be used in your study, but this short set would be useful for the experiments and models that you, as a scientist, would be expected to develop and study before making any conclusions about the unknown material in that box.

12–1 STATES OF MATTER

All matter exists as a solid, a liquid, or a gas. A **solid** is rigid; strong forces are usually required to change its shape. Also, the volume of space taken up by solid matter is fixed. Common examples of solids include ice, wood, steel, cloth,

and paper. **Liquids** are not rigid; they easily change shape when poured from one container to another. The volume of a liquid does not change when the shape of its container changes. **Gases** are not rigid, nor are their volumes fixed. A gas that is moved from one container to another immediately expands to fill the volume of the new container and adopts the shape of the new container. By changing conditions like temperature and pressure, matter can also change from solid to gas, from gas to liquid, from liquid to solid, and so on.

Take water as a specific example. Water in

Figure 12.1

States of Matter: Solid, liquid, and gas.

Solid

A physical state of matter that is characterized by rigidity and resistance to changes in size and shape.

Liquid

A physical state of matter that readily changes shape to match its container but that resists changes in volume.

Gas

A physical state of matter that readily changes both shape and volume to match its container.

Plasma

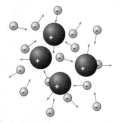

A physical state of matter characterized by fluid properties but in which positive and negative charges move independently.

its liquid form becomes solid at 32° F (0° C) and yet can easily be changed back to a liquid or to a gas. The volume of an ice cube is determined by the size of the partitions in the ice cube tray. If you want crushed ice, you must exert a considerable force on the cubes to break them down into smaller bits. Liquid water, however, flows freely from the tap. You can measure a liter of liquid water using a graduated cylinder. If you pour that liquid into an irregularly shaped vase you still have a liter of liquid. No strong forces have to be applied to get the liquid to assume the inside shape of the vase. Steam, the gaseous form of water, escapes from a boiling tea kettle and expands to fill the size of the kitchen.

In addition to these three states, or conditions, in which all matter exists, physicists also consider a fourth state in which matter may exist. This state is called a **plasma**. A plasma is a gas that consists of positively and negatively charged particles. The positively charged particles are atoms that lose their electrons. The negatively charged particles are the electrons that the atoms lost.

Although you may have only heard the word "plasma" to describe a type of TV, plasmas are the most common form of matter in the Universe. Two naturally occurring examples of plasmas are the phenomenon known as the Northern Lights, which have mystified sky watchers since the dawn of civilization, and solar

winds blowing off the surface of the Sun. Photos of these are shown in *Figure 12.2*.

Your most frequent experience with a plasma is probably when you turn a fluorescent light in your home on or off. Inside every fluorescent light tube is a plasma of ionized argon and mercury atoms, as well as freely moving electrons. You may own (or hope to own) a plasma-screen television set to hang on your wall. The flat-screen plasma TV uses a more sophisticated form of the familiar fluorescent light tube to produce images that entertain and hopefully instruct.

The establishment of four distinct states of matter is somewhat arbitrary, because there are, in fact, important materials that do not fall cleanly into any of those four categories. Consider Silly Putty® or Jello® at room temperature. These materials have physical characteristics that fall somewhere between a solid and a liquid. A ball of Silly Putty has a fixed volume but it is not rigid. Unlike a liquid, however, it doesn't immediately change its shape when it is moved to a new container. But over time relatively weak forces like gravity can cause it to change its shape (see *Figure 12.3*). Materials like Silly Putty often behave more like one or another state of matter by changing temperature or pressure. If a lump of Silly Putty is put in the freezer, at the lower temperature it becomes brittle and hard, like a solid. If the lump is heated to a high

Figure 12.2

Four examples of plasmas.

b.

A plasma display screen displaying a picture of the Aurora Borealis. During times of high solar activity, the atmospheric gases can be ionized to form plasmas and give rise to the beautiful Northern Lights.

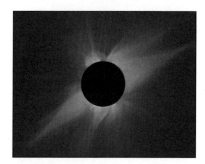

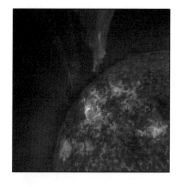

a.

Fluorescent lamp. A fluorescent lamp contains a plasma (a mixture of positively charged argon and mercury ions plus electrons). Energy from the plasma causes a coating inside the lamp to give off white light. In this picture, part of the coating is removed so that you can see the actual blue glow of light given off by the plasma.

c.

A solar eclipse showing the corona, a plasma that makes up the sun's atmosphere.

d.

Another photo of the sun's corona. Ionized gases stream from the surface forming the solar wind.

Figure 12.3
Time-elapsed pictures show that Silly Putty® changes its shape slowly over time under the influence of gravity.

enough temperature, it may become fully liquid-like.

Carbon dioxide, which we exhale as a gas, has some liquid-like properties when it is maintained under a high pressure. This condition is referred to as a **supercritical fluid**. Supercritical fluids have some interesting applications as described in the definition box to the side.

Thinking Like a Scientist: What do these observations tell us about the nature of matter? They give us our first clues about the forces that hold the tiniest particles of matter together, and that allow those clumps to form larger pieces of matter, from elephants, to mountain ranges and to the Universe itself. These observations tell us that the forces that hold bits of solids together are somehow different from those that keep liquids together, and even more different from those associated with gases.

You already know a little about atoms and molecules, so it's not spoiling the ending of the story to tell you that those "bits" of matter are atoms or molecules, depending upon the nature of the material.

12-2 TEMPERATURES AT WHICH MATTER UNDERGOES CHANGES IN STATE

Table 12.1 shows the melting and boiling temperatures for some common materials. A table of data like this can be intimidating, but don't worry, because you needn't memorize any of the numbers. Instead, let's see what information you can pull out of this table by asking yourself a few questions. What substances have the lowest melting temperature? What ones have the highest melting temperatures? Does the substance with the lowest melting temperature also have the lowest boiling temperature? How do the melting and boiling points of water compare to the lowest and the highest temperatures found in Table 12.1?

• Supercritical Fluid

Materials dissolve more easily in a liquid than in a gas. A supercritical fluid has the property of filling the volume of its container like a gas, but dissolving materials like a liquid. Both carbon dioxide and water can be put into super-critical states at temperatures and pressures that are pretty close to room temperature and pressure. Cola and coffee beans are decaffeinated by passing one of these supercritical fluids over them. The caffeine dissolves in the fluid, leaving most of the other chemicals in the beans behind. Advertisers proclaim the process is "natural" because both carbon dioxide and water occur in nature.

Table 12.1 – *Properties of Materials*

	Melting Temperature °C	Boiling Temperature °C (under 1 atm pressure)	Density solid	Density liquid	Density gas
Helium	doesn't form solid except under high pressure!	−269	doesn't form a solid	0.122	.00018
Hydrogen	−259	−253	0.078	0.071	.0001
Neon	−249	−246	0.77	1.21	.00082
Nitrogen	−210	−196	1.09	0.81	.0013
Ethanol	−117	78.5	1.3	0.80	.0020
Water	0	100	0.90 (0° C)	1.00	.0006
Table salt	801	1413	2.2	not available	not available
Copper	1083	2567	8.9	not available	not available
Gold	1065	2807	19.3	not available	not available
Magnesium Oxide	2830	3600	3.6	not available	not available

Table 12.1

Properties of materials: Melting and boiling temperatures of representative materials. Densities are given at temperatures near the state changes. Densities are hard to measure at high temperatures, so information for liquid salt and the metals is not available.

Water undergoes its changes of states in the middle of the temperature range, which has important implications for life on our planet Earth. Organisms living on Earth's surface have adapted to live within this temperature range. Another material in the table, ethanol, also changes state at mid-range temperatures like water.

You may have noticed that there is no melting point for helium. Helium, the gas that makes both party balloons and the Goodyear® blimp rise above the crowds, is a truly remarkable material. It is the only known substance that does not form a solid when it is cooled. Helium only solidifies when it is both very cold **and** subjected to strong pressure. Helium even boils at a very cold temperature.

Of all the substances shown in the table, only helium, nitrogen and neon can exist in plasma form. To turn these gases into plasmas, they must be heated to around 8,000° C.

Thinking Like a Scientist: What can you learn about matter from the data in Table 12.1? Let's make two hypotheses now and test them in upcoming chapters.

Hypothesis 1: The temperature at which a change in state takes place tells us something

---

* In the next few chapters that deal with atoms and molecules, we shall occasionally use the terms "strong force" and "weak force" to characterize the magnitudes of forces between atoms or molecules, just as we needed to do in Hypothesis 2. Sometimes in science, as in life, words can have very different meanings. Chemists who rarely deal with processes taking place inside atomic nuclei don't have to worry about those two fundamental forces, the Strong force and the Weak force, that occur within the nucleus. Nuclear physicists don't worry about the interactions between atoms that lead to molecules or that influence melting and boiling points. Since the two sets of scientists rarely talk to one another, confusion doesn't reign. We will hope that you can recognize our different uses for the same terms from the context of the chapter.

about the strength of the force that holds bits of matter together in that particular state.

Hypothesis 2: A type of matter whose particles are held together strongly in its solid state will melt at a higher temperature than will one in which the forces between particles are weaker.*

You might form a similar hypothesis about the change in state of a liquid to a gas.

What predictions can we make based on these hypotheses? Here are a few: Table salt and metals like gold and copper are held together by stronger forces than water or ethanol. Water and ethanol boil at higher temperatures than are required to boil helium and neon, so forces holding bits of liquid helium or neon in place are weaker than forces holding together bits of water or ethanol. Are these predictions accurate? Keep reading.

12–3 DENSITY

You learned about density when Archimedes' Principle was presented in Chapter 6. Now consider how the density of a substance changes as the material undergoes a change of state from a solid to a liquid to a gas. Remember that density is defined as the "mass per unit volume of a substance," or:

$$\text{density} = \frac{\text{mass}}{\text{volume}}$$

Table 12.1 shows the density of some materials presented in units of grams per cubic centimeter (g cm^{-3}). On this scale, the density of liquid water is 1.00 g cm^{-3}. That means that 20

Table 12.2

There are three common temperature scales. Americans tend to use the Fahrenheit scale (°F) while the rest of the world uses the Celsius or Centigrade scale (°C). Scientists often use a scale in which the lowest possible temperature is set at 0 (absolute zero). The unit on this scale is called a Kelvin (K) in honor of Lord Kelvin who made major advances to our understanding of temperature. The table gives temperatures on these three scales for different phenomena.

Table 12.2 – Temperature Scales

K	°C	°F	
0	−273	−459	Absolute zero
100	−173	−279.4	
273	0	32	Water freezes
310	37	98.6	Normal human body temperature
373	100	212	Water boils at sea level
755	482	900	Oven on "clean" setting
5,773	5,500	9,900	Our Sun's temperature
10,273	10,000	18,000	Temperature of a blue star

cm³ of liquid water would have a mass of 20.0 g. Twenty cm³ of solid gold would have a mass of 386 g.

Notice in Table 12.1 how the density of a substance changes as it goes from one state to another. Again, look for general patterns. Which states tend to be the densest? Which the least dense? Are there any exceptions to the general trends?

Big changes in density occur as a material undergoes a change of state. As a general rule, matter is denser when it is a solid than when it becomes a liquid, and much denser than when it is in its gaseous state. Notice that the materials on Table 12.1 that show the highest densities are the metals. They also have high melting points, while the materials shown in this table having the lowest densities also have very low melting points.

Thinking Like a Scientist: What do these observations tell us about the nature of matter? When any of the materials in Table 12.1 changes state, its density changes, but whatever is most fundamental to making it "helium" or "water" or "copper" does not change. When water, for instance, changes state from liquid to solid, its fundamental "bits" must be packed much closer together, and when it changes from liquid to gas, its basic "bits" become much farther apart.

An interesting aside: The density of a material can be used to distinguish it from other materials. Diamonds and cubic zirconia look very much alike to the unaided eye. Diamond, by far the more desirable gem of the two, is extremely hard but is not as dense as cubic zirconia. *Figure 12.4* shows how the two materials can be distinguished by their flotation behavior in a liquid of an appropriate density.

Water is a rare exception to the general rule about density changes stated above. Near its melting temperature, ice is less dense than liquid water. That's the reason ice cubes and icebergs float. There would be serious consequences for life on planet Earth if water behaved like most liquids. Ice that formed in the winter would sink to the bottom of the ocean, lake or pond. Because it would be at the bottom of the body of water, it would not experience enough of the warming rays of the Sun to melt in the spring and summer. Each winter more ice would freeze and sink, never to melt. Eventually there would be no liquid water on the planet and life as we know it would cease to exist.

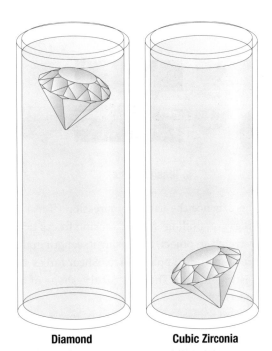

Diamond   Cubic Zirconia

Figure 12.4
In a liquid whose density is about 4 g cm⁻³, diamonds float while cubic zirconia sinks.

12–4 RESPONSE OF MATTER TO FORCES

In Chapter 1, we learned about the origins of forces (gravity, electromagnetism, and two types of nuclear forces). Then we saw how the motion of a rigid object could be explained by the application of Newton's laws to the forces acting on the object. Now, as you know from your earlier reading in this chapter, only solids are rigid. As part of our goal to gather some observations about the behavior of matter, let's characterize the different states of matter according to the effect forces have on them.

A simple activity, pictured in *Figure 12.5*, will help you understand these new ways to think about forces. First, hold this textbook between the palms of your two hands. Push the front and back covers toward each other. You have just exerted a **compression**-type force on the book. Now, grab the top and bottom edges of the book with your fingers and try (gently) to pull the edges apart. In this case, you are applying a **tension**-type force. Finally, place the book flat on a table. Push against the right edge of the top of the book with your right index finger, while simultaneously pushing in the opposite direction with your left index finger against the book's bottom of the left edge. You have just exerted a **shear**-type force on the book.

Compression forces are "pushing" type forces. They tend to reduce the volume of an

• **Compression Force**
A force that is applied in such a way as to compress a material.

• **Tension Force**
A force that is applied in such a way as to stretch a material.

• **Shear Force**
A force that is applied in such a way as to twist or deform a material.

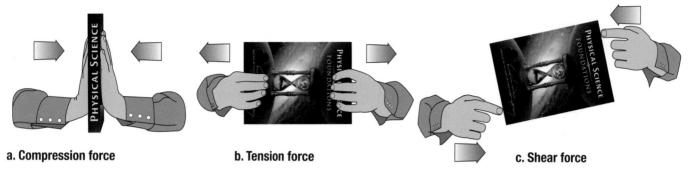

a. Compression force   **b. Tension force**   **c. Shear force**

Figure 12.5
Types of forces.

object, hence the name compression. Tension forces are "pulling" forces. Tension forces tend to stretch an object, increasing its length in the direction of the applied force. Shear forces are twisting forces. They distort the shape of an object.

You applied all three types of forces to the book, which is a solid. You met resistance to your efforts to apply force in all three cases. (The book didn't squeeze down to a thin sliver, for example.) We can generalize your result for all solids. Scientists say that solids can "sustain" or "support" all three types of forces. What they mean is that when you exert a force, there is a resistance to your applied force.

Would you get the same results if you made the same pushing, pulling, and twisting exercises with a liquid or gas? Imagine pushing down a plunger on a syringe filled with water. You can feel the resistance to the compression force you exert. Similarly, if you try to stretch a column of liquid, such as sucking water up a straw, it would resist your efforts. Liquids can be compressed; they can also be stretched. Therefore, we say that a liquid supports compression and tension forces.

Now, what about shear forces? Imagine putting your hands into a large bucket of water. Try to exert a shear force on the water between your hands as you did for the book. Do you feel any resistance? Does the volume of water start to rotate or change shape? This simple experiment shows us that liquids do not support shear forces.

What happens when similar forces are applied to helium or some other gas? Matter in a gaseous state will not support tension or shear forces. You can't draw out a column of gas nor can you twist or reshape it. However, gases do sustain compression forces. You can squeeze on a gas sample and compress it into a smaller volume.

Plasmas will not be considered here because plasmas contain ionized particles. Their behavior is dominated by the electromagnetic force and conclusions about it are more complicated than we can deal with at this level of your studies.

Thinking Like a Scientist: What might the differences between the responses of solid, liquid, and gaseous states of matter to forces reveal about fundamental differences between those states? We have already hypothesized that there are differences in the nature or type of forces that hold bits of matter together in different states of matter. The observations just made strengthen that connection.

The different response of liquids and solids to shear forces will become important when you study Earth's interior in a later chapter. The difference allows us to infer from other measurements the state of matter at the center of Earth's center, which is something we can't directly observe.

12–5 COLOR

Isaac Newton, already well-known to us for his laws of motion, also discovered that the white light of sunlight could be separated into all the colors of the rainbow (*Figure 12.6*). The combination of colors gives rise to what you perceive

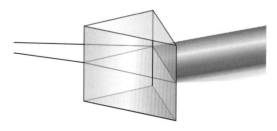

Figure 12.6
White light goes through the prism and is separated into its component colors.

as white light. As you learned in the previous chapter, there are also "colors" of light that are invisible to the human eye. Light has wave properties, and the color of a photon is determined by its frequency. The whole range of colors (frequencies) of light is referred to as the **electromagnetic spectrum**. Some living creatures, bumblebees, for example, can sense ultraviolet light, which is in a higher frequency range than the violet and blue our human eyes can detect. Snakes, on the other hand, are sensitive to infrared light, which is light with frequencies lower than the red that our eyes can see.

Whether an object absorbs or reflects the various colors of light determines what color our eyes perceive when we look at that object. We see red tulips because the pigments in the petals of the flower reflect the red colors of the spectrum, absorbing the other colors. The flower's green leaves reflect green, but absorb other colors (*Figure 12.7*).

The color of a material is related to the internal structure of that object. The warm yellow color of pure gold is different from the cool white color of pure silver, which tells us that there is something different about the two materials.

All materials give off light when they are heated to high temperatures. The burner on your stove begins to glow red when it reaches a temperature of about 700° C. Our Sun, whose surface temperature is near 5,500° C, gives off all colors of light. That is why bright sunlight appears white. We say the Sun has a **continuous spectrum**.

Gases of pure materials like hydrogen, helium, and neon, however, give off only a few colors of light when they are excited by an electrical discharge. We call these **discrete spectra**. *Figure 12.8* shows the continuous spectrum of the Sun contrasted with discrete spectra obtained from different materials. The spectrum of each material is distinctive and can be used to identify it. The element helium was first identified from light coming from the Sun, long before it was discovered on Earth.

12–6 ELECTRICAL CONDUCTIVITY

There is one last set of observations to add to your results. What kinds of materials conduct electricity? We will use as our test an electrical

- **Electromagnetic Spectrum**
The entire range of radiation including, in order of decreasing frequency, cosmic-ray photons, gamma rays, x-rays, ultraviolet radiation, visible light, infrared radiation, microwaves, and radio waves.

- **Continuous Spectrum**
A spectrum in which the colors blend gradually together without noticeably abrupt changes or missing colors.

- **Discrete Spectra**
A spectrum of separate and distinct colors in which not all colors are present.

Figure 12.8
This figure contrasts the continuous spectrum of the Sun (top) with the discrete spectra of gaseous materials. The numbers 400 nm and 700 nm refer to the wavelengths of light at each end of the spectrum. Black represents the absence of color.

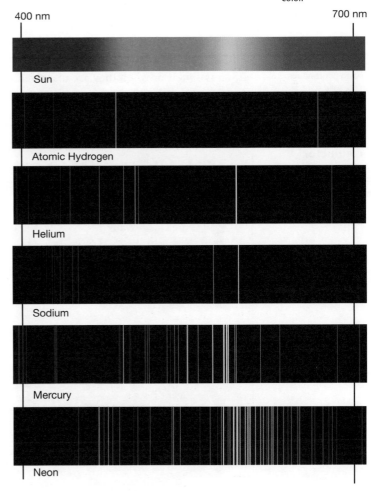

Figure 12.7
The tulip petals appear red because the red light is reflected from the petals while other colors are absorbed.

circuit of the type shown in *Figure 12.9*. To generate electricity, we need a battery in the circuit to provide electrical potential energy. When electricity is flowing, the light bulb in the circuit will light up. If no electricity is flowing, the bulb remains dark.

Figure 12.9

The circuit used to test the electrical conductivity of a material.

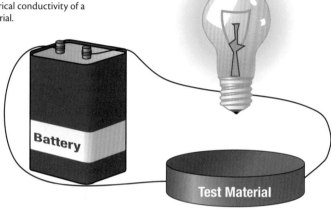

Table 12.3

Observations of electrical conductivity.

• **Conductors**

Materials that conduct electricity in the solid and liquid state.

• **Ionic Conductors**

Materials that do not conduct electricity in the solid state, but do when molten or dissolved in water.

• **Non-conductor**

A material which does not conduct electricity in any of its physical states.

Table 12.3 gives the conductivity results for some of the materials you studied in Table 12.1.

Metals conduct electricity in their pure solid and liquid states. These materials are called **conductors**. Other materials do not conduct electricity in their pure solid state, but they do conduct electricity when in the liquid state, either as a melt or when they are dissolved in

water. These materials are called **ionic conductors**. Sodium chloride, common table salt, is an ionic conductor, although it is unlikely you have ever used it for that purpose.

A material which does not conduct electricity in any of its physical states or when dissolved in water is referred to in science as a **non-conductor** or insulator. Sugar and ethanol are common non-conductors. Table 12.3 illustrates the electrical conductivity behavior of representative materials.

Extremely pure water does not conduct electricity either in its solid or liquid state. Impurities in common tap water can make water slightly conductive, however. This is a good reason why electrical appliances should never be used near a bathtub or swimming pool.

Gases do not normally conduct electricity. Lightning bolts and the sparks associated with static electricity are brief discharges of electrical energy through a gas (air). The electrical energy ionizes the air, making it a plasma. Plasmas do conduct electricity.

12–7 MODELS OF MATTER

You now have a set of observations, results from simple experiments designed to measure

---

Table 12.3 – Electrical Conductivity of Materials

Non-Conductors	Conductors	Ionic Conductors
Pure Liquid Water	Solid Copper	Table Salt Crystals
Pure Solid Water	Solid Gold	Table Salt Dissolved in Water
Liquid Ethanol	Solid Aluminum	Magnesium Oxide Crystals
Sugar Crystals	Solid Iron	Liquid Magnesium Oxide
Sugar Dissolved in Water	Solid Titanium	

physical properties of matter. In the next chapters, we will see how these observations, coupled with the laws of force, conservation of energy, knowledge of light, etc, will enable us to begin to answer the "why?" questions about matter.

Scientists form mental pictures to explain their observations. These models can be very simple and qualitative, or very complex and rigorous, with lots of equations and numerical predictions attached to them. In the quest to understand the basic nature of matter, we will start with simple models and adapt them as new experiments show the limitations of current thinking.

What is the simplest model we could form? What would one be like, if it was based on observations made just with our naked eyes? Looking at matter from that perspective, we could conclude that matter has no internal structure. We can subdivide solids, liquids and gases into smaller and smaller masses of each, but the properties stay the same. We could simply formulate as our model that "all matter is continuous."

A scientific model is supposed to provide a mental picture. It should supply explanations of observations and suggest new experiments to test those observations. With this simple model, we can immediately see deficiencies. The model offers no insights about why the densities of the different states are so different. Nor can it say anything about why different substances have such radically different melting and boiling temperatures. It offers us nothing to explain the phenomenon of electrical conductivity, either.

We have many improvements to add to the model to begin to get explanations for these diverse observations. As we propose new models, we will keep the principle of Occam's razor constantly in mind: accept the simplest model as most likely if it explains all the observed facts.

CONCLUSION

The set of observations about matter that we have assembled in this chapter will form the basis for the next evolution in our understanding of matter. For example, gases, liquids and solids behave differently with respect to the different types of forces, so this tells us that there are differences at some internal level in these different states. We will explore what these different observations have to tell us about matter over the next few chapters.

Chapter Framework

A. States of Matter
1. Solid
2. Liquid
3. Gas
4. Plasma
5. Supercritical fluid

B. Melting and Boiling Temperatures
C. Densities and States of Matter
D. Response to Forces
1. Compression
2. Tension
3. Shear

E. Color
1. Electromagnetic spectrum
   a. Continuous spectrum
   b. Discrete spectra

F. Electrical Conductivity
1. Conductors
2. Non-Conductors
3. Ionic Conductors

Comprehension

Matching

1. _____ Force that distorts or twists the shape of an object.
2. _____ A spectrum of separate or distinct colors.
3. _____ A force that when applied compresses the material.
4. _____ A physical state of matter that is characterized by rigidity and resistance to changes in size and shape.
5. _____ A physical state of matter characterized by fluid properties but in which positive and negative charges move independently.
6. _____ A material that is a non-conductor of electricity as a solid but that conducts electricity when melted or dissolved in water.
7. _____ The whole range of colors (frequencies) of light.
8. _____ A physical state of matter that readily changes both shape and volume to match its container.
9. _____ A substance that readily allows an electric current to flow through it.
10. _____ A force that stretches material.
11. _____ A characteristic of matter associated with the light reflected off the matter to an observer.
12. _____ A physical state of matter that readily changes shape to match its container but that resists changes in volume.
13. _____ A spectrum in which the colors blend gradually together without noticeable abrupt changes or missing colors.
14. _____ Mass per unit of volume of a substance.
15. _____ A substance that does not readily allow electric current to flow through it.

a. Gas
b. Electromagnetic spectrum
c. Continuous spectrum
d. Liquid
e. Insulator
f. Ionic conductor
g. Plasma
h. Compression force
i. Shear force
j. Solid
k. Color
l. Tension force
m. Density
n. Discrete spectrum
o. Conductor

True/False

1. _____ Typically, solids are the densest state of matter and gases are the least dense.
2. _____ The continuous spectrum consists of separate, distinct colors.
3. _____ All materials become plasmas if heated to a high enough temperature.
4. _____ Gold's physical state is always a solid.
5. _____ Liquids assume the shape of their container.
6. _____ All materials fall cleanly into the categories of solid, liquid, gas, or plasma.
7. _____ All matter melts at 0° C (32° F) and boils at 100° C (212° F).

Fill in the Blank

1. An object appears blue if it _____ (reflects, absorbs) blue light.
2. Scientists formulate _____ (models, hypotheses) to provide a mental picture of material, such as matter.
3. _____ (Compression, Tension) forces are pushing forces, and _____ (tension, shear) forces are typically stretching forces.
4. _____ _____ (Supercritical fluid, Silly Putty) has the gas-like property of filling the volume of its container like a gas, but dissolving materials like a liquid.
5. Glass is an example of a(n) _____ (insulator, conductor).

Analysis

1. Which of the following processes does not produce a change in states?

   a) melting gold
   b) condensing steam
   c) freezing water
   d) boiling ethanol
   e) falling objects

2. Which of the following is not a fluid?

   a) steam
   b) air
   c) oil
   d) gasoline
   e) all of the above are fluids

3. Neither sugar nor salt conduct electricity when they are in the solid state. Salt, however, does conduct electricity as a liquid while sugar does not. In classifying these materials we say that

   a) sugar is an ionic material and salt is nonionic.
   b) sugar is a nonionic material and salt is ionic.
   c) both are nonionic.
   d) both are ionic.
   e) both are equally good conductors in solution.

4. Which of the following can sustain shear forces?

   a) liquid helium

   b) steam

   c) chocolate milk

   d) rocks

   e) two of the above

5. Which of the following statements is FALSE?

   a) The solar wind is a plasma.

   b) Gases and liquids are fluids.

   c) A gas will expand to assume both the size and shape of its container.

   d) In all materials, the solid form is more rigid than the liquid form.

   e) In all materials, the solid form is denser than the liquid form.

Synthesis

1. Which has greater density, an ice cube or an iceberg?

2. Describe what is meant by "plasma" and give an example of plasma that occurs in nature.

3. Show, in a sketch, how compression, tension, and shear forces can be applied to a material.

4. Why is tap water a conductor while pure water is not?

5. Choose five materials and list them in order of increasing density.

6. List and briefly describe the different characteristics used to classify matter. With each category of characteristics give examples of matter that demonstrate those characteristics.

7. Why would an object look different when illuminated by a mercury vapor lamp than when seen under sunlight? (See Figure 12.8 for the colors of light given off by such a lamp.)

8. Give examples of materials that don't fall clearly into one of the four states of matter. Justify your answer with a description of one or more of their properties. (Use examples outside those given in the book.)

9. The liquid-solid change of state for water occurs with an important difference from most other matter. What is this difference and why is it important for life on Earth?

10. Summarize what observations you have made from Table 12.1 by answering the following questions:

    a) For most types of matter, what sequence of states corresponds to increasing density?

    b) For a given type of matter, which has the higher temperature: melting or boiling?

    c) If a material has a low melting temperature, what can you predict about its boiling temperature?

    d) Do metals (copper and gold) and salts (table salt and magnesium oxide) have high or low melting temperatures?

11. During an unmanned expedition to another planet, a new material is discovered. The material conducts electricity in its solid state and has a high melting point. This new material resembles what substance(s) in Table 12.1?

THE MOLECULAR MODEL OF MATTER

A scientific model attempts to explain why nature behaves the way it does and to make logical predictions about its future behavior. Models are developed and used in many different fields outside the natural sciences. Economists trying to predict the future financial health of the U.S. Social Security program create models to guide their projections. Built into all economists' models are fundamental economic laws (e.g., supply and demand) and mathematical equations such as the one that governs the compounding of interest. Models vary according to the assumptions that underlie them.

For example, different Social Security models vary in their projections of growth for the senior citizen population. Other assumptions that can be varied to test the outcomes predicted by economic models include age and level at which benefits are provided, interest rates, rate of national economic growth, etc.

Developing accurate models is a constant challenge for meteorologists. You may have noticed that weather forecasters on different local television newscasts frequently differ in their predictions about upcoming weather patterns and temperature highs and lows. The different projections reflect the effect of different variables in the models these weather forecasters use. Each meteorologist's model starts with the same basic facts (e.g., It is mid-summer, a major storm front is moving south into the state, daytime temper-

atures for the past week have been in the upper 90s, the Great Salt Lake is a stable heat sink, etc.). Weather forecasters then build in factors they consider pertinent to the upcoming local weather conditions. Several different models will be developed, each assuming slightly different conditions and emphasizing different factors. For example, one model might suggest a shift in the jet stream as it comes over the Rocky Mountains resulting in a slowing of the coming storm front. Another model might predict no shift in the jet stream and an earlier arrival of the storm front. Different assumptions lead to different models and different predictions.

Every researcher constructing models, like the economic modeler or weather forecaster, strives to use complete, reliable data and to make reasonable assumptions so that the model yields accurate predictions. In the case of scientific models, however, testing that yields unexpected results can be as exciting as a confirmation. As we shall see, science progresses by pushing the limits of our understanding.

13–1 THE MOLECULAR MODEL OF MATTER

In the previous chapter, you collected a database of some physical properties for different

> *[The scientist] doesn't speak of the last analysis but rather of the next approximation.*
>
> ~ Gilbert N. Lewis

LEARNING OBJECTIVES

When you are finished with this chapter, you should be able to

- Describe the four essential assumptions of the Molecular Model of Matter.
- Discuss how this model explains Brownian motion.
- Discuss how this model accounts for the different states of matter and changes between them.
- Discuss how this model explains temperature, heat, and internal energy.
- Discuss how this model explains heat conduction and gas pressure.
- Identify several limitations of this model.

kinds of matter. These include its states (gas, liquid, solid, plasma), the relative densities of those states, their different responses to forces, and the color and electrical properties of matter. You also saw that the first of our models proposed to describe matter, the continuous model, had serious limitations. Clearly, a better model is needed.

The subject of this chapter is an improved model, called the **molecular model**. This model deals with some, but not all, of the limitations of the continuous model. It enables predictions of new behavior that can be tested; many of its predictions have been shown to be accurate. Even where the model fails, it still gives insight into fundamental behavior.

Experimental Basis for the Model

PROPERTIES OF MATTER

What are the key parts of a model in the physical sciences? The basis for any model is a set of observations (results of experiments). The database of physical properties that you assembled in Chapter 12 forms an important foundation for the molecular model.

BROWNIAN MOTION

Another set of experiments specifically provides evidence for the existence of tiny, invisible particles that are in constant motion. In 1827, Robert Brown observed the motion of pollen grains suspended in a liquid under a microscope. He found that the pollen grains would occasionally twitch and jump for no apparent reason. This motion became known as **Brownian motion.** An early explanation of Brownian motion was that the particles possessed some life force that triggered the motion. However, dust particles that showed no other characteristics of living things also exhibited this motion, and so this interpretation was abandoned.

Almost a century later, Einstein proposed that the Brownian motion could be caused by collisions of particles, much too small to be seen under the microscope, with the pollen grain. In 1905 he derived a theoretical expression that predicted how far the pollen grain would move in a given period of time if it were subjected to random collisions with very much smaller particles. In Einstein's calculation, both the smaller particles and the pollen grain were assumed to

153

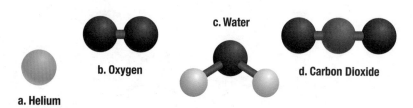

c. Water

b. Oxygen

d. Carbon Dioxide

a. Helium

Figure 13.1

A first glimpse at atoms and molecules. For ease of reference we will use balls to represent atoms. Molecules are combinations of atoms. Pictured here is an atom of helium (He), a molecule of oxygen as it exists in nature (two oxygen atoms (O) combined), a molecule of water (two atoms of hydrogen (H) attached to one atom of oxygen (O)), and a molecule of carbon dioxide (one carbon (C) and one oxygen atom).

obey Newtonian laws of motion and the conservation of energy. Experiments conducted four years later verified Einstein's calculation, and his theory was accepted as being the correct explanation: Particles too small to be observed through a microscope must exist. These particles are what we now call molecules.

Assumptions of the Model

Next, there is a set of rules or assumptions that the model postulates to govern behavior. (These will be described in detail momentarily.) Then, logical deductions, based on the data and the rules, can be made to provide not only expla-

nations of the behavior, but also new insights. These insights suggest new experiments to test the validity of the model. A good model will not only explain the previously collected data, but will also accurately predict the results of new experiments.

The molecular model was constructed to explain the behavior of gases, but some aspects of this model are also appropriate for solids and liquids. The following four assumptions are key points of the molecular model:

1. All matter consists of tiny particles.

The simplest kind of matter is composed entirely of atoms. This kind of material is called **atomic matter**. More complex kinds of matter are made of particles called **molecules**. A molecule contains two or more atoms. Molecules can contain multiple atoms of the same kind, or atoms of different kinds. For brevity, when we speak in general terms, we will use the term "molecule" to represent the smallest unit of both atomic matter and molecular matter.

◆ **Molecular Model**

The essential defining characteristics of the Molecular Model are: 1. Matter consists of tiny particles called molecules. 2. Each different kind of matter consists of a different kind of molecule. 3. The molecules in matter are in constant motion. 4. Molecules move and interact in accord with laws of motion, the laws of force and the laws of conservation.

◆ **Brownian Motion**

The constant, irregular motion of very fine particles (such as fine dust or smoke) suspended in a fluid and observed with a microscope. Brownian Motion is taken as evidence for molecules, which collide with the observed particles and cause the jittery motion.

◆ **Atomic Matter**

Matter composed simply of atoms, not molecules.

◆ **Molecules**

The tiny constituent particles of which matter is composed. At this stage in our model, we do not distinguish between atoms and molecules nor do we worry about their sizes or shapes. We only postulate that different kinds of matter consist of different kinds of molecules.

ATOMIC MICROSCOPY

Scientists now use sophisticated instruments called scanning tunneling microscopes (STM) to see atoms more directly. *Figure 13.2* shows a photograph taken through an STM of a solid crystal of nickel atoms. This image was magnified at least 1 billion times (as compared to the 1,500 times maximum magnification power of many standard light microscopes). Each blue cone represents a nickel atom. The

diameter of each cone is related to the diameter of a nickel atom plus a little additional space to allow for the jiggling motion described earlier. Another STM image (*Figure 13.3*) shows some iron atoms placed on a layer of copper atoms. The copper atoms appear only as the soft hills in the blue layer. They are not well resolved in the image.

Figure 13.2

An image of a layer of nickel atoms taken by a scanning tunneling microscope. The magnification is about 1 billion times.

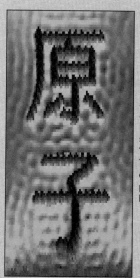

Figure 13.3

An image of iron atoms deposited on a layer of copper atoms spelling the word "atom" in Japanese. The copper atoms are only visible as the ripples in the blue background.

Molecules are so small that one teaspoonful of water contains more molecules than there are teaspoonfuls of water in all the oceans put together. We can't see molecules with even the highest magnifying light-based microscopes. Only since about 1990 have instruments called electron microscopes been developed that allow us to see these small particles more directly.

2. Different kinds of matter are made up of different molecules.

The helium gas that is in the balloons you buy for a birthday party is an example of atomic matter; helium gas contains just atoms. The molecules of oxygen and nitrogen (both gases present in the air that we breathe) each contain two atoms of the same type. Molecules of carbon dioxide (a gas that we exhale with each breath), and molecules of ordinary drinking water each contain two kinds of atoms. A carbon dioxide molecule contains one atom of carbon and two atoms of oxygen; a water molecule contains one atom of oxygen and two atoms of hydrogen. By contrast, the molecules that make up our hair and skin contain many thousands of atoms, mostly carbon, hydrogen, nitrogen, and oxygen. We will learn more about such complicated molecules in later chapters.

3. The molecules in matter are in constant motion.

Within each state of matter, the molecules are moving constantly. In gases, molecules move freely throughout the entire volume of their container. They can even escape into the atmosphere if the container has a hole in it. Molecules in a liquid state move throughout the liquid's volume but they are not completely free of their neighboring molecules. There are interactions between the molecules in a liquid that help to keep them relatively close to one another. In the solid state, there is a different kind of motion than one sees in the liquid and gas states.

To visualize that motion, imagine some lumps of Jello® arranged on a flat plate as shown in *Figure 13.4*. If you gently shake the plate back and forth, the Jello® pieces jiggle around, but do not move from one end of the plate to another. Molecules in a solid move like the lumps of Jello®. Molecular centers are fixed in position while the outer parts of the molecule vibrate back and forth.

Collisions among molecules and between molecules and container walls take place in both the liquid and gas states of matter, but not generally in solid matter. This constant molecular motion allows gases and liquids to assume the shape of their containers, while the jiggling of a solid object's molecules is not enough to make the solid flow like a liquid or expand like a gas.

4. The motion of gas molecules is governed by Newton's laws of motion, the electromagnetic force, gravitation laws, and the conservation laws.

A gas molecule is assumed to move in a straight line until it collides with another molecule or the wall of its container. When molecular collisions occur, Newton's third law describes the interaction between the colliding objects. Also, during collisions, molecules can exchange energy with each other and change their direction. The speeds of the molecules and their directions after collisions are determined by Newton's second law and the laws of conservation of energy and momentum.

The molecular model was developed long before Dr. Albert Einstein proposed the theory of relativity that you studied in Chapter 7. Knowing about relativity, you might wonder if point 4 is valid. However, since molecules rarely

a. Jello on a stationary plate ⇧

b. Jello on a shaken plate ⇩

Figure 13.4

The quivering, jiggling motion of Jello pieces on a gently shaken plate resembles the nature of molecular motion in the solid state.

travel at speeds approaching that of light, we can safely assume the simple classical description of molecular motion.

13–2 EXPLANATIONS PROVIDED BY THE MOLECULAR MODEL

Physical States of Matter

Chapter 12 detailed the physical characteristics of four states of matter: solid, liquid, gas, and plasma. *Figure 13.5* shows how the molecular model helps us to picture these first three states.

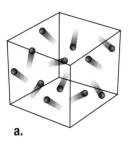
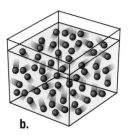
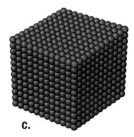

a. b. c.

Figure 13.5
The states of matter as pictured in the molecular model of matter. In all three states the molecules are in motion.

a) In gases, the molecules can move throughout their container.
b) In liquids, they move less freely, but stay within a certain volume.
c) In solids, each molecule only jiggles about a central point.

The molecules in a solid are arranged in an orderly fashion, with the molecules packed so close to one another that they almost touch. In a liquid, molecules are not packed tightly together, but are still relatively close. Molecules in a gaseous state are in contact with each other only when they collide.

Why States of Matter Have Different Densities

Can you explain, using the pictures in Figure 13.5, the trends in density that you noted in Table 12.1? Which cube contains the most molecules and therefore has the most mass? Each cube in this figure has the same volume, so the cube with the most molecules will have the greatest density. The close packing of molecules in the solid compared to the liquid and gas means that the solid has the greatest density. In the gas, there is much empty space between molecules, which are far apart on the average. The low density of a gas is due to the small number of gas molecules (and therefore lower mass) in a given volume. A liquid has a density that is between the density of a gas and a solid because a liquid contains more molecules than gases, but fewer molecules than a solid having the same volume.

13–3 NEW INSIGHTS PROVIDED BY THE MOLECULAR MODEL

States of Matter and Internal Energy

In Chapter 9 you learned that internal energy has two forms: microscopic kinetic energy (also known as thermal or heat energy) and microscopic electrical potential energy (also known as chemical potential energy). The molecular model can help you more clearly picture these two forms of internal energy.

Molecules are in a state of constant motion and so possess microscopic kinetic energy. Atoms and molecules contain both positive and negatively charged bits. Therefore, they possess an electrical potential energy that depends upon the average distance between molecules. Figure 13.5 illustrates that molecules are close together in solid matter and much farther apart in gases. The molecular model implies that the different states of matter have different amounts of internal energy because of the differences both in their microscopic kinetic energy and in their potential energy.

Internal Kinetic Energy and Temperature

Remember Scottish physicist James Clerk Maxwell from Chapter 11? In addition to developing his equations for electromagnetic fields, Maxwell used the molecular model assumptions and several mathematical and statistical principles to derive an equation that revealed important properties of a large collection of gas molecules. Maxwell's derivation is seen as a true thing of beauty, a grand example of scientific logic and mathematical rigor, by those who appreciate mathematical elegance.

To put Maxwell's results in a meaningful context, let's consider two situations. First, think of driving on a moderately busy six-lane freeway. Some cars (perhaps driven by senior citizens or folks talking on cell phones) are driving significantly below the speed limit. Others (perhaps those driven by teenage boys or anyone in a cherry-red convertible) can be found going much, much faster than the posted speed. Most cars will be going at the speed limit.

Then, think of driving on a suburban street in a school zone. In a school zone, just about all of the cars would be expected to be moving at 20 mph with a small number moving a bit slower or faster. It would be unusual (and unlawful) to find cars going 65 mph in this zone.

A state trooper sitting with a radar gun on the side of the freeway or a police officer by the school could count the number of cars going at each speed and create graphs to represent their results. Since there are many more cars passing by on the freeway than by the school, it makes sense to report the results as a fraction: number of cars going a particular speed/the total number of cars that were counted. That way, the results from both observations would cover the same range: 0 to 1, and they could be plotted on the same graph.

Now back to Maxwell. Maxwell's equation tells us that in a large collection of many gas molecules there will be a range of molecular speeds. Molecules, like cars on roads, travel at different speeds. Maxwell's formula actually lets us calculate the fraction of molecules going a particular speed if we know the gas temperature and molecular mass.

Let's look at Maxwell's results for molecular systems by supposing that you have three balloons, each filled with one of three gases, helium (He), nitrogen (N_2), and argon (Ar) and all at room temperature. Atoms of helium have less mass than do atoms of argon. The masses of nitrogen molecules are in between helium and argon atoms. *Figure 13.6* displays what you would observe if you could track the speeds of the molecules (atoms) inside the balloons. The y-axis of each plot gives the fraction of molecules going at a particular speed. A large fraction means that many molecules travel at that speed, and a very small value means that very few molecules can be found moving at that speed.

Notice that each plot has a speed with a maximum or peak value of the fraction. The speed at which the maximum fraction occurs can be thought of as the most popular speed of gas molecules in that balloon. That is, the largest number of molecules move at that speed.

The peak for argon occurs with a large fraction, so it is a very popular speed indeed. If you were to track the speed of argon atoms, you would find many atoms moving with this speed. The fraction of helium atoms moving at its most popular speed is low.

You can understand why this might be so by considering the range of speeds with which the different gases move. Atoms of Ar (the heaviest gas) move with a small distribution of speeds. Their speed distribution is like that of the cars in the school zone. Just as it would be unlikely to see a car moving at 65 mph near a school, it is unlikely that heavy Ar atoms will move very quickly.

Helium atoms behave like the cars on the freeway. The range of freeway speeds is very large; some cars are going very fast, others slowly. Likewise, the light He atoms show a broad distribution. Since the He atoms have more speeds to choose from, the most popular speed is found for a smaller fraction of atoms.

Molecules don't have state troopers patrolling their speed nor do they ride in red convertibles, so what causes the distribution of speeds? Gas molecules continually collide with one another, exchanging energy and changing speeds with each collision. When fast molecules collide with slow ones, the slow ones may speed up and the fast ones slow down.

Maxwell's formula also predicts what happens if we change the temperature for a given type of molecule. *Figure 13.7* shows

James Clerk Maxwell

In addition to his equations on electromagnetic fields, Maxwell did revolutionary work on the kinetic theory of gases.

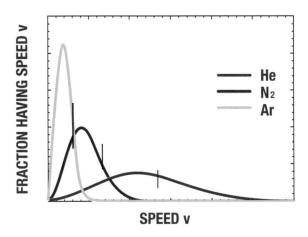

Figure 13.6

These graphs show the distribution of speeds for collections of different molecules at room temperature (25°C). The speed associated with the average kinetic energy is shown by the position of the vertical line for each graph.

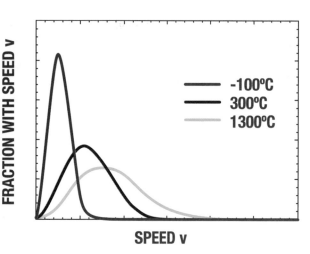

Figure 13.7
The distribution of speeds for a collection of nitrogen molecules at three different temperatures.

FRACTION WITH SPEED v

— -100°C
— 300°C
— 1300°C

SPEED v

For matter in any state, temperature is a measure of the average kinetic energy of the molecules.

Therefore, when gas and liquid molecules are at the same temperature, they have the same average kinetic energy. When matter changes temperature, its internal kinetic energy also changes.

You can deduce from this that increasing the temperature of matter causes an increase in its internal energy. Next, let's see about the relation between internal energy and changes in state.

Relative Order of Internal Energy in States of Matter

The connection between temperature and the average microscopic kinetic energy enables us to conclude which state of matter has more internal energy for a given particular substance. To see this, imagine doing the following experiment:

Take a closed pan containing water with a thermometer immersed in the liquid like that shown in *Figure 13.8* and put it into a freezer. Leave it there until all the liquid is frozen and the temperature is below 0°C. Then take the container out, put it onto the kitchen counter and allow it to warm up. When all the ice has melted, put the pan on the stove and turn on the heat. (You will need to stir the water gently so that the heat gets distributed evenly.)

If you watched the temperature carefully as the process was taking place, you would see the temperature of the water change as shown in *Figure 13.9*. Initially, when all the water is solid ice, the temperature begins to rise. Then, when the ice begins to melt, the temperature stays the

the distribution for helium atoms at three different temperatures. Notice that the distribution is narrower at low temperatures—most of the molecules are moving at close to the same speed (Think cars near the school). As the temperature increases, molecules move with a wider range of speeds (think cars on the freeway).

The mathematics of the molecular model tells us that the average kinetic energy (KE) of a collection of gas molecules is related to its temperature:

$$\text{Average KE} = \tfrac{1}{2}m\,(v^2)_{ave} = 3k_B T$$

where k_B is a constant and T is the temperature on the Kelvin Scale ($T = t + 273.15$, where t is the temperature in Celsius). Increasing the temperature of a gas increases its average kinetic energy.

This equation says the average kinetic energy of all gases will be the same at the same temperature. All three gases in Figure 13.6 are at the same temperature, so the three collections of gases all have the same average kinetic energy. Mathematically, we can write that as:

$$\tfrac{1}{2}m_{He}v^2_{He} = \tfrac{1}{2}m_{N2}v_{N2}{}^2 = \tfrac{1}{2}m_{Ar}v^2_{Ar}$$

where v is an average speed of each type of molecule. This relationship shows that light molecules must have higher average speeds than heavy ones. In Figure 13.6, the speed associated with the average kinetic energy of each gas is marked by a vertical black line. Verify that the black line for helium occurs at a higher speed than the one for argon or nitrogen.

This general conclusion about average kinetic energy and temperature also applies to the other states of matter. We can state the following:

Figure 13.8
A closed vessel with a small amount of water and a thermometer to measure temperature.

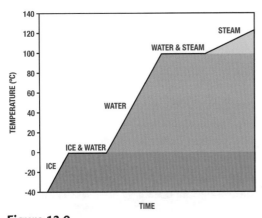

Figure 13.9

A graph of the changes in temperature of the closed vessel in Figure 13.8, as heat energy is put in at a constant rate. Temperature increases when there is only one state present, but is constant when one state is converting to another.

same. It stays the same for as long as both liquid and solid are present. When all the ice is gone and only liquid is present, the temperature begins to rise again. It keeps going up until the liquid starts to boil. Then the temperature stays constant until all of the liquid has evaporated.

The key points to keep in mind from this experiment: 1) Energy is constantly being put into the pan of water. 2) Figure 13.9 shows that the temperature increases only when the pan holds a single state of matter: just solid, just liquid, or just gas. 3) When two states of matter are present, the temperature stays the same: 0 °C for ice/water and 100 °C for water/steam.

Thinking Like A Scientist: Let's see what we can conclude about the relative ordering of internal energies of solid, liquid, and gas from this experiment and our new knowledge about temperature and kinetic energy.

Think back to the experiment and the graph of Figure 13.9. Notice that when the temperature was changing, only one state was present (just ice or just liquid or just steam). When two states of matter were present, the temperature stayed the same (0°C for water/ice and 100°C for water/steam). What does that tell you about the different contributions of microscopic kinetic and electrical potential energy?

Ice at a low temperature has a low internal kinetic energy. Energy flowing in from the warm kitchen causes the ice to heat up, increasing the average kinetic energy of its molecules. The jiggling motion of the molecules increases with temperature. Eventually the molecules have enough kinetic energy and begin to break free of the solid. The solid begins to melt, forming

the liquid. At this point, even though heat energy is still flowing into the pan, the temperature of the liquid/solid mixture does not increase. Therefore, the internal kinetic energies of the two states must be the same.

Because heat flows into the mixture but its temperature is not changing, you can conclude that the additional energy must increase the electrical potential energy. The liquid must have a higher potential energy than the solid. When all of the ice has melted, continued heating causes the temperature to rise again. Similarly, when enough energy has been added from the hot stove to the liquid, molecules begin to break free and evaporate to form the gas. The average kinetic energy of the molecules in the two states is the same during the evaporation process at 100°C. The additional energy input from the stove appears as the increased potential energy of the gas molecules.

To summarize, solids have the least electrical potential energy, gases the most, and liquids are somewhere in between. Since solids are usually found at lower temperatures than liquids, and liquids at lower temperatures than gases, we can arrive at the ordering in total internal energy: solids, then liquids, then gases.

Heat Flow: Conduction

When a cold pan is placed on a hot stove burner, the pan molecules and the burner molecules come in contact where the two surfaces touch. Both objects are solid, so their molecules, while moving, are really not going anywhere. The hot burner molecules are jiggling wildly while the cold pan molecules jiggle just a little. The burner molecules occasionally bump into

COLD

HOT

Figure 13.10

The effect of temperature on the motion of molecules in solids, using the lumps of green Jello of Figure 13.2. In cold molecules, the jiggling back and forth motion is small and molecules can be very close together. In hot molecules, the jiggling motion covers more space, and molecules move apart to accomodate the expanded motion.

◆ **Heat**
That portion of internal energy that is associated with the kinetic energy of molecules.

◆ **Conduction**
The flow of heat energy from a hot region to a cold region within solid matter.

◆ **Pressure**
Total force divided by the area over which force is applied.

the pan molecules, transferring some of their kinetic energy. Over time, the burner's molecules make the pan's molecules move faster.

The molecular model of matter gives us insight into what heat is and why it flows in the direction that it does. **Heat** is associated with the kinetic energy of molecules. Heat always flows from a hot object to a cold one, because molecular collisions between cold, slow-moving molecules and hot, rapidly moving ones speed up the slow ones and slow down the fast ones. **Conduction** is the term used when describing heat flowing within solid matter because of a temperature difference.

It is important to distinguish between the flow of heat and temperature itself. Put a metal spoon and a wooden spoon in the freezer for several hours, long enough for both of them to reach the temperature inside the freezer. Now pick them up. Which *feels* colder? Both are at the same temperature, yet the metal spoon feels colder. What our nerve endings sense and our brains interpret as temperature is really heat flow. The molecular model cannot provide an explanation of why the molecules in metals transmit energy faster than the molecules in wooden spoons. We will have to wait for a more sophisticated model to explain this observation.

Gas Pressure

The molecular model provides an explanation of why gas molecules exert pressure on the walls of their container (*Figure 13.11*). Molecules in a gas are in constant motion. They collide continually with the walls of the container that holds them. Each collision exerts a force on the container wall. Remember in Chapter 6 that you saw

that it is useful to speak of **pressure** when many different forces are exerted on an object. Therefore, we can consider the gas pressure to be a measure of the collective force exerted by many molecules colliding over a given area of the container at the same time.

Thinking Like A Scientist: The molecular model allows us to make a prediction about the effects of increasing the temperature of gas. Increasing the temperature of the gas increases the average kinetic energy of the gas's molecules. Molecules will hit the wall faster. Their acceleration at the time of collision will be greater (their change in speed is greater if they go from 600 meters/sec to 0 meters/sec at the wall, than if they go from 300 meters/sec to 0 meters/sec at the wall). Acceleration determines force, so increasing the acceleration means increased force. Therefore, the average force of a collision will increase. If average force increases, then pressure should increase. To see if this prediction is accurate, measure the air pressure in your bicycle or automobile tire before and after a long ride on a hot road. When is the pressure higher?

13-4 LIMITATIONS OF THE MOLECULAR MODEL

The molecular model has given us some explanations for observations like the states of matter and their densities. It has provided us with the insight that temperature is connected to kinetic energy and that changes in internal energy occur when matter changes state.

The molecular model is not perfect, however. Notice that nothing has been said about why gases, solids, and liquids respond differently to compression, tension, and shear forces. Also, we have not offered any explanations about why objects differ in color. The molecular model cannot deal with either of those issues. We have also noted that it does not explain why metals and wooden objects conduct heat differently. These are challenges for future models.

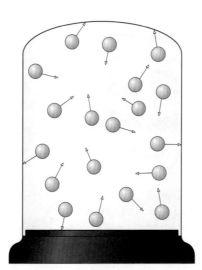

Figure 13.11
Gas molecules hitting the wall of a container cause pressure.

Chapter Framework

A. The Molecular Model of Matter
1. Experimental Basis
   a. *Properties of matter*
   b. *Brownian motion*
2. Assumptions
   a. *Tiny particles*
   b. *Different molecules*
   c. *Constant motion*
   d. *Gas molecule motion*

B. Explanations from the Model
1. Physical States
2. Differing Densities

C. New Insights
1. States of Matter and Internal Energy
2. Internal Kinetic Energy and Temperature
   a. *James Clerk Maxwell*
3. Relative Order of Internal Energy in States of Matter
4. Heat Flow: Conduction

Comprehension

True/False
1. _____ Pressure in a hot tire is greater than the pressure when the tire is cold.
2. _____ For a given material, the solid state has a higher internal energy than the gaseous state.
3. _____ Molecules, even in solids, are in constant motion.
4. _____ The molecular model is limited in that it cannot explain the color of an object.
5. _____ Heat is the amount of energy associated with electrical potential energy.
6. _____ In the molecular model, molecules are assumed to move according to the laws of special relativity.
7. _____ According to Maxwell, all of the gas molecules in a balloon are traveling at the same speed.

Fill in the Blank
1. _____ are the invisible tiny particles that make up matter.
2. Liquids are typically _____ dense than solids. Water is an exception.
3. When an object's temperature increases, the average kinetic energy of the molecules inside the object _____.
4. When a liquid transforms to a gas in a closed container, and both liquid and gas are present simultaneously, the temperature of the substance _____ (stays the same, increases, decreases).
5. Ice and liquid water are present in the container of Figure 13.8 at the same temperature. The

_____ (internal kinetic energy, internal potential energy) of the two states is the same.

Matching
1. _____ The tiny constituent particles of which matter is composed.
2. _____ A measure of average kinetic energy of the molecules that make up an object.
3. _____ The constant, irregular motion of very fine particles suspended in a fluid and observed with a microscope.
4. _____ The transfer of microscopic kinetic energy between two solid objects (a hot one and a cold one) that are in physical contact with each other.
5. _____ Model that explains the behavior of gases observed by Maxwell.
6. _____ Force per unit area.

a. Molecular Model
b. Heat Conduction
c. Pressure
d. Temperature
e. Molecules
f. Brownian Motion

Analysis

1. Between two objects, heat always travels
   a) from a cooler to a warmer object.
   b) from a warmer to a cooler object.
   c) randomly between the two objects regardless of their temperature.
   d) Heat doesn't travel between objects.

2. According to the Molecular Model, the density of physical states increases in the order:
   a) solid, gas, liquid
   b) liquid, gas, solid
   c) solid, liquid, gas
   d) It is not possible to determine using the Molecular Model.

3. Molecules of the air around us are thought of as:
   a) Compressible particles like little tufts of wool that are nearly at rest and touching one another.
   b) Objects that fill the otherwise empty space of atoms.
   c) Compressible particles like little tufts of wool that are in rapid motion in a fine fluid called ether.
   d) Particles in rapid and chaotic uniform motion until they strike one another or the walls of a container.

4. If a large bucket of water and a small bucket of water have the same temperature,
   a) both have the same total internal energy.
   b) both have the same total molecular kinetic energy.
   c) the average molecular speed is the same for both.
   d) both have the same total energy.
   e) the water molecules in the small bucket are moving faster than those in the large bucket.

5. Heat conduction occurs from a warm room through a closed window on a cold day because

a) the molecules in the glass window are moving faster than those in the air inside the room.

b) fast molecules go through the window to the outside.

c) slow molecules enter the room from the outside.

d) slow molecules transfer energy to faster ones with which they collide, on the average.

e) fast molecules transfer energy to slower ones with which they collide, on the average.

6. Evaporation of water from the skin has a cooling effect. This is because

a) the most massive water molecules escape into the surrounding atmosphere.

b) water molecules with the greatest speed escape into the surrounding atmosphere.

c) water molecules with least kinetic energy escape into the surrounding atmosphere.

d) the surrounding atmosphere transfers its energy into the water.

e) the least massive water molecules escape into the surrounding atmosphere.

Synthesis

1. What are the four main assumptions of the Molecular Model of Matter?

2. At room temperature, liquid water has a density of about 1 g/cm³ while that of liquid mercury is about 13.6 g/cm³. How might the molecular model account for this difference?

3. What is actually "seen" in Brownian motion and how is Brownian motion explained by the Molecular Model?

4. Using the Molecular Model, explain why gases readily change volume when pressure is applied, while liquids and solids do not change volume appreciably, even under enormous pressure.

5. Using the Molecular Model, explain why solid material resists changes in shape, while liquids readily assume the shape of their container?

6. The temperature of boiling water does not rise above 100° C until all the water has evaporated, even though considerable energy is added to the water during this time. Where does the energy go?

7. Outline the key aspects of the molecular model: What experimental observations are at its foundation? What assumptions does the model make?

What explanations does the model provide? What new insights are gained from the model or predictions that the model led to?

8. Use the Molecular Model to explain each of the following:

a. The density of solid nitrogen molecules is greater than the density of nitrogen molecules in the atmosphere.

b. Why heat moves from hot objects to colder ones.

c. Why placing an ice pack on your head cools you down.

d. How fluids exert pressures.

9. The pressure of all gases rises when their temperature is increased. For example, the air pressure in the tire of a car is higher when the tire is hot than when it is cold. Using the Molecular Model, explain why this is so.

10. Figure 13.6 shows how the distribution of speeds varies for gas molecules of different masses at the same temperature. Use this figure to predict the behavior of two different gas samples, hydrogen and sulfur dioxide, at the same temperature. Sulfur dioxide molecules have more than 32 times as much mass as hydrogen molecules.

a. In which sample will the molecules travel with a wider distribution of speeds? That is, which molecules behave more like cars on the freeway than cars near the school?

b. Which sample will have the highest, sharpest peak in the distribution of speeds?

11. In the process described in Figure 13.9, we started with a cold ice cube and ended with hot steam. Describe how the internal energy of the molecules changes as this process takes place.

12. The details of Figure 13.9 apply to changes of state for many substances other than water. Pick one of the substances (other than water) in Table 12.1 and sketch a graph like Figure 13.9 for your substance. Things to consider: At what temperatures will you have plateaus? Between what temperatures will you have sloping lines?

13. "Thermal pane" windows are designed to reduce the heat that flows out of your warm house into the cold outside via the house's glass windows. These windows are constructed with two pieces of glass with an evacuated space (no gas molecules) in between. Using the Molecular Model, explain why less heat gets transferred to the cold outside window pane from the hot interior window pane in this design than if a single piece of glass was used.

More Test-Taking Strategies:
Test-Taking Tips For Specific Types of Tests

(Tips A–C on page 51)

D. Sentence Completion Or Fill-In the Blank Questions

1. Read the question with the intent to give an answer and make the sentence grammatically correct.
2. Concentrate on the number of blanks in the sentence and the length of the space.
3. Provide a descriptive answer when you cannot think of the exact word or words.

E. Essay Questions

1. Organize your thoughts before you begin to write.
2. Paraphrase the original question to form your introductory statements.
3. Write your answer clearly, so the reader will be able to decode your writing and understand your ideas.
4. Read each essay question carefully with the intent to identify the verbs or words that give you direction.
    –Circle the direction verbs that ask you:
      • to review an idea or concept (Summarize, Survey, Discuss, Explain).
      • for a set of items (Trace, Outline, List, Diagram, Solve).
      • to speak in favor of a concept or give the reasons why it should be accepted as valid (Defend, Argue, Debate, Contend, Justify).
      • for a specific meaning or picture of a concept (Define, Clarify, Describe, Depict, Illustrate).
      • to show differences in several ideas or situations (Contrast, Compare, Distinguish, Differentiate)
5. Use good principles of English composition when answering all types of essay questions.
    –Form a clear thesis statement.
    –Use examples to back up your answers.
    –Always include a conclusion!
6. Keep to the point: Try for quality, not just quantity.
7. Proofread your completed answer.

General Guidelines for Test Preparation

• Know the testing format; Multiple Choice, True/False, Fill-in etc.
• Review the material throughout the week
• DON'T CRAM!!! When you have a cram session and then go purge all the information on the test, you're not really learning. It's like a farmer who plants his field in the morning and then tries to harvest it in the evening. It's not going to happen.
• Get enough sleep and have a good meal!
• Don't hold last minute reviews while waiting in line at the testing center. They will more than likely cause you to be more stressed.
• Arrive to the exam area early. Use the restroom and get a drink before you start.

During the Exam

1. Sit in an area where you can concentrate; i.e., avoid doors and windows.
2. Bring supplies: pencils, calculators, scratch paper, late fees, snacks, water, etc.
3. Write down test formulas and other memorized facts. Free your mind.
4. Review directions.
5. Don't spend too much time on any one question. If you don't know the answer come back later.
6. Guess, unless there is a penalty.
7. Relax! Take a minute to laugh before the exam. Relieve a little tension.

THE NUCLEAR ATOM

The opposite of a correct statement is a false statement. But the opposite of a profound truth may be another profound truth.

~ Niels Bohr

The molecular model of Chapter 13 provides a mental image around which to explain properties of states of matter. Perhaps most importantly, the molecular model establishes a critical connection between an object's temperature and the average kinetic energy of the molecules that make up the object. Maxwell's equation that describes the distribution of molecular speeds, derived on the basis of the molecular model, remains very useful for the study of gases even today.

However, the molecular model is a very simple model. It says nothing about the internal structure of an atom. A look at the atom's interior is needed to further develop our understanding. Chapter 14 describes the early models of an atom and the scientific process that led to those models. Important experiments and the logical reasoning from experiments to models of the atom provide one example of the scientific method at work.

Usually, a transition from one model to a new one occurs only after many experiments. Occasionally, however, a new model springs forth immediately from dramatic and unexpected results of a single experiment. Our understanding of the atom progressed via both slow, evolutionary processes and quick, abrupt pathways. Study this chapter both for an understanding of the various models, and for its explicit examination of the scientific process at work.

14–1 EARLY EXPERIMENTS AND THE ELECTRICAL NATURE OF THE ATOM

Watch how a toddler explores her world. Chances are good that at least one toy gets ripped or chewed open to see what's inside. Scientists, too, recognize that a good way to understand how something works is to take it apart. To study the atom, experiments were designed to tear it apart and observe the pieces.

J. J. Thomson and his colleagues found that gas atoms could be pulled apart by applying an electrical charge across a tube containing a low-pressure gas (see Chapter 4). Both positively-charged fragments and negatively-charged fragments were created. Positive fragments produced in tubes containing different gases (e.g., nitrogen, oxygen, mercury) had masses nearly identical to the original gas particles. The negative particles, on the contrary, had the same charge and the same mass, regardless of the gas inside the tube. These negative, small-mass particles became known as electrons.

Robert Millikan's oil drop experiment (also detailed in Chapter 4) established that every electron had the same amount of negative charge. The charge on an electron did not change from experiment to experiment. Thomson's and Millikan's experiments provided strong evidence for the atom's electrical nature.

LEARNING OBJECTIVES

When you finish with this chapter, you should be able to

• Discuss the key experiments (gas discharge tubes, oil-drop experiment, gold-foil experiment, atomic spectra) that led to our understanding of atomic structure.

• Describe the Thomson model of the atom, also known as the Plum Pudding model, and its limitations.

• Describe the Rutherford model of the atom, also known as the Nuclear or Solar System model, and its limitations.

• Describe the Bohr model of the atom, also known as the Modified Solar System model, and its limitations.

14–2 THE PLUM PUDDING MODEL

By 1904, the results of many atom-blasting experiments had established the following facts about atoms:

1. The atom consists of positively-charged fragments and negatively charged bits of matter.

2. The negative bits, called electrons, have the same characteristics (mass and charge) in every kind of atom.

3. The positive fragments from a given kind of atom have the same characteristics. Positive fragments from one kind of atom differed from those of other kinds. For example, positive bits from nitrogen had less mass than positive bits from mercury.

4. The mass of an electron is much, much smaller than the mass of the lightest positive fragment measured in any gas-discharge experiments.

In an article published in 1904, Thomson combined these four observations into a simple model for the atom. *Figure 14.1* represents Thomson's picture of the atom. Thomson proposed that the positive charge of an atom was uniformly distributed, like a cloud, throughout

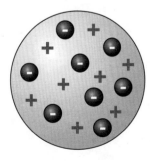

Figure 14.1

The plum pudding model proposed by J. J. Thomson. The positive charge is spread diffusely throughout the atom; electrons are sprinkled throughout the positively-charged region.

the space occupied by an atom. Electrons were embedded randomly within the positively-charged region. Each atom had just enough electrons to balance out the positive charge of the atom.

Thomson's model came to be known as the plum pudding model. Plum pudding, a favorite British dessert, contains bits of plum sprinkled throughout a cake-like base. For Americans who don't eat much plum pudding, a better image might be an oatmeal-raisin or chocolate-chip cookie. The positive charge resembles the cookie dough with the electrons sprinkled throughout like the raisins or chips.

14–3 RUTHERFORD'S GOLD FOIL EXPERIMENT

• **Alpha Particles**

A positively charged particle that is given off by some radioactive materials including uranium, plutonium, and polonium. Alpha particles are now known to be nuclei of helium atoms.

Figure 14.2

Rutherford's Gold Foil Experiment. Alpha particles emitted by a radioactive source were shot at a thin gold foil. Particles were detected when they hit a screen and caused the zinc sulfide coating to glow. When the screen was in front of the gold foil, a few particles bounced back and were detected when they hit the screen.

The next advance in atomic models was made by a former student of J. J. Thomson, Ernest Rutherford (1871–1937). Rutherford had participated in many gas-discharge experiments with Thomson, gaining expertise in that technology. After moving to Canada to establish his own laboratory, Rutherford began a set of experiments that would lead to a Nobel prize. Some of those experiments produced high-energy, positively-charged particles, called **alpha particles**. (Scientists now know that alpha particles are helium nuclei, given off by some radioactive materials during their decay. This topic will be pursued in Chapter 25.)

Rutherford realized that these particles could be used to test Thomson's plum pudding model. He would shoot the particles at atoms in

a gold foil, using them as atomic-sized bullets. Rutherford hypothesized that the rapidly moving alpha particles would slice right through the diffuse positive charge of the gold atoms. An alpha particle would experience only weak repulsive interactions with the diffuse positive charge of the gold atoms as the particle passed through the foil. Attractive encounters of an alpha particle and an electron would occur rarely. At best, an alpha particle would experience a slight deflection from its original motion on passing through the foil.

In 1911, Rutherford and two junior colleagues set up an apparatus like that shown in *Figure 14.2*. The radioactive sample of polonium emitted a beam of alpha particles. These particles, moving in a straight line, were shot at an ultra-thin piece of gold foil. A moveable screen was coated with zinc sulfide. (Zinc sulfide emits flashes of light when alpha particles slam into it.) The screen could be moved to different positions around the gold foil. With this arrangement, the investigators could see what happened to an alpha particle as it passed through the gold foil. A flash of light appearing on the screen would indicate the particle's path after it hit the gold foil.

Because the light given off by the detector screen was very weak, the experiments had to be conducted in the dark. Each experiment took a long time. An observer would turn on the lights, position the screen, turn out the lights and let his eyes adapt to the darkness. Sitting quietly with attention focused on the screen, the observer counted the blips of light that appeared on the screen during a set time interval. Then the process would be repeated, with the screen placed in a new location around the gold foil.

Rutherford was not a patient man, and he allowed two junior colleagues to actually collect the data. Fortunately, his colleagues were both patient *and* meticulous. Given the working hypothesis, the pair might have concentrated their observations at screen locations directly behind or a few degrees on either side of the foil. Instead, they moved the detector to many locations, going almost 360° around the gold foil.

The number and pattern of hits on the screen were counted at each location. Most of the alpha particles were found to behave just as Rutherford expected, hitting the screen behind the foil with small deflection angles. But occa-

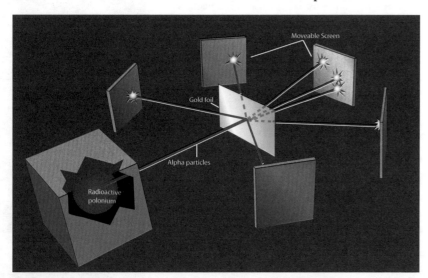

Moveable Screen

Gold foil

Alpha particles

Radioactive polonium

sionally, about one in every 8000 particles, a flash was detected in a most unexpected place, somewhere in front of the gold foil!

The junior colleagues' report that alpha particles were occasionally observed to reflect backwards astounded Rutherford. He later wrote:

It was quite the most incredible event that has happened in my life. It was almost as incredible as if you fired a 15-inch (artillery) shell at a piece of tissue paper and it came back and hit you.[1]

14–4 THE ATOM HAS A NUCLEUS

Rutherford and his colleagues analyzed the recoil patterns of the alpha particles. They realized that only one interpretation of the results was consistent with Newton's laws of motion and the electrical force law. Their reasoning went like this: To reflect backwards, a particle had to stop and change direction. That particle experienced large accelerated motion. Large accelerations require large forces. Therefore, those particles had to have encountered a very strong repulsive force. Such a large repulsive force could only result if the positive charge of the gold atoms were concentrated in very small, very dense particles. Thomson's plum pudding model was wrong!

The scientists called the dense, positively-charged particle the **nucleus**. Since only a few alpha particles recoiled backward, repulsive encounters with the nucleus had to be infrequent. Most of the alpha particles passed directly through the foil, experiencing little deflection. Rutherford concluded that both the mass and positive charge of the atom must be concentrated in the nucleus while the rest of the atom was empty space.

Rutherford's calculations indicated a nuclear diameter of 10^{-15} meters. Other types of experiments showed the atomic size to be about 10^{-10} meters. The nucleus is about 100,000 times smaller than the atom!

To understand the relative size of the nucleus compared to the atom, imagine a marble. Now put the marble at the center of a sphere with a diameter about the width of the BYU campus. If the nucleus were a marble located

at the Wilkinson Student Center, the outer limits of the atom would extend from the Marriott Center on the north to the Botany Pond on the south.

Rutherford's experimental results required that the atom's mass had to be concentrated in a very small space. Lots of mass in a small space gives rise to a very high density. The nuclear density can be calculated to be about 10^{16} (1 with 16 0's after it!) grams in a cubic centimeter. That is equivalent to squeezing 90 billion 250-lb linebackers into a space with a volume of 1 cubic centimeter.

How did Rutherford account for Thomson's electrons? The electrons were presumed to be outside the nucleus. Because of their small size and mass, electrons were thought to take up very little space.

Solar System Model

Rutherford's model resembles a solar system where planets exist in mostly empty space at large distances from a very dense sun. The parallel with the solar system was too good to ignore, and additional characteristics of the solar system crept into Rutherford's model. For example, the electrons orbited the nucleus in elliptical paths as planets orbit around the sun. Rutherford envisioned the atom to look much like the model shown in *Figure 14.3*. Not surprisingly, this new model was sometimes called the **solar system model** of the atom.

Scientists quickly became aware that this model couldn't be quite right. James Maxwell (Chapter 11) had demonstrated that accelerating charges produce light. Electrons that move in elliptical paths are charged particles undergoing accelerated motion. Where was the light that should be produced? And because electrons, like planets, could orbit with any possible speed, shouldn't electrons emit light with a continuous spectrum? Conservation of energy would require that eventually electrons would have no more kinetic energy and fall into the nucleus.

However, Thomson's other gas discharge tube experiments (described in Chapter 12) showed that atoms didn't usually emit light at all. The atoms in gas discharge tubes had to be stimulated with lots of electrical energy to produce radiation. As we saw in Chapter 12, these

♦ **Nucleus**
The atomic nucleus is the very dense, positively charged center of the atom.

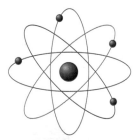

Figure 14.3
The Rutherford model of the atom.

♦ **Solar System Model**
A model of the atom in which the electrons orbit the small, dense, positively-charged nucleus in elliptical paths. The model proposed by Rutherford.

tubes emit radiation with discrete colors or wavelengths of light, not a continuous spectrum of light. Clearly, a new model was needed to resolve these problems.

14–5 EMISSION SPECTRA

A successful model must explain why atoms in gas discharge tubes produced the discrete **emission spectra**. One that also explained the continuous emission spectrum of the sun and other hot objects would be an added bonus.

Discrete versus Continuous Emission Spectra

The differences between discrete emission spectra and continuous emission spectra were discussed briefly in Chapter 12. The more extended discussion now emphasizes the role these spectra played in the development of atomic models.

White light emitted by the sun can be separated into all the colors of the rainbow. Newton discovered this using a simple prism. (*Figure 14.4a*) Hold a piece of white paper on one side of the prism and direct the separated light on to the paper. You should see that the colors change continuously from red through orange to yellow, green, blue, ending in violet. Exactly where one color ends and the next one begins

* **Emission Spectrum**

An emission spectrum is the set of colors of light given off, or emitted by, an object.

is impossible to identify. The colors of light change smoothly and continuously from one end of the rainbow to the other in a continuous emission spectrum.

Thomson and his colleagues discovered that the gas in discharge tubes also gave off light. A tube containing neon gas gives off a bright red-colored light. Atomic hydrogen gas in a discharge tube gives off a reddish light. Passing the reddish light through a prism to separate the colors yields only a few colors of light (see *Figure 14.4b*). It is easy to distinguish between the red light and the blue-green light in the discrete spectra. There are no other colors in between, hence the black regions in the images of the spectra. Black signals the *absence* of color in emission spectra.

Recall that emission spectra in which the colors of light change abruptly and many colors are missing are called discrete emission spectra. Back in Chapter 12, Figure 12.8 showed other examples of discrete emission spectra. Because the colors appear as sharp lines in these spectra, scientists often speak of "emission lines."*

Both continuous and discrete emission spectra may also contain emissions in the ultraviolet and infrared regions. Recall that our eyes detect only those wavelengths of light in the visible region of the electromagnetic spectrum. Using the colors of the rainbow to set the direction of colors, ultraviolet light is "bluer than blue" and infrared light is "redder than red." Scientists have ways to observe these invisible colors. The night vision goggles used by the military are sensitive to the infrared radiation emitted by warm-blooded creatures. T-shirts designed to "glow" in the presence of black lights do so by absorbing uv light and emitting visible light.

Atomic Hydrogen Discrete Emission Spectra

Scientists had studied the spectrum of atomic hydrogen in gas discharge tubes in great detail. Hydrogen was known to have several families of emission lines. Only one family of lines is located in the visible region (Figure 14.4b). Others are in the ultraviolet region and in the infrared region. A Swedish mathematician

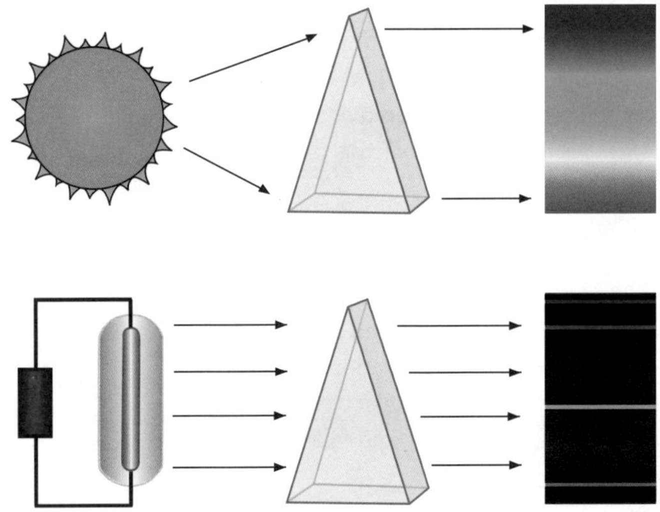

Figure 14.4

Comparison of Continuous and Discrete Emission Spectra. a) Continuous Spectra—The sun gives off white light. Passing the white light through a prism reveals all the colors of the rainbow. The colors change continuously from red to violet. b) Discrete Spectra—Gases in discharge tubes give off only a few colors of light. Light from a tube containing atomic hydrogen looks reddish. When the red light is passed through the prism, only four colors are found. The colors are very distinct. The color red that our eyes detect is a result of the combination of those four colors.

---

* A mathematical analogy might be helpful. The set of real numbers is continuous. There are an infinite number of numbers between 3.1415 and 3.1316. Integers are discrete. There are no integers between 3 and 4.

named Janne Rydberg (1854–1919) had discovered, just by trial and error, a formula that reproduced the frequencies of different families of emission lines.

The formula*, published in 1890, was:

$$f = C \left[\frac{1}{n_2^{\,2}} - \frac{1}{n_1^{\,2}} \right]$$

where "f" is the frequency of emitted light, n_1 and n_2 are integers: 1,2,3,4. . . . C is a constant. Scientists commonly use the letter "*n*" to represent a variable that can take on integer values. The subscripts 1 and 2 provide a way to distinguish two different integers. The ellipses. . . . indicate that the series of numbers can continue to infinity.

Rydberg associated each family of spectral lines with a fixed value of n_2. Then, Rydberg assigned each line within a given family its own n_1.

To illustrate the formula, consider the four lines in the visible spectrum of atomic hydrogen. Rydberg set $n_2 = 2$ for this family. Then, with $n_2 = 2$, he set $n_1 = 3, 4, 5$ and 6. Rydberg's formula calculated the frequencies of the red, blue-green, blue and violet lines, respectively. With $n_2 = 1$ and $n_1 = 2, 3, 4 . . .$, the formula calculated the frequencies of ultraviolet lines. Frequencies of a family of infrared lines resulted when $n_2 = 3$, and $n_1 = 4, 5, 6, . . .$ For each family of lines, Rydberg found that the smallest n_1 was 1 unit higher than the family's n_2 value.

The equation worked incredibly well for the known emission lines in the hydrogen spectrum. Rydberg predicted that additional lines existed, and he calculated their frequencies. Knowing where to look, scientists found these lines. Rydberg's predictions were "spot on" as his British colleagues would say. However, it would be more than 20 years before a reasonable explanation could be given for why this formula worked!

The Continuous Emission Spectra of the Sun and Other Hot Objects

Rydberg's formula gave encouragement that the atom had an underlying structure. Unfor-

tunately, the formula gave no clues what that structure might be. The critical clue actually came from a study of *continuous* spectra.

Ten years after Rydberg, in 1900, a German scientist named Max Planck made an important discovery. Planck had been investigating the emission spectra of hot materials. Matter heated to very high temperatures, like the sun or other stars, emits a continuous spectrum**. The colors in the spectrum depend on the object's temperature, not what the object is made of. The heating element on your stove begins to glow "red-hot" at a temperature of about 1200° F while a "white-hot" object like our sun is around 10,000° F. *Figure 14.5* shows the emission spectra for an object at several temperatures.

Planck had a radical idea to explain the continuous emission spectra. He assumed that light energy could only be emitted in discrete amounts. What, you say? Discrete energy emission associated with continuous spectra! How can this be?

Recall from Chapter 13, the motion of molecules in solid matter was described in terms of lumps of Jello jiggling back and forth. Planck***

** In fact, all matter emits electromagnetic radiation. The temperature of the object determines what its emission spectrum looks like. Human bodies and other mammals ("hot-blooded organisms") give off infrared radiation. Night goggles detect IR radiation. In a later chapter you will read that a star's color reveals its temperature.

*** Planck was wrong about the source of the light, but his idea of quantized energy was exactly right.

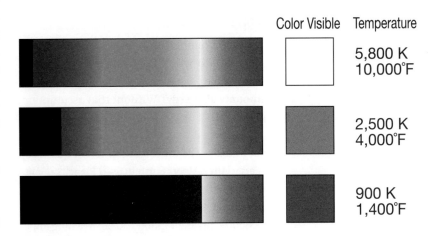

Color Visible	Temperature
	5,800 K 10,000°F
	2,500 K 4,000°F
	900 K 1,400°F

Figure 14.5
The continuous emission spectrum from hot objects at different temperatures. Black represents the absence of color. The squares represent the approximate color that the eye would see. Remember that white light is a balance of all the colors. If some colors are missing, or present in excess, the perceived color will not be white.

---

* You don't need to memorize this formula. What is important is it showed that there were predictable patterns to the emission lines. Discovering patterns is the first step in a breakthrough to understanding.

proposed that the light emitted by hot objects was due to this same type of jiggling or vibrational motion. Planck decided that the vibrating motion was governed by a new principle: Jiggling atoms could only absorb or emit energy in parcels obeying the following relationship:

Energy of a parcel = *n* h f

In Planck's equation, *n* also represents positive integers: 1, 2, 3, to infinity, but otherwise it does not have the same physical significance as in the Rydberg formula. "f" is the frequency of the vibration, and "h" is a constant that now bears Planck's name. Planck's constant is such a very small number most non-scientific calculators would treat it as being equal to zero.

Planck called a parcel of energy a quantum (plural quanta). Because Planck's constant is extraordinarily small*, the sizes of allowed energy parcels can also be small. Just how small can a quantum be? The size depends on the jiggling frequency. Let's take f to have a frequency of 89.1 megahertz (the frequency at which KBYU radio station broadcasts). When *n* = 1, the allowed energy is 10^{-29} food calories. That is small. Looking at it from another perspective, one food calorie (a kilocalorie) would correspond to *n* = 9×10^{29} for the 89.1 megahertz frequency.

Using Planck's formula and the KBYU frequency for f, the energy of a particular red photon corresponds to *n* = 5,112,997. The next most energetic photon corresponds to *n* = 5,112,998. The difference in energy between these two photons is too small to resolve so the spectrum appears continuous.

Is it a tempest in a teapot or a matter of semantics to worry about discrete parcels of energy if the parcels can differ by incredibly small amounts of energy? Without that assumption, Planck could not explain the spectrum of hot objects; with it he could. Still, many scientists did not initially accept the assumption of quantized energy. After Albert Einstein used Planck's quanta to explain the photoelectric effect (Chapter 11), acceptance came grudgingly. Physicists began to recognize this assumption had far-reaching implications. A new physics, now called quantum mechanics, had just been born.

---

* You have seen Planck's constant before. "h" is the proportionality constant between the energy of a photon of light and its frequency.

14–6 THE BOHR MODEL OF THE ATOM

Quantization of Angular Momentum

Niels Bohr (1885–1962), a Danish scientist, gets credit for the next model of the atom. Bohr had worked with Thomson and Rutherford. He wanted to solve the problems of the solar system model. Bohr knew of Planck's quantum, he knew about gas discharge spectra, and he knew about Rydberg's formula. Bohr's genius was to synthesize these facts into a new model.

Bohr recognized that the discharge spectra were due to the electrons of an atom. He applied Planck's idea of quantization to the angular momentum of an electron. This required circular rather than elliptical electron orbits. The angular momentum of a particle moving in a circle has been discussed in Chapter 8. There it states that:

Angular momentum = mass x speed x radius

Bohr postulated that the angular momentum was only allowed to take on values given by the formula:

Angular momentum = *n* h

where *n* is a positive integer from 1, 2, 3. . . to infinity and h is Planck's constant. The integer *n* is sometimes called the quantum number.

Bohr's assumption of quantized angular momenta led to restrictions on electron orbits and energy states. Electrons could only orbit the nucleus with radii that maintained the angular momentum requirement. Bohr also concluded that the energies of electrons are quantized.

He derived an equation for electron energies and found that the electron energies were inversely proportional to the square of the quantum number *n*:

$$\text{Energy} \propto \frac{1}{n^2}$$

The Bohr Model in Pictures

THE ELECTRON ORBITS

Let's look in a little more detail at the Bohr model. *Figure 14.6* shows the geometric arrangement of electrons around a positively-charged nucleus. Electrons orbit the nucleus in circular paths whose radii satisfy Bohr's assumptions. Electrons never occupy the space between the allowed orbits.

Bohr's quantum number *n* provides a convenient label to identify an electron orbit and the energy of an electron in that orbit. The smallest allowed value of the quantum number, *n* = 1 , corresponds to the orbit having the smallest allowed radius. As *n* increases, the orbital radius also increases.

The Bohr model has circular orbits at special radii, while the solar system model (Rutherford model) postulated elliptical orbits with no restrictions on the orbital motion. Because of these two differences, the Bohr model is sometimes called the **modified solar system model.**

Energy States in the Model

Figure 14.7 represents the ordering of electronic energy states in the Bohr model. Horizontal lines represent electronic states; each state is labeled by its quantum number, *n*. Moving upward in the vertical direction corresponds to higher energy states.

The lowest energy state, *n* = 1 is at the bottom of the figure. As *n* increases, the energy of that state also increase. States with *n* greater than 1 are sometimes called **excited states.**

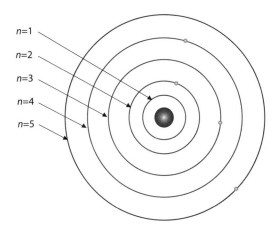

Figure 14.6

The Bohr Model of the Atom. Electrons move around the nucleus in circular orbits. (These are not drawn to scale.) The first orbit is many times larger than the nucleus. As the quantum number *n* increases, the energy of the electron and the radius of its orbit increases.

Discrete Emissions Explained at Last

The energy diagram in Figure 14.6 explains the origins of the discrete emission lines in atomic spectra graphically. An electron can jump from one orbit to another only if its energy changes. An emission spectrum is produced when an electron drops from a high energy orbit to a lower energy one. During the emission process, the electron jumps into an orbit closer to the nucleus.

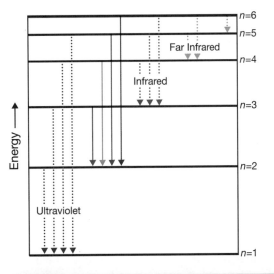

- **Modified Solar System Model**

The Bohr model with restricted circular orbits of electrons around a dense nucleus.

- **Excited States**

Electronic states with quantum number *n* greater than 1.

Figure 14.7

The energy levels of a Bohr atom. The arrows represent differences between two energy states. They also represent photons that are emitted when electrons jump between states. The colors of the arrows are those of the photons in the emission spectrum of hydrogen. Solid arrows represent visible photons. Dashed arrows represent photons outside the visible region. Reversing the direction of the arrows would give an absorption spectrum.

LOOKING CLOSER AT BOHR'S AND RYDBERG'S ENERGY FORMULAS

When talking about electronic states and electronic energies, two important concepts arise. The first is the absolute energy. The absolute energies identify the ordering or sequencing of the quantum states. They specify which state is lowest in energy, which state next lowest, etc. States which have high absolute energies are identified by horizontal lines high up in Figure 14.7.

The second concept is the energy *difference* between two states. The arrows of Figure 14.7 represent the sizes of energy differences between several pairs of states. Look at the length of the arrow between states *n* = 6 and *n* = 5 and then look at the length of the arrow between *n* = 2 and *n* = 1. Which arrow is longer? The arrow between *n* = 2 and *n* = 1 is longer. That means the energy difference between the first and second states is greater than the difference between the 5th and 6th

states. This is a general result: In the Bohr model, energy differences between successive states gets smaller and smaller.

Bohr's energy equation calculated *absolute* electron energies for a given *n* state. Bohr recognized that Rydberg's formula calculated energy *differences*. Rydberg's n_1 and n_2 numbers correspond to initial (n_1) and final (n_2) quantum numbers of Bohr. Bohr's model also reproduced the value of Rydberg's constant C.

What Rydberg had come up with by trial and error, Bohr derived from a few assumptions and the classical laws of force, motion, and conservation. In addition, Rydberg's formula only worked for hydrogen, Bohr's formula could be adapted to correctly predict the energies of emission lines in the spectra of several other atoms. It was considered a great success.

The energy *difference* between the two orbits determines the color of light:

(Energy of outer orbit) – (Energy of inner orbit) = hν

The arrows in Figure 14.7 show several allowed changes in quantum state. The length of the arrow is a measure of the energy difference between the two states. Long arrows correspond to big changes in energy. Short arrows correspond to small energy changes.

We can use the general energy diagram of Figure 14.7 to understand the specific emission spectrum of hydrogen. In the visible region, hydrogen has four lines. Figure 14.7 shows four arrows that stop at $n = 2$. Each arrow represents an emission line; the arrow color is that of the emission line.

Violet photons arise when electrons in the $n = 6$ orbit fall down to the $n = 2$ orbit. Red photons are produced when electrons fall from the $n = 3$ to the $n = 2$ orbits. If you recall that violet photons are more energetic than red photons, this assignment should seem reasonable. What changes in electron state give rise to the blue and blue-green photons?

The diagram can also explain the emission lines of hydrogen that are found in the ultraviolet and infrared regions. Jumps from excited states to the $n=1$ orbit generate ultraviolet photons; jumps between highly excited states generate low energy photons in the infrared or far infrared regions.

The conservation of energy law requires photon emissions when an electron drops to a lower energy state. To change from one orbit to another, an electron must change its energy. A drop from a high energy state to a low energy state means that the electron must get rid of some energy. It does so by emitting a photon. The size of the energy drop determines how much energy the photon must take away.

ABSORPTION SPECTRA

Are you wondering how an electron gets into excited states in the first place? The electron in an undisturbed hydrogen atom (not hot, not sitting between the plates of a discharge tube) is in the $n = 1$ state. Suppose a photon happens to pass by with just the right energy to kick the electron upstairs to a state with a higher n. The electron can absorb that photon. On doing so, it jumps to the new orbit. Conservation of energy governs photon absorption just as it does photon emission.

Photon absorption is the reverse process of photon emission. An absorption spectrum can be represented using the diagram of Figure 14.7 simply by reversing the directions of the arrows. There is a correspondence between an absorption spectrum and an emission spectrum.

The pattern of light absorbed by matter is called an absorption spectrum. *Figure 14.8* depicts the absorption spectrum of atomic hydrogen and compares it to the emission spectrum. The hydrogen absorbs photons from the white light passing through it. The correspondence between emission and absorption can be seen if you match the colors of emitted photons with the black regions in the absorbance spectrum. Recall that black is the absence of color in these figures.

Application to Other Atoms

The Bohr model was found to give qualitative agreement with atoms other than hydrogen. The quantitative agreement was not so spectacular. The model did not predict the correct numbers of lines in emission spectra. When the model did get the number of lines correct, the predicted frequencies did not match the measured ones. Clearly there was still more to be learned.

Other Problems with the Model

The careful reader will recognize that Bohr adroitly sidestepped one critical issue that plagued Rutherford's solar system model. Bohr's electrons are still accelerating charges. Accelerating charges emit radiation. Bohr postulated that radiation was emitted only when electrons changed their orbits. While the assumption enabled him to successfully account for the hydrogen spectrum, there was really no justification for it.

Bohr's model introduced a new problem. Why should the angular momentum be quan-

Figure 14.8
Comparison of emission and absorption spectra. In an absorption experiment, light from a white source passes through a tube containing hydrogen gas. The hydrogen absorbs red, blue-green, blue and violet photons from the light, leaving black gaps. The lower figure shows a gas discharge tube. A high electrical voltage is applied to the gas and causes it to emit photons. The colors of photons absorbed are the same as the ones emitted in a gas discharge tube.

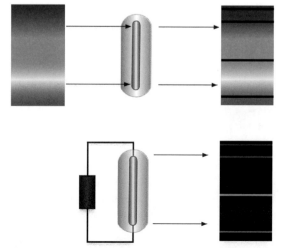

tized? Bohr could offer no other explanation than to say that this assumption led to a successful explanation of the hydrogen spectrum and Rydberg's formula. Having yielded such a spectacular success, the assumption had to be correct. The critical "why" question remained unanswered by Bohr.

14-7 CONCLUSION

Science progresses as new experiments provide new observations. Sometimes the new observations are inconsistent with the explanations provided by old models. Usually, old models are not completely thrown out. Instead, an old model may be "decorated" when new information becomes available. Or, the old model may be "patched" up like a pair of favorite blue jeans when a hole develops.

The molecular model of matter provided a basis to explain the behavior of matter associated with collections of atoms acting as a whole. The plum pudding model served as the beginning model for the interior design of the atom. Rutherford's gold foil experiment singlehandedly overturned the plum pudding model. The solar system model retained the existence of electrons and positive fragments, but the image of a diffuse cloud with embedded electrons morphed into the image of a dense nucleus with electrons in elliptical orbits. Bohr kept the nucleus but quantized angular momentum and energy and came up circular orbits.

The images of the Bohr and Rutherford models may not seem so different. A circle is just a special kind of ellipse, isn't it? In fact, the idea that nature operates with discrete rather than continuous energies was revolutionary. The ability of the Bohr model to explain so many observations about the hydrogen atom spectra gave it immediate credibility. The old picture of nature had to be discarded. The new picture was, in the words of Alice's Cheshire cat: "Curiouser and curiouser."

References

1. From the 1936 essay, "The Development of the Theory of Atomic Structure," by Lord Rutherford, in *Background to Modern Science*, New York: Macmillan, 1940.

CAMBRIDGE, COPENHAGEN, AND THE INTERNATIONAL NATURE OF SCIENCE

Many of the key experiments in the development of atomic models were done in the Cavendish Laboratory at Cambridge University in England. The Cavendish Laboratory was established in 1874. Its first director was James Clerk Maxwell (Chapter 11), who made key discoveries about electromagnetic radiation and its wave nature. At the turn of the 19th century, J. J. Thomson directed the Lab.

Thomson's ground-breaking experiments on the electron made Cambridge the place to be for physicists. Ernest Rutherford came from New Zealand to work in the Cavendish laboratory. He did important gas discharge tube experiments before taking a brief appointment in Canada, where he studied radioactivity, another hot topic of the time. Rutherford moved back to Britain, where he performed the gold-foil experiments with assistant Hans Geiger and undergraduate student Ernest Marsden at Manchester University. Ultimately, in 1919 Rutherford returned to Cambridge as head of the Cavendish Laboratory.

In 1911, Niels Bohr came to the Cavendish Laboratory to work with Thomson. But after meeting Rutherford at a party, Bohr moved to Manchester to study in the Rutherford laboratory. Bohr published his model of the atom in 1913. He returned to Copenhagen and his fame spread throughout the scientific world. Many scientists then came to Copenhagen to work at the institute Bohr established there. In 1944, Bohr fled to England because his Jewish heritage put him at risk during the Nazi invasions; he returned after the war was over.

International travel was surprisingly common among scientists, even before the days of commercial aviation. During the early 20th century England was seen as the dominant contributor to scientific advances and scientists flocked there for study. The United States replaced England as the leader during the second-half of the 20th century. However, declining enrollments and public interest in science and engineering in the U.S. in the 21st century may well mean that some new country will claim the role as the leader in the pursuit of scientific knowledge.

Chapter Framework

A. The Plum Pudding Model
  1. J. J. Thomson
B. The Solar System Model
  1. Rutherford
  2. Gold Foil Experiment
     a. Alpha particles
     b. Nucleus
  3. Elliptical orbits
C. Emission Spectra
  1. Discrete vs. Continuous
  2. Janne Rydberg
     a. Atomic hydrogen discrete emission formula
  3. Max Planck
     a. Hot object emissions
     b. Quantum energy
D. The Bohr Model
  1. Angular Momentum Quantized
  2. Discrete circular orbits (energy states)
  3. Discrete emissions explained

Comprehension

True/ False

1. _____ The electron has no mass.
2. _____ The red photons found in the emission spectrum of atomic hydrogen are less energetic than the purple photons.
3. _____ The rare, backward reflection of alpha particles convinced Rutherford that the atom consisted of a dense, positively-charged nucleus.
4. _____ In gas discharge tube experiments, positive fragments from different types of atoms are similar to one another.
5. _____ To explain the continuous spectrum, Planck proposed that light could only be absorbed or emitted in discrete amounts.
6. _____ The Molecular Model of Matter says nothing about the internal structure of an atom.
7. _____ Bohr failed to explain why an accelerated electron does not radiate energy.
8. _____ Rutherford fully expected alpha particles to bounce off of the gold foil.
9. _____ The nucleus of an atom occupies more than half of the atom's volume.
10. ___ The color of a hot object is related to its temperature.

Matching

a. Nucleus
b. Alpha particle
c. Plum Pudding model
d. Solar system model
e. Discrete spectra

1. _____ Dense, positively-charged center of the atom.
2. _____ Rutherford Model.
3. _____ Spectra in which the colors of light change abruptly and many colors are missing.
4. _____ Thomson Model.
5. _____ Positively charged particle emitted by some radioactive materials (a helium nucleus).

Fill in the Blank

1. The conservation of _____ (energy, mass, angular momentum) law explains why photon emission occurs when an electron drops from a high to a low energy state.
2. Thomson's and Millikan's experiments provided strong evidence for the atom's _____ (nuclear, electrical) nature.
3. Rutherford's orbits were _____ (elliptical, circular); Bohr's orbits were _____ (elliptical, circular).
4. An electron with a large value of n (quantum number) in the Bohr model is _____ (close to, far away from) the nucleus and has _____ (not much, lots of) energy.
5. That nature functions using discrete rather than continuous energy is an assumption of the _____ (Thomson, Rutherford, Bohr) model.

Analysis

1. The oil drop experiment (Millikan)
   a) measured the charge of an electron.
   b) measured the charge of a neutron.
   c) measured the charge of a nucleus.
   d) measured the mass of an electron.
   e) proved the quantum model of the atom.

2. Experiments on beams of charged particles derived from neutral gases (Thomson's gas discharge tube experiments) provide direct experimental evidence for the
   a) Exclusion Principle.
   b) Nuclear Model of atoms.
   c) Bohr model of atoms.
   d) idea that all atoms are made of charged particles.
   e) idea that electrons in atoms behave as waves.

3. In the Thomson (plum pudding) model of the atom, an atom is described as
   a) a neutral "pudding" with small lumps of positive and negative charge distributed throughout.
   b) a positive "pudding" with small lumps of negative charge distributed throughout.
   c) a negative "pudding" with small lumps of positive charge distributed throughout.
   d) a negative "pudding" with one large lump of positive charge in the middle.
   e) a neutral "pudding" with lumps of negative charge around the outside and lumps of positive charge in the middle.

4. In what model do electrons orbit the nucleus so that any orbit allowed by Newtonian physics can be occupied by an electron? (i.e., there are no restrictions on allowed electron energies.)
   a) quantum model

b) Thomson or "plum pudding" model

c) Rutherford or "solar system" model

d) Bohr or "modified solar system" model

e) the molecular model

5. White light (containing all visible colors) passes through a gas that absorbs some of the light. The spectrum of light that passes through the gas is then analyzed. That spectrum could best be described as

a) continuous.

b) a discrete spectrum of colored lines.

c) a mostly continuous spectrum that is missing some colors.

d) a discrete spectrum of colored lines that corresponds to the absorbed light.

e) a completely black spectrum.

6. When gases like hydrogen, neon, or nitrogen are excited by passing an electrical discharge through them, a few lines of colored light are seen when the light is separated into its colors. The light observed in such a spectrum is emitted when an electron in an atom

a) "jumps" from one energy level up to a higher energy level.

b) "jumps" from one energy level down to a lower energy level.

c) is completely removed from the atom.

d) is converted to the pure energy of a photon.

e) is absorbed by the nucleus.

7. Which of the following is TRUE?

a) The absorption and emission spectra from a given type of gas occur at the same "colors."

b) The lines of absorption and emission spectra of a given gas occur at different "colors."

c) Absorption spectra result from electrons moving from higher energy levels to lower energy levels in an atom.

d) Emission spectra result from electrons moving from lower energy levels to higher energy levels in an atom.

e) Only emission spectra may be used to identify unknown atoms present in gases. Absorption spectra cannot be used for this purpose.

Synthesis

1. What four facts did "atom-blasting experiments," such as the gas discharge tube, establish about the atom?

2. Describe and explain Rutherford's gold foil experiment.

3. Outline the main elements of Rutherford's solar system model.

4. List and explain the weaknesses in Rutherford's model of the atom.

5. What role did Rydberg's formula play in the development of Bohr's model?

6. Outline the main element of Bohr's model.

7. List and explain the weaknesses of the Bohr model.

8. Use a qualitative (no numbers needed) time line to map out the sequence of events (experiments) and models that led to the Bohr model.

9. Use the laws of force and motion to explain Rutherford's hypothesis (alpha particles would travel in either straight lines or experience small deflections on passing through the gold foil) based on the Plum Pudding Model. Use these same laws to explain why the results of the gold foil experiments ruled out this hypothesis and required the existence of a dense, small, positively-charged nucleus. (It is the logic of Rutherford's arguments that we are most interested in. You need not give equations.)

10. How can a continuous spectrum be made up from discrete amounts of energy? What role does the size of Planck's constant h play in your answer?

11. What is the relationship between the frequencies present in an emission spectrum and those missing in an absorption spectrum? What law(s) require that there be this type of correspondence?

12. Neither Rutherford nor Bohr's model could explain why electrons didn't radiate energy as they accelerated around the nucleus, so why is Bohr's model considered an improvement?

DUALITY OF MATTER

Chapter 11 introduced the theory that light has both wave and particle properties. Science considers phenomenon that come in countable bundles as "particle-like." Back in 1900, Max Planck's theory of radiation from hot bodies relied on the idea that light consists of small bundles of energy. When detected, light from a very dim beam strikes a small point on the detector in bundles of energy called **photons.** When Einstein presented his theory of the Photoelectric Effect in 1905, he relied on photons to explain how high-frequency light knocked electrons off the surface of a metal when low-frequency light would not.

Other experiments trying to answer the question of the nature of light, such as Young's Two-Slit Experiment, demonstrated that light exhibited properties of waves. In Young's experiment, a beam of light sent through two narrow, closely spaced slits resulted in interference patterns appearing on a screen placed behind the slits. When the light passed through a single narrow slit, it spread out in a diffraction pattern. Diffraction and interference are wave properties, not particle properties.

The apparent inconsistency between experimental results showing the wave and particle nature of light created a dilemma. This dilemma was resolved by suggesting that light has both wave and particle properties depending on the context.

Light's particle properties become evident when being measured. Measurements that detect light at the smallest possible energy scales show particle effects. Light's wave nature is evident in how light travels. As light travels it diffracts and interferes, showing the properties of waves.

In his 1924 Ph.D. thesis, Louis de Broglie proposed that matter has the same wave-particle duality as light. This dual wave/particle nature is usually only evident when things are much smaller than what we can see with our naked eyes. When this matter is detected, it manifests particle properties. However, it shows wave properties in how it moves.

Matter's particle nature becomes fairly evident from everyday experience with objects all around us. Imagining electrons, protons, or neutrons that come in countable units or bundles is not difficult. Likewise, once we understand the basic principles of matter, assigning particle properties like mass or charge to these objects becomes relatively simple.

The wave nature of matter is more complicated and likely not part of a normal person's everyday experiences. The wavelength of matter, as given by de Broglie, is Planck's con-

Actually, we need not speak of particles at all. For many experiments it is more convenient to speak of matter waves . . . The two pictures are of course mutually exclusive, because a certain thing cannot at the same time be a particle . . . and a wave . . . but the two complement each other. By playing with both pictures, by going from the one picture to the other and back again, we finally get the right impression of the strange kind of reality behind our quantum experiments."

~ Werner Heisenberg

stant divided by its momentum. In other words, if w is the wavelength, h is Planck's constant and p is the momentum (the mass times the speed):

$$w = \frac{h}{p}$$

Planck's constant h is a very small number if we use the common units of kilograms, meters and seconds. Dividing this small number by the momentum of people-sized things, we get an extremely short wavelength. For instance, the wavelength of a woman walking down the street would be about 10^{-35} meters (an unimaginably small number, considerably smaller than the smallest entity that could exist). Even an object of incredibly small macroscopic momentum, like a droplet of water moving one centimeter per year, would have a wavelength of one thousandth the diameter of an atomic nucleus! It's no wonder that we don't notice the wave nature of matter in our day-to-day experience.

The thrill and the challenge of studying extremely small objects comes from learning something different from what we would intuitively expect, based on our experience with the macroscopic world. As Richard Feynman (who received a Nobel Prize for his work in this area)

Louis de Broglie

de Broglie proposed that matter, like light, exhibited a wave-particle duality.

said, "Because atomic behavior is so unlike ordinary experience, it is very difficult to get used to, and it appears peculiar and mysterious to everyone—both to the novice and to the experienced physicist. Even the experts do not understand it the way they would like to, and it is perfectly reasonable that they should not, because all of direct, human experience and of human intuition applies to large objects."[1]

On the other hand, the wave properties of matter do become noticeable for things the size of atoms. For instance, the wavelength of an electron in a hydrogen atom is about 10^{-10} meters, the same size as the atom. Thus, we would expect the wave nature of matter to be important in describing the motion of electrons in atoms.

If things are small enough and move slowly enough, their wavelengths can even have macroscopic dimensions. For example, a very slow neutron moving about 1/2 millimeter per second would have a wavelength of about one millimeter. These neutrons diffract while moving through slits that are large enough to be seen with the naked eye. Recently, macroscopic collections of atoms have been created with a temperature at billionths of a degree above absolute zero. These collections of extremely cold atoms exhibit the strange kind of wave behavior seen in individual atoms.

Because of their dual wave and particle behavior, Newton's equations are not sufficient to describe the behavior of very small particles and dim light. They are described instead by a branch of physics and chemistry called **quantum mechanics**. Quantum mechanics was developed independently by Werner Heisenberg and Erwin Schrödinger in 1925 and 1926. Their very different formulations have since been shown to be equivalent.

15–1 Experiments

The simplest experiment that conceptually illustrates the wave and particle aspects of matter is Young's Two-Slit Experiment, with the light replaced by a beam of electrons. It is actually much more difficult to use electrons in the double-slit experiment than light. Because the charged electrons repel each other, the electrons

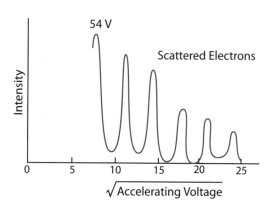

Figure 15.1
Results from the Davisson–Germer experiment.[2]

need to be moving fairly fast to stay in the beam. And because fast electrons have large momenta, they have short wavelengths (about the size of the space between individual atoms in a solid). To see interference effects, the slit's spacing needs to be close to the electron's wavelength.

In order to get slit spacing equal to the spacing of atoms in a solid, the first experimental verification of de Broglie's hypothesis was made by passing electrons through crystals. A crystal is a solid with a regular arrangement of atoms which are equally spaced. These regularly spaced atoms were analogous to the slits in Young's light experiments. In 1927, Clinton Davisson and Lester Germer performed the first of these experiments. They observed interference patterns from electron beams reflecting from a nickel crystal. They received a Nobel Prize in 1937 for their work. Figure 15.1 shows the interference maxima and minima they saw in their experiment.

To appreciate the results of these two-slit experiments, imagine a beam of macroscopic particles and a macroscopic wave passing through two slits. For the particle beam, imagine bullets being shot from a rickety machine gun at two narrow slits cut in a wall (*Figure 15.2*).[3]

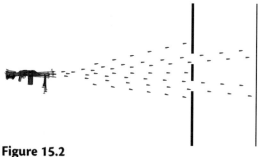

Figure 15.2
What kind of results would you expect if you fired a machine gun at a wall with two slits?

♦ **Photon**
A particle of light. It possesses energy, frequency, and wavelength but neither mass nor charge.

♦ **Quantum Mechanics**
The branch of physics used to describe the wave properties of light and matter.

Erwin Schrödinger
Schrödinger won the Nobel Prize in 1933 for his wave equation that described the behavior of electrons in an atom.

If one slit is covered, the pattern of holes in a target placed behind the slits might look like *Figure 15.3a*.

The pattern from uncovering the other slit would be similar, but shifted a little to the side, as in *Figure 15.3b*.

When both slits in the wall are open, one would see a pattern consisting of the pattern for each hole overlapping each other. Remember these are what the patterns would look like if particles pass through the slits (*Figure 15.3c*).

Now let's consider what patterns would form if waves instead of particles passed through the slits. To help you visualize waves passing through the slits, consider what one sees when a water wave passes through slits. When the wave passes through a single slit, it spreads out in a fan-like pattern as shown in *Figure 15.5*.

With both slits open, the waves hit the edge of the tank at lower and higher elevations than normally expected (*Figure 15.6*). The higher and lower elevations show regions of constructive and of destructive interference, respectively. Remember from Chapter 10 that constructive interference occurs when two waves enhance

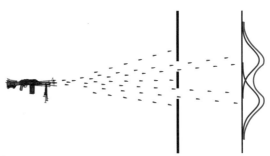

Figure 15.4
The blue curves on the screen at the right illustrate the density of bullet holes seen from the individual holes in the wall. The red curve is the density of bullet holes created by combining the two blue patterns.

one another and destructive interference occurs when two waves cancel one another out.

When electrons pass through the slits, they exhibit an interference pattern with places of constructive and of destructive behavior as seen with water waves. Apparently, like light, electrons (and similarly small objects) have a wave nature that permits them to interfere and diffract just as macroscopic waves do.

"But wait!" the conscientious student might (and should) say at this point. "Electrons are also similar to bullets. I can count them and they have individual masses and charges. What will I see if the electrons pass through the slits one at a time?"

As one might expect, the electrons would be detected as individual spots on the screen. This shows the particle behavior one sees when electrons are detected. However, when many

a.

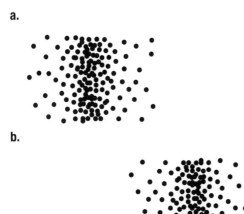

b.

c.

Figure 15.3
The resulting pattern of bullet distribution one would expect from the machine gun in *Figure 15.2* with:
a) one slit covered,
b) the other slit covered,
c) neither slit covered (patterns combined).

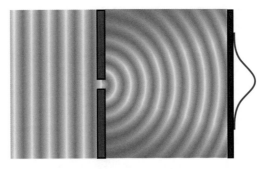

Figure 15.5
A water wave passing through a single slit diffracts and spreads out in a fan shape.

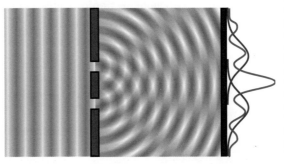

Figure 15.6
When a water wave passes through two slits, the diffraction from each slit combine to form an interference pattern. The blue curves are the height of the water waves at the edge of the tank from the waves passing through the individual holes. The red curve is the combined height of the waves hitting the edge of the tank. Note that the interference peaks seen in this curve are very different from the ones in *Figure 15.4*.

electrons accumulate on the screen, they do so in a way that forms an interference pattern as one would expect from the wave nature of the electrons (*Figure 15.7*).

To summarize these experiments, electrons have the same wave-particle nature as light. Electrons travel in a way that has a wave nature, exhibiting diffraction and interference effects just like those seen in macroscopic waves, like water waves. However, when detected, electrons are detected as particles with definite positions, countable numbers, and properties like a specific mass, energy, and charge.

Later experiments duplicated the two-slit geometry using neutrons instead of electrons. The results using the neutrons were similar to the experiments using electrons, further confirming the nature of matter.

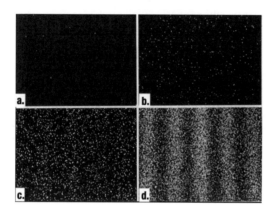

probability of striking the screen where the wave has constructive interference. A beam with many electrons will result in a lot of electrons accumulating in regions of constructive interference.

Electrons have a low probability of striking the screen where the wave has destructive interference. A beam of many electrons will accumulate few electrons on the screen in regions of destructive interference.

These probability waves are similar to **probability curves** encountered in everyday life. For instance, consider a bell-shaped curve that might represent the distribution of grades on a test (*Figure 15.8*).

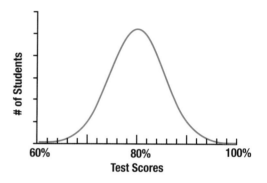

Figure 15.8
Bell-shaped curve that might represent a grade distribution on a test.

In this sample curve, it is apparent that the most likely grade would be 80%, as more students received this grade than any other. There is little chance that a student would have been fortunate enough to get a grade of 100%, or unfortunate enough to get a grade as low as 60%.

If a professor predicted the grade of a student picked at random from the class, there could be no certainty about that particular student's grade, but the instructor would know some probabilities based on the curve. The student likely scored close to 80%, and probably did not score above 95% or below 65%.

Similarly, when an electron passes through a double slit, the researcher cannot predict exactly where it will strike the screen. However, the researcher does know the probability of where it will and will not strike. Based on the electron's different probabilities, the experimenter *can* predict what pattern will be produced when many electrons strike the screen. The curve representing the probabilities of where an electron will strike a screen is also called a probability curve.

• Probability Curve
A curve giving the probability of where an object might be detected. The particle is likely to be found where the curve is high and unlikely to be found where the curve is low.

Figure 15.7
Result of a double-slit electron experiment performed at Hitachi. Electrons, after passing through two slits, strike a screen, appearing as little white dots. The accumulation of many dots eventually forms an interference pattern.

15–2 PROBABILITY WAVES

An interesting question yet to be addressed concerns the nature of the wave associated with matter. It certainly does not seem reasonable to classify it as a disturbance moving through a medium as we did in Chapter 10, because even a single electron seems to exhibit this wave behavior. In fact, the two-slit experiment discussed in the previous section provides a clue about what kind of wave this must be. The build-up of interference patterns from single electrons implies that these waves tell us how likely it is that the electrons will hit various locations on the screen. We refer to such waves as **probability waves**.

This wave gives the probability of where an individual electron will strike the screen after passing through the slits. Electrons have a high

• Probability Wave
A probability curve that moves in time. At a given moment in time, the places where the wave is high are where the object associated with the wave is most likely to be found.

Moving electrons have moving probability curves associated with them, indicating the probability of where to find them at various moments in time. *Figure 15.9* shows what the probability wave of an electron might look like as it progresses through time.

The probabilistic nature of these waves explains why the electron's wave nature changes to a particle nature when a measurement is made of its position. Before making a measurement, the electron has the probability of being in a number of places. After the measurement, it becomes known exactly where the electron is, changing the probabilities and hence the probability curve. This collapse of the curve to a single line is illustrated in *Figure 15.10*.

15–3 HEISENBERG UNCERTAINTY PRINCIPLE

The position of an object is not the only variable that has probability curves and probability waves associated with it. Probability waves can also describe an object's momentum, energy, and other properties.

The probability wave associated with an object's momentum is interesting because it relates to the probability wave associated with its position.

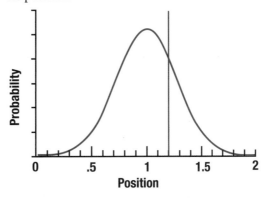

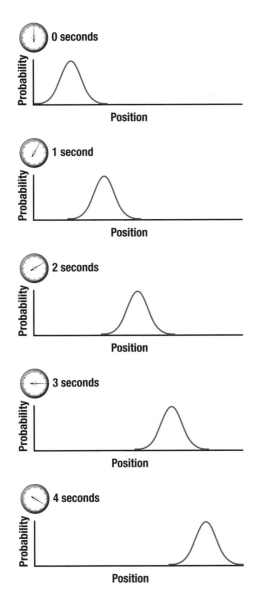

Figure 15.10

Probability curves for an electron just before (red) and just after (blue) it is detected at position 1.2. Before being detected the electron has a range of positions between 0 and 2 where it could be detected. After it has been detected, we know exactly where it is (at position 1.2).

ELECTRON MICROSCOPE

High-energy electrons have wavelengths that are much shorter than those of visible light. The shorter wavelength is employed in the design of electron microscopes that create images of objects much smaller than objects visible under conventional light microscopes. Images of objects are limited in their resolution by diffraction of light or of electrons at the object's edges. Diffraction of light by objects smaller than the wavelength of light smears the image so that the object cannot be resolved. High energy electrons have a short enough wavelength that electron microscope images are limited by the quality of the electron optics rather than the diffraction of the electrons. *Figure 15.11* is an image from an electron microscope that shows a small (7.5×10^{-9} meters wide) Iron-Platinum particle (dark area) on a carbon support film (light area). The light lines running diagonal across the dark section are planes of atoms that are 2.2×10^{-10} meters apart, a distance typical of atomic spacings in solids. This image allows the user of an electron microscope to examine an object that is thousands of times smaller than could be seen through the highest-powered light microscope.

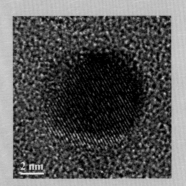

Figure 15.9

For a moving electron, the probability of its location changes with time. After 4 seconds, this electron is most likely to be found in a very different location from its starting point.

The relationship between position probability waves and momentum probability waves can be understood by considering de Broglie's hypothesis that objects have a wavelength associated with them. When we assign a definite momentum to a wave, de Broglie's relationship gives it a definite wavelength. This means it has an oscillating pattern of repeating peaks that extends forever (*Figure 15.12*).

Figure 15.12

A section of a position probability wave with a definite wavelength. This pattern repeats itself indefinitely to the left and to the right of this section.

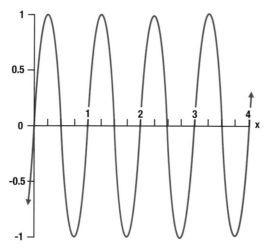

Because this wave extends forever, there is a non-zero probability of finding the electron anywhere. It has no definite position. A wave can be created with a more definite position (similar to the Bell Curve in Figure 15.10, for instance) by adding together probability waves with a variety of wavelengths. In fact, a wave could be created where the electron was at a single point by combining waves of every possible wavelength. However, locating the particle at a definite position has made its momentum totally uncertain, because it could have a momentum associated with *any* of the wavelengths that were combined to locate the electron.

For example, consider adding up a set of oscillating waves like those in Figure 15.12 to make a probability curve like the bell-shaped curve in Figure 15.10. *Figure 15.13* is an example of such a sum with a width of about 2.

The collection of wavelengths that had to be used to create this bell curve gives rise to the momentum probability curve shown in *Figure 15.14*.

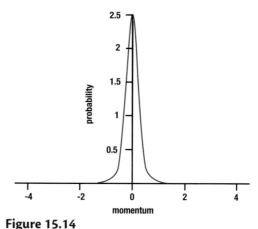

Figure 15.14

Bell-shaped momentum probability curve reflecting the range of wavelengths needed to build the bell-shaped position probability curve shown in *Figure 15.13*.

Notice that it also has a bell shape, arising from a range of different momenta. It has a width of about 1/2.

If one wants to decrease the width of the position probability curve, it can be done by adding oscillating waves with a wider range of wavelengths. For example, *Figure 15.15* is a position probability curve with a width of 1/2, one quarter the width of the curve in Figure 15.13.

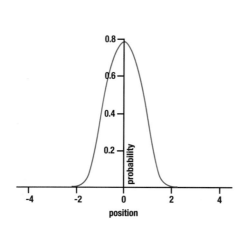

Figure 15.13

Bell-shaped wave packet obtained by adding together oscillating waves with a range of wavelengths.

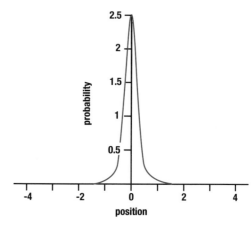

Figure 15.15

Position probability curve with a width of about 1/2.

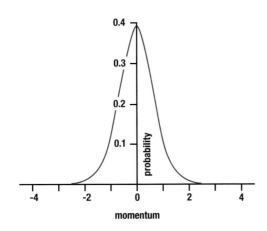

Figure 15.16

Momentum probability curve corresponding to the position probability curve in *Figure 15.15*.

The larger range of wavelengths that had to be added together to get this curve results in the wider momentum probability curve shown in *Figure 15.16*.

This momentum curve has a width of 2. Evidently, making the position curve narrower results in the momentum curve getting broader by the same factor.

Werner Heisenberg, one of the fathers of quantum mechanics, expressed this trade-off between knowing an object's position and its momentum in the **Heisenberg Uncertainty Principle**. It states that the uncertainty in an object's position (Δx) and the uncertainty in its momentum (Δp) are related by the formula

$$\Delta x \times \Delta p \geq h$$

where h is Planck's constant. (The product of the uncertainty in an object's position and the uncertainty in an object's momentum is greater than or equal to Planck's constant.) In other words, narrowing down an object's position makes its momentum less certain. Narrowing down an object's momentum (or speed) makes its position less certain.

Note that the Heisenberg Uncertainty Principle is not a matter of how carefully or accurately measurements can be made. Rather, it is a fundamental limit on how well two complementary quantities can be determined. An analogous situation would be a student going to a party the night before an exam. The more time the student spends at the party, the less time the student will have to spend studying. The more the student studies, the less time the student has to party. The student can choose to get a good grade on the exam or have fun at the party, but not 100% of both. Likewise, an experimenter can know an object's position with high accuracy or how fast it is going with precision, but not both.

A good example of the Heisenberg Uncertainty Principle is the diffraction of slow neutrons passing through a slit. If the slit is wide, the beam does not diffract very much. In other words, the momentum of the neutrons in the direction perpendicular to the slit is well known, since it is close to zero. Thus, we have a case where there is a lot of uncertainty in the position (the neutron could come through the wide slit anywhere) and little uncertainty in the momentum. If the slit is narrowed, there is less uncertainty in the position of the neutrons. They have to be located somewhere in the narrow slit. However, the neutron beam diffracts in this case, giving rise to a range of different momenta perpendicular to the direction of the slit. In this case, the position is fairly certain, but the momentum is more uncertain. There is always a trade-off between how well the position is known (how narrow the slit is) and how well the momentum is known (how much diffraction there is). This effect is illustrated in *Figure 15.17*.

15-4 PHILOSOPHICAL IMPLICATIONS

A fundamental difference exists between the descriptions of the motion of objects using Newton's Laws of Motion and Quantum Mechanics. Newton's Laws provided precise descriptions about how objects move. Using Newton's Laws one could, at least in principle, know the precise values of an object's position and

Werner Heisenberg

Heisenberg won the Nobel Prize in 1932 for the creation of quantum mechanics, which includes his Uncertainty Principle concerning a particle's momentum and position.

◆ **Heisenberg Uncertainty Principle**

The product of the uncertainty in an object's position and the uncertainty in its momentum must be greater than or equal to Planck's Constant.

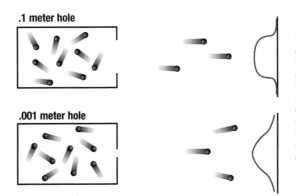

Figure 15.17

A beam of slow neutrons passing through a wide slit and a narrow slit. In the top figure, the position of the neutrons is uncertain because of the width of the slit. In the bottom figure, the momentum perpendicular to the slit is uncertain because the beam is spread out by diffraction.

momentum. Knowing these quantities and the object's interactions with other objects, one could predict exactly where it would be and how fast it would be moving for all times in the future. An extrapolation backward in time could also be made to determine where it had been and how fast it had been going in the past.

Quantum Mechanics, on the other hand, describes the location and motion of objects in terms of probability waves. One can predict the statistical results of a number of repeated experiments, but not the precise results from a single experiment. The Heisenberg Uncertainty Principle prohibits precise determination of an object's history or future from measurements made in the present.

On the microscopic level, the difference between Newtonian Mechanics and Quantum Mechanics has important philosophical implications. In Newton's deterministic universe, the physical world is akin to a giant machine that continues on its predetermined course once set in motion. For those who take the extreme position that the physical Universe is a complete description of reality, this means that our future is cast in stone, totally determined by events which were set in motion long ago.

Quantum mechanics, on the other hand, postulates a universe where actions do not lead to pre-determined effects. The probabilities are well determined, but the results of individual encounters are not.

Note, however, that these two views are not as divergent as they might initially seem, at least on the macroscopic level. Probabilities in quantum mechanics are well known, even though the results of individual events are not. Knowing these probabilities means that one can accurately predict the results of a large number of events. In other words, a pilot may not know precisely what each component of every atom in an airplane is doing, but she can predict with confidence how the airplane will respond to the various controls.

Another interesting philosophical question related to quantum mechanics is the nature of the probabilities associated with its statistical predictions. Are the probabilities that are used to describe the outcomes of events a result of the observer's ignorance of the inner workings of the objects involved or

are their behaviors intrinsically random? In other words, are the outcomes of these events unknown or unknowable?

Two Nobel Prize-winning physicists took opposite sides in this debate at the beginning of the 20th century. Albert Einstein took the view that quantum mechanics required probabilities in its description of experiments because the theory was incomplete. He maintained that the results of experiments appeared to be random only because of scientists' lack of complete knowledge of all of the factors influencing the results. In other words, the reason scientists don't know exactly where the electron will hit the screen is because there isn't enough information available.

Neils Bohr, on the other hand, argued that where an individual electron would hit the screen was not determined until the moment that the electron actually struck the screen. He claimed that it was impossible to predict what

Figure 15.18
Albert Einstein (left) and Neils Bohr at a conference in Brussels in 1930. Einstein and Bohr disagreed on whether quantum probabilities were intrinsically random. (Photo by Paul Ehrenfest.)

would happen in the quantum mechanical experiment, even if the experimenter had all possible available information about the system.

For many years, it seemed as if this philosophical argument would remain unresolved by science. It wasn't until many years after Einstein's death in 1955 that this issue was finally resolved.

The first theoretical work to help resolve this dilemma was done by David Bohm and John Bell. They devised an experimental arrangement where the results would be statistically different for Einstein's and Bohr's interpretations of quantum mechanics. Being theoreticians, they didn't actually conduct this difficult experiment.

An experiment using Bohm and Bell's arrangement was finally conducted with conclusive evidence by Alain Aspect, Jean Dalibard, and Gérard Roger in 1982. Aspect's results were inconsistent with Einstein's hidden variables interpretation and consistent with Bohr's idea of things being intrinsically random.

15-5 SUMMARY

Matter, as well as light, has both wave and particle properties. The wave properties (like diffraction and interference) are evident when we see how the object travels. The particle properties are evident when we actually detect the particle.

The waves associated with matter are probability waves. They give the probability of where the object is likely to be found. The particle properties are evident when the objects are detected as individual "lumps." These lumps can be counted and identified with properties like mass and charge.

The wave properties for macroscopic objects are not evident because their wavelengths are so small. Seeing things like diffraction or interference would require experiments whose size is considerably smaller than anything that exists in nature.

An object's position and momentum (and consequently, its speed) are complementary quantities that can't be independently determined to arbitrary accuracy. The Heisenberg Uncertainty Principle states that the product of the uncertainty in these two quantities must always be greater than or equal to Planck's Constant.

Quantum mechanics changed our fundamental model of the interactions between the smallest particles in nature. It requires us to consider these interactions in terms of probabilities rather than with the deterministic viewpoint possible using Newton's Laws.

References

1. Richard P. Feynman, Robert B. Leighton, Matthew Sands, "The Feynman Lectures on Physics, Quantum Mechanics," Vol. III, Addison-Wesley (Reading, Massachusetts), p. 7.

2. Davisson, C. J., "Are Electrons Waves?," Franklin Institute Journal 205, 597 (1928).

3. Richard P. Feynman, Robert B. Leighton, Matthew Sands, "The Feynman Lectures on Physics, Quantum Mechanics," Vol. III, Addison-Wesley (Reading, Massachusetts), p. 11.

Chapter Framework

A. The Duality of Matter
1. Wave–Particle Duality
2. Wavelength of Matter

B. Experiments
1. Davisson-Germer Two-Slit Experiment
2. Building Interference Pattern One Electron at a Time.

C. Probability Waves

D. Heisenberg Uncertainty Principle
1. Relationship between Position and Momentum
2. $\Delta x \times \Delta p \geq h$

E. Philosophical Implications
1. Determinism vs. Indeterminism
2. Nature of Probability
   a. *Einstein: unknown*
   b. *Bohr: unknowable*

Comprehension

True/ False

1. _____ The more you know about position, the more you know about momentum.

2. _____ An object's momentum is the only property associated with probability waves.

3. _____ Several thousand electrons passing through a single slit would create an interference pattern on a screen behind the slit.

4. _____ If moving slowly enough, small objects can have wavelengths that reach macroscopic dimensions.

5. _____ After passing many electrons through two slits, an interference pattern on the screen looks like the probability curve in Figure 15.10.

6. _____ Performing the double-slit experiment with light is more difficult than performing it with electrons.

a. Constructive interference
b. Probability curve
c. Destructive interference
d. Quantum Mechanics
e. Heisenberg Uncertainty Principle
f. Probability wave
g. Newtonian Mechanics

Matching

1. _____ The wave indicates where the particle will likely strike rather than where the particle is.

2. _____ The more you know about position the less you know about momentum, and the more you know about momentum the less you know about position.

3. _____ Phenomenon that creates areas of high probability where the electron will strike the screen.

4. _____ Curve representing the probabilities of where an electron will strike a screen.

5. _____ Phenomenon that creates areas of low probability where the electron is unlikely to strike the screen.

6. _____ Postulates a Universe where actions do not lead to pre-determined effects.

7. _____ The physical world continues on a predetermined course once set in motion.

Fill in the Blank

1. Louis de Broglie proposed that matter has the same _____ duality as light.

2. _____ and _____ were the first to verify de Broglie's hypothesis about the wave nature of matter.

3. In addition to light and electrons, _____ have also been used in the double-slit experiment.

4. To see interference fringes (patterns), the slit's spacing needs to be close in size to the electron's _____.

5. Electrons have a low probability of striking the screen where the wave has _____ interference.

Analysis

1. The wavelength of a particle moving with a certain speed is given by
   a) particle speed divided by Planck's constant (v/h).
   b) Planck's constant divided by momentum (h/p).
   c) Planck's constant divided by 2 ($h/2$).
   d) frequency divided by speed of light (f/c).
   e) mass times speed of light squared (mc^2).

2. Which of the following could NOT be caused to form a diffraction pattern?
   a) visible light
   b) x-rays
   c) ultraviolet light
   d) electrons
   e) none of these; all could form diffraction patterns

3. For which phenomenon would the Heisenberg Uncertainty Principle be a significant consideration in describing motion?
   a) Electrons in atoms.
   b) Planets in orbit around the sun.
   c) Space shuttle in orbit around the earth.
   d) Billiard balls on a pool table.
   e) Brownian motion of dust particles.

4. The Heisenberg Uncertainty Principle seems to conflict with the concept of
   a) operationalism
   b) the quantum theory
   c) Newtonian determinism
   d) duality
   e) mass

5. Electrons passing one at a time through a two-slit apparatus strike a screen. The resulting pattern on

the screen after many electrons have struck the screen is

a) a single band of points about as narrow as one slit.

b) a single broad band of points, i.e., broader than the combined width of the slits.

c) a completely random pattern of points.

d) two narrow bands of points about the width of each slit.

e) a pattern of bands where electrons hit separated by areas where no electrons hit.

Synthesis

1. Explain how the double-slit experiment can show both the particle and wave nature of matter.

2. Why can electron microscopes create images of objects much smaller than visible-light microscopes can?

3. How is quantum mechanics deterministic?

4. When is matter considered a particle? When is matter considered a wave?

5. Discuss the differences between Newtonian Mechanics and Quantum Mechanics.

6. Why does the separation of the slits need to be approximately equal to the wavelength of an electron for an interference pattern to appear?

7. An experiment passing neutrons through two slits smaller than their wavelength is devised. Before passing through the slits, the experiment locates the neutron's position. Several thousand neutrons pass through the two slits. What type of pattern is seen on the screen behind the two slits?

8. Neutrons are sent through a single slit whose width can vary. Behind the slit is a screen to detect the neutrons. Answer the following questions.

   a. The slit's width is very narrow. Almost narrow enough to locate the neutrons as they pass through the slit. What do you know about position and momentum? What type of pattern will form on the screen?

   b. The slits width is dramatically increased. What do you know about position and momentum? What type of pattern will form on the screen?

   c. What principle helps explain these two different results?

9. Why is the Heisenberg Uncertainty Principle only relevant to microscopic objects but unimportant when dealing with objects that we encounter on a daily basis? (Your answer should include reasoning that uses the equation that determines wavelength.)

10. The equation for wavelength is $w = h/p$ (wavelength=Planck's constant/momentum). If a large object and an electron were traveling the same speed, why would the electron have a larger wavelength?

THE QUANTUM MODEL OF THE ATOM

The quantum theory was born in 1900, with the twentieth century, and future centuries will list it among our own's most remarkable achievements. Designed to account for the puzzling behavior of matter at the submicroscopic scale of individual atoms, the theory has enjoyed phenomenal success. It has accounted in a quantitative way for atomic phenomena with numerical precision never before achieved in any field of science.

~ N. David Mermin

Now that Chapter 15 has introduced the dual wave-particle nature of matter, we are prepared to discuss the modern view of the atom. The Bohr model of the atom, as described in Chapter 14, did not answer two very important questions that needed to be resolved. Why did electrons not radiate when in Bohr's special orbits? And why did electrons prefer to be in Bohr orbits?

16–1 ORBITALS

The key to answering the problems with the Bohr model of the atom lies in electrons' wave character. These waves can form standing waves around an atomic nucleus, just like the standing waves we learned about in Chapter 10. Recall that standing waves are waves whose disturbances remain stationary in space. The regions of destructive and constructive interference (nodes and anti-nodes) do not move. In one dimension, these standing waves are created by adding waves together that are traveling in opposite directions and have equal amplitudes. Electron standing waves in atoms are called **orbitals**.

When electrons form standing waves around a nucleus, the amplitude of the orbitals at a given location in space indicates the probability of finding an electron at that location. The probability of locating them doesn't change in time. In other words, the electrons actually remain stationary. They do not accelerate like they would in a Bohr orbit and as a result they don't "radiate" energy. The problem with Bohr's accelerated energy is solved.

Orbital Shapes

Only certain waves can fit within the prescribed geometry when standing waves are created. This can be illustrated simply by considering a mechanical wave in a string that is clamped at both ends. The wave can't move at the clamped ends, making it so only standing waves of certain wavelengths can be created in the string. The wave with the longest wavelength looks like the one shown in *Figure 16.1a*. The next longest wavelength for a standing wave in a string looks like *Figure 16.1b*

The longest wavelength after that has three bumps, followed by waves with an increasing number of bumps.

As we consider waves in two dimensions, they take on shapes that are extensions of their one dimensional counterparts. For example, the

LEARNING OBJECTIVES

When you finish this chapter you should be able to

- Identify the main elements of the quantum model of the atom.
- Explain how the quantum model of the atom resolves the problems with the Bohr model of the atom.
- Explain the difference between an orbit and an orbital.
- Recognize the shapes of the lowest-energy orbitals.
- Know how many orbitals each shape has.
- Know how orbitals are grouped in shells and which orbitals can be in each shell.
- Know the relative energies of each shell and of the orbitals within each shell.
- State the Exclusion Principle and apply it to the filling of atomic orbitals.

wave on a circular drumhead with the lowest frequency looks like *Figure 16.2*.

With some imagination, you can picture this as Figure 16.1a rotated horizontally about its center point—a one-dimensional wave extended to a circular domain.

The next lowest frequency wave looks like *Figure 16.3*. You can probably see how this resembles Figure 16.1b rotated in a circle around its highest point.

Finally, the next mode looks like *Figure 16.4*. Notice that a cross section of its middle from left to right also resembles Figure 16.1b.

Extending these standing waves to three dimensions gives another set of shapes. In three dimensions, it is hard to represent what the "sur-

Figure 16.2
Lowest frequency wave on a two-dimensional drumhead.

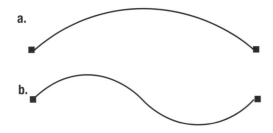

Figure 16.1
A stationary string can only have standing waves of certain lengths.
a) Longest possible wavelength for a standing wave in a stationary string.
b) Next longest wavelength for a standing wave.

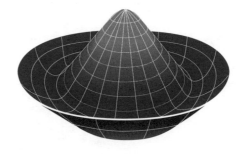

Figure 16.3
Second lowest frequency in a circular drumhead.

- ◆ **Orbital**

A standing wave giving the probability of finding an electron in various locations around the nucleus of an atom.

Figure 16.4

Third lowest frequency in a circular drumhead.

- ◆ **Spectroscopy**

The study of the brightness and wavelengths of the different frequencies of light emitted by excited atoms and ions.

face" of such a wave would be on paper. Instead, we will show the volume in which 90% of the wave amplitude is contained.

These three-dimensional waves are the kind of standing waves that are formed by electrons around atomic nuclei. The orbital shapes are classified by letters: "s," "p," "d," "f," and so on. Why was this sequence of letters chosen rather than "a," "b," "c" and so on, which would be a seemingly more natural sequence? This type of classification goes back to the early days of atomic **spectroscopy**. When scientists separated the light from excited atoms and ions into its various wavelengths, they saw sets of lines of various frequencies (and hence colors). Some of the lines were very sharp, others were quite bright and others were more diffuse. Scientists called orbitals associated with sharp lines "s" orbitals, those associated with bright ("principle") lines "p" orbitals, and those associated with diffuse lines "d" orbitals.

The "s" orbitals are spherical in shape and are the only orbital in which the electron has a non-zero probability of being at the nucleus. We will use this fact when we later consider the nuclear decay process called electron capture. There is only one kind of "s" orbital (*Figure 16.5*).

To understand this shape in terms of probability, the spherical shape means that finding an electron in the "s" orbital is equally likely in any direction. In a hydrogen atom, the lowest energy "s" orbital has a diameter of about 10^{-10} meters. This means that a hydrogen electron is likely to be found within a sphere of diameter 10^{-10} meters. The Rutherford Model predicted the atom's diameter to be about this same size.

The next most complicated shape is the "p" orbital (*Figure 16.6*). The "p" orbitals all have the same basic shape of a dumbbell that can have three possible orientations (aligned with the x-axis, the y-axis, or the z-axis). This gives rise to three types of "p" orbitals.

Figure 16.6

"p" orbital shape.

The "p" orbitals have lobes, so electrons in these orbitals are more likely to be found in one direction of space than another. This directionality gives rise to characteristic shapes of atoms and molecules. These shapes can dictate the shapes of crystals and the rate and types of chemical reactions that occur.

Figure 16.5

"s" orbital shape.

THE QUANTUM MODEL IN THE NUCLEUS

The quantum model can also apply to the nucleus of an atom. The protons and neutrons are found in orbitals that have characteristic energies and shapes. However, because of the nature of the strong force and characteristics of the particles involved, the energies and shapes differ from those found in atomic electrons. In the atomic nucleus, the orbitals have diameters of about 10^{-15} meters. Thus, the quantum model remains consistent with Rutherford's measurements that indicated the positively charged nucleus has a very small volume compared to the volume of the entire atom.

Figure 16.7
One possible "d" orbital shape.

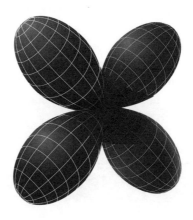

Figure 16.8
Another possible "d" orbital shape.

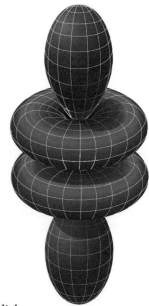

Figure 16.9
One of the possible shapes of an "f" orbital.

The "d" orbitals have two general shapes. One is shaped like a dumbbell with a bagel in the center (*Figure 16.7*).

Another shape resembles a fat four-leaf clover (*Figure 16.8*). There are four orientations of this shape, resulting in a total of five different kinds of "d" orbitals.

Orbitals identified by letters further in the sequence have, as might be expected, increasingly complicated shapes with more bumps on them. For instance, one of the "f" orbitals is shown in *Figure 16.9*.

Shells

There are many possible orbitals in atoms with each of the general shapes discussed above. However, even though the orbitals share the same general exterior shape, each differs in size, energy, and **radial shape**, which is what a cross section of an orbital would look like if it were sliced in two.

If the orbital were a large onion, the radial cross section is what you would see when you slice the onion down the middle.

To illustrate these differences, consider a set of "s" orbitals. Many different types of "s" orbitals can exist around an atom. The various "s" orbitals are distinguished by a number called the **shell** (explained in more detail below). The lowest-energy "s" orbital (which is the lowest-energy orbital in an atom) is called the "1s" orbital. It is the smallest of the "s" orbitals. It has no nodes in its radial shape. The next most energetic and next largest orbital is the "2s" orbital. It has one node in its radial shape. The "3s"

orbital comes next with two nodes in its radial shape. The radial cross sections of these three orbitals are shown in *Figure 16.10*.

Two trends are important to notice. The first is that electrons in higher-numbered orbitals are more likely to be found farther from the nucleus than lower-numbered orbitals. The second trend is that higher-numbered orbitals have more nodes than lower-numbered orbitals. Both of these trends hold true for orbitals with other shapes as well as for "s" orbitals.

A shell consists of orbital groups that have approximately the same energy and size. The various shells can only contain certain orbitals. The first shell only has an "s" orbital. The sec-

• **Radial Shape**
A cross section of what an orbital would look like if it were sliced in two.

• **Shell**
A group of orbitals having similar energies and sizes.

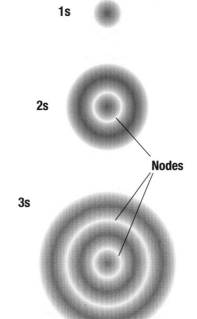

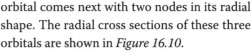

Figure 16.10
Radial cross sections of the "1s," "2s" and "3s" orbitals. The colored areas are where the electron has the highest probability of being found. The white areas are where the electron has the smallest probability of being found. The nucleus is in the very center of each of these orbitals.

• **Spin**

A characteristic of an electron, giving the direction of its intrinsic magnetic field.

Figure 16.11
Energy levels of the first few orbitals in an atom. The number of lines for each orbital indicates the number of orbitals of that kind in the atom.

• **Electron Volt**

A small amount of energy used to measure energies of particles in atoms and nuclei. It is equal to 1.6×10^{-19} joules.

Table 16.1

Orbital Energies
(lowest to highest)

1s
2s
2p
3s
3p
4s
3d
4p
5s
4d
5p
6s
4f
5d
6p
7s
5f
6d
7p
8s

ond shell has "s" and "p" orbitals. The third shell has "s," "p" and "d" orbitals. This pattern continues for increasing shell numbers.

Figure 16.11 is a schematic diagram of the energies of the different orbitals in an atom. The energy spacings are qualitatively (but not quantitatively) correct.

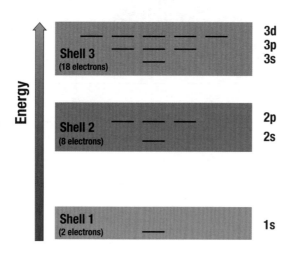

As we learned in Chapter 9, electrical potential energy decreases as opposite charges are brought closer together. Therefore, the energies of the electrons in orbitals closest to the nucleus are the lowest and those electrons far away from the nucleus have a lot of energy.

The first shell is the lowest-energy shell, followed in order by the second, third, and fourth shells. Within a shell, the lowest-energy orbital is the "s" orbital, followed by the "p" orbitals and the "d" orbitals.

The shell diagram in Figure 16.11 has been simplified by excluding shells higher than the third. Beyond the third shell, the orbitals begin to overlap between shells. For instance, the "4s" orbital is actually lower in energy than the "3d" orbital. The actual general order of energies is shown in *Table 16.1*.

Spin

Besides their orbital shape and shell, electrons in an atom have a third characteristic called **spin**. The electrons do not actually spin within their orbitals, however. The electron's spin is the direction of the electron's magnetic field. Each electron has a magnetic field associated with it, just like a bar magnet, and like a bar magnet, this field has a north pole and a south pole. The spin of an electron can point in one of two directions. We call the two directions "up" and "down."

16–2 COMPARING WITH THE BOHR MODEL

The quantum model of the atom has some similarities to and some important differences from the Bohr Model of the atom. These similarities and differences will be examined from the standpoint of atomic spectra, radiation, and atomic stability.

Bohr explained atomic spectra as transitions between special stable orbits with various energies. Photons could be emitted or absorbed when their energies matched the energy difference between the various orbits. Bohr could offer no good explanation of why his orbits would be special stable ones with given energy levels.

The quantum model is similar to Bohr's model, except that orbitals replace orbits. The various lines from absorption or emission spectra can be accounted for by the energy differences between electron states in the different orbitals.

For example, the 1s orbital in hydrogen has an energy of –13.6 **electron Volts** (or eV). The energy is negative because the electron has less electrical potential energy than it would have if it wasn't near a positively charged nucleus. The "2p" orbital has an energy of –3.4 electron Volts. If a hydrogen atom has an electron in the "2p" orbital that jumps down to the 1s orbital, it will

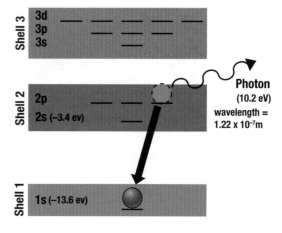

Figure 16.12
An electron jumping from the "2p" to "1s" orbital. A photon is emitted with an energy of 10.2 electron Volts and a wavelength of 1.22×10^{-7} meters.

lose 10.2 electron Volts of energy (the difference between –3.4 electron Volts and –13.6 electron Volts). We can compute the corresponding wavelength of light for a photon of this energy by using Planck's formula from Chapter 11 and the relationship between wave speed, frequency, and wavelength from Chapter 10. Doing so, we get a value of 1.22×10^{-7} meters, exactly the wavelength of the emitted light that is observed (see *Figure 16.12*).

In addition to not accounting for why atoms had specific energy levels, Bohr's model did not account for why electrons did not radiate when orbiting the nucleus in the special Bohr orbits. Classical experiments demonstrate that accelerating charges emit radiation. Electrons in circular orbits are constantly changing direction, and hence accelerating.

Again, the quantum model answers this dilemma by replacing Bohr orbits with orbitals. As we noted at the beginning of this chapter, the electrons in orbitals are not orbiting the nucleus, but rather consist of standing waves with constant probabilities of being in various locations. In this sense, they are not moving and thus are not accelerating. Because they are not accelerating, they do not radiate.

A final problem with the Bohr model concerns the stability of the electron orbits. If electrons were constantly radiating, they would be losing energy and spiraling lower and lower. What keeps them from eventually losing all of their energy and spiraling into the nucleus?

In the quantum model of course, the electrons are *not* accelerating, and therefore not radiating and losing energy, so they would not be spiraling lower. Furthermore, it is not possible for electrons to be between the orbitals defined by the wavelength of their probability waves. Because even the lowest energy orbital (1s) has a very high probability for the electron to be a considerable distance from the nucleus (about 100,000 times the diameter of the nucleus in hydrogen), the atomic structure remains stable.

16–3 THE EXCLUSION PRINCIPLE

Common experience teaches us that two macroscopic objects cannot be in the same place at the same time. A similar principle exists in the quantum model called the **exclusion principle.** The exclusion principle states that even though two electrons can have a probability of being in the same place at the same time, they cannot be in the same "state." The electron's state is a combination of its shell, orbital, and spin. For example, the exclusion principle prohibits two electrons from being in an atom if both are in the "1s" orbital and if both have "spin up."

An electron's state is like an address. The address has three pieces—the shell, the orbital, and the spin. Think of these as a street number, street name, and city. The exclusion principle essentially says that two electrons cannot have the exact same address.

Electrons in an atom prefer being in the lowest possible energy states. An electron in a high-energy state will eventually drop down to a lower energy state, emitting a photon in the process. The exclusion principle therefore provides a rule we can use to determine which states in various atoms are filled.

Lithium, for instance, has an atomic number of 3, meaning it has three protons in the nucleus and three electrons. Looking at the energy level diagram in Figure 16.11, one can see that the lowest energy orbital is the "1s" orbital. One electron can be placed in that orbital with spin up and another in the same orbital, only with spin down. At that point, the exclusion principle prohibits putting any more electrons in that orbital. Otherwise it would have the same "address" as one of the two electrons already there. Therefore, the third electron must be in the "2s" orbital (*Figure 16.13*).

We can represent the electron occupancy of the various orbitals in atoms using the following shorthand notation. Each orbital is represented by its shell number, its letter corresponding to an

• **The Exclusion Principle**

The rule that two electrons cannot be in exactly the same state in an atom. In other words, no two electrons in the same atom can have exactly the same shell, orbital, and spin values.

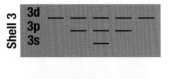

Figure 16.13

The electronic structure of lithium. When filling in an energy level diagram, arrows are used to indicate electrons. Lithium has two electrons in the 1s orbital, one with spin up and one with spin down. It has one electron in the 2s orbital.

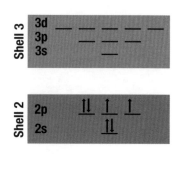

Figure 16.14

The electronic structure of oxygen. Notice that the electrons fill the orbitals in an energy level spin up first. This is because an electron has slightly less energy when oriented spin up.

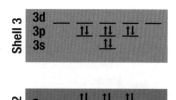

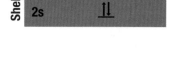

Figure 16.15

The electronic structure of argon.

orbital type, and the number of electrons in that shell. For example, the electron configuration of lithium is $1s^2 2s^1$. The number to the left of an orbital identifies the orbital's shell number, and the superscript to the right gives the number of electrons in that type of orbital. For p and d type orbitals, the total number of electrons in the orbital set are given, not the distribution amongst individual orbitals.

A more involved example would be the electronic structure of oxygen, which has eight electrons. Applying the exclusion principle, two electrons can fit in the "1s" orbital (one spin up and one spin down). Two more electrons can fit in the "2s" orbital (one spin up and one spin down). There are three "2p" orbitals, each of which could hold two electrons, so the remaining four electrons go into these orbitals. To summarize, oxygen has two "1s" electrons, two "2s" electrons, and four "2p" electrons. We represent this in shorthand notations as $1s^2 2s^2 2sp^4$.

Lastly, consider the case of argon with its 18 electrons. Applying the exclusion principle, there is room for two "1s" electrons, two "2s" electrons, six "2p" electrons, two "3s" electrons and six "3p" electrons, for a total of 18. In shorthand, this is represented as $1s^2 2s^2 2p^6$.

The next chapter will explain how the quantum model and the exclusion principle can be used to explain the periodic proper-

ties we see in elements as shown by their location in the Periodical Table.

16–4 SUMMARY

The quantum model removes the problems with the Bohr Model by replacing electron orbits with orbitals. Rather than giving the path the electrons travel, orbitals are standing waves giving the probability an electron will be found in a given location. The problems raised by the Bohr Model (why some orbits are special, why these electrons don't radiate, and why electrons don't crash into the nucleus) are all neatly resolved by the quantum model.

Each of these orbitals has a specific energy associated with it. When an electron moves from a higher-energy orbital to a lower-energy orbital, it releases the energy it has lost as a photon. The energy of the photon exactly equals this energy difference between orbitals. An electron can also be moved from a lower-energy orbital to a higher-energy orbital by absorbing a photon of the required energy difference. The frequency (and hence color) of the photon is related to its energy by Planck's formula:

$$E = hf$$

where E is the energy, h is Planck's constant, and f is the frequency.

Chapter Framework

A. Electron Orbitals
1. Standing Waves
2. Orbital Shapes
   a. "s," "p," "d," and "f"
   b. *Number of orbitals with each shape in a shell*
3. Shells
   a. *Radial shape*
   b. *Nodes*
   c. *Which orbitals can be in each shell*
4. Spin
B. Comparing Quantum Model to Bohr Model
C. The Exclusion Principle

Comprehension

True/False
1. _____ The quantum model remains consistent with Rutherford's model that the nucleus is very small compared to the rest of the atom.
2. _____ Orbitals' shapes become more complex as they move further along in the sequence ("s," "p," "d," etc.).
3. _____ Two electrons within the same orbital may have the same spin
4. _____ "d" orbitals have a possibility of eight different kinds of orbitals.
5. _____ Electrons actually do not accelerate around the nucleus as Bohr proposed.

Matching
1. _____ A standing wave formed by an electron surrounding an atomic nucleus.
2. _____ A group of orbitals having similar energies and sizes.
3. _____ Two electrons cannot be in the same state.
4. _____ A cross section of what an orbital would look like if it were sliced in two.
5. _____ The only orbital that has the probability of an electron being in the nucleus.
6. _____ The direction of an electron's magnetic field.

Fill in the Blank
1. In addition to electrons, the quantum model of the atom can also apply to the _____ of an atom.
2. The spin of an electron can point either _____ or _____.
3. Higher numbered shells have _____ energetic electrons than lower numbered shells.
4. An electron's state includes a combination of its _____, _____, and _____.

5. The dumbbell shape of the "p" orbital can have _____ possible different orientations.

Analysis

1. An electron in which of the following orbitals would have the largest energy?

   a) 1s
   b) 2p
   c) 2s
   d) 3d
   e) 3s

2. An unexcited atom has its most energetic two electrons in the 3s orbital. How many electrons does it have?

   a) 1 (hydrogen)
   b) 4 (beryllium)
   c) 6 (carbon)
   d) 9 (fluorine)
   e) 12 (magnesium)

3. The maximum number of electrons that can be placed in the "p" orbitals of one shell is

   a) 2
   b) 3
   c) 6
   d) 8
   e) 10

a. "s" orbital
b. Radial shape
c. Shell
d. Orbital
e. Spin
f. Exclusion principle

4. The shape of a p-orbital most closely resembles that of

   a) a sphere
   b) a cloverleaf
   c) a dumbbell
   d) concentric circles
   e) a cone

5. According to present understanding, which of the following is true of an electron in an atom?

   a) It travels in a circular orbit.
   b) It travels on the surface of a sphere.

c) It is confined within the nucleus most of the time.

d) Its probable position is determined by which orbital it is in.

e) It is confined within a sphere about twice the diameter of the nucleus.

6. What orbital(s) would you expect to find in the 3rd shell (energy level) of an atom?

   a) s
   b) p
   c) d
   d) two of the above
   e) all three of the above (s, p, and d)

Synthesis

1. What are two important trends for orbitals?

2. How does the quantum model resolve the problem of accelerated electrons radiating energy and spinning into the nucleus?

3. Name and describe three characteristics that determine an electron's state (address) in an atom.

4. According to the quantum model, why are only certain orbitals possible in the atom?

5. What is the difference between an orbital and an orbit?

6. Why is the s orbital the only orbital with the possibility of an electron being in the nucleus?

7. Draw electrons for the following elements in the energy level diagrams provided:

   a) H (1 electron)

   b) Li (3 electrons)

   c) Na (11 electrons)

   d) What similarities do you notice among the patterns of filled orbitals for H, Li, and Na?

7a:

3d	__ __ __ __ __
3p	__ __ __
3s	__
2p	__ __ __
2s	__
1s	__

7b:

3d	__ __ __ __ __
3p	__ __ __
3s	__
2p	__ __ __
2s	__
1s	__

7c:

3d	__ __ __ __ __
3p	__ __ __
3s	__
2p	__ __ __
2s	__
1s	__

Improving the Listening and Notetaking Experience
Recommendations and Notes

Preparation
- Review previous class notes
- Read assigned text
- Prepare questions
- Prepare an individualized outline
- Be adequately rested and nourished
- Arrive early—"make sure you arrive"

Attitude
- Decide to listen
- Avoid labeling subject, e.g., mundane, boring, or odd
- Avoid labeling professor, e.g., weird, boring, out-of-it
- Avoid labeling presentation style, e.g., slow, hard, simple, boring

Posture and Position
- Sit near the front
- Sit away from doors or windows
- Sit away from peer distractions
- Avoid the "lounger" zone
- Maintain eye contact

Tracking—Lecture and Self
- Listen for main points
- Use notes as reminders not as full text
- Don't ignore materials written on the board
- Stick with challenging materials
- Reflect upon information, asking: "What does this mean?" or "How does this relate?"
- Catch yourself zoning

After the lecture?
- Review notes immediately
- Annotate notes with material from text
- Compare notes with fellow student
- Meet with instructor or teaching assistant to clarify points
- Rate your "attention"

Special Skills or Resources
- Develop writing speed
- Develop special abbreviations or codes
- Use a note-taking system
- Tape lectures . . . with instructors approval and only as necessary . . . but avoid zoning!

Courtesy of the BYU Counseling and Career Center

CHAPTER 17

THE PERIODIC TABLE

The mere accumulation of facts, even an extremely extensive collection, does not constitute scientific method; it provides neither a direction for further discoveries nor does it even deserve the name of science in the higher sense of that word. The cathedral of science requires . . . a design for the harmonic composition of parts and to indicate the pathway by which the most fruitful new material might be generated.'   ~ Mendeleyev

The quantum model of the atom successfully explains the behavior of electrons in isolated atoms. However, most of us don't encounter matter as isolated atoms. Our food, our bodies, the chairs we sit on, all contain atoms interacting with each other.

This chapter begins a move from the study of isolated atoms to the study of interacting atoms. The discipline of **chemistry** investigates how atoms interact with each other. Chemistry and chemists study how atoms form partnerships with other atoms and exchange old partners for new ones. Some atoms dance solo, others in pairs or in lines or even complex formations like the opening ceremonies for an Olympic games.

Chemists refer to the interactions between and among atoms as bonds. Chemical bonds form because the positively charged nuclei of atoms attract the electrons of other nuclei. Amazingly, the quantum model description of electrons explains all of the different ways in which atoms bond. Chapters 17 through 24 introduce the chemistry and bonding of the elements, of simple substances, and even of ones as complex as proteins and minerals.

Medieval alchemists, striving to transmute "base" metals such as mercury into "noble" metals such as gold, laid the first foundations for chemistry. Mystical forces and secret spells were invoked. Gradually, scientists searching for natural laws replaced wizards chanting spells.

Early chemists knew that many substances could be broken down into simpler substances. They called a substance which could not be broken down any further an **element**. We know now that elements contain only one kind of atom. In other words, every atom in the element contains the same number of protons in its nucleus.

During the middle of the 19th century, scientists were discovering many new elements and characterizing the chemical properties of all the known elements. A Russian scientist, Dmitri Mendeleyev (1843–1907) was fascinated, perhaps to the point of obsession, by the properties of the elements. His single-minded passion led him to make an important discovery: Physical and chemical properties of the elements vary periodically with atomic number. The underlying principle responsible for the patterns remained unknown for more than 30 years. Can you guess what it is? The quantum (wave) model of the atom explains many of the observed patterns!

We begin this chapter with a quick look at the early history of chemistry. Then we move to Mendeleyev's discovery. We conclude by establishing the connection between the periodic

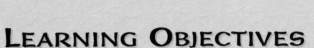

trends in elemental properties and the quantum model of the atom.

Remember that you continue on a journey to learn both how nature works and how science works to understand nature. Mendeleyev contributed to both endeavors. Mendeleyev's organization of the elements provided a concise way to convey much chemical information; his plan of attack solidified the way scientists approach their tasks, and was the first example of using knowledge to predict the existence of new materials.

17–1 EARLY CHEMISTRY AND CHEMISTS

Modern science developed rapidly in the latter part of the 18th century. Rudimentary scientific techniques and methods of investigation were developed. For example, French chemist Antoine Lavoisier, working in 1789, formulated the Law of Conservation of Mass (Chapter 8). Lavoisier studied how substances react with oxygen. As part of his investigations, Lavoisier measured the masses of his starting materials. After the process was over, Lavoisier measured the masses of the new substances. These measure-

ments established that the total mass of the first substance plus oxygen were equal to that of the substances produced during the reaction. Lavoisier's careful, quantitative, experimental measurements established a methodology for many future chemical studies.

Other scientists studied the decomposition of substances into its elements. They observed that the decomposition of a particular substance always produced the same elements, in the same relative amounts. For example, 100 g of a substance containing cadmium and sulfur always decomposed to give 78 g of cadmium and 22 g of sulfur. Decomposition of a lead-sulfur compound always gave 87 % of its mass as lead and 13 % as sulfur. This observation became known as the **Law of Constant Composition**.

Occasionally, different substances were found to contain the same elements, but in different proportions. Rust, an iron-oxygen compound, is 69% iron by mass, but another

Figure 17.1

Illustrations of the Laws of Constant Mass and of Constant Composition.
a) One hundred grams of the orange substance always contain 78 grams of cadmium and 22 grams of sulfur.
b) One hundred grams of the black substance always contain 87 grams of lead and 13 grams of sulfur.

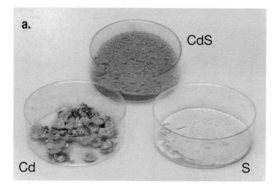

• **Chemistry**

Chemistry is the discipline in which the interactions of atoms with each other are studied.

• **Element**

Matter that contains only one kind of atom.

• **Law of Constant Composition**

Substances contain a fixed, definite proportion of elements by mass.

• **Atomic Theory**

The model that matter is made up of atoms.

• **Physical Properties**

Properties like melting or boiling temperature, density, ionization potential.

• **Chemical Properties**

Properties associated with the chemical reactivity of a material. Some examples: Does a substance combine with oxygen or react with water?

iron-oxygen substance with different properties is 72% iron by mass. Gradually, scientists recognized that a particular substance contained a definite combination of elements in a fixed proportion. Changing the proportions of the elements produced new substances with different properties.

John Dalton (1766–1845), an English school teacher, pulled together many experimental observations to propose what has come to be known as the **Atomic Theory**. Dalton included five basic assumptions in his model of matter:

1) Matter is composed of small indivisible particles called atoms.

2) An element contains only a single kind of atom. Atoms of a given element are identical in every respect, including mass and chemical behavior.

3) Atoms of different elements have different mass and chemical reactivity.

4) Chemical *compounds* are composed of two or more atoms that are joined together in fixed ratios.

5) Chemical *reactions* correspond to the rearrangement of atoms to form different compounds.

Dalton's assumptions, we now know, contained some flaws. Atoms *are* divisible. They contain positively-charged nuclei and negatively-charged electrons. Dalton's second assumption needs refinement. Elements can differ slightly

in mass without significantly affecting chemical behavior. The details will be discussed in Chapter 25. Finally, Dalton's fourth assumption is true for most, but not all substances. Many compounds are now known to exist with variable compositions.

Dalton's theory provided a simple way to represent the chemical composition of different compounds. Every element was given a simple one- or two-letter abbreviation. Specifying the elements and the number of atoms identified a compound. For example, The magnesium-oxygen compound can be represented as MgO, since Mg is the symbol for magnesium and O is the symbol for oxygen. Sodium (Na) forms two compounds with oxygen, one has the formula Na_2O and the other is NaO_2. The first compound contains two atoms of sodium for every atom of oxygen. The second compound switches the

Figure 17.2

Different combinations of the same elements can produce different compounds. Rust (Fe_2O_3) and magnetite (Fe_3O_4) are both iron-oxygen containing materials, but the relative amounts of iron to oxygen differ.

ELEMENT NAMES AND SYMBOLS

The symbol assigned to an element reflects when the element was discovered. Medieval alchemists assigned symbols derived from the original Latin names. Sodium, then called Natrium, got the symbol Na. Gold, called Aurium, appeared as Au. Modern scientists often name an element after its discoverer or the location where the discovery was made. For example, Seaborgium is named after Glen Seaborg and Californium is named in honor of the state in which it was discovered.

ratio: One atom of sodium is found for every two atoms of oxygen. In Dalton's notation, the subscript *following* an element's symbol specifies the number of that kind of atom in the compound. No subscript after a symbol implies one atom in the formula.

17-2 THE DEVELOPMENT OF THE PERIODIC TABLE

Families of Elements

By 1850 scientists had identified about fifty elements. Chemists began to group the known elements into families that shared similar **physical properties** and **chemical properties**. Three important families were identified. Lithium, sodium, and potassium were called alkali metals. Beryllium, magnesium, calcium, strontium,

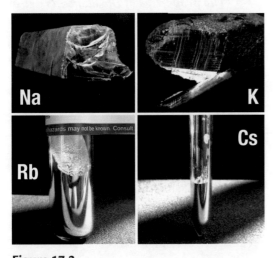

Figure 17.3
The alkali metals sodium (Na) and potassium (K) were known to Mendeleyev; rubidium (Rb), and cesium (Cs) were discovered later.

Figure 17.4
Three halogen family members: chlorine (yellow gas), bromine (red-orange liquid) and iodine (purple solid).

and barium were called alkaline earth metals. Chlorine, bromine, and iodine made up the halogen family.

The eight members of the alkali and alkali earth families known to Mendeleyev are all solids at room temperature. Pictures of sodium and potassium, along with rubidium and cesium (family members not yet discovered by 1850), are shown in *Figure 17.3*. Alkaline earth metals have a similar luster. Members of both families also conduct electricity easily. The two families differ in their chemical properties, however. The alkali metal elements form compounds with oxygen that contain two metal atoms for every oxygen atom. Oxygen-containing compounds of the alkaline earth metal elements contain one metal atom for every oxygen atom.

The halogen family of elements has more diverse physical properties than the metallic families. Chlorine is a gas, bromine is a liquid that vaporizes easily, and iodine a solid that easily transforms to a gas. They are all colored. *Figure 17.4* shows that chlorine is yellowish-green, bromine red, and iodine purple. The halogens were grouped as a family because each element consists of two atoms bonded together. Also, they react similarly with oxygen.

The existence of element families so fascinated the Russian scientist and teacher Mendeleyev that the elements became his obsession. With single-minded passion, Mendeleyev worked to discover a relationship between an element and its properties. Mendeleyev created a card game to detect relationships or patterns. He wrote the known physical and chemical properties of each element on cards. Mendeleyev dealt the cards out into rows and columns, playing his own form of Solitaire. Relentlessly he sorted and re-sorted the cards according to different properties, looking for patterns.

Mendeleyev's Process

To illustrate Mendeleyev's approach, let's consider one chemical property of the elements. A property called the oxide combining ratios presents the patterns nicely. The *oxide combining ratio* of an element gives the atomic ratio of element to oxygen in a compound. *Table 17.1* shows this quantity for the elements known to Mendeleyev at the beginning of his studies.

Thinking Like a Scientist: Look carefully

Dmitri Mendeleyev
The Russian scientist and teacher who discovered the Periodic Law and constructed the first Periodic Table.

Table 17.1 – Periodic Trends in Combining Ratios

Oxide Formula	I. R_2O	II. RO	III. R_2O_3	IV. RO_2	V. R_2O_5	VI. RO_3	VII. R_2O_7
Combining Ratio	2	1	$\frac{2}{3} = 0.67$	$\frac{1}{2} = 0.5$	$\frac{2}{5} = 0.4$	$\frac{1}{3} = 0.33$	$\frac{2}{7} = .28$
	Li 7	Be 8	B 11	C 12	N 14	O* 16	
	Na 23	Mg 24	Al 27	Si 28	P 31	S 32	Cl 35.5
	K 39	Ca 40		Ti 48	As 75	Se 79	Br 80
		Sr 87					

*O does not fit with respect to this particular property. It falls in line if other properties are considered.

Table 17.1

Periodic trends in the combining ratios of elements with oxygen for elements known at the time of Mendeleyev. Numbers below the element symbols are the atomic masses.

• **Periodic Law**

The properties of the elements are a periodic function of their atomic masses.

at *Table 17.1*. The elements are sequenced by their atomic masses, but grouped in columns by their combining ratios. What do you notice about the combining ratio as the atomic mass increases? What is the largest value of the ratio? What is the smallest value?

Mendeleyev discovered a trend to the numbers. He had found a repetitive pattern: The oxide combining ratio started at 2 with lithium, then it decreased systematically for a few elements, and then jumped back up to 2 with sodium. The pattern repeated in this fashion as Mendeleyev sorted through all the elements.

Mendeleyev grouped the elements with the same combining ratios together. This arrangement left several gaps in his table. For example, there was no known element in Column III of Table 17.1 to put between calcium and titanium.

Mendeleyev believed that nature would not permit such gaps. Confident that his patterns revealed something fundamental about nature, Mendeleyev predicted in 1869 the existence of a new element that would fill the gap. He estimated the physical and chemical properties of this unknown element based on its family members. Nine years later an element with mass of 45, now known as scandium, was discovered. Scandium had an oxide combining ratio of 0.67 and other properties close to those predicted by Mendeleyev. Mendeleyev formulated his observations into the **Periodic Law:**

The properties of the elements are a periodic function of their atomic masses.

Mendeleyev's contributions were of two kinds. He contributed scientific knowledge: the Periodic Law and the first Periodic Table. The table's structure organized and succinctly conveyed information about element families. Gaps became evident where elements were not yet discovered. In addition, Mendeleyev helped to change how knowledge could be manipulated for good. Mendeleyev recognized that he could use nature's patterns to make predictions about unknown elements and their properties. Science progressed from simple data collection and categorization to a more sophisticated level: one that included predictive powers.

17–3 AN IMPROVED PERIODIC TABLE WITH MORE ELEMENTS

New Elements

Mendeleyev published his first Periodic Table in 1861 with about 50 elements. Other scientists had isolated or discovered another 25 elements by 1900. More than one hundred years later, the total of elements stands at 111.

The last naturally-occurring element (element 92) was discovered in 1928. Since then, scientists working in high-energy laboratories have created all new elements. In these laboratories, atoms are accelerated to very high speeds and allowed to collide into one another. Sometimes those collisions lead to the formation of new elements.

For example, in 1994, scientists at the Institute for Heavy Ion Physics (see *Figure 17.5*) slammed very rapidly moving nickel atoms (element 28) into a piece of bismuth (element 83). Element 111 resulted from the collision. Several additional elements (atomic numbers 112, 114, and 116) have been reported, but verification of their existence by other scientists has not yet occurred.

Elements with atomic numbers heavier than 92 (uranium) are all man-made elements. Many heavy elements do not live for very long before decomposing into other kinds of nuclei. However, a few heavy elements, like plutonium (element 94), can exist for thousands of years before undergoing changes. You will study these unstable, or radioactive, nuclei in Chapter 25.

Figure 17.5

Element 111, named Roentgenium, was discovered in 1994 at the Institute for Heavy Ion Physics at Darmstadt, Germany.

Improved, Extended Table

Improvements have been made to the Periodic Table as new knowledge about the atom became available. Mendeleyev first sorted elements according to their atomic masses. However, the number of protons in the atomic nucleus distinguishes one element from another rather than atomic masses. Re-sorting the table by **atomic number** made no significant changes in family structure from Mendeleyev's first version and improved the agreement of family properties for a few elements in the middle of the table.

• **Atomic Number**

The number of protons in a nucleus. This number defines an element.

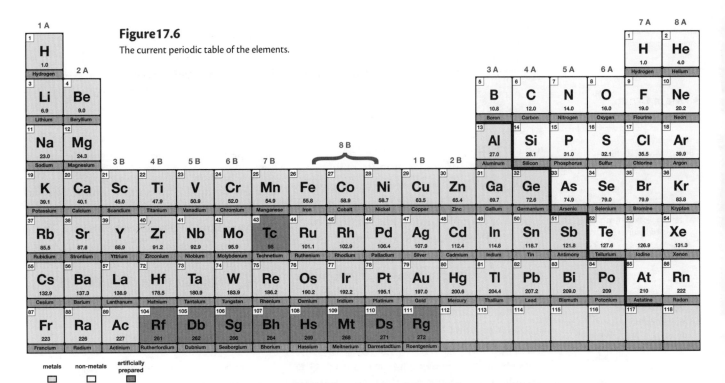

Figure 17.6

The current periodic table of the elements.

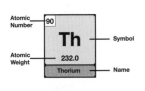

• Metals

Elements that are good electrical and thermal conductors and can be hammered into thin sheets or drawn into fine wires.

• Non-Metals

Elements that do not conduct electricity.

• Families or Groups of Elements

Elements that were grouped together because they had very similar chemical properties and are now known to have the same number of valence electrons. An element family occupies a vertical column in the Periodic Table.

• Periods

Horizontal rows in the periodic table within which physical and chemical properties change systematically.

• Main Group

The set of metal and non-metal elements designated with A column headings. They have valence electron configurations involving only s and p electrons.

• Transition Metals

The set of metal elements designated with B column headings. They have valence electron configurations involving d electrons.

• Atomic Size

An estimate of the volume occupied by an atom. The number is obtained from the density of the solid state of the element.

• Ionization Energy

The amount of energy needed to completely remove an electron from an atom. The energy need to remove the first electron from a neutral atom varies periodically with atomic number.

Figure 17.6 presents the most current version of the Periodic Table, including element 111. The elements can be broadly classified into two categories, **metals** and **non-metals.** As a general rule, metals occupy the left-hand and middle portions of the Periodic Table. The black line running below boron (B), silicon (Si), etc. divides metals from non-metals. The non-metal elements sit on the right-hand side of the table, above and to the right of the black dividing line.

The property of electrical conductivity establishes an element as a metal. Metals conduct electricity; non-metals do not. About three-fourths of the known elements are metals. All but one metallic element, mercury (number 80), is a solid at room temperature. Metals have other properties in common. They are shiny and reflective. They can also be hammered into thin sheets and stretched into fine wires. The elements of gold, copper, and aluminum are metals whose properties with which you may already be familiar. You will study metals in greater depth in Chapter 21.

Non-metals show much more variety in their properties. There are non-metal elements that are gases, others that are liquids, and still others that are solids at room temperature. Some are highly colored, while others are colorless. The chemistry of non-metals will be discussed in Chapters 22 and 23.

The modern Periodic Table still retains a structure that conveys how chemical and physical properties of the elements vary. The vertical columns of the periodic table are Mendeleyev's **families,** now also called **groups.** The elements of a given family have similar properties. For example, the formulas of oxide compounds with elements in a family will all be the same. However, the ease or vigor with which the reaction of the element with oxygen to form the oxide may change as you go down a column.

The horizontal rows of the Periodic Table are called **periods**. Within a given row, physical and chemical properties change systematically from element to element. A row represents the period or length of the repeating pattern observed by Mendeleyev. Moving from the last element in a row to the first element in the next row corresponds to restarting the pattern.

Some of the family names from early groupings are retained in the modern Periodic Table. Alkali metals and alkaline earth elements form

Columns 1A and 2A, respectively. The halogens make up Column 7A in the modern table. A new column, 8A, contains the noble gas elements. These elements were not discovered until 25 years after Mendeleyev published his first table. The elements with "A" labels are sometimes called the **main group** elements.

The elements in the large block in the center of the Periodic Table are collectively referred to as the **transition metals**. Many precious gemstones such as rubies and sapphires owe their colors to the presence of small amounts of transition metals in otherwise colorless substances. Transition metal chemistry is a rich but challenging field. Because of their complexity, we shall not study these materials in depth.

Two additional series of elements exist. The lanthanide series contains the elements from 58 to 71. The series gets its name from lanthanum, element 58. The actinide series consists of elements from actinium, element 90, to lawrencium, element 103. All of the actinide series are radioactive. Uranium and plutonium are the two most famous (infamous) elements of this series.

17–4 PERIODIC TRENDS IN ATOMIC SIZE AND IONIZATION ENERGY

When all the known elements are included, periodic trends of atomic properties stand out with increased clarity. Let us consider two important physical properties, **atomic size** and **ionization energy**, to further illustrate the periodic variations and repeating patterns. These two properties dramatically portray the trends hinted at by Mendeleyev's oxide combining ratios. In addition, these properties will prove useful for further discussions of bonding.

Atomic Size Variations

Figure 17.7 shows the variation of the atomic size (expressed as a volume that can be estimated from the density of the element in a solid state) with atomic number. The x axis in Figure 17.7 identifies the atomic number of the element. The y axis gives the atomic size. The graph shows recurring peaks and valleys. The peaks correspond to atoms that have large atomic volume;

the valleys arise from elements with smaller atomic volumes.

Thinking Like a Scientist: Can you identify what family of elements tends to have the largest volume in every period? Now, look just at the trend in the peak volumes. Do these volumes increase or decrease with atomic number?

Peaks in atomic volumes occur with the members of the alkali metal family. The alkaline earth elements, just one element to the right in each period, have significantly smaller volumes than their alkali metal neighbors.

Figure 17.7 shows that the atom volumes of the alkali metals increase as you go down the column. This same trend is true, but less apparent, for other element families.

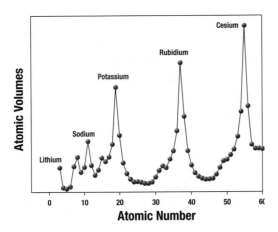

Figure 17.7
Atomic sizes vary periodically. This graph shows the variation of the atomic volume with the atomic number. All known elements are shown here, not just those known to Mendeleyev.

Ionization Energy Variations

The first ionization energy measures the energy needed to strip one electron away from a neutral atom. The chemical behavior of an element directly relates to how easily the element loses electrons, so this is an important property to understand. We will refer back to this extensively in Chapters 21 and 22.

Like the atomic size, the ionization energy varies periodically with atomic number of the elements (*Figure 17.8*). Again we see a set of peaks. In this figure, a peak signifies an element that really likes to hold on to its electrons. That is, to pull away an electron from such an atom requires a great deal of energy. The ionization energy drops immediately following a peak to a minimum value. Atoms with minimum energies lose electrons easily.

Thinking Like a Scientist: Which element family has high ionization energies? Which element family tends to have low ionization energies? Looking as a group at metallic elements versus non-metallic elements, how do you characterize the ionization energies of the two groups? (Hint: Try to arrive at an answer to this last question by comparing elements in a given period, then formulate a general description for each group.)

The noble gas (Group 8A) element family needs the largest energy to give up an electron. Those large-sized alkali metals turn out to be very easy to ionize. In fact, as a group, metals ionize much more easily than their non-metal peers in a given period.

Certain properties of elements correlate well with ionization energy. For example, all metals have low ionization energies. Metals are shiny and electrically conducting. Non-metal elements have large ionization energies. The different ionization energies of the two classes of elements play a significant role in the different chemistry of the two groups.

The highest ionization energies (the peaks in Figure 17.8) come from the noble gases (helium, neon, argon, krypton, and xenon). The ionization energies are so high, in fact, that these gases do not interact with other atoms. Only xenon forms chemical compounds at room temperature. The compound formation occurs even then only with the most reactive element, fluorine.

The appearance, natural state, and chemical aggressiveness of elements vary periodically

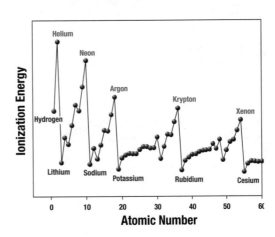

Figure 17.8
It takes energy to remove an electron from a neutral atom. This energy, called the ionization energy, varies with atomic number.

♦ **Electron Configuration Diagram**

An enumeration of how electrons populate atomic orbitals that is consistent with the "lowest-energy filled first" and "exclusion" principles.

with atomic number. That so many properties exhibited the same periodicity tantalized scientists for many years after Mendeleyev. Surely some underlying fundamental principle could explain everything. The explanation became apparent after Schrödinger and others solved the mathematical equations of the quantum model of the atom.

17–5 THE QUANTUM MODEL EXPLAINS THE PERIODIC TABLE

How does the quantum model explain Mendeleyev's puzzling patterns? Let's follow Mendeleyev's lead and look for patterns. Get in the spirit of this and consider each question posed below. See if you come up with the answers on your own before you read our answers and explanations.

Thinking like a Scientist: Look first at *Figure 17.9* to refresh your memory of the ordering of electronic energy levels from the quantum model. Figure 17.9 also reminds you of the maximum number of electrons each shell can hold.

Now, count the number of elements in the first two periods of the modern Periodic Table (Figure 17.6). Row 1 has 2 elements; Row 2 has 8 elements.

How many electrons can the first shell of an atom hold? How many electrons can the second shell hold? Do the numbers 2 and 8 seem familiar?

Perhaps now you think you are onto something. What hypothesis might you form? Suppose you hypothesize that a connection exists between the rows in the Periodic Table and electronic shells of the quantum model.

To test the hypothesis, work your way across the first two rows of elements. (Write out the energy level diagrams for each atom. The practice will cement the ideas in your head.) Look at what electron orbitals are populated as you go from atom to atom. In assigning electrons to orbitals, remember two principles: 1) electrons want to be in the lowest energy orbital possible, but 2) no orbital can hold more than two electrons. Scientists call these orbital population diagrams **electron configurations.**

Hydrogen has one electron, it must go into the 1 s orbital. Helium has one more electron. Putting two electrons into the 1s orbital fills that orbital up. Shell 1 is complete.

Move down to Row 2. Lithium, the first element of row 2, has 3 electrons. Two electrons must go into the 1s orbital. The third electron of lithium goes into the next available orbital, which is a 2s orbital. Beryllium, atom 4, puts its 4th electron into the 2s orbital. The 2s orbital is now filled.

Atoms 5 through 10 have more electrons than beryllium. What orbitals do their electrons go into? The set of 2p orbitals must be filled next. Boron, atom 5, must put its 5th electron in to one of the 2p orbitals. The remaining 5 elements (carbon through neon) must each add their additional electron to the 2p orbitals. At atom 10, the 2 p orbitals have 6 electrons. Shell 2 is complete.

Once you have completed the configurations on your own, check them against *Figure 17.10*. For clarity, only the outer most electrons are shown in this figure.

You are on a roll now. Looking over your electron configuration diagrams, (or the first two rows of Figure 17.10), you see that your hypothesis looks viable. Rows 1 and 2 of the periodic table correspond to the filling of electrons in the first two shells of the quantum model.

Furthermore, you see some other patterns developing. The two atoms in column 1A each have a single electron in the s orbital of the outer,

Figure 17.9

Simple atomic orbital energy diagram. Remember that each orbital can only hold at most two electrons.

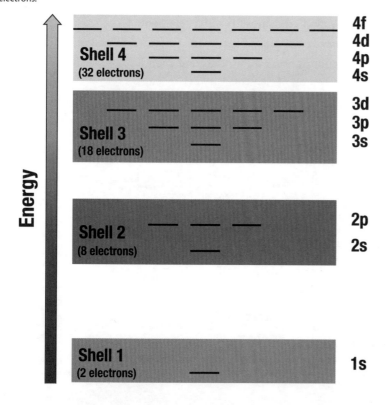

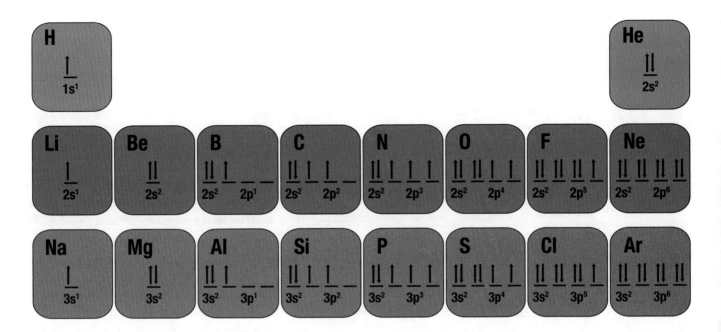

Figure 17.10
Valence electron configurations of the elements in rows 1–3 of the periodic table.

or higher numbered, shell. In fact, each member of a group has the *same* orbital population description for its outer electrons.

Then you notice something even more significant. The first two noble gases in Column 8A each have completely filled shells. Noble gases are unreactive, you know.

Wow, you've got the connection, you think with building excitement. Time for a second hypothesis: "Atoms with completely filled shells are unreactive." Try this new hypothesis out by checking it out on Row 3 of the periodic table.

Atom number 11, the element sodium, starts off Row 3. Sodium's first 10 electrons fill up Shell 2, so electron 11 must go into Shell 3, specifically into the 3s orbital, because Figure 17.9 tells us that's next in energy.

Working across the third period the same way you did the second period takes you to argon. Argon has 18 electrons, 8 more electrons than neon. Argon's last electron completes the 3p orbital set.

Check to see if the patterns you observed earlier are still holding up, and if the two hypotheses still seem valid.

Yes, each element of Period 3 has the same outer electron configuration as its family members. Argon, an unreactive noble gas element, has completely filled 3s and 3p orbitals. Shell 3, however, can take ten additional electrons; it has the set of 3d orbitals. According to the Periodic Table, moving to atom 19 (potassium) takes you down to a new period.

Time to step back and re-evaluate things. Can it be that periods don't correspond to shells after all? Are your hypotheses about reactivity and completely-filled shells completely off-base? Maybe reactivity isn't about filled shells after all. What's going on?

The early atomic scientists, at this point in their own mental exercises, began to scratch their heads. The simple energy scheme developed by Schrödinger and others for atomic hydrogen worked so well for the first 18 elements! What went wrong at atom number 19?

The scientists realized that the energy levels of Figure 17.9 were appropriate only for atoms with one electron. Unfortunately, only one neutral atom, hydrogen, has a single electron. The presence of additional electrons complicates the simple picture developed for hydrogen.

Scientists thrive on finding explanations to improve models. But the improvement of the quantum model for many-electron atoms requires concepts not considered in this course and we won't elaborate here. However, an overview illustrates how scientific theory and experimental results work hand in hand.

Scientists had confidence in both the Periodic Table and the fundamental correctness of the quantum model of the atom. The structure of the Periodic Table, established by experimental measurements, was taken as the best indicator of electron orbital energies. Theoretical calculations were "tweaked" until the energy ordering scheme they predicted matched the atom sequence dictated by the Periodic Table.

Figure 17.11 presents the revised energy scheme appropriate for most atoms. Notice that the 3d orbitals are now higher in energy than the 4s orbital. With this new energy scheme, the outer electrons of potassium and calcium (atoms number 19 and 20, respectively) go in as $4s^1$ and $4s^2$, respectively, rather than as 3d electrons.

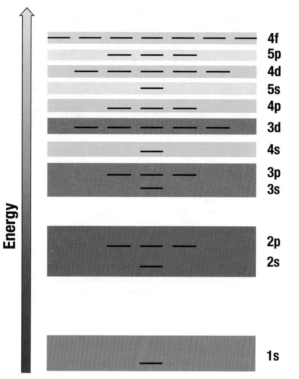

Figure 17.11

An atomic orbital energy diagram modified to show the correct ordering of the 4s and 3s orbitals.

Following calcium, the first row of transition metal elements appears. The last electrons of these 10 elements, beginning with scandium, fill in the set of five 3d orbitals. The outer electrons of atoms 31 (gallium) through 36 (krypton) go into the next available orbitals, the 4p orbitals.

Krypton's full electron configuration is given as $1s^2 2s^2 2p^6 3s^2 3p^6 4s^2 3d^{10} 4p^6$. Krypton is another noble gas. The revised energy scheme restores the pattern of electron configurations for the main group elements (1A through 8A) you observed earlier. All the members of a column have the same outer electron configuration. The quantum number n that identifies the shell of the outermost s and p orbitals locates the row in which the element is found. Your first hypothesis about the connection between shell and periods turns out to be correct after all.

The second hypothesis relating filled shells with unusual chemical stability has not been sig-

nificantly improved, even with the energy reordering. The $ns^2 np^6$ configuration of the elements in Group 8A does not always correspond to closed shells. The experimental observations that these elements are chemically unreactive and have high ionization energies suggests that there is something special about that configuration. The quantum model does not easily provide an explanation why. However, knowing that the $ns^2 np^6$ configuration confers energetic stability enables chemists to make simple predictions about the chemistry of many elements. We shall mention this briefly as the octet structure in a later chapter.

Periods 5, 6, and 7 also have ten transition metals associated with the filling of five d orbitals. If you look closely at the sequence of atomic numbers after lanthanum and actinium, you will see that periods 6 and 7 have additional elements.

These additional elements are called the lanthanides and actinides after the first member in each series, lanthanum and actinium, respectively. There are fourteen elements in each of these series. Moving from one element to another within each series corresponds to populating sets of f-type orbitals.

The chemistry of these f-electron elements is very complex. Other than to note that these are metals, we will not discuss them further.

Let's summarize what you've learned. Mendeleyev's patterns arise from the sequential filling of atomic orbitals by electrons, and the existence of electron shells. The experimentally-determined structure of the Periodic Table provided the evidence to improve the simple quantum model of the atom, good only for hydrogen. The quantum model–Periodic Table connection established that an element's chemical reactivity is determined by its outermost (most energetic) electrons. Scientists now call these outer electrons the **valence electrons**.

• **Valence Electrons**

One or more electrons in the outermost populated electron shell of an atom. Valence electrons determine an element's chemical reactivity.

17–6 CONCLUSION

The single-minded passion of Mendeleyev led him to an important discovery. Periodic patterns exist in the properties of elements. The organizing principle responsible for the patterns is the quantum (wave) nature of the atom.

Scientists find beauty in simple, elegant ways of understanding nature. From that perspective, the Periodic Table is like Michelangelo's famous *Pieta*. The beautifully sculpted statue conveys to even an unfamiliar observer a story of physical suffering and compassionate love. To a religious Christian, familiar with the story of Jesus and Mary, the statue takes on a more profound meaning.

On one level, the Periodic Table conveys information about elemental properties. To the educated observer, the table also portrays electron configurations and shell structures. New predictions about chemical properties and reactivities become possible. The Periodic Table is elegant and simple in its conciseness, yet powerfully capable of providing a wealth of chemical and physical information. We shall continue to refer back to it in many subsequent chapters.

Figure 17.12
Michelangelo's *Pieta* (1498, St. Peter's Basilica, Rome)

Chapter Framework

A. Early Chemistry and Chemists
1. Law of Constant Composition
2. Atomic Theory

B. The Development of the Periodic Table
1. Families of Elements
   a. *Physical properties*
   b. *Chemical properties*
2. Dmitri Mendeleyev
3. Periodic Law

C. Improved Periodic Table
1. New Elements
2. Sorted by Atomic Number
3. Metals and Non-metals
4. Families or Groups
   a. *Main group*
   b. *Transition metals*
   c. *Lanthanide and actinide series*
5. Periods

D. Periodic Trends
1. Atomic Size Variations
2. Ionization Energy Variations

E. The Quantum Model and the Periodic Table
1. Electron Configurations
2. Valence Electrons

Comprehension

Matching

1. _____ Properties like melting or boiling temperature, density, and color.
2. _____ Good electrical and thermal conductors that can usually be hammered into thin sheets or drawn into fine wires.
3. _____ Two or more atoms that are joined together in fixed ratios.
4. _____ Electrons that are in the outermost, usually unfilled shell of an atom.
5. _____ Elements that do not conduct electricity.
6. _____ Elements that occur in the same row of the Periodic Table.
7. _____ The science of matter and the transformations that it can undergo to form new or different types of matter.
8. _____ Elements in the periodic table which are placed in the same column and have similar chemical properties.
9. _____ A kind of matter that contains only one type of atom.
10. ___ Properties associated with the reactivity of a material.

a. *Metals*
b. *Chemical property*
c. *Periods*
d. *Non-metals*
e. *Chemistry*
f. *Physical property*
g. *Element*
h. *Family*
i. *Valence electrons*
j. *Compound*

True/False

1. _____ Dmitri Mendeleyev is the father of the Periodic Table of elements.
2. _____ Elements that have similar chemical properties are categorized into periods.
3. _____ Elements with atomic numbers heavier than 92 (uranium) are all man-made elements.
4. _____ Carbon, silicon, and lead belong to the same family.
5. _____ Alchemy first started in the Middle Ages while trying to form precious metals such as gold.

Fill in the Blank

1. The two categories of elements are _____ and _____.
2. _____, a missing element, was discovered to fit in between calcium and titanium in the Periodic Table according to oxidation levels.
3. The density of an element is found by dividing atomic _____ by atomic _____.
4. Different substances can contain the same elements but in different _____.
5. Mendeleyev discovered a trend in the elements using _____ _____ _____.

Analysis

1. According to Figure 17.6, which of the following is a metal? (Hint: Metals have ionization energies less than 8 electron volts and non-metals have more than 10.)

   a) H, Hydrogen
   b) Li, lithium
   c) C, Carbon
   d) Br, Bromine

2. List Fe, Rh, and Pt in order of increasing density. (They all have about the same diameter.)

   a) Pt Rh Fe
   b) Rh Fe Pt
   c) Fe Rh Pt
   d) Pt Fe Rh
   e) Fe Pt Rh

3. List the following atoms in order of increasing diameter: nitrogen, oxygen, and phosphorus.

   a) O N P
   b) N O P
   c) N P O
   d) P N O
   e) P O N

4. The atomic mass of a potassium atom is about 39. The atom has

   a) 39 protons
   b) 39 neutrons
   c) 39 electrons
   d) 19 neutrons
   e) 19 protons

5. How many and in what orbitals does oxygen have valance electrons? (Hint: Could be multiple answers.)

a) 8 in p orbitals

b) 6 in p orbitals

c) 4 in p orbitals

d) 4 in s orbitals

e) 2 in s orbitals

6. Which atom has the lowest ionization energy?

a) Hydrogen

b) Helium

c) Beryllium

d) Lithium

e) Aluminum

7. Which of the following statements is false?

a) Elements in a row progress from metal to non-metal.

b) Elements in a column are chemically similar.

c) Li, Na, and K are chemically similar.

d) Ne, Ar, and Kr are chemically active solids.

e) F, Cl, ad Br are chemically active gases.

8. Which of the following pairs are most like $_{15}P$?

a) $_{46}Pd$ and $_{82}Pb$

b) $_{14}Si$ and $_{16}S$

c) $_{07}N$ and $_{33}As$

Synthesis

1. Which two of the following atoms are most similar in size: $_{09}F$, $_{30}Zn$, $_{47}Ag$, or $_{56}Ba$?

2. Is $_{12}Mg$ or $_{79}Au$ (gold) denser? Use the quantum model of the atom to explain your answer.

3. Which neutral atom is smaller, $_{38}Sr$ or $_{16}S$? Use the quantum model of the atom to explain your answer.

4. Which element is most similar to $_{09}F$? Use the quantum model of the atom to explain your answer.

5. Why is the second ionization energy of Li so much higher than the first?

6. Which gaseous element has the largest number of protons in each atom?

7. Technetium, $_{43}Tc$, does not exist naturally on the earth and is prepared by nuclear bombardment. If you were looking for it, would you expect to find it as a solid, liquid, gas, metal, or nonmetal? (This element reduces the corrosion of steel remarkably.

At one time it cost $2,800 per gram, now it is below $100 per gram.)

8. On the basis of its neighbors, describe the characteristics of $_{46}Pb$.

9. Which two elements are most like $_{35}Br$?

10. Compared to chromium, $_{24}Cr$, what can you say about molybdenum, $_{42}Mo$? Compare density and metallic nature.

11. Match the atoms that belong to the same family.

$_{20}Ca$ $_{18}Ar$

$_{03}Li$ $_{12}Mg$

$_{35}Br$ $_{33}As$

$_{10}Ne$ $_{11}Na$

$_{07}N$ $_{09}F$

12. Describe three important patterns of the properties of the chemical elements that correlate to their placement on the Periodic Table. What are the main elements of the quantum model of the atom (including a statement of two fundamental principles upon which it is built)? How does the quantum model of the atom explain the patterns?

13. The quantum model of the atom offers some insights into the trends in atomic size (Figure 17.7). Consider the following questions and state some observations we can make by comparing the theory with experiment. What type of electron configuration is associated with the largest atomic volumes in a given period? As the *n* designation of an element's valence electron increases (e.g., $1s^1$, $2s^1$, $3s^1$ etc), what happens to the atomic size of that element?

14. The trend in ionization energy as you go down Group 1A can be explained, qualitatively at least, by the electric force law. Why does it get easier to pull away a valence 6s electron than a valence 3s electron? Hint: which electron is further away from the nucleus, on the average?

15. Atoms that contain unpaired electrons can exhibit magnetic properties. Write the electron configurations for iron (Fe, atomic number 26) and zinc (Zn, atomic number 30) and predict which metal might be magnetic. Remember that electrons don't pair up in orbitals until they have to.

THE LAW OF INCREASING DISORDER

In previous chapters, we learned that there are various forms of energy, and that energy can be converted from one form to another, including mass. Evidence also shows that the conservation laws govern any energy transformation. Mass and energy (or mass-energy in relativistic processes) are always conserved. In this chapter, we will see that there is an additional constraint on the transformation of one type of energy into another. This constraint is associated with the direction of the energy conversion process. If energy can be completely converted from one form to another, the reverse process cannot take place with perfect conversion. We will categorize the types of energy in terms of their ability to do work and assign each type of energy a qualitative ranking. Using this ranking system we will find that while the quantity of energy may be conserved, the quality of the energy is generally degraded, making it less useful to do work. These observations form the basis of the **Law of Increasing Disorder**. This law impacts every aspect of life.

In the early 19th century, the invention of the steam engine drove the Industrial Revolution. While crude and inefficient by today's standards, these engines were true marvels of that age. Steam engines, also called heat engines, used the thermal energy in hot steam, produced by burning wood, coal, and—later—petroleum to do work (*Figure 18.1*). Remember that we defined work in Chapter 9 in terms of the energy required to move an object against a force. In the steam engine, the expansion of hot gases provided a force that turned crankshafts to propel steam ships or push pistons to drill coal mines.

Figure 18.1
The steam engine was a marvelous invention that used thermal energy to do work.

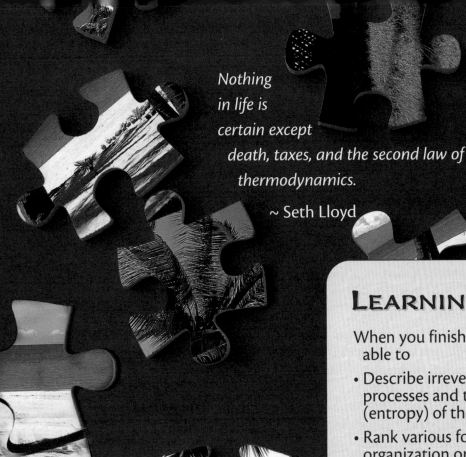

Nothing in life is certain except death, taxes, and the second law of thermodynamics.

~ Seth Lloyd

LEARNING OBJECTIVES

When you finish this chapter, you should be able to

- Describe irreversible and reversible processes and their effect on the disorder (entropy) of the Universe.

- Rank various forms of energy in terms of its organization or usefulness to do work.

- Discuss the implications of converting energy from one form to another with respect to the Law of Increasing Disorder.

- Recognize the implications of the Law of Increasing Disorder on society's long-term energy needs.

Scientists and engineers began to study the engine carefully with the hopes of improving its performance. In some cases it was a matter of national pride. (See the sidebar on Sadi Carnot, a French scientist and engineer, below.) The investigators wanted to produce an engine that could completely convert all the heat energy available in the hot steam into useful work energy. The reverse process, conversion of work into heat, occurred with no trouble. (A simple

SADI CARNOT—SCIENTIST AND PATRIOT

Carnot was born in France in 1796, the son of a leading government official of the French revolution. While a student at the École Polytechnique, Carnot requested permission from Napoleon to allow him and his fellow students to fight in the 1814 battle for Paris. Permission was granted, and they fought bravely, but unsuccessfully. After graduation from the École Polytechnique and additional military service, Carnot took additional courses at the Sorbonne. Carnot also made many visits to factories and workshops to observe how the academic principles he learned at the university were at work in the fledgling French industries. He wanted to improve the performance of steam engines, recognizing that technological prowess could keep France as a world power.

Carnot developed an idealized heat engine based on his observations of real engines. He is credited with making the initial observations that led to the statement to the Law of Increasing Disorder. Unfortunately, Carnot died of cholera at the age of 36. Most of Carnot's papers and other belongings were buried with him so his work did not receive recognition until years after his death.

♦ **Law of Increasing Disorder**

Changes occurring in natural systems always proceed in such a way that the total amount of disorder in the universe is either unchanged or increased. If total disorder is increased, the process is irreversible.

♦ **Irreversible**

An irreversible process is one which goes in only one direction; its effects often cannot be undone. Most processes which occur in nature are irreversible.

♦ **Reversible**

A reversible process goes both forward and backward at the same time. Reversible processes are relatively rare in nature.

⇦ **Figure 18.3**

Is this a natural order of events?

example of the reverse process is to rub your hands together. Your muscles are doing work, moving your hands back and forth. The action creates friction which is manifest as heat.) However, all the experiments conducted with the heat engines showed that only partial conversion of heat energy into work could be achieved. Some heat was always left over.

At about the same time, other experiments were being conducted to understand the operation of another 19th century invention, the refrigerator. Prior to the invention of the refrigerator, an icebox was used to keep food cold for a short time. An icebox worked by conduction; heat flowed from the hot food to the cold ice, melting the ice in the process. The food could never get colder than the ice.

A refrigerator, however, removes heat energy from a cold object, making the object even colder. Its operation is described in the accompanying side box. Engineers found that the operation of a refrigerator always required that some work be done (see *Figure 18.2* in the "Quick Look at How a Refrigerator Works" box). The reverse process, transferring heat from a hot object to a cold one, takes place with no work being required.

The study of these two very different inventions, steam engines and refrigerators, yielded a surprisingly common observation: there was a preferred directionality to processes involving heat. Work can be completely converted to heat, but not vice-versa, and heat flows naturally from hot objects to cold ones; to reverse the natural direction requires doing work.

We shall see in the next section that many natural occurrences have a preferred or spontaneous direction. These, like the operations of steam engines and refrigerators, have their roots in what we shall state as the Law of Increasing Disorder, or the Second Law of Thermodynamics.

18–1 IRREVERSIBLE AND REVERSIBLE PROCESSES

We are all familiar with events whose effects can't be undone. As a child you probably sang, "All the King's horses and all the King's men couldn't put Humpty together again." If you saw a video clip of a swimmer who suddenly emerged, feet first, from a placid swimming pool, and arched upward, landing on a diving board, you would probably laugh, realizing the video clip had been played backwards (*Figure 18.3*). We often find humor in the "unnatural." A diver never dives *upward* from a swimming pool, just as scrambled eggs never spontaneously unscramble and a pet dog doesn't get younger. Our experience in everyday life shows us that nature tends to run in one direction.

The examples above illustrate processes that are, in scientific terms, **irreversible**. The described actions do not spontaneously go in a reverse direction. Some irreversible processes can be undone, but these require actions, work that someone or something does to reverse the process.

For example, to imitate the backward-playing videotape, the diver could be hoisted back up to the diving board with a rope and pulley, but to date, no process for unscrambling eggs or making faithful old Fido a puppy again has been discovered.

There are some processes that can occur with equal ease in both forward and reverse directions. Such processes, which occur on the molecular level, are characterized as being **reversible.** The simplest reversible transformations are the changes in state that we studied in Chapter 12. The state transformations that water undergoes provide good examples of reversible processes and illustrate some key features of reversibility.

Imagine a beaker filled with liquid water and ice cubes at exactly 0° C sitting in a freezer that is exactly at 0° C. If you observe this beaker over time, you will find that the shape of the ice cubes change, but that the total volume (and mass) of ice doesn't change. At this temperature, water molecules on the surface of the ice cube leave and go into the liquid state at the same rate that other liquid water molecules freeze onto the sur-

A Quick Look at How a Refrigerator Works

We have already seen a few of the key principles behind the operation of a refrigerator in Chapter 13:

1. When the pressure on a gas is increased, the gas temperature rises; expanding a gas (lowering its pressure) drops the gas temperature.
2. It takes heat energy to evaporate a liquid; condensing a gas gives off heat energy.
3. Heat flows from hot objects to cold ones.

A refrigerator takes advantage of these principles to transfer heat from food in the fridge to your kitchen, causing the food's temperature to drop. In Figure 18.2, we can see a picture of the back of a refrigerator and a schematic showing the major components of a refrigerator. Several are visible at the back or inside of the refrigerator, depending upon its design. Others are hidden underneath the refrigerator's casing. The functions of each component are summarized below:

Refrigerant—the material that is evaporated and condensed, compressed and expanded during the refrigeration cycle. These may include freon, one of a family of compounds containing chlorine, fluorine, and carbon, that are sometimes abbreviated CFC's (for chloro-fluorocarbons) or ammonia, a nitrogen-hydrogen compound.

Compressor—the engine that transports the fluid (liquid/gas refrigerant), compressing and expanding it. It is usually at the back of the refrigerator near the bottom.

Heat-exchangers—coils of pipes where heat is absorbed or dissipated

Evaporator: a set of coils inside the refrigerator that becomes cold because evaporation takes place within the coils. Heat is absorbed from the refrigerator/contents into the evaporator.

Condenser: a set of coils outside the refrigerator that becomes hot because gas is condensed to a liquid inside the coils. Heat is dissipated from the coils into the air outside the refrigerator.

Expansion valve—the place where the high-pressure liquid crosses to the low pressure region. There the liquid expands and evaporates to become a low-pressure gas.

Notice that the components form a closed loop. The refrigerant moves from one point to another in the loop during a refrigeration cycle. Let's imagine starting the cycle at the compressor. The compres-

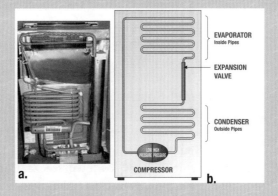

Figure 18.2

a) The back of a refrigerator showing the compressor and condenser.
b) A schematic showing the major components of a refrigerator. The yellow color of the compressor represents the region where heat is dissipated into the surroundings around the refrigerator. The blue color of the evaporator indicates the region (usually in the freezer) where cooling takes place.

sor begins to exert compression forces on the refrigerant. The refrigerant, in the gaseous state, is pressurized. It goes from a low-pressure state to a high-pressure one. Attached to the high pressure side of the compressor is the condenser. While flowing through the condenser pipe, the high-pressure gas condenses to form a liquid, giving off heat. (The yellow color of the condenser in Figure 18.2b represents the high temperature where heat is dissipated.)

On the other end of the condenser pipe a tiny, narrow-diameter copper tube is attached. The liquid, at high pressure, is forced through the narrow tube, traveling up inside the refrigerator, often into the freezer section. There, at the expansion valve, the tube connects to the evaporator pipe. The liquid refrigerant experiences a large pressure drop as it moves into the larger diameter pipe of the evaporator. Because of the pressure drop, the liquid transforms back to the gas state. The temperature of the gas falls, and heat is transferred from the warm food to the cold gas. The compressor then sucks the low pressure gas back outside the refrigerator, and the process can begin again.

To consider refrigeration from the point of view of the law of increasing disorder, the key points are:

1. The compressor does work on the gas by compressing it to the liquid state.
2. The expansion process that cools the gas allows heat to be extracted from the refrigerator contents, which are warmer than the gas.
3. During the condensation process, heat is dissipated out into the kitchen environment.

face of the ice cube. We can represent the process as:

Ice ⟺ Liquid

where the double headed arrow indicates a reversible process.

Contrast that example with a glass of water at room temperature to which ice cubes are added. Over time, all of the ice cubes will melt (*Figure 18.4*). No amount of watching will transform the water into ice cubes again. Is this process reversible or irreversible? What will happen if you put warm water into a freezer at a temperature below 0° C? It will freeze. Under these conditions, the liquid to solid transformation is irreversible.

Figure 18.4

A glass of ice-water is standing on a kitchen counter. Is the melting of the ice cubes a process that can be reversed?

What is the fundamental difference between the three examples? It is the temperature of the water. These examples illustrate an important point about reversible processes. Reversibility occurs only within a narrow set of experimental conditions such as temperature and pressure. Changing the temperature and pressure can alter the irreversibility/reversibility of a process. The specific temperature and pressure at which reversible state transformations occur depend upon the material. In *Table 12.1*, the melting and boiling temperatures represent the conditions of reversibility for each material. Since reversibility occurs at fixed temperatures and pressures,

reversible processes even on the molecular level are relatively rare in nature.

It can probably be stated that there are no mechanical processes which occur reversibly. Friction always occurs when two surfaces rub against each other, and this friction causes irreversibility.

18–2 ORDER AND DISORDER

What fundamental principle explains the fact that nature has a tendency to run in one direction? The principle has been stated in a variety of ways, one of which is, "If you think things are mixed up now, just wait a while." The key idea is that things tend to get more mixed up as time goes on. Consider *Figure 18.5*, which shows a messy dorm room and the same room after it has been cleaned up. Over time, the cleaned room tends to once again get messed up. It takes work to straighten it up again. Which would your mother prefer to see if she came to visit? Nature, unlike your mother, apparently prefers disorder and chaos.

Let's consider order and disorder on a molecular level. Remember the images the molecular model gave us for how molecules are arranged in the various states of matter? In solids, molecules are arranged neatly in a regular, predictable array, and they take up a relatively small space. In gases, molecules move chaotically throughout the entire volume of their container. The solid state is more ordered, the gaseous state more disordered.

Now consider the two images in *Figure 18.6*. Image *18.6a* is a container that has two compartments, each containing only one kind of gas. Below in *18.6b* is the same container after the divider between the two compartments has been removed and the two gases have mixed. Which image represents the ordered arrangement, and

Figure 18.5

A room in a state of disorder can be cleaned and organized (with a lot of work). However, over time it will return to a state of chaos.

Figure 18.6
a) Two kinds of molecules separated in a container.
b) If the divider is removed and they are allowed to mix, will they ever spontaneously separate to their original state?

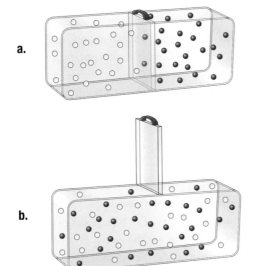

which the disordered one? Can the process be reversed? Will the mixture of two gases ever spontaneously separate?

This example illustrates disorder resulting from the various arrangements of molecules in space. Disorder can also arise from the partitioning of energy among molecules. Recall the distribution curves in Chapter 13 for the probability of molecular speeds in gases (Figures 13.8 and 13.9). At low temperatures the distribution is sharply peaked, so the molecules in a gas sample all have about the same kinetic energy. At high temperatures there is a much broader distribution of speeds and the energy is dispersed in a more disordered way throughout the molecules.

Scientists use the word **entropy** to describe the amount of disorder in a system. Strictly speaking, it is the disorder associated with the dispersal of energy throughout the molecules that make up a system, but often this is related to the geometric description of the system, such as the chaos of a messy room, or the probability of finding a particular type of molecule in a particular compartment of the container.

The entropy can be calculated if we can determine the mathematical probability of obtaining a system in its given state. The details involved in making this calculation are beyond the scope of this textbook but we can summarize the situation with two observations: More

disordered systems have a higher probability of occurring, and thus have greater entropy. In general, increasing the temperature of matter increases its entropy.

We have used the term "system" without being specific about its scientific definition. In science it is often useful to put a box, either literally or figuratively, around that portion of the world that we want to study. We isolate it, either physically or mentally, from that rest of the world that we don't want to consider. We use the word "**system**" to denote the stuff inside the box, and "**surroundings**" to identify everything outside the box. Finally, we use the word "**universe**" to describe the combined environment of the contents of our box (the "system"), plus everything outside our box (the "surroundings").

18-3 THE LAW OF INCREASING DISORDER

Now that we have introduced the concepts of reversible/irreversible processes and disorder, we can formally state the Law of Increasing Disorder:

A reversible process does not change the total amount of disorder in the Universe.

An irreversible process increases the total amount of disorder in the Universe.

Notice that the law has two parts, one for reversible processes, a second for irreversible processes. The Law of Increasing Disorder says that we must consider the *total* disorder (entropy) of the Universe. Mentally dividing our world into the system and the surroundings is a helpful way to think about this aspect of the law. A process going on in the system can decrease in its disorder as long as somewhere in the surroundings a compensating process leads to a greater increase in disorder. The net effect of the two processes must be to increase disorder in the Universe as a whole.

At 0° C, water transforming to ice is a reversible process; the transformation does not change the total disorder of the Universe. Liquid water below 0° C will irreversibly transform to solid water; while the disorder decreases for the system (water), the overall amount of disorder in the Universe must increase. This law provides

♦ **Entropy**
A quantitative measure of disorder. It increases as the disorder increases. It can be calculated mathematically from the probability of obtaining the system in its current state.

♦ **System**
A small piece of the world around which we mentally draw a box and upon which we focus our attention. It may be a beaker containing an ice cube and warm water or a refrigerator or a living organism.

♦ **Surroundings**
Everything outside what we have defined to be the system. For the examples given above, the surroundings can be considered to be the immediate area around the system: the laboratory bench on which the beaker is sitting, the kitchen in which the refrigerator is working, or the Petri dish and agar on which the organism is growing.

♦ **Universe**
The combination of system plus surroundings.

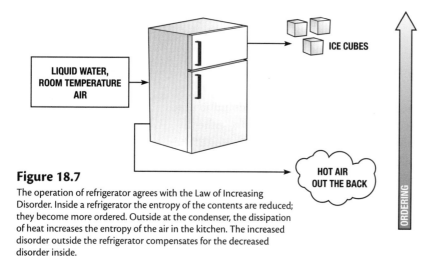

Figure 18.7
The operation of refrigerator agrees with the Law of Increasing Disorder. Inside a refrigerator the entropy of the contents are reduced; they become more ordered. Outside at the condenser, the dissipation of heat increases the entropy of the air in the kitchen. The increased disorder outside the refrigerator compensates for the decreased disorder inside.

us with an explanation for why the reverse process (solid water below 0° C melting to liquid) is never observed. Such a process must *decrease* the total amount of disorder in the Universe.

A more detailed example will be helpful to illustrate the law of increasing disorder (*Figure 18.7*). Consider a refrigerator and its contents to be the system. In the refrigerator, a tuna-fish sandwich placed on one of the refrigerator's shelves is cooled to a lower temperature. An ice-cube tray filled with warm water placed in the freezing compartment is cooled to a lower temperature and eventually turns into ice. In both compartments, there is a decrease in temperature, and in the freezer, liquid transforms to solid. Both of these effects lead to a *decrease* in the entropy of the system. If that was all that was happening, the refrigerator would be violating the Law of Increasing Disorder. However, something else has been taking place in the refrigerator at the same time ice was forming and the tuna-fish sandwich was becoming cold. At the back of the refrigerator hot air is dissipated out into the kitchen, increasing the room temperature of the kitchen. Remember that increases in temperature represent increases in entropy, so there is an increase in the entropy of the surroundings. The net effect must be that the increase in entropy of the surroundings is greater than the decrease in entropy of the system, and the entropy of the Universe increases.

Sometimes people use the Law of Increasing Disorder to argue against the theory of evolution. These folks claim that evolution represents a decrease in the entropy of organisms since evolution leads to more organized (in the sense of being more complex) organisms. Such an argu-

ment ignores the fact that as organisms become more complex they can interact with their surroundings in such a way as to increase the entropy of the Universe. A simple one-celled organism absorbs nutrients and energy from its environment and excretes waste products. Humans also absorb nutrients and energy from their surroundings. One might argue that the waste products of human existence (not just our metabolic waste products but also toxic exhaust fumes from our badly tuned cars and all the plastic, paper, and worn-out jogging shoes that fill our garbage dumps) are sufficiently great to increase the entropy of the Universe!

The law of increasing disorder provides an important criterion to use in predicting whether a potential process can take place or not. If the process will increase the entropy of the Universe, it just might work. If calculations show that the process will decrease the Universe's entropy, don't bother trying it, you will waste your time.

When NASA sent two rovers to Mars, those robots discovered certain forms of iron oxides. The discovery prompted NASA scientists to proclaim that water must have existed on Mars. Fundamentally, this claim is rooted in the Law of Increasing Disorder. Earth-based experiments have shown that, of the possible chemical reactions that could produce these oxides, the only ones that obey the Law of Increasing Disorder require water.

18–4 ORDER AND ENERGY

As stated in the introduction, the Law of Increasing Disorder arose from studies designed to improve the performances of early steam engines. Those studies showed that even in the best designed engines, not all the energy available from the fuel can be captured, controlled and put to use, like turning the wheels of your car, or propelling you uphill. Even the human body, which is among the most efficiently designed "engines," can't completely convert all the chemical potential energy in the food it takes in into useful work, like contracting and expanding muscles and transporting molecules (O_2) from one part of the body (lungs) to other parts of the body (blood cells.) Some energy is expelled as body heat while additional energy is elimi-

Figure 18.8
Illustrations showing the origins on an atomic level of the ordering of different energy types. a) Water molecules falling over Niagra Falls under the influence of gravity are generally moving downward. Gravitational potential and macroscopic kinetic energy are represented here. b) Electrons flowing through a circuit are generally moving in the same direction. Electrical potential energy is represented here. c) Water molecules in the Great Salt Lake, essentially a large pond, move chaotically, with no net organization to their motion. Microscopic kinetic energy is represented here.

nated in the form of bodily waste products (urine and feces.)

These observations can be explained in light of the law of increasing disorder. The forms of energy described in Chapter 9 can be ranked in terms of the organization or order of the energy. In the illustrations in *Figure 18.8* we see three forms of energy: the **macroscopic kinetic energy** associated with water molecules going over Niagara Falls, the **electrical potential energy** associated with electrons flowing through an electrical circuit, and the **microscopic kinetic energy** (thermal energy) associated with the water molecules in the Great Salt Lake. In each of these three figures we see a macroscopic (large-scale) object with an inset that shows a magnification to illustrate motion at the atomic level.

Water molecules going over Niagara Falls have an overall uniform direction to their motion—they are going downhill. Electrons flowing through a circuit have a similar uniformity to their direction of motion. The motion of the water molecules and electrons in these two illustrations show some coherence or directionality. The water molecules in the Great Salt Lake, however, are moving around, but they are not going anywhere. Like gas molecules, they undergo random collisions, but there is no net direction to their motion.

ASIDE: These are simplifications, of course. Water molecules in Niagara Falls do move in directions other than down hill and electrons experience resistance as they flow through wires and collide with nuclei in the passage. Still, the contrast with the random motion of molecules in that big pond we call the Great Salt Lake is a good picture around which to frame our images of "organized energy."

In addition to these three forms of energy there are nuclear potential energy, a highly organized form of internal energy associated with the subatomic particles in the nucleus, and chemical potential energy, the internal energy associated with the electrostatic interactions between the electrons and nuclei of atoms that hold molecules and also that hold atoms or molecules together in liquids and solids. Chemical potential energy is intermediate in organization between electrical potential and ambient temperature thermal energy.

Table 18.1 summarizes the various forms of energy and their ranking with respect to organization of the energy. A form of energy can be converted completely into all forms below it in Table 18.1. If we want to convert a less-organized form of energy into a more-organized form, nature requires that we pay a price in order to satisfy the Law of Increasing Disorder. Only

- **Macroscopic Kinetic Energy**

The kinetic energy possessed by moving objects given by 1/2mass x (speed)^2.

- **Electrical Potential Energy**

Potential energy due to the relative positions of charged particles.

- **Microscopic Kinetic Energy**

The kinetic energy associated with atomic and molecular motions. A stationary object can have microscopic but not macroscopic kinetic energy.

Table 18.1 – Forms of Energy and Their Ranking in Terms of Organization

Gravitational Potential Energy and Macroscopic Kinetic Energy

Nuclear Potential Energy

Electrical (*Household*)

Chemical Potential Energy

Thermal Energy (also known as *Heat or Microscopic Kinetic Energy*)

ordered

↓

disordered

Table 18.1
Energy can be ranked according to its order or organization.

part of the mid-level energy can be converted upwards and the remainder must be degraded to a lower form, usually heat.

The ranking of energy can be understood in terms of partitioning a given quantity of energy into various quantum energy states. One thousand kilojoules (about 250 food calories) of chemical potential energy contained in gasoline, an intermediate form of organized energy, is contained in one or two energy states associated with the bonds that hold the fuel together. In highly disordered heat energy, that same quantity of energy is spread out over many, many millions of quantum states. These quantum states are associated with the microscopic kinetic energy of the molecules.

Figure 18.9 illustrates the application of the Law of Increasing Disorder to the operation of the combustion engines that power motor vehicles. The desired outcome is to move the vehicle forward, giving it macroscopic kinetic energy. The energy comes from the chemical potential energy stored in the gasoline. Only some fraction of that energy is converted to the higher energy form, the majority is downgraded to heat that is expelled as hot gases from the exhaust pipe.

Life forms are also governed by the Law of Increasing Disorder. Sunlight is energy that

results from nuclear reactions on the Sun. Sunlight is fairly high-quality energy. Plants on Earth absorb the sunlight and partially convert it into chemical potential energy through the chemical reactions of photosynthesis. Then, when the plants die, the complex molecules in the plant decay into simpler molecules with heat as a major product; chemical potential energy is converted to thermal energy. Through biochemical processes in animals (including humans) that consume the plants, the chemical potential energy can be partially converted to higher forms of energy. For example, conversion to macroscopic kinetic energy allows the animal to flee a pursuer, while conversion to electrical potential energy powers the respiratory pathways of cells. But nature, operating through the Law of Increasing Disorder, always takes a toll during the process, and a major portion of the chemical energy stored in the plant is discarded as heat.

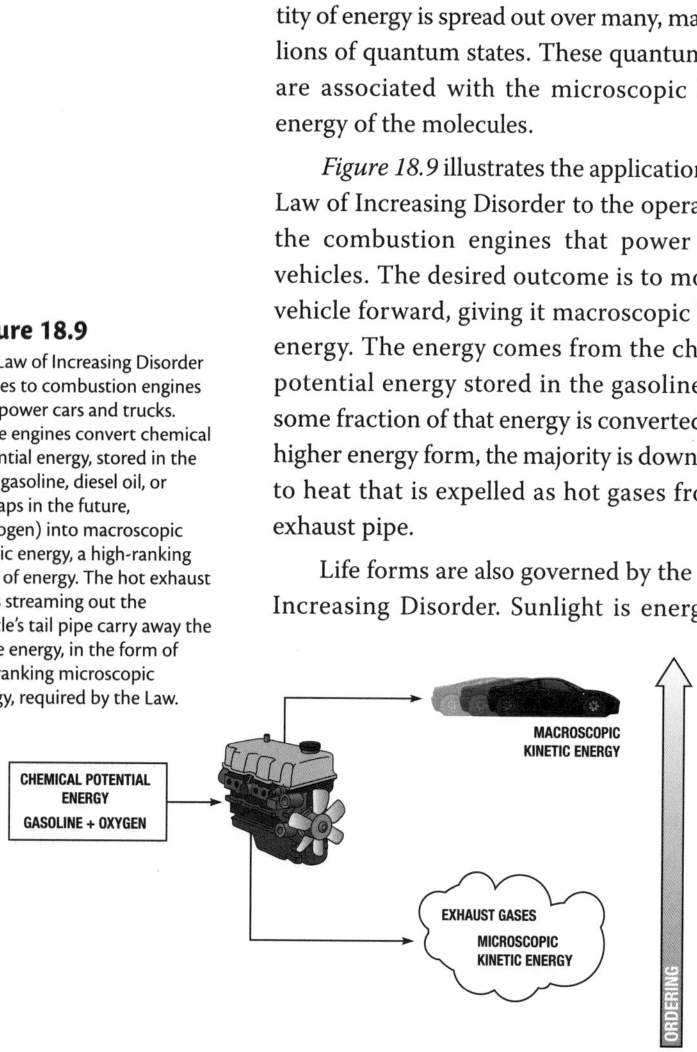

18–5 ENERGY CONSERVATION AND SOCIAL ISSUES

The Law of Increasing Disorder requires every irreversible process to increase disorder in the Universe. If you want to convert energy from a more disordered form to a more ordered one, the law requires some of the energy to be converted downward to an even more disordered form.

Engineers talk about the efficiency of an engine as a measure of the price nature requires for the upward conversion of energy. If an engine could be perfectly efficient, all the chemical potential energy stored in its fuel would be converted to the higher quality macroscopic kinetic energy. However, in even the best-designed and well-tuned engine, the Law of Increasing Disorder requires that a fraction of the energy

Figure 18.9
The Law of Increasing Disorder applies to combustion engines that power cars and trucks. These engines convert chemical potential energy, stored in the fuel (gasoline, diesel oil, or perhaps in the future, hydrogen) into macroscopic kinetic energy, a high-ranking form of energy. The hot exhaust gases streaming out the vehicle's tail pipe carry away the waste energy, in the form of low-ranking microscopic energy, required by the Law.

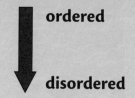

CHEMICAL POTENTIAL ENERGY
GASOLINE + OXYGEN

MACROSCOPIC KINETIC ENERGY

EXHAUST GASES
MICROSCOPIC KINETIC ENERGY

ORDERING

in the fuel be exhausted in a more disorganized form, usually as thermal energy (heat). The more disordered the source of energy is, the greater the amount of energy that will be wasted in use. You might think of the implications of this law as "You can't win; you can't even break even!"

Some philosophers in the latter half of the 19th century believed that the Law of Increasing Disorder would ultimately result in the end of all life. They reasoned that the Universe would eventually run down, as all the useful energy gradually degraded to thermal energy. Some years later, after Hiroshima and Nagasaki, T. S. Eliot, in his poem, "The Hollow Men," described it this way: "This is how the world ends . . . Not with a bang but a whimper." Sydney Harris has depicted the Law of Increasing Disorder in several of his cartoons. One is shown in *Figure 18.10*.

The Law of Increasing Disorder tells us that every irreversible action ultimately impacts the Universe's quantity of useful energy. While we can't do much about the eventual death of the

Figure 18.10
How does this cartoon illustrate the Law of Increasing Disorder?

Sun, we can consider our use of Earth-based energy sources. To anyone concerned about the availability of the world's natural resources for future generations, prudence and good stewardship of those resources means that human activities should be conducted as efficiently as possible. In today's free-market society a manufacturer can earn a greater profit in the sale of a large sport utility vehicle with poor gas mileage than in the sale of a smaller, more energy-efficient compact car. Often what is good for capitalism may be in conflict with what is good for the energy balance of the Universe.

Chapter Framework

A. Law of Increasing Disorder
  1. Sadi Carnot
B. Irreversible and Reversible Processes
C. Order and Disorder
  1. Entropy
D. Order and Energy
E. Energy Conservation and Social Issues

Comprehension

True/False

1. _____ An increase in temperature also means that disorder increases.

2. _____ Irreversible processes are always spontaneous and occur on their own without any intervention.

3. _____ From our current understanding, sometime in the future engineers will design a car that is completely efficient; i.e., a car that creates no additional disorder in the universe.

4. _____ Gravitational potential energy is a more ordered form of energy than electrical potential energy.

5. _____ A salt shaker and a pepper shaker get knocked off the table and break onto the floor. Separating the salt and pepper can be considered an irreversible process.

Fill in the Blank

1. An ice cube melts in a warm glass of water. This is an example of a(n) _____ process.

2. Complete conversion of one energy form to another energy form only takes place only if the energy converts to a _____ energy form.

3. The "energy" crisis is not well-named. It should really be called a(n) _____ crisis.

4. The universe is the combination of a(n) _____ plus its _____.

Matching

1. _____ Everything outside what we have defined to be the system.

2. _____ A process which goes in only one direction; its effects cannot be undone. Most processes which occur in nature are this way.

3. _____ A process which goes both forward and backward at the same time.

4. _____ A small piece of the world around which we mentally draw a box and upon which we focus our attention.

5. _____ A quantitative measure of disorder. It increases as the disorder increases.

6. _____ Disorder in the universe increases or stays the same anytime a process occurs.

a. System
b. Entropy
c. Irreversible process
d. Reversible process
e. Surroundings
f. The Law of Increasing Disorder

Analysis

1. Overall disorder remains unchanged in
   a) reversible processes.
   b) chemical processes.
   c) mechanical processes.
   d) irreversible processes.

2. If analyzing a fridge in relationship to its surroundings, what would the fridge be considered?
   a) Entropy
   b) Surroundings
   c) System
   d) Both (b) and (c)

3. Which of the following is a reversible process?
   a) A man diving into a pool.
   b) Water falling down Niagara Falls.
   c) A pendulum swinging in a frictionless environment.
   d) Scrambling eggs.
   e) None of the above.

4. Which of the following processes is closest to an ideal reversible process?
   a) A falling golf ball falls into the mud and sticks there.
   b) Water evaporates from a glass sitting on the kitchen table.
   c) A book sliding on a horizontal table comes to rest because of friction.
   d) A ripe peach rotting.
   e) An ice cube changes shape while floating in a glass of water at 0° C.

5. An auto engine cannot convert all of its fuel's chemical potential energy into macroscopic kinetic energy because
   a) energy would not be conserved.
   b) energy would be conserved.
   c) mass would not be conserved.
   d) disorder would be decreased.

6. The Law of Increasing Disorder places limits on the efficiency of energy conversion. Which of the following is allowed?
   a) 100% conversion of ambient temperature thermal energy to kinetic energy.
   b) 100% conversion of chemical potential energy to kinetic energy.
   c) 100% conversion of sunlight to kinetic energy.
   d) 100% conversion of electricity to ambient temperature thermal energy.
   e) 100% conversion of ambient temperature thermal energy to chemical potential energy.

7. Of the quantities listed, the one associated with the most disorder is
   a) chemical potential energy.

b) gravitational potential energy.

c) macroscopic kinetic energy.

d) nuclear potential energy.

e) thermal energy in a glass of water.

8. In an old-fashioned ice box (literally a box containing ice with room for food containers), the food's temperature could never get lower than 0° C. Explain why.

9. In the freezer in your refrigerator, food probably gets down to about −10 °C. What can you conclude about the temperature that the refrigerant gas reaches during the expansion portion of a refrigeration cycle?

10. In the following scenarios, identify which of the two situations is more disordered.

   a. A large, solid chunk of table salt and a beaker of pure water or a solution made by mixing the salt and water together.

   b. A solid chunk of ice or a container filled with the same mass of water in the gaseous state.

   c. A balloon filled with helium at room temperature at sea level or the same balloon at an altitude of 8000 feet where the air is colder.

   d. A chamber with two compartments, one containing pure oxygen and the other containing pure nitrogen or the same chamber in which the two gases have been allowed to mix.

11. Pure aluminum melts at a temperature of 660° C. When liquid aluminum solidifies at this temperature, is the process reversible or irreversible? What effect does the process have on the total disorder in the universe?

Synthesis

1. An object slides across the table, and comes to a rest because of friction. Explain how there is more "order" in the beginning and more "disorder" at the end of this process.

2. State the Law of Increasing Disorder in you own words.

3. Illustrate the Law of Increasing Disorder by describing an irreversible process.

4. No process can occur in which the total effect results in heat flowing from a cooler object to a hotter object. Why?

5. Stacey drops a bottle of perfume on the floor of a large room. The bottle completely shatters. Ashley smells the perfume on the other side of the room a few seconds later. Using the molecular model of matter and the Law of Increasing Disorder, explain why Ashley smells the perfume on the other side of the room.

6. For each of the following situations:

   • Describe what would happen to the system.

   • Name and state, in you own words, the fundamental principle that could explain what would be observed.

   • Explain what would happen to the order of the system in terms of the fundamental principle. Be sure to describe the order at the beginning and how it changes with time.

   a. A car is moving along a flat highway. The engine is off and the car coasts to a stop.

   b. A drop of ink is released into a large flask of water.

   c. An ice cube is placed into a pan of warm water.

7. State both the Law of Conservation of Energy and the Law of Increasing Disorder. What happens to the energy and to the entropy when:

   a. Fossil fuel is burned.

   b. Water from behind a dam is used to make electric current and the electric current is used to operate a toaster.

8. A refrigerator causes a transfer of thermal internal energy from a cooler region to a hotter region. The separation of hot and cold causes an increase in order. The door on the refrigerator is left open.

   a. What happens to the temperature of the kitchen?

   b. Explain the temperature change using the Law of Increasing Disorder.

   c. If the fridge door were shut, order would appear to increase with the separation of hot and cold. Explain how this is possible using the Law of Increasing Disorder.

9. A tractor trailer truck driving down a mountain at 60 mph hour comes to a complete stop when he rounds a bend and sees a line of traffic ahead. The truck's brakes become so hot that they start to smoke. Describe this event in terms of an energy conversion: a) what kind of energy did the truck have coming down the hill and b) what kind of energy did it have when fully stopped. Explain why this process is allowed by the Law of Increasing Disorder.

10. Cars and trucks vary widely in their gas consumption efficiencies. A subcompact car may get 30 miles per gallon of gas consumed while a large, heavy, military-type vehicle now sold for popular use may get fewer than 10 miles per gallon. Discuss the effect on the disorder in the Universe by burning a gallon of gas in the small car as compared to the large military vehicle.

11. Explain how the Sydney Harris cartoon in Figure 18.8 illustrates the Law of Increasing Disorder.

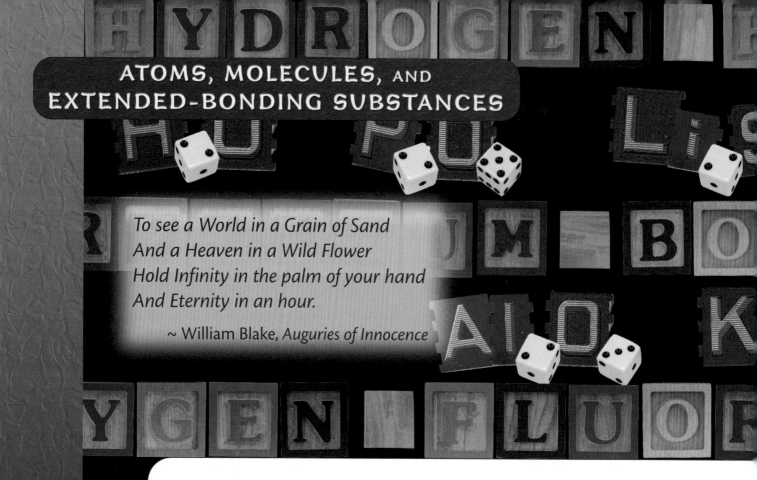

ATOMS, MOLECULES, AND EXTENDED-BONDING SUBSTANCES

CHAPTER 19

*To see a World in a Grain of Sand
And a Heaven in a Wild Flower
Hold Infinity in the palm of your hand
And Eternity in an hour.*

~ William Blake, *Auguries of Innocence*

When physicists talk about matter, they may mean anything from subatomic particles to galaxies. When chemists talk about matter, they usually mean matter at the atomic and the molecular level. Chemists study why different forms of atomic and molecular matter exist. They often want to recreate in the laboratory substances first discovered in plants or other living organisms and then found to have useful properties. For example, tamoxifen, the drug used most-widely to treat and prevent breast cancer, was first obtained from needles of a Pacific yew tree. Since the yew tree grows very slowly, scientists vigorously pursued methods to synthesize the drug on a large scale. Scientists continue to synthesize new substances

Figure 19.1

The branches, needles, and fruit of a Pacific yew tree from which tamoxifen is obtained.

based upon the tamoxifen molecule in hopes of improving the therapeutic performance, by boosting the kill rate of cancer cells or minimizing side effects like hair loss.

Thinking on the molecular scale poses some challenges. Although we have all gazed up at stars, experienced gravitational forces, played with magnets, and seen electricity at work, none of us has direct experiences with molecules. Is this course your first opportunity to think about those tiny particles that make up chemical substances? If so, don't hyperventilate at the thought. We will keep it simple but relevant.

Chemists use various methods to represent molecules and compounds and convey important information simply, concisely and accurately. In this chapter, you will encounter several of these methods. You will also learn how atoms connect to form molecules and larger structures.

Often a molecular structure provides important clues to why the molecule behaves the way it does. When James Watson and Francis Crick discovered the double helical structure of DNA, for example, they immediately recognized how the molecule might function in genetics and evolution. In a later chapter, we shall consider several complex materials that also illustrate the relation between chemical and physical properties and chemical structures.

LEARNING OBJECTIVES

When you are finish with this chapter, you should be able to
• Distinguish between compounds and elements.
• Interpret a chemical formula for the type and for the number of atoms in a molecule or for the relative numbers of atoms in materials that form extended or network structures.
• Recognize that characteristic atomic groupings or fragments give rise to molecular families.
• Inspect molecular structures for connectivity and for bonding geometry within the molecules.
• Identify several instrumental techniques that give elemental and structural information about molecules and compounds.

Someone once said, "Beauty is in the eye of the beholder." Chemists find beauty in the form and structure of molecules. In the opening quote for this chapter, William Blake speaks of seeing the world in a grain of sand and holding infinity in the palm of his hand. The numbers of atoms in a grain of sand or molecules in a handful of sugar border on infinity. The order in the physical world that is the subject of this course is manifested on the level of atoms and molecules as well as galaxies. We encourage you to find beauty in atomic and molecular order.

19-1 CLASSIFICATION OF MATTER—PURE SUBSTANCES AND MIXTURES

Pure Substances: Elements and Compounds

A **pure substance** has a defined, fixed chemical composition. There are two types of pure substances: elements and compounds. **Elements** contain just one kind of atom. The Periodic Table lists the 111 known elements. Elemental substances you may have encountered include helium gas (in balloons), liquid mercury

(in thermometers) and aluminum foil (covers for last night's leftovers.)

Compounds contain two or more types of atoms in a fixed, definite proportion. Both water and hydrogen peroxide (a popular disinfectant and bleach) contain hydrogen atoms and oxygen atoms. In water, the ratio is two hydrogen atoms to one oxygen atom; in hydrogen peroxide, the ratio is one to one. Common table salt has one sodium atom for every chlorine atom. Sucrose, the sugar you sprinkled on your cereal this morning, contains carbon atoms, hydrogen atoms and oxygen atoms in the ratio 12:22:11.

Mixtures, Solutions and Alloys

MIXTURES

In our daily lives, we rarely encounter matter that is a pure substance. We deal most commonly with **mixtures** of pure substances. Often, mixtures can be physically separated into the

225

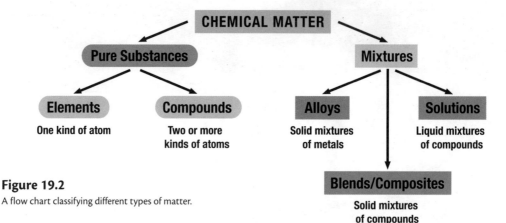

Figure 19.2
A flow chart classifying different types of matter.

- ◆ **Pure Substance**

  Chemical matter that has a defined, unchanging chemical composition.

- ◆ **Elements**

  Matter that contains only one kind of atom.

- ◆ **Compounds**

  Matter that contains two or more atoms in a fixed, definite proportion. New compounds form when the relative proportions of atoms change.

- ◆ **Mixtures**

  Matter that contains multiple substances. Many mixtures can be physically separated into their pure components.

- ◆ **Solutions**

  A liquid mixture containing two or more compounds.

- ◆ **Alloy**

  A solid solution of metals.

component substances. Imagine dumping the contents of a salt shaker and a pepper shaker into a bowl and stirring. You have just prepared a mixture. Even though it might be tedious, you could separate out the salt from the pepper.

Not all mixtures are as obvious as the salt and pepper example, nor as easy to separate components. For example, you likely wear clothes made of a "blended" fabric. Different mixes of natural and/or synthetic fibers are blended together. Each fiber has a different property (stretchy, wrinkle-free, shrink-resistant) based on the properties of its chemical matter. Blending fibers produces a fabric possessing the desirable properties of the individual components. Additional substances may coat the fibers to promote stain-resistance or reduce flammability. Looking at the fiber with the native eye may not reveal its "mixture" aspect.

Foods are mixtures of complex substances. Different foods contain different mixtures of substances. Healthy foods contain lots of complex carbohydrates, proteins, vitamins, and minerals. They are also low in fats and simple forms of carbohydrates, such as sugar. Unfortunately for our health, most fast foods incorporate large quantities of fats and simple carbohydrates.

Solutions

Solutions are mixtures of substances, one of them a liquid, such that the other components completely dissolve in the liquid. Your favorite soda pop is a solution that contains sugar (about 8–10 teaspoons per 16 oz.), food coloring, flavorings, and carbon dioxide gas to make it fizzy. When the open soda can stands on the counter or warms up, the dissolved carbon dioxide comes out of the solution, making the soda taste "flat." Milk and orange juice, on the other hand, are not simple solutions, because they contain solid particles that are suspended in water-based liquid solutions.

Unlike pure compounds, the compositions of solutions can vary. Solutions of table sugar or of salt in water have a large composition range. Dilute solutions contain just a few ions of sodium and chlorine or a few sugar molecules; concentrated solutions contain relatively little water and mostly salt or sugar. Gases like CO_2 have a limited solubility in liquids. Because of this, sodas are actually bottled with a large pressure of CO_2 above the liquid to increase the solubility. The small amount of high pressure CO_2 at the top is what makes the hissing sound when you open a can of soda.

Alloys

Alloys form when one or more metals dissolve in each other and then solidify. The relative amounts of the metals in an alloy can vary, sometimes substantially, from one type of alloy to another. Brass (copper and zinc), gold jewelry, and stainless steel "silverware" are common alloys.

An alloy can have very different properties from the pure metals that make up the alloy. Pure metals are soft and malleable (we shall see why in chapter 20). Adding small amounts of other metals can produce alloys with a hardness higher than that of the pure metal.

Scientists usually start by studying properties of pure substances before tackling mixtures or solutions. Generally, pure materials behave more reproducibly. Characterizing and identifying structural or chemical factors responsible for a particular property becomes easier. Like scientists, we will focus our initial study of chemical matter on pure substances.

IN THE MARKET FOR A WEDDING RING?

An Introduction to Buying Gold Jewelry

Pure gold is a very soft metal. Because of its softness, pure-gold jewelry dents or deforms very easily. Adding other metals to pure gold produces a harder substance, one that resists shape changes. For this reason, jewelers use gold alloys rather than pure gold to fashion typical gold rings, pendants, and earrings.

The term *karat* identifies the amount of gold in the alloy. A karat is defined as 1/24 ounce. An 18-karat gold alloy signifies that the fraction of gold is 18/24. Expressed as a weight percent, 75% (18/24 = 0.75) of the alloy is gold. A 22-karat piece has (22/24) or 91.7% of its weight as gold. Even 24-karat gold, nominally (24/24) gold by weight, has small amounts of other metals. The other metals used in the alloy are often silver, copper, and zinc.

In addition to hardness, the color of the gold piece can vary with chemical composition of the alloy. Alloys of gold with platinum or gold with palladium yield "white" gold. Chemical reactivity also varies with composition. A 9 karat gold piece has less than half (by weight) of its metal as gold; typically copper makes up most of the remaining mass. Metallic copper, present in a high proportion in 9 karat rings, can react with the moisture on your skin. The green copper oxide that results can leave an unsightly green circle around your finger. Jewelry pieces with higher gold contents do not react with skin moisture or oils.

19–2 STRUCTURAL ORGANIZATION OF MATTER

Three different kinds of atomic-level organization have been observed in pure substances.

Atomic Matter

Helium and the other members of the Group 8A noble gases exhibit the simplest kind of matter. In their three physical states (gas, liquid, solid), Group 8A elements exist as simple atoms. The pictures of Figure 13.5 adequately portray the organization in these materials: each ball in those figures represents one atom. We shall refer to Group 8A elements as **atomic matter.**

Molecular Matter

Water exemplifies the next kind of organization. In its three physical states, water exists as discrete molecules. Each water molecule contains two hydrogen atoms connected to a central oxygen atom. In ice, the solid form of water, the water molecules arrange themselves in a very specific pattern. Each hydrogen atom on one molecule aligns itself with an oxygen atom on a neighboring molecule. Water molecules in ice do

not move much, except to jiggle a bit about their central location, like the lumps of Jello on the tray in Chapter 13 (Figure 13.2). Liquid water molecules move more freely than those in ice, but they still remain loosely connected with neighbors. Gaseous water molecules, on the other hand, are free to move throughout the entire container. *Figure 19.3* illustrates the arrangement of molecules in the three states of water. We shall refer to substances like water that contain discrete molecules as **molecular substances.**

- **Atomic Matter**

  Matter that exists in the solid, liquid, and gaseous states as single atoms.

- **Molecular Substances**

  Matter that exists as molecules in the solid, liquid, and gaseous states.

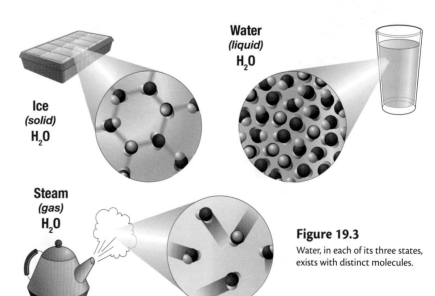

Figure 19.3

Water, in each of its three states, exists with distinct molecules.

Network Matter

Magnesium and aluminum, table salt (sodium chloride), and the quartz in beach sand (silicon dioxide) represent the third kind of atomic-level organization of matter. You might suspect that elemental magnesium and aluminum would be classified as atomic matter, like helium. You might also suspect that sodium chloride would exist as discrete molecules containing sodium atoms and chlorine atoms.

Neither supposition would be true. These materials are classified as **network or extended-bonding substances**. In extended-bonding substances, every atom or ion interacts strongly with many neighbors. A linked network forms.

Figure 19.4 provides a representation of the three network solids discussed above, showing all the atoms or ions as space-filling balls. The arrangement of magnesium atoms in solid metal does not look noticeably different from those of solid helium or neon. In sodium chloride, each sodium ion interacts very strongly with the six negatively-charged chloride ions that surround it, but they also interact with other chloride ions that are further away. In turn, every chloride ion interacts very strongly with its immediate neighbors, six positively-charged sodium ions, and less strongly with sodium ions further away. In the quartz, every silicon atom connects to four oxygen atoms, and every oxygen atom connects to two silicon atoms.

- **Network or Extended-Bonding Substances**

Substances in which every atom or ion interacts strongly with many neighbors. An extended network of linked atoms or ions form. Distinct molecules or ion pairs do not exist in these materials.

Figure 19.4

Examples of extended or network solids. Atoms and ions are shown as space filling balls. a) Magnesium, a metallic element, is a network solid. b) Sodium chloride, an ionic compound is also a network solid. c) Quartz, the major component of sand has the formula SiO_2, but discrete molecules with this formula do not exist in quartz.

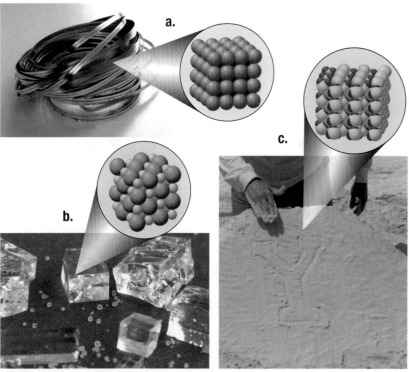

Thinking Like A Scientist: Scientists have only been able to look at matter on the atomic level for about fifty years. Yet the three differences in the organization of matter have been known for more than one hundred years. How did scientists recognize these divisions so many years before direct observation was possible? Particularly, how did the difference in structural organization between helium and aluminum come to be understood?

Go back and look at Table 12.1. Can you categorize the materials represented there in terms of atomic, molecular, or network types of matter? Helium and neon belong to the category of atomic matter; hydrogen, nitrogen, water and ethanol typify molecular matter; the remaining substances are network substances. Now, do you notice anything about the values of the melting and boiling temperatures of each type of matter? Which grouping tends to have the lowest values? Which grouping tends to have the highest values?

As you have just noticed, the melting and boiling points tend to group together for a particular type of substance. Atomic substances have very low melting and boiling points; network substances have extraordinarily high ones. Molecular substances tend to have melting and boiling points somewhere in between. (Hydrogen, an especially low mass molecular substance, has melting and boiling temperatures lower than neon, an atomic substance.) This grouping of substances by melting and boiling point characteristics provided the first clues to scientists that matter was organized differently in atomic, molecular, and extended structures.

Remember our hypotheses to explain the observations of the melting and boiling points—that they have something to do with the strengths of forces holding the solids and liquids together. Given this new distinction between atomic, molecular, and network substances, we can refine the hypotheses.

The weak interactions (forces) between neon atoms in its solid or liquid states must be very different in origin from the strong interactions between magnesium, aluminum, or other metal atoms in their solid and liquid states. The interactions that hold together solids or liquids of hydrogen, nitrogen, water and ethanol occur between molecules, not atoms. Given the melting and boiling point temperatures, forces between molecules must be stronger than those in atomic solids, but not as strong as those in extended materials.

Also, we can recognize that the strong forces that hold metals together must differ from those that hold salts together. While the melting and boiling points of both types of extended solids are comparable, other properties such as electrical conductivity are not.

19–3 CHEMICAL BONDS

Chemists use the term **chemical bond** to refer to the attractive forces that hold atoms together in molecules or that hold atoms or ions together in network solids. At the simplest level, bonds arise from electrostatic interactions. Positively-charged nuclei attract electrons, both their own, and those of their neighbors.

There are three principal types of bonds: metallic, ionic, and covalent bonds. Other types of interactions, such as van der Waals and hydrogen bonds, are weak electrostatic interactions. Upcoming chapters show how extensions of the quantum model of the atom explain all these bonding types.

19–4 CHEMICAL FORMULAS AND STRUCTURES

Chemical Formulas of Atomic or Molecular Substances

Chemical formulas give the chemical composition of a compound. In its simplest form, a chemical formula lists the kinds of atoms in an atomic or molecular substance and their relative numbers. Here are some examples of chemical formulas and reasons you might have heard of these substances:

He   helium gas—party balloon gas

H$_2$ hydrogen molecule—potential source of energy in future automobiles

N$_2$ nitrogen molecule—air we breathe

S$_8$ sulfur molecule—elemental form of sulfur

CO$_2$ carbon dioxide—greenhouse gas produced by burning carbon-based fuels

H$_2$O   water—does this need an introduction?

H$_2$O$_2$ hydrogen peroxide—bleach and antiseptic agent

C$_{13}$H$_{18}$O$_2$ ibuprofen—a non-steroidal anti-inflammatory agent

C$_{257}$H$_{383}$N$_{65}$O$_{77}$S$_6$ insulin—an enzyme produced in the pancreas

PtCl$_2$N$_2$H$_6$ cisplatin—an anti-tumor agent

A chemical formula strings together the atomic symbols for the elements in the compound. A *subscript* placed to the *right* of an atom identifies how many times that atom is present in the molecule. The lack of a subscript indicates that only a single atom of that element is present in the molecule.

Molecules can be very simple and contain as few as two atoms. Hydrogen and nitrogen exist in nature as two atoms of the same element. The term **diatomic molecule** is used to identify such molecules. "Dia" comes from the Greek word for "two."

Molecules can also contain large numbers of atoms. Insulin, for example, contains almost 800 atoms. In fact, insulin belongs to a family of molecules called proteins. The largest proteins found in the human body can contain many thousands of atoms. The body uses insulin to break down sugar molecules. People with diabetes have problems producing insulin.

Chemical Structures of Molecular Substances

Molecules have three-dimensional structures. Scientists use different methods to represent molecular structures. In the simplest method, colored balls represent atoms and sticks between atoms represent the bonds that connect them. Using balls with small atomic sizes relative to the stick bonds most clearly portrays the details of **connectivity**, which atoms connect to what other atoms.

Other methods better reflect the extent to which electron density spreads out from the nuclei. We have used this method, sometimes referred to as "space-filling" balls in representing the structures in Figure 19.4. Space-filling

• **Chemical Bond**
The attractive force between nuclei and electrons that hold atoms together in molecules or atoms and ions together in network substances.

• **Chemical Formula**
Way to represent the the kind of atom and its number in a molecule. The chemical formula of a water molecule that contains two hydrogen atoms and one oxygen atom is given by H$_2$O. The subscript to the right of the atomic symbol indicates the number of that kind of atom in the molecule.

• **Diatomic Molecule**
A molecule containing only two atoms of the same kind of element. Hydrogen, nitrogen, oxygen, fluorine, chlorine, bromine, and iodine exist in nature as diatomic molecules.

• **Connectivity**
The details of how atoms connect to one another in molecules or extended structures.

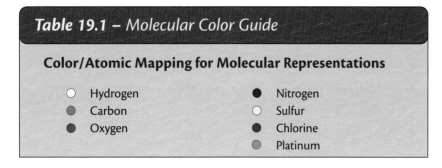

Table 19.1 – *Molecular Color Guide*

Color/Atomic Mapping for Molecular Representations

○ Hydrogen   ● Nitrogen
● Carbon   ○ Sulfur
● Oxygen   ● Chlorine
                    ● Platinum

Figure 19.5
Images of selected molecules. Balls represent atoms (not to scale) and sticks represent bonds.

a. CO₂
Carbon dioxide
Linear molecule

b. H₂O
Water
Bent shape

c. H₂O₂
Hydrogen peroxide
Non-planar shape

d. CH₄
Methane
Tetrahedral shape

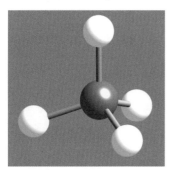

e. C₃H₈
Propane

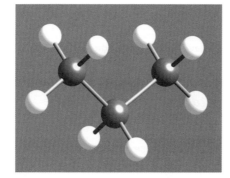

f. C₈H₁₈
Octane

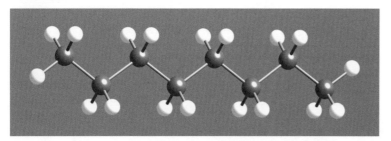

balls hide structural details that will be of interest to us in this section. For this reason, we will rely on the simplest ball and stick representations for most of our molecular pictures. *Table 19.1* shows the color/element assignment that we will use in our representations.

The following section presents an opportunity for you to look at molecules. Don't worry about memorizing formulas or structures. Approach the experience the way you might look at a photo album of your new fiance's extended family. No one will ask you to recognize Aunt Josephine from the photograph or guess what her weight is. But, by looking at the pictures, you can get a sense of what your new family looks like. Are they tall or short, dark or blond? Are there lots of kids, or mostly senior citizens? How many of the grandchildren have Grandpa Joe's protruding ears or Grandma Beth's nose?

CONNECTIVITY OF ATOMS IN MOLECULES

Use the following suggestions and questions to guide your inspection of the molecules in *Figure 19.5*. In this first glimpse at molecules, look in particular at the different ways in which atoms connect to each other.

I. Practice matching formulas to structures.
    1. Look at the chemical formulas in Figure 19.5 and verify that you can match atoms to the formula.

II. Look for bonding patterns within each structure and between different structures.
    1. Describe to yourself what atoms connect to other atoms.
    2. In the molecules that contain carbon atoms, to how many other atoms is

MODEL STRUCTURE

The orientation of an atomic group or fragment shown in the picture of one molecule may differ from the orientation shown in another molecule's picture. What matters to a chemist is the number and nature of atoms connected to each other; not whether the fragment is pictured on the right hand side rather than the left hand side of the picture.

each carbon attached? How many attachments do hydrogen atoms tend to make? What about oxygen?

3. Notice that some fragments or groupings of atoms appear in many molecules. Can you find $-CH_3$ (a carbon atom attached to three hydrogen atoms) fragments in propane (e), octane (f), alanine (k), and ibuprofen (r)? Does this fragment appear in any other molecules?

4. Can you find $-O-H$ fragments in any of the molecules? What atom(s) connect to the $-O-H$ fragment?

III. Methane (d), propane (e), and octane (f) are three substances that serve as fuels. Methane is also known as "natural gas." Camp stoves burn propane, while octane is one component in gasoline.

1. What atoms does each molecule contain? Why might they be called "hydrocarbons?" What structural units do you find in all three molecules?

2. What other molecules in Figure 19.5 contain long chains of carbon and hydrogen atoms?

3. A molecule called hexane (not shown in Figure 19.5) has a formula C_6H_{14}. Hexane resembles propane and octane. Could you sketch out what its structure might look like?

IV. Look at the structure of benzene (g) which has 6 carbon atoms. Hexane, described above in III.3, also has 6 carbon atoms. Besides having a different number of hydrogen atoms, how does the benzene molecule differ from the hexane molecule? How many atoms is each carbon bonded to? Contrast the arrangement of atoms around the carbons in hexane with those in benzene. Notice that the carbon atoms in benzene form a ring structure, and that all the atoms are in the same plane. Do you expect that to be true for hexane?

V. Compare the structures of glycine (j), alanine (k), and tryptophan (l). These molecules are examples of amino acids. Amino acids make up the proteins in your hair, skin, fingernails, and enzymes. What

g. C_6H_6

Benzene

Planar molecule

Looking down ⇨

(3 double bonds between alternating C's are not shown in this picture)

Looking edge on ⇩

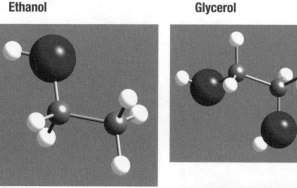

h. C_2H_6O

Ethanol

i. $C_3H_8O_3$

Glycerol

j. $C_2H_5NO_2$ ⇨

Glycine

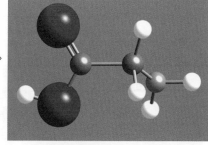

k. $C_3H_7NO_2$

Alanine

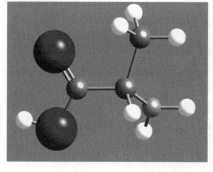

l. $C_{10}H_{12}N_2O_2$ ⇨

Tryptophan

m. $C_{12}H_{24}O_2$

Lauric acid

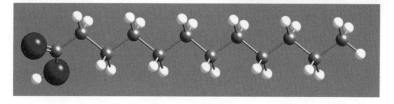

n. $C_{18}H_{34}O_2$
Oleic acid

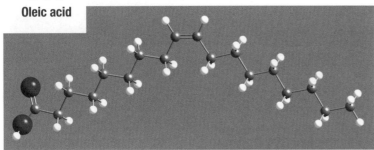

o. C_2H_2
Acetylene

p. $C_9H_8O_4$
Aspirin

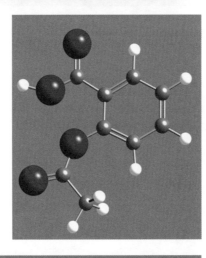

q. $C_{14}H_{14}O_3$
Naproxen

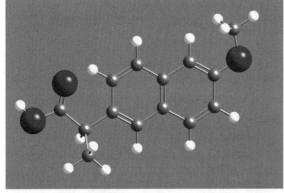

r. $C_{13}H_{18}O_2$ ⇓
Ibuprofen

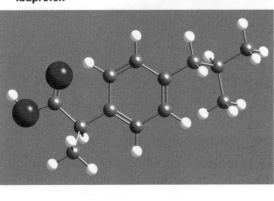

s. S_8 ⇨

Elemental sulfur molecule

Looking down ⬀

Looking sideways ⇨

groups of atoms do these molecules have in common?

VI. Consider the structures of lauric acid (m) and oleic acid (n). Look at the right ends of the molecules first. What group of atoms do these two molecules have in common with the amino acids?

VII. Finally, look at the molecular structures of three common painkillers: acetyl salicylic acid (p) (aspirin), naproxen (q) (Aleve® and Naprosyn®) and ibuprofen (r) (Advil® and Motrin®). What atomic fragments do these molecules have in common? Can you find molecular fragments within these molecules that you found in other molecules in Figure 19.5?

By studying these pictures, you gain some important insights into molecules. First, perhaps you realized that molecules can be very diverse, even when containing many of the same fragments. Second, you should have noticed that each kind of atom tends to prefer a particular type of connectivity.

Carbon atoms, for example, tend to make a total of four bonds. Carbon exhibits versatility in exactly how it satisfies its craving for four bonds. In many of the pictures you've looked at, carbon connects with four other atoms. But carbon can also form two or three bonds with the same atom, and then bonds with as many other atoms as needed to reach a maximum of four. When carbon forms two bonds with another atom, the interaction is referred to as a **double**

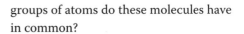

t. $PtCl_2N_2H_6$ *Pt*   pink
      Cisplatin   *Cl*   green
                  N   blue
                  H   white

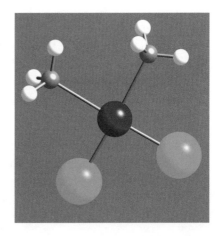

bond. Double bonds appear as two connecting lines between the atoms in representations of molecular structures. A triple bond occurs when carbon forms three bonds with a single atom; three lines connecting two atoms represent a **triple bond** in a structures like those of Figure 19.5. Only one molecule in Figure 19.5 has a triple bond: acetylene (o).

Oxygen has a tendency to form two bonds, and hydrogen one.

Just as human families share characteristics like long straight noses or pointy chins, families of molecules share structural and chemical characteristics. On the molecular level, the family characteristics derive from the presence of similar atomic groupings in molecules. For example, the **hydrocarbon** family consists of molecules that contain only carbon and hydrogen atoms. Many of the molecules you have looked at belong to a molecular family called organic acids. All **organic acids** have the fragment

$$-C-O-H$$
$$\|$$
$$O$$

within in the molecule. The amino acid family contains the acid group plus the $-NH_2$ group. This molecular group is called the **amine group** because it is related to ammonia, a molecule with the formula, NH_3.

GEOMETRIC ARRANGEMENT OF ATOMS IN MOLECULES

The molecular pictures also enable you to study the shapes of molecules and of molecular fragments. Some bonding connections lead to planar arrangements, but most give nonplanar or bent geometries. Look at the propane, octane, and lauric acid molecules. Describe the shape of the carbon backbone. Is it linear or zigzag? Compare the ring of the S_8 molecule (s) to the ring of six C atoms in benzene (g), or in the middle of the ibuprofen molecule (q). Are the rings in all three molecules planar?

The number of bonds that one atom forms with other atoms determines the bonding geometry around that central atom. *Figure 19.6* illustrates the bonding geometry around carbon atoms with different connectivities. Carbon atoms connected to four different atoms give rise to a tetrahedral arrangement of outer atoms. A

tetrahedron is a four-sided pyramid with triangular faces on all sides. Each of the four outer atoms are located at the corners of the pyramid, with the central carbon at the interior.

When a carbon atom bonds to three atoms, the bonding can be represented as a double bond plus two single bonds. All four atoms lie in the same plane, with approximately 120° angles between the outer atoms. The bonding geometry about a triple-bonded carbon atom is linear.

A simple picture of bonding within these molecules helps to rationalize these observed arrangements. Bonds within molecules can be modeled as the sharing of electron pairs between two atoms. *Figure 19.7* shows how a simple bond forms from the combination of s-type atomic orbitals on two atoms. Each atom contributes one electron to the bond. The resulting bond concentrates the electrons in the region between the two nuclei.

You can think of the electrons as creating a "blob" of glue that holds the two nuclei together. Molecules adopt a bonding geometry that keeps the blobs of glue as far away from each other as possible. This arrangement minimizes the repulsive electrostatic interactions of electrons in different bonds around the central atom. Additional details of bonding within molecules will be studied in Chapter 23.

- **Double Bond**
  Atoms connected by two bonds. Double bonds usually involve four electrons, two per bond.

- **Triple Bond**
  Atoms within a molecule connected by three bonds.

- **Hydrocarbon Molecules**
  Molecules that contain only carbon and hydrogen atoms.

- **Organic Acid**
  A molecule that contains the fragment CO_2H attached to another carbon atom.

- **Amine Group**
  The grouping of NH_2 attached to a carbon atom.

✍ **Figure 19.7**
Simple picture of bond formation.

Two isolated atoms with an electron in an s orbital

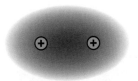
Two atoms bonded together

⇩ **Figure 19.6**
Geometric arrangement of bonds around carbon atoms.
a) Tetrahedral shape when four bonds are formed to four different atoms.
b) Planar shape when four bonds are made to three different atoms.
c) Linear shape when four bonds are made to two different atoms.

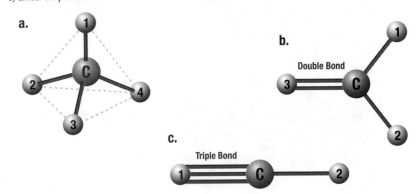

Chemical Formulas and Structures of Extended Substances

In substances with extended bonding interactions, the chemical formula gives the relative atomic composition for the entire structure. Elemental magnesium contains only magnesium atoms; its formula is Mg. Sodium chloride has the formula NaCl. Quartz, an extended solid that is the major component of beach sand, contains silicon and oxygen, with the formula SiO_2. Extended substances exist as solids at room temperature and normal, atmospheric pressure. Under these conditions, a single atom of Mg or single "molecules" of NaCl or of SiO_2 do not exist. Rather every atom or ion bonds with many other atoms that are, in turn, bonded to additional atoms.

Let's look more carefully at the structures of several extended substances mentioned briefly. Figure 19.4a shows the structure of elemental magnesium. Every Mg atom is surrounded by six other atoms. The structure looks like the arrangement of oranges or grapefruit in the produce section of your grocery store.

Figure 19.4b shows the arrangement of ions in sodium chloride. Each Na ion is surrounded by six Cl ions, and each Cl ion is surrounded by six Na ions. The Cl ions are larger than the Na ions. You can think of this arrangement as being like the grocer's arrangement of large grapefruit, with smaller oranges going into the holes produced by the stacked grapefruits.

A different representation of quartz's structure is given in *Figure 19.8*. There you can see the bonding environment a little more clearly. Every Si atom is bonded to four O atoms, and

every O atom is bonded to two Si atoms. As you might suspect from our earlier discussion, the oxygen atoms form tetrahedra around each silicon atom. The O–Si–O connections are bent like water, rather than being linear like O–C–O in carbon dioxide.

Inspection of extended structures illustrates an additional feature in these materials. Extended structures usually form **crystals**. Crystals are characterized by a regular repeating arrangement of the atoms or ions that make up the solid.

Sometimes an extended substance can form crystals with the same chemical formula but a different repeat pattern. TiO_2, for example, forms one crystal called rutile and another one called anatase. The structures are shown in *Figure 19.9*. These two crystals have different electronic properties and different applications. White paints and pigments, including those used in sunscreens, consist largely of the rutile form of TiO_2. Anatase is used in solar cells and other electronic devices.

In chapter 24, we shall see in more detail how the geometry of the repeating pattern influences the properties of extended solids.

19–5 MODERN INSTRUMENTAL TECHNIQUES

Chemists have developed a wide variety of techniques to determine the composition and structure of matter. These techniques employ fundamental properties encountered in previous chapters. Learning about them illustrates

• **Crystal**
A solid with a regular repeating arrangement of molecules or ions.

Figure 19.8
a) The ball and stick representation of the quartz crystal (SiO_2).
b) The tetrahedral arrangement of oxygen atoms around every silicon atom.
c) The connectivity of silicon atoms through bonding with oxygen atoms.

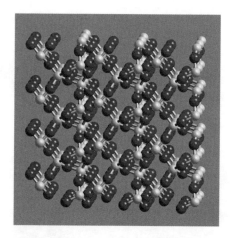
a.

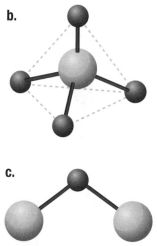
b.

c.

Figure 19.9
Two different crystals of TiO_2: a) Rutile and b) Anatase. (Red balls are oxygen atoms; grey balls are titanium atoms.) The two crystals have different electronic properties. Rutile is the white pigment in paint and anatase is used in solar cells.

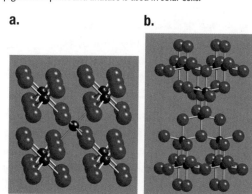
a. b.

how scientists apply fundamental principles to design new technologies. Besides, these technologies lie at the basis of many modern medical diagnostic and forensic science tools. You can be a more informed consumer with some basic understanding of these technologies.

Spectroscopy

In Chapter 16, we saw that electrons in atoms occupy discrete electronic energy levels. In fact, nature exhibits discrete energy levels of all kinds. The term "spectroscopy" applies to many techniques in which photons are used as probes to characterize or measure energy differences in matter.

Electronic Spectroscopy

Atoms and molecules emit photons of a particular frequency when their electrons jump to lower energy levels; they absorb photons when electrons jump to higher levels. The pattern of absorptions or emissions can be used to identify a substance.

Transitions between electronic states in colorless substances have photon energies in the ultraviolet region of the electromagnetic spectrum. Colorless, transparent window glass absorbs light in the ultraviolet region. This is the reason why it is hard to get a suntan sitting inside the house beside a closed window!

Pure compounds containing transition metal elements may be highly colored because transition metal ions can have electronic transitions in the visible region. *Figure 19.10* provides some examples. The colored materials in Figure 17.1 and 17.2 also contain transition metals. Colored glass and many gemstones get their

Figure 19.10

The color in each of these compounds arises from chromium, a transition metal.

brilliant color by incorporating small amounts of transition metals into an otherwise colorless substance.

Vibrational Spectroscopy

The chemical bonds that hold atoms together in a molecule behave like mattress springs. Bonds compress and expand, like a Slinky® toy. Bonds can also move in and out, in a scissoring-type motion that changes the angle between bonds. Both motions are called vibrations. As a simple example, we show in *Figure 19.11* the different types of vibrations that the atoms in water molecules undergo.

Complex molecules with many atoms have a large number of different types of bonds, so many types of vibrational motions become possible. Each type of bond occurs with a characteristic energy in the infrared (IR) region. For example, molecules that contain the fragment with a carbon-oxygen double bond

$$\begin{array}{c} \backslash \\ C = O \\ / \end{array}$$

have a strong absorption in the electromagnetic spectrum at a frequency near 5×10^{13} Hz. This absorption is associated with the stretching and compression of the C=O bond.

IR absorption spectra that arise from vibrational motions look very different from the visible electronic absorption shown in Figure 14.8. Three IR absorption spectra are shown in *Figure 19.12*. The x axis of each figure represents a quantity related to the frequency of photons. (The 5×10^3 Hz noted above corresponds to a value of 1670 on the x axis of these figures.) High numbers on the frequency axis correspond to energetic photons; small numbers represent less energetic photons. The y axes of these figures run from 100 at the top to 0 at the bottom. A value of 100 corresponds to no absorption of photons, while a value of 0 means that the substance absorbs every photon of that particular energy. (Screwy convention, isn't it?)

Figure 19.11

The three kinds of vibrational motion that the water molecule undergoes.

a. Water in its equilibrium position.

b. Symmetric bond stretch—Expansion (left) and contraction (right)

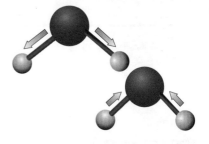

c. Asymmetric bond stretch—One bond compresses while the other expands

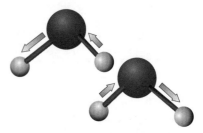

d. Bond angle bend—Scissor motion in and out

Let's look at the aspirin, ibuprofen, and naproxen IR spectra (Figure 19.12). All three drugs contain the C=O bond, and all show the tell-tale absorptions near 5×10^{13} Hz (approximately "1600"), mentioned previously, because of it. Notice that all three drugs absorb some photons in the energy region marked as "3000" on the x axis. However, all three absorb few photons at "4000."

The absorptions near the "3000" region arise from stretching motions involving C–H bonds. Since all three molecules have lots of C–H bonds, lots of absorption in this region make sense.

Other structural features lead to characteristic absorptions in different regions of the IR spectrum. Scientists use a table of characteristic absorptions to identify molecular fragments, such as –O–H or –NH$_2$, within a molecule. Then they assemble the fragments together to determine the complete molecule, just as you do when putting together a jigsaw puzzle.

Sometimes the spectrum is too complicated to determine the complete structure just from an analysis of the peaks. That would probably be the case for these three molecules. Scientists would use additional information from the other techniques described in this section to arrive at a structure.

Even when the spectrum is to complicated to fully "analyze," the spectrum can still serve a useful purpose. The spectrum, like a fingerprint, can identify a known molecule.

Consider the following hypothetical scenario: Suppose an unlabeled pill was found in the pocket of the victim at a crime scene. Investigators might obtain the IR spectrum of the pill to help identify it. Knowing that the victim suffers from arthritis, the investigators might first suspect a painkiller.

All three drugs show complicated absorption patterns differing enough from one another that their spectra can probably be used to identify the pill. Look specifically at the region between the two lines marked in red. Notice that the pattern of absorptions in this narrow region are not the same for all three molecules. Aspirin contains two different C=O groups, and each one has its own absorption. Ibuprofen has only one band, while naproxen shows a band that is partially split into two. These spectral differences can help the investigators to identify or eliminate one of these three painkillers as the pill in the pocket.

Mass Spectrometry

One of the first techniques used to prove the existence of molecules was the mass spectrometer, a variation on the gas discharge tubes of J. J. Thompson. Today scientists use many different kinds of mass spectrometer designs. All designs employ the same basic operating principle: high energy particles bombard and ionize molecules, causing many of the molecules to fragment into smaller parts. The instrument separates and detects the fragments according to their masses. *Figure 19.13* shows the mass spectra of the same three painkillers discussed above.

Figure 19.12

Infrared spectra of three painkillers. Each dip downward represents an absorption of IR photons of a given frequency due to molecular vibrational motions. The y axis measures the IR photon absorption. A value of 100 means no photons were absorbed. The x axis is given in wavenumbers, which is a way to represent photon frequencies. The region between the red lines mark the location of C=O bond stretching motions.

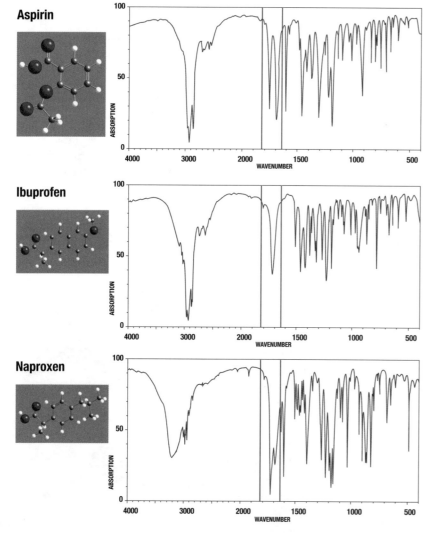

The y axis identifies how often a molecular fragment appears, the x axis locates the mass to charge ratio (m/e) of the fragment. Usually the charge on the fragment is +1, so the mass can be directly inferred. The peak with the largest (m/e) value usually comes from the unfragmented molecule with a charge of +1. This allows the chemist to determine the mass of the neutral molecule. Looking at these three spectra, can you determine which painkiller has the most massive molecule?

As with infrared spectra, the fragmentation pattern can be used as a fingerprint to identify a compound. Drug-testing organizations often use this technique to screen for the presence of illegal drugs such as steroids or other performance-enhancing substances in Olympic athletes. Security screeners at airports also use mass spectrometry techniques to detect high energy explosives in carry-on luggage. If your hands or luggage have been swiped by an inspector using a wand with a small cloth at one end, then you have experienced this screening technique first hand. Dangerous explosives have characteristic fragmentation patterns that the spectrometer can recognize and alert the screener that you shouldn't be flying on a plane.

Crystallography

In part II, we studied the phenomenon of diffraction of both light and electrons. Early electron diffraction studies provided the first detailed information about bond angles and bond lengths in gaseous molecules. Using X-rays or neutrons, diffraction can be applied to study molecules in crystals. In crystals, there is a regular arrangement of the molecules in layers. Beams of X-rays or neutrons can be diffracted through the "slits" formed by crystal layers. The X-ray or neutron beams form interference patterns just as electrons do when they pass through multiple slits (Chapter 15).

Figure 19.14 shows the X-ray diffraction pattern obtained from a small molecule. Each white spot represents a constructive interference from diffracted X-ray beams. The sample holder and crystal specimen cast shadows in the X-ray beam. Their shadows appear in Figure 19.14 as the dark wedge coming from the top, and the circle in the center.

The pattern and arrangement of the white

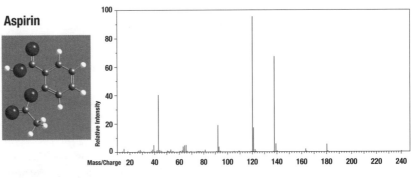

Aspirin

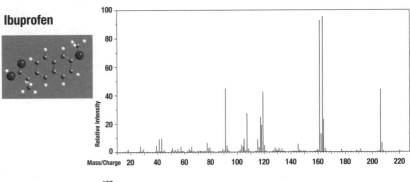

Ibuprofen

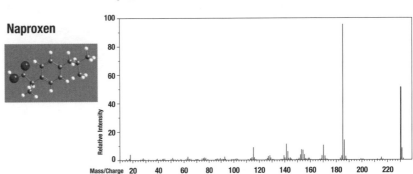

Naproxen

⇧ **Figure 19.13**

The mass spectra of three painkillers. The molecular fragment which appears most often is assigned an intensity of 100; other peaks are scaled relative to the intensity (popularity) of the most intense one. The x axis represents the ratio of fragment mass to charge on the fragment. (Most often the charge is +1, but it may be +2 or +3.) The highest mass peak is usually the unfragmented molecule with a charge of +1. Each of these three molecules fragments easily, so the highest mass peak is barely visible.

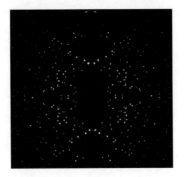

⇦ **Figure 19.14**

An X-ray diffraction pattern obtained from a small molecule. White spots locate the regions of constructive interference; dark regions come from destructive interference. The black spindle coming from the top and the black circle in the center are the sample holder and sample, respectively.

spots tells the chemist how the molecule arranges itself in its crystal. As amazing as it seems, chemists can extract from the relative intensities of the spots, specific details of what atoms are present in the molecule, and how the atoms are connected to each other, as well as the distances between them.

19–6 CONCLUSION

You now have some idea of what matter looks like on an atomic level. You have seen that molecules consist of atoms bonded to each other with definite geometries. Perhaps you have recognized that atoms differ in their preferred ways to interact with other atoms. Some sets of atoms tend to form discrete molecules while others form extended networks.

Carbon and silicon tend to form four bonds with other atoms, oxygen forms two and hydrogen one. The number of bonds around an atom determines the geometry of bonding and ultimately the shape of molecules.

The perspective so far has been static: matter exists in particular arrangements of atoms. The details of the atomic arrangements (molecules vs. extended networks; connectivity and geometry) determine physical properties. The next thing to consider about molecules has a more dynamic aspect. Atoms can change partners, creating new molecules, or new networks. Scientists talk about the exchange of atomic partners that creates new molecules and new materials as chemical reactions.

In chemical reactions, small molecules can come together to form large molecules, and large molecules can be split into smaller ones. Sometimes the bonding geometry about a central atom can change; other times the geometry can stay the same but one bonding partner may be exchanged for a different kind of atom.

In the next chapter you shall learn how several familiar, fundamental principles govern chemical reactivity. By applying these principles to the study of interacting molecules, scientists can gain powerful insights into ways to create new molecules. These principles also provide insights into the chemical reactions that sustain life and foster growth in living organisms. Understanding the chemical reactions associated with cell division, for example, can lead to the synthesis of molecules better suited to treat cancer.

Chapter Framework

A. Classification of Matter
1. Pure Substances
   - a. Elements
   - b. Compounds
2. Mixtures
   - a. Solutions
   - b. Alloys

B. Structural Organization of Matter
1. Atomic Matter
2. Molecular Matter
3. Network Matter

C. Chemical Bonds

D. Chemical Formulas
1. Connectivity
2. Geometric Arrangement of Atoms

E. Modern Instrumental Techniques
1. Electronic Spectroscopy
2. Vibrational Spectroscopy
3. Mass Spectrometry
4. Crystallography

Comprehension

True/False
1. _____ Compounds containing transition metals are often brightly colored.
2. _____ Sodium chloride (NaCl) and Magnesium (Mg) are examples of network substances.
3. _____ Molecular substances melt at very high temperatures.
4. _____ In a chemical formula, subscripts are placed to the left of the chemical symbol to indicate the number of that type of atoms in a molecule.
5. _____ Mass spectrometry provides information about the energy associated with motions within molecules.

Fill in the Blank
Write the chemical formula of these compounds. Refer to Table 19.1 for the atom color guide.

1. Butane—the fuel used in cigarette lighters

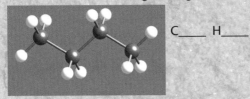

C_____ H_____

2. Acetic Acid—component of vinegar

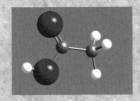

C_____ H_____
O_____

3. Ascorbic Acid—the major component of Vitamin C

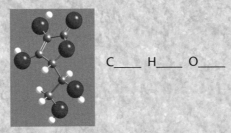

C_____ H_____ O_____

4. Caffeine—a stimulant found in colas and coffee

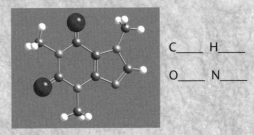

C_____ H_____
O_____ N_____

5. Refer to the figure below.

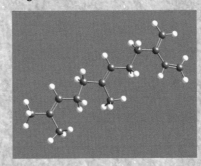

a. How many double bonds are in the compound called beta-farnesene (a compound used by many insects to communicate with one another and by plants to protect against insects)? _____

b. How many bonds does each carbon atom form? _____

c. How many bonds does each hydrogen atom form? _____

d. Is this molecule a hydrocarbon or an organic acid? _____

Matching
1. _____ The geometry around a carbon atom with four single bonds.
2. _____ The geometry around a carbon atom with a triple bond.
3. _____ The attractive interaction that holds atoms together in molecules.
4. _____ The structural organization of water.
5. _____ The structural organization of salts and metals.
6. _____ The structural organization of Group 8A elements.

- a. Extended or network substances
- b. Atomic matter
- c. Molecular substances
- d. Tetrahedron
- e. Linear
- f. Chemical bond

Analysis

1. Which of the following is not a compound?

   a) Sulfur dioxide

   b) Nitrous oxide

   c) Water molecule

   d) Oxygen molecule

   e) Rust

Synthesis

1. Classify each of the following as an element, compound, mixture, solution, or alloy.

   a. 7-Up _____

   b. Brass _____

   c. White gold _____

   d. Orange juice _____

   e. Air _____

   f. Water in a swimming pool _____

   g. Oxygen _____

   h. Sucrose (table sugar) _____

2. Figure 19.5 contains pictures of molecules that belong to several different molecular families. Each group of molecules identified below belongs to a different family. Predict what atomic grouping or structural characteristic might be associated with each family.

   i.   d, e, and f

   ii. h and l

   iii. j and k

   iv. m, n, p, and r

3. The IR spectra and the mass spectrum obtained from acetic acid are shown below, along with the molecular formula.

   a. Predict what molecular feature is responsible for the IR absorption observed between the two red lines. Estimate the mass of an acetic acid molecule from its mass spectrum.

   b. Describe the three levels of structural organization of matter—atomic, molecular, and network or extended substances. How are they different?

   c. Describe how a forensic scientist would use the techniques of spectroscopy to identify an unknown white crystalline powder found in the locker of a professional athlete.

   d. How many atoms of hydrogen are there in each molecule of propane that has the formula $H_3CCH_2CH_3$? Use this formula to draw a diagram of the molecule of propane.

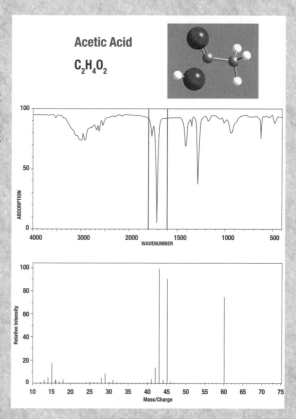

Acetic Acid
$C_2H_4O_2$

In Praise of a General Education

by Don Fossum, BYU Bookstore

For many students, the "general education" science course that brings you to read this textbook will be your only university exposure to the physical sciences. If you have a major outside of the physical sciences, it may be easy to think of the class as something to be "gotten out-of-the-way." As you become swamped with quizzes, tests, and papers, it is worth remembering that, as noted by Aristotle, "The roots of education are bitter, but the fruit is sweet."

Shortly after I took my current position as General Book Buyer for the BYU Bookstore, one of my former English 115 students stopped by and proudly proclaimed, "I have finally finished my stupid GE requirements!"

I told him that I was sorry to hear it. He was further disturbed when I told him that I remembered that he was going into nuclear physics and that I figured he needed as much humanity as he could get—that he was of the ilk who was more than happy to view humans as organisms.

This conversation and others with similar themes have lead to an interesting introspection regarding education and the purpose of universities. None of what I have decided is original, but like many things, we need to be reminded of what we already know.

For me, the role of education is to make one more human and humane, and the role of the university is to bring as much knowledge as possible together in place and time in a setting that encourages access to this breadth and depth of knowledge. This, of course, flies in the face of current practices, where students are asked as early as the seventh grade to start making career choices—but then, that is the rub, because all learning has become focused on careers and not on education. As noted by Robert Bruen in *The Chronical of Higher Education*, "Education is about the improvement of the individual, not about training for the work force. It is just that educated people generally do better in the work force. The abilities to understand, interpret, evaluate, and create are not the same as being trained to perform a series of tasks structured by someone else."

It seems that the university is increasingly disinterested in making the person whole and more interested in producing graduates with good placement possibilities -- and to do it as quickly as possible. The persistent pressure for students to specialize ever earlier in their "academic" career puts their development into a whole person at greater risk.

There are disturbing indicators of many problems. The NEA study "Reading at Risk," released last July, shows the trend of decreased reading by various age groups. Most alarming was the drastic drop in reading by the teen and early adult age groups. I encountered a study 15 years ago, which claimed that 78% of the adult population of the U.S. never finish 2 books on their own after they get their termi-

nal degree, and that was consistent whether their terminal degree was junior high, high school, Bachelor's, Master's, or PhD. (The study excluded training manuals or documents which had to be read for employment.)

Perhaps the most disturbing trend to my mind is the overwhelming lack of curiosity and feeling of boredom expressed by the current student-age population. Eliot Butler, a former vice-president of Brigham Young University, defined education as "a sense of total curiosity." His father had urged him to take at least one class outside his area of emphasis no matter what level of degree he was pursuing. I personally think that this is wisdom for the ages.

As John Henry Newman wrote is his 1854 book *The Idea of a University*:

A person with a well-trained intellect is a useful person, socially and in every other way. Such persons raise the intellectual tone of society, cultivate taste, public spiritedness, give enlargement and sobriety to the ideas of an age, and refine private life. The kind of education a university should provide is the education which gives a man a clear conscious view of his own opinions and judgments, a truth in developing them, an eloquence in expressing them, and a force in urging them. It teaches him to see things as they are, to go right to the point, to disentangle a skein of thought, to detect what is sophistical and to discard what is irrelevant. It prepares him to fill any post with credit, and to master any subject with facility. It shows him how to accommodate himself to others,... how to influence them, how to come to an understanding with them, how to bear with them. He is at home in any society, he has common ground with every class; he knows when to speak and when to be silent; he is able to converse, he is able to listen; he can ask a question pertinently and gain a lesson seasonably, when he has nothing to impart himself; he is every ready, yet never in the way.

We need to be more aware of the positive influences that people with a broad background will have on society and the world.

CHAPTER 20

PRINCIPLES OF CHEMICAL REACTIVITY

Rates of cooking, or growth of muscles, or tightening of muscles, or using the brain—everything involves the speed of some reaction. Understanding these reactions really means getting acquainted with the molecules as if they were your friends and knowing what their nature is and what they will do . . .

~ Henry Eyring

One of the most important advances in the history of humanity was the discovery of how to make and control fire. This discovery was really a discovery about chemical reactivity. We have made many observations about the interactions of matter since then. For instance, the gases on the right side of the periodic table tend to not react. In fact, neutral helium and neon atoms have never been observed to form chemical compounds, and argon, krypton, and xenon do so only with difficulty. These five gases are found in nature as individual atoms. Because of their low reactivity, they are called **noble gases**.

Other gases, such as hydrogen, oxygen, and nitrogen, are not observed as individual atoms, but exist as molecules with pairs of atoms tightly bound to each other. In contrast to the noble gases, the metallic elements along the left side of the periodic table—lithium, sodium, potassium, rubidium, and cesium—are all quite reactive. For example, cesium reacts violently (and explosively!) when exposed to water. Because these five elements are so reactive, they are rarely found in nature except when they are combined with other chemical species.

The rates at which reacting materials are consumed also vary widely. Some reactions are so slow they require time scales of millions to billions of years, while other reactions occur in less than one billionth of a second. The same materials can be converted into the same products with widely different rates. For example, when a tree falls in the forest and begins to rot, the carbon in its wood eventually converts to carbon dioxide. This process requires years for complete conversion, but if that same wood is placed in a fire pit and ignited, conversion to carbon dioxide takes only minutes.

The chemical world may seem extremely complex, but all these observations actually correlate closely with, and can be predicted from, the periodic table. Ultimately, all can be understood in terms of the quantum model of the atom. In this chapter we will examine some of the basic principles that determine chemical reactivity. You will find that you are already familiar with most of them.

20–1 A BRIEF INTRODUCTION TO CHEMICAL BONDING

The quantum model of the atom predicts that 3-dimensional standing waves, called orbitals, describe the electron probability distributions of atoms. The general shapes of the

LEARNING OBJECTIVES

When you are finished with this chapter, you should be able to

• Discuss the roles of molecular orbitals, entropy, and energy in determining why some atoms form chemical bonds while other atoms do not.

• Be able to balance simple chemical equations reflecting the conservation of mass in chemical reactions.

• Discuss the roles of temperature, energy and entropy in determining the rates of chemical reactions.

• Describe chemical equilibrium as the state where forward and reverse reaction rates are equal, and where energy is minimized and entropy is maximized.

orbitals are the same for all atoms. Details such as the size of a particular orbital depend on the nuclear charge. As the total energy (kinetic and potential) of the electron is changed, the probable locations of the electron change; they are described by a different orbital.

All the positive charge in an atom is concentrated in a single small volume, the atomic nucleus. What happens if two atoms are brought close together? In that case, there are two regions of positive charge, corresponding to the two atomic nuclei. With two nuclei, the single-nucleus standing wave patterns no longer describe the electron probabilities; new and different-shaped orbitals become possible when two atoms come together. These new standing wave patterns are called **molecular orbitals**. If the electrons from the two atoms can achieve a lower energy arrangement in the molecular orbitals than they had in the atomic orbitals of the isolated atoms, the molecular arrangement is more stable than the isolated atoms and the two atoms stick or "bond" together. This bonding is what happens when two hydrogen atoms come together. They can achieve a lower-energy standing wave pattern than would be possible for two isolated hydrogen atoms. The new arrangement is at lower energy, so the "extra" energy is released (in the form of emitted pho-

tons), the two atoms form a bond, and they stay together. Energy would be required to break the bond to produce two free hydrogen atoms, because that is a higher energy arrangement.

Molecular orbitals are more complex than atomic orbitals and tend to be different for every combination of atoms forming a molecule; they don't follow the same simple patterns that atomic orbitals do. Two molecular orbitals for the hydrogen molecule, H_2, are shown in *Figure 20.1*.

a.   **b.**

Figure 20.1

The two lowest molecular orbitals for the H_2 molecule. The lowest energy orbital (a) has high electron density between the two hydrogen nuclei and is therefore a bonding molecular orbital. In the H_2 molecule, two electrons occupy this bonding orbital. Going up in energy, the next orbital (b) has a node between the two hydrogen nuclei and high electron density outside the internuclear axis. This is an anti-bonding orbital, but it is not occupied in H_2 because the two electrons are in the lower-energy bonding orbital.

MOLECULAR ORBITALS

Because molecules have more than one atom and therefore more than one atomic nucleus, the standing wave shapes and sizes of their orbitals differ from those of individual atoms. Each molecular orbital can accommodate up to two electrons, as long as those electrons have opposite spins.

Molecular orbitals may be "bonding," "anti-bonding," or "non-bonding," depending on whether they involve high electron density between atoms (bonding), or not (anti-bonding), or about the same between and not between the atoms (non-bonding). Molecular orbitals are filled with electrons beginning with the lowest energy orbital and working up in energy to account for all the electrons in the molecule. Both bonding and anti-bonding orbitals may be occupied at the same time, depending on the energies of the orbitals and the number of electrons in the atoms.

◆ Noble Gases

Gaseous elements in the right-most column of the periodic table (helium, neon, argon, krypton, xenon, and radon) that exist in nature as individual atoms. They are quite unreactive and are very unlikely to form chemical compounds.

◆ Molecular Orbitals

Standing electron probability waves for molecules. These standing wave shapes and sizes are different from those for individual atoms because of the multiple atomic nuclei.

◆ Bonding Molecular Orbitals

Molecular orbitals that have high electron probability *between* atomic nuclei in a molecule. When bonding molecular orbitals are occupied by electrons, the high electron density between the nuclei helps hold the nuclei together, contributing to a bond between the atoms.

◆ Anti-Bonding Molecular Orbitals

Molecular orbitals that have low (or no) electron probability *between* atomic nuclei in a molecule and high electron density in areas not between the nuclei. When anti-bonding orbitals are occupied by electrons, the resulting electron density in the anti-bonding orbital helps pull the nuclei apart, weakening any chemical bond that may exist between them.

The shapes represent the regions around the nuclei where an electron is likely to be found.

Notice how the lowest energy orbital (Figure 20.1a) differs from the next higher energy orbital (Figure 20.1b). The lowest orbital has high electron probability in the region between the two nuclei, while the next one puts most of the electron density on either side of one atom, with no density in the middle. Each hydrogen atom contributes its 1s electron to the molecule, and the two electrons go into the lowest available molecular orbital, just as in atomic energy diagrams.

More complicated, higher energy orbitals exist even for the H_2 molecule, but the general principles of molecular orbitals can be grasped from just these two examples. Orbitals that concentrate electron density between nuclei contribute to holding the molecule together. These are called **bonding molecular orbitals.** Orbitals that have no electron probability between the nuclei are called non-bonding or **anti-bonding molecular orbitals**, because they either don't contribute to bonding or actually weaken bonds. The strength of chemical bonds depends on the orbital energies and shapes, and on how the electrons are distributed among the molecular orbitals. We can extend these ideas to more than two atoms, making larger molecules that are more complex. Some molecules contain hundreds of thousands of atoms, but the principles behind bonding are the same as for simple two-atom molecules, only more complex.

20–2 PREDICTING CHEMICAL BONDING

Whether or not a chemical bond will form depends ultimately on two things: the energy involved and the disorder (entropy) involved. Spontaneous processes tend to go "downhill" in energy. Two materials are likely to react if they can achieve a lower-energy state, and this is true for the process of chemical bond formation. If formation of a bond results in a lower-energy arrangement of the nuclei and atoms, bonding is likely to happen. Similarly, spontaneous processes increase the entropy of the Universe (i.e., such spontaneity increases disorder). Two materials are likely to react and form new bonds if that reaction increases the disorder of the Universe.

Both energy and entropy determine reactivity. A favorable downhill energy change can lead to reaction when the entropy change for the reacting materials is unfavorable, if the release of energy to the surroundings is large enough to maintain a positive entropy change for the Universe. A favorable entropy change can enable a process to go "uphill" in energy.

For example, in the reaction of sugar with oxygen (called combustion or oxidation of sugar), large amounts of energy are released as heat. Thus, the products are at lower energy than the starting materials. The reaction goes downhill energetically. In addition, while the reactants are a highly ordered solid and a gas, the products of this reaction are disordered gaseous materials: carbon dioxide and water vapor. Thus, disorder increases in this reaction; disorder also increases in the surroundings because of the large heat release. Both the energy change and the entropy change in the combustion of sugar favor reaction, so this kind of reaction is very likely to take place.

We can also react hydrogen gas with oxygen, to produce water. At first glance, this looks like an unfavorable thing to do: we are taking two disordered gases and making a more ordered single gas. However, the product, water vapor, is at much lower energy than the reactant gases, so this energetically favorable reaction releases large amounts of energy into the surroundings. The large energy release causes disorder in the surroundings, so the overall entropy change in the Universe when hydrogen burns is still positive, even though the entropy change for the system is not.

The math behind predicting chemical bonding using the quantum model is extremely complex. In fact, it is not known how to solve the equations exactly. Fortunately, we do know how to obtain approximate solutions and how to make the approximations very accurate. It is not necessary to solve the equations to get a good, qualitative understanding of bonding.

In general, when the energy and entropy are in the right direction, nature makes favorable chemical bonds. Bonds can be formed in one of three ways. Each of the three ways will be mentioned briefly here, leaving more detailed discussion of each of these important topics for later chapters.

Strong bonds can be formed when a large number of atoms collectively share their electrons. This kind of bonding is what holds metal atoms together. It is why the gold in Fort Knox does not evaporate into atoms. Chapter 21 explains more in detail about metallic bonding.

Some atoms (in particular the metal atoms toward the left of the periodic table) achieve especially low energy electron standing wave patterns when they lose their **valence electrons** and become positively charged **cations**. Other atoms (especially the nonmetals toward the right side of the periodic table) achieve low energy electron standing wave patterns when they gain additional electrons to become negatively charged **anions**. When these two kinds of atoms come together, strong interactions occur because the metals, which need to lose electrons to achieve lower energy, give their "extra" electrons to the non-metals, which need to gain electrons. We call the resulting materials "ionic" because they consist of cations and anions rather than neutral atoms. Common table salt, sodium chloride, is an example of an ionic material. More about ionic reactivity will be found in Chapter 22.

When nonmetals interact with each other, especially low energy electron standing wave patterns can be realized through *sharing* of electrons between the atoms, as in the example of H_2 discussed above. This sharing mode of bonding is called **covalent bonding**, a subject explained in greater detail in Chapter 23. Other common covalent materials include the nitro-

gen and oxygen molecules that make up the Earth's atmosphere, and water, on which all known forms of life depend.

20-3 BALANCING CHEMICAL EQUATIONS
(CONSERVATION OF MATTER)

All but the simplest chemical reactions are difficult to describe in words. Chemists have developed a shorthand notation for describing reactions. This involves writing the **reactants** (starting materials) on the left, with plus signs indicating reactants are combining. An arrow or an equal sign (arrows and equal signs are used interchangeably) separates reactants from **products** (the material produced in the reaction), and the products are listed to the right of the equal sign, again separated by plus signs. Therefore, for the reaction of H_2 and O_2 to make water, we could write:

$$H_2 + O_2 = H_2O$$

There is a not-so-subtle problem with what we have written. Remember the law of conservation of matter from Chapter 8? On the left (reactant) side of our chemical equation, the oxygen molecule contains two oxygen atoms. However, the water molecule on the right contains only one oxygen atom. Just as in mathematical equations, the equal sign (or arrow) means exactly what it says; the matter on the reactant side is equivalent to the matter on the product side. The reaction simply rearranges the atoms (*Figure 20.2*).

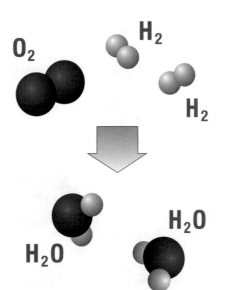

- **Valence Electrons**

Electrons in the highest-energy, outermost quantum shell of an atom. Only the valence electrons are involved in chemical reactions.

- **Cations**

Atoms, or groups of atoms bound together, that have a net positive charge. In a cation, the number of electrons is less than the number of protons in the atom or group of atoms.

- **Anions**

Atoms, or groups of atoms bound together, that have a net negative charge. In an anion, the number of electrons is greater than the number of protons in the atom or group of atoms.

- **Covalent Bonding**

Bonding between atoms accomplished by sharing electrons to achieve low-energy arrangement of the electrons between the nuclei.

- **Reactants**

The starting material(s) in a chemical reaction, written on the left-hand side of a chemical equation.

- **Products**

Material(s) produced in a chemical reaction, written on the right-hand side of a chemical equation.

Figure 20.2

Schematic representation of the reaction $2H_2 + O_2 = 2H_2O$. Note that the number of hydrogen and oxygen atoms does not change in going from reactants to products. Matter is always conserved. The arrangement of the chemical bonds is what changes in the reaction.

◆ **Rate of Reaction**

The speed at which reactants are consumed and products are produced in a chemical reaction per unit time.

Matter is always conserved in chemical reactions, and the energies involved in chemistry are not large enough to change one kind of atom into another. Therefore, when writing reactions, it is important to make sure that the number of each kind of atom is the same on both the reactant and product sides of the equation. The process of making sure this is so is called "balancing" the chemical reaction.

How could we balance the reaction for combustion of water above? The easiest way would be to put "1/2" in front of the O_2:

$$H_2 + \tfrac{1}{2}O_2 = H_2O$$

The numbers work out this way, but this isn't a very accurate representation of the reaction, because we don't really have half an oxygen molecule. Multiplying everything by 2 fixes the problem:

$$2H_2 + O_2 = 2H_2O$$

Now we have four hydrogen atoms (as two molecules) on the left, and four hydrogen atoms in the two water molecules on the right. We have two oxygen atoms in the O_2 molecule on the left, and two oxygen atoms (one in each of the two water molecules) on the right. We are balanced. This is a good way to describe the reaction. It really does take two molecules of hydrogen for every molecule of oxygen to make water, and for every oxygen molecule used, two water molecules will be produced. Whenever we write a chemical equation, it is important to accurately reflect the relationships between the numbers of each kind of atom or molecule in the reaction by properly balancing the equation.

Figure 20.3

Diamond, a form of pure carbon, is at higher energy than graphite, another form of pure carbon. Diamond and graphite differ in the way the carbon atoms are bound to each other. If it is downhill in energy from diamond to graphite, why doesn't diamond spontaneously convert to graphite and release the energy?

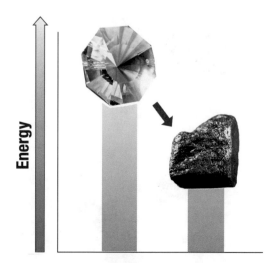

20–4 RATES OF CHEMICAL REACTIONS

We've seen how to predict in general whether or not a chemical reaction will occur, and we've also seen how to reflect conservation of matter in the way we write chemical equations. However, so far nothing tells us about how fast the reactions will go. We can measure **rates of reactions** by monitoring disappearance of reactants (the stuff you start with) or by watching appearance of products (the stuff that forms in the reaction).

Consider the reaction of sugar with oxygen to make carbon dioxide and water, which has already been shown to be especially favorable. What happens to one of the reactants (sugar) over time? Well, it depends. Sugar left out in the air at room temperature reacts only very slowly, so sugar can be safely stored for years (and even longer if oxygen is removed). Sugar taken into the body at 37° C (98.6° F, the temperature on a hot day) undergoes the same reaction much more quickly, in a matter of hours. Powdered sugar burns rapidly and even explosively under some circumstances. This is an example of the same reaction going at different speeds.

Another well-known example deals with two naturally-occurring forms of pure elemental carbon. There are three known forms of naturally occurring, pure carbon: diamond, graphite, and fullerene. Each differs in how its carbon atoms are bound to each other. At room temperature and pressure, the atomic arrangement of carbon atoms in diamond (one of the hardest materials known) is a higher-energy arrangement than is found in graphite (the soft lubricant used on the wheels of pinewood derby cars, among other places). It is "downhill" in energy to go from diamond to graphite. So why isn't nature making pencils out of diamond rings? Fortunately for diamond lovers, even though the reaction is energetically favorable, it is very slow (it is one of those reactions that works on the billion-year time scale), so slow that a newly engaged young lady doesn't have to worry about her ring turning into soot.

What controls the speed of a chemical reaction? And why are some reactions explosively fast, while others are glacially slow? We can begin to understand by looking at chemical reactions up close. For two atoms (or molecules) to react, they must get close enough together for their electron clouds to overlap. In science, this close approach is called a "collision." Because collisions are required for reaction, collision rates must influence reaction rates; reactions can't go faster than the reactants can get together. Collision rates are determined by such factors as the concentration (or pressure) of the reactants and the speed of the reactant molecules, which is determined by the temperature. At higher temperatures, collision rates increase and the kinetic energies of the colliding particles are greater, so reaction speeds are strongly influenced by temperature. Usually, the higher the temperature, the faster the reaction will be.

However, collision rates do not give a complete explanation. Many reactions go much slower than the collision rate; perhaps only one in 100 or 1,000 or 1,000,000 collisions results in reaction. Why? The energies and entropies involved as the reactants collide turn out to play crucial roles in determining whether or not a collision will result in transformation of, for example, the Hope Diamond into a lump of coal.

Energy and Reaction Rates

Often, energy is required to start the reaction, even though more energy will be released when the reaction is complete. For example, a mixture of hydrogen and oxygen in a balloon at room temperature does not react to produce water unless energy is supplied (usually in the form of a spark or heat), even though the arrangement of electrons in water is a much lower energy configuration than that of the electrons in the reactant hydrogen and oxygen molecules. Energy is needed to begin the process, and at room temperature the collisions between the molecules are not energetic enough. In some ways the reaction is like a roller coaster ride. The ride won't start until the coaster is pulled to the top of the track (energy is put in), even if the end of the track is lower than the start.

We can describe the energy requirements for a reaction with a diagram that shows the energy change as a reaction progresses. On the diagram, a simple example of which is shown in *Figure 20.4*, we indicate the energies of the reactants, the products, and the energy of the colliding molecules needed to start the process. We

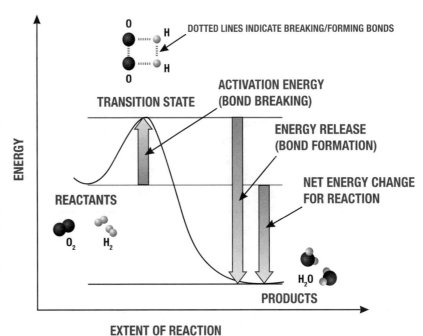

Figure 20.4

Part of the potential energy surface for the reaction of H_2 with O_2. The H_2 and O_2 reactant molecules on the left are at lower energy than the transition state, which involves breaking H–H and O–O bonds and formation of H–O bonds. Several additional steps (not shown) are involved in forming the final product, H_2O.

call this graph a **potential energy surface** because it is a plot of the potential energy that exists between two interacting reactants. The surface shown here is for a very simple reaction of just a few atoms. More complex reactions for multi-atom molecules have three-dimensional surfaces or even many dimensions that we can't visualize. However, the principles that control multidimensional surfaces are the same as for the two-dimensional surfaces we can easily picture.

We call the arrangement of reactants that leads to product formation the **transition state**, because this is the critical point that determines whether or not the molecules react. For instance, it is often necessary to break a chemical bond to promote a reaction. In our example, we need to break H–H and O–O bonds in the reactants to get the water formation reaction going. The transition state would involve breaking the bonds in the reactants. Energy is required to do this. The energy difference between the reactants and the transition state is referred to as the **activation energy**, because this amount of energy is needed to "activate" the reactants to enable them to form products. Subsequently, a new, stronger bond may form (such as the O–H bonds in water), so that overall the reaction is downhill

- **Potential Energy Surface**

A diagram plotting the total energy of reactants and products as a function of the "completeness" of a chemical reaction. For all but the simplest reactions, these are multidimensional hypersurfaces that are difficult to visualize.

- **Transition State**

The critical point that separates reactants from products on a potential energy surface. Usually this corresponds to the point on the path from reactants to products where the energy is highest.

- **Activation Energy**

The difference between the energy of the isolated reactant molecules and energy of the transition state. If the activation energy is added to a set of reactant molecules, it is possible for them to reach the transition state and go on to form products. Reactants with less than the activation energy do not normally form products.

- **Activation Entropy**

The difference between the entropy (or disorder) of the isolated reactant molecules and the entropy (or disorder) of the transition state. Frequently, the activation entropy is unfavorable so that colliding molecules do not always react even if they have sufficient energy to react.

- **Catalyst**

A chemical whose presence increases the rate of a chemical reaction without being consumed by the reaction. Catalysts make the energy and/or entropy of the transition state more favorable, without affecting the energies or entropies of the initial reactants or final products.

- **Enzymes**

Protein molecules that function as catalysts in biochemical reactions.

Figure 20.5

Just as a key must be oriented properly to enter a keyhole and turn to open a lock, in many reactions the molecules must collide with a certain orientation in order for reaction to occur.

in energy, but the initial energy to break the original bonds has to come from somewhere.

In reactions of gases, the energy comes from the kinetic energy of the colliding molecules. (For liquids and solids the situation is essentially the same, but it is harder to describe because there are so many nearby molecules participating in the collisions.) If the collision isn't "hard" enough, there is not enough kinetic energy to start the reaction and it does not go.

For fast reactions, the transition state may be at the same or lower energy than the reactants. Most of the colliding reactant molecules have enough energy to react, so most collisions have enough energy to go over the transition state "hill" and result in product formation. For slower reactions, it is often uphill in energy from the reactants to the transition state. If the initial hill is too high, very few molecules will have enough energy to reach the transition state. Few collisions will lead to formation of products.

Entropy and Reaction Rates

Energy alone does not explain all we observe about rates of chemical reactions. For instance, even though a collision may be quite energetic, it may still fail to result in product formation. For example, if the reacting molecules have to collide with a particular orientation, not all collisions will be effective, even if the collision involves a lot of energy.

An analogy from everyday life may help to simplify this (see *Figure 20.5*). A key being placed in a keyhole must be oriented just right to go into the hole, and then must be turned the right way to move the tumblers and open the lock. It doesn't matter how hard the key hits the hole or how hard the key is turned if the key is turned the wrong way. Similarly, for many reactions the reacting molecules must fit together properly or no products are formed (*Figure 20.6*).

Many orientations of reacting molecules are possible in a collision, but the transition state leading to products is only a very small subset of the possible arrangements. Thus, the transition state represents a particular, ordered arrangement of the reactants. This is related to an entropy requirement for the reaction—a certain amount of order is often required in a collision, corresponding to a certain amount of unfavorable entropy. The entropy associated with formation of the transition state is called the **activation entropy** because it is required to "activate" the reactants so they can form products.

Catalysts

Rates of reaction can also be affected by the presence of a **catalyst**. Catalysts are chemicals that speed up reactions without themselves being consumed. For instance, the reason sugar oxidation in the body is so much faster than it is for sugar sitting on the shelf at the same temperature is because catalysts in living organisms speed up the reaction.

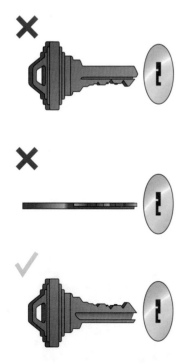

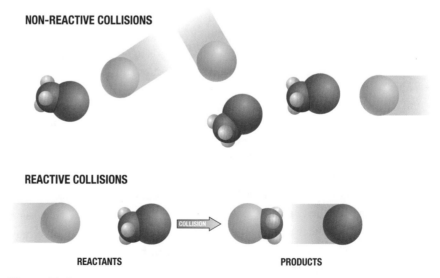

NON-REACTIVE COLLISIONS

REACTIVE COLLISIONS

COLLISION

REACTANTS   PRODUCTS

Figure 20.6

In the reaction of iodide (yellow) with methyl bromide (grey, white, and orange), the iodide must hit the methyl (grey and white) end of the methyl bromide molecule for the reaction forming methyl iodide to occur. Collisions involving other orientations of the two colliding species do not lead to reaction; if the orientation is wrong, the iodide just bounces off rather than forming methyl iodide.

Life on the Earth as we know it would not be possible without the vast array of catalytic molecules, called **enzymes**, that exist and function in various ways in all living organisms. Without catalysts, the reactions of life at room temperature would be too slow to supply energy at the rates needed by living things. Raising the temperature to speed up the reactions would not work either, because reactions that decompose the proteins, fats, nucleotides, and other molecules of life also speed up at higher temperatures. Catalysts speed up specific reactions for molecules only if those molecules are of just the right size and shape, so with the right catalytic enzymes, needed reactions are accelerated while reactions that cause destruction are not.

Catalysts work by decreasing the energetic or entropic (or both) requirements for the reaction, without affecting the energies or entropies of the reactants or products. In other words, they lower the energy or increase the entropy of the transition state. The effect of a catalyst is easy to picture on the potential energy surface (*Figure 20.7*). The catalyst lowers the transition state "hill" between reactants and products, without affecting the positions of the reactants or products, as shown on the diagram.

A few simple examples illustrate how this works. Let's look at catalysis operating in the combustion of hydrogen to form water and in the oxidation of a simple sugar, glucose.

Remember that the reaction of hydrogen and oxygen to form water requires energy. At room temperature, a spark is needed to start the reaction. However, in the presence of the metal palladium, the reaction proceeds rapidly without the spark (see *Figure 20.8*). Why? Hydrogen molecules interact strongly with palladium atoms on the surface of the metal. The palladium atoms are farther apart on the surface than the normal hydrogen-hydrogen distance in the molecule. Strong interactions between hydrogen and palladium atoms stretch and weaken the hydrogen-hydrogen bond, drastically lowering the activation energy. Palladium is not used up in the reaction; it merely acts as a "helper." The catalyst can be reused many times (but not for-

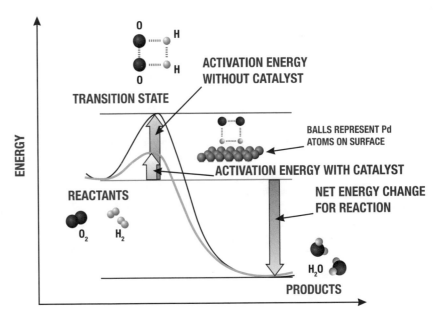

Figure 20.7

Potential energy surfaces showing the effect of a catalyst. The catalyst lowers the energy and/or increases the entropy of the transition state, making it easier (and faster!) for reactants to become products. The energies and entropies of the reactants and products are not affected by the catalyst. In this example, the presence of palladium metal causes the H–H bond of H_2 to stretch, weakening this bond, which must break to allow formation of water.

a.

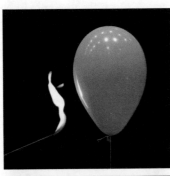

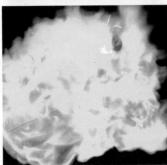

b.

Figure 20.8

a) Hydrogen and oxygen mixed in a balloon do not react to form water vapor unless activation energy (in the form of the flame) is applied, even though the water vapor product is at much lower energy than the H_2 and O_2 reactants. The release of energy from just a few activated molecules forming products supplies energy to activate the rest of the reactants.

b) In the presence of a palladium catalyst, no flame is needed to start the reaction. The catalyst lowers the activation energy so that reactant molecules at room temperature have sufficient kinetic energy to react and become products, explosively releasing more energy.

ever; eventually, impurities contaminate and "poison" the surface so the catalyst stops working).

The reaction of glucose (sugar) with oxygen to produce carbon dioxide and water in living cells is a complex process involving many steps, each sped up by a biological catalyst called an enzyme. One of the first steps involves reaction between the glucose molecule and another molecule called ATP. The catalyst is a large molecule called hexokinase. The hexokinase is shaped just right to hold the glucose and ATP molecules close together, in the right orientation to react. This makes the subsequent reaction much more likely than it would be if the glucose and ATP had to rely on random collisions (*Figure 29.9*).

Figure 20.9

Hexokinase (depicted as ribbons) is a large molecule that functions as a biological catalyst (enzyme). It binds glucose (a kind of sugar) and ATP so that these two reactants are close together and have the proper orientation to form products. This makes both the energy and entropy of activation much more favorable for the reaction of glucose with ATP than would be the case in the absence of the enzyme.

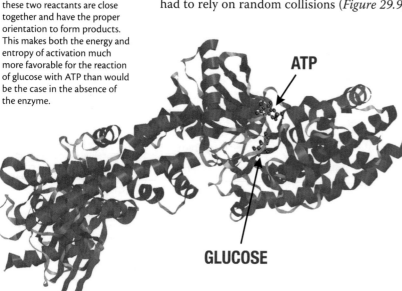

ATP

GLUCOSE

When the reaction is finished, the products no longer fit properly to bind to hexokinase, so they are released and the catalyst is ready to assist in another reaction; it is not used up. The catalyst in this and many other cases is highly selective. It only works with molecules that have just the right shape. So in this case, hexokinase catalyzes the reaction of glucose, but doesn't work for other sugars that have the wrong shape. Further, hexokinase speeds up only the desired reaction; it does not promote decomposition that would be destructive to the living system.

The lock and key analogy may help here to illustrate how specifically the catalysts operate. The relationship between a catalyst and the molecules it acts upon is much like the relationship between a lock and key. Only the correctly shaped key fits in and turns the lock; if the shape is wrong, it doesn't work. Further, the lock only

opens the door to which it is attached. Opening the door lock has specific and limited results. The correctly fitted and turned key won't also open all the windows or turn on the television set.

20–5 CHEMICAL EQUILIBRIUM

In the molecular model of matter, molecules are in constant motion. They continually collide with each other. These collisions can sometimes lead to chemical reaction, the breaking of some chemical bonds and the formation of new ones. For example, if a hydrogen molecule collides with an oxygen molecule with the right orientation and with enough energy, the H–H and O–O bonds break and new O–H bonds form, making water and releasing energy. What about the reverse process? Can water molecules collide in such a way as to break the O–H bonds and re-form H–H and O–O bonds? Can the products react and turn back into reactants?

The answer is yes. If product water molecules collide with enough energy and the right orientation, it is possible to re-form H_2 and O_2 (*Figure 20.10*). There is nothing special about the "direction" of a chemical reaction. The molecular model suggests that if we look at matter at the scale of molecules, matter is dynamic. It is in constant motion and is constantly changing. This extends to the chemistry. Because random collisions are constantly happening, reactions are constantly going on, in both "for-

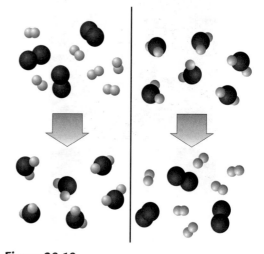

Figure 20.10

Under the proper conditions, H_2 and O_2 react to form water (left), but if conditions are changed, it is possible to produce H_2 and O_2 from water (right).

ward" (the direction we have written the reaction) and "reverse" directions.

So if the reaction can go in either direction, what determines whether reactants become products or products become reactants? Maybe an analogy (no, not the key and the lock again) will help. A person is trying to fill the kitchen sink with water from the tap, but can't close off the drain all the way. Whether or not the sink fills up will depend on how fast the water is draining out and on how fast the tap is running to put water in (*Figure 20.11*). If water is put into the sink faster than it can drain away, the sink will fill up (and overflow, unless the tap is turned off). On the other hand, if the drain empties the sink faster than the tap can fill it, then all the water put in will go down the drain and the sink will not fill. Similarly, the rates of the reverse and forward reactions determine whether reactants or products accumulate. If the forward rate is faster than the reverse rate, reactants disappear and products form. However, if the reverse rate is faster, products disappear and reactants form; essentially, the reaction runs backward!

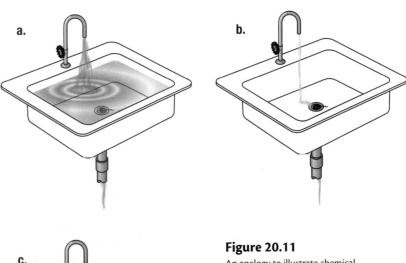

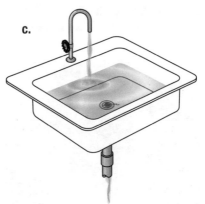

Figure 20.11

An analogy to illustrate chemical equilibrium. If the tap flows faster than the drain, the sink fills (a), but if the drain is faster than the tap, the sink never fills (b). If the tap and drain flow at the same rate, the level of water in the sink remains constant, because the system is at equilibrium (c). No net change is observed at equilibrium, even though filling and draining are going on constantly.

Chemical Equilibrium Occurs When the Forward and Reverse Rates are Equal

If the tap on the sink can be adjusted just right, the rate that water flows in will be equal to the rate at which it flows down the drain. In this situation, the amount of water in the sink does not change, even though water is constantly flowing in and out. This is an example of **equilibrium**. The rate of water flowing in and the rate of water flowing out are in balance.

In the same way, when the forward and reverse rates of a chemical reaction are equal, the amounts of product and reactant do not change. We say that the reaction has reached chemical equilibrium, because the forward and reverse rates for the reaction are in balance. Even though the reaction may be occurring rapidly, no net change is observed because the reverse reaction is happening just as rapidly. In writing reactions, equilibrium is indicated by double arrows, reminding the person reading the equation that the reaction is dynamic and is going in both the forward and the reverse direction. So, for example, at the freezing point of water, where both liquid water, $H_2O_{(l)}$, and ice, $H_2O_{(s)}$, are pres-

ent at the same time, we could write a chemical equation representing the equilibrium as

$$H_2O_{(l)} \rightleftharpoons H_2O_{(s)}$$

If the amount of ice and water remains constant as is implied in the reaction above, the mixture is at equilibrium. The mass of ice cubes in liquid water at the freezing point does not change, but the cubes do change their shapes over time. Why? Because the equilibrium is dynamic, the ice cubes are melting at the same rate that water is freezing back into ice. The freezing and melting occur at random locations on the ice cubes, so the shapes change as time passes.

Equilibrium is the State of Minimum Energy and Maximum Entropy

In the kitchen sink analogy, the person filling the sink has to adjust the tap just right to balance the flow out of the drain. This may be hard to do. But for reacting molecules, the equilibrium condition is not difficult to achieve. In fact, the equilibrium state is the state toward which

• **Equilibrium**

The condition where the forward and reverse rates of a chemical reaction are equal, so the system experiences no net change. Equilibrium is also the state of most favorable energy and entropy for a chemical system.

all reacting systems tend. Why? For a collection of molecules, the lowest energy and most disordered (highest entropy) state is the equilibrium state. Therefore, both energy and entropy favor the establishment of equilibrium.

It follows that energy is required to move a system away from equilibrium. In the ice water example, increasing the amount of water in the liquid form would require addition of energy to the system to speed up the rate of melting. Increasing the amount of ice in the system would

require a large decrease in entropy and removal of energy from the system as the disordered liquid molecules are organized into a regular array in the solid crystal lattice. Removing heat from the system to the surroundings to create order in the system always requires additional expenditure of energy in the surroundings so that the overall entropy of the Universe increases.

As the state of minimum energy and maximum entropy for a system, chemical equilibrium is special. All systems are eventually headed

HENRY EYRING'S CONTRIBUTION

Henry Eyring was a brilliant Utah chemist. He was born in 1901 in Colonia Juarez, Mexico (one of the Mormon colonies). He grew up on a ranch there until the Mexican revolution of 1912 forced the family to leave for Arizona. Henry won a scholarship at the University of Arizona, where he studied mining engineering and metallurgy. As a Ph.D. student at the University of California, Berkeley, he turned to chemistry. He taught at the University of Wisconsin, then moved to Princeton where he rubbed shoulders with Einstein and came into his own as a scientific leader. In 1946 he moved to the University of Utah, where he became dean of the graduate school.

Henry Eyring was the first to realize the connection between the energetic and entropic requirements for chemical reaction and the rate of the reaction. He was able to describe these requirement with beautiful mathematics. The resulting "absolute rate theory" he developed is still widely used to understand and make predictions about the rates of chemical reactions.

Eyring was a member of the National Academy of Science, held fifteen honorary doctorate degrees, and won a virtually all the prestigious prizes in his field, including the National Medal of Science, the Priestly Medal, the Berzelius Medal in Gold awarded by the Swedish Academy, and Israel's $100,000 Wolf Prize. It is surprising to most chemists that Eyring was not awarded a Nobel Prize, but bone cancer took his life before that happened. He served as president of the two most important scientific organizations in his field, the American Chemical Society and the American Association for the Advancement of Science. Eyring published more than 600 journal articles and several influential books, often with the student coauthors' names first. The chemistry building at the University of Utah is named for him.

Eyring has been described as "a truly interesting character." From the age of about 60 for the next 20 years, each year he ran a 50-yard dash challenging all comers among his students. He may not have been able to beat all of them, but he never came in last. Occasionally he would welcome visiting scientists by challenging them to a floor-to-table-top jumping contest. Usually he would then demonstrate the feat and take the win by default. He was as comfortable and considerate in talking with and learning from waiters, gas station attendants, and high school students as he was with Nobel laureates.

Eyring was also a man of great faith, and made no secret of his convictions. His book, *Reflections of a Scientist* (Deseret Book: Salt Lake City, 1983), describes some of his ideas on science, religion, and life and has been a great source of inspiration for many students. For instance, Eyring once wrote, "If you picked up a watch far from human habitation and found it running, you would ask not only 'Who made this watch?' but 'Who wound it up?' So it is with the universe." (*Reflections of a Scientist*, p. 75). Eyring served in many different capacities in The Church of Jesus Christ of Latter-day Saints and is the father of current LDS apostle Henry B. Eyring.

toward equilibrium. The "heat death" of the Universe described in Chapter 18 is the ultimate equilibrium. Fortunately, the rate at which the Universe is headed in that direction is not very fast!

Energy and entropy play important roles in determining, first, whether or not a chemical reaction will happen and second, if a chemical reaction will happen, how fast it will happen. Matter is always conserved in chemical reactions, and this conservation is reflected in the way scientists write reactions; the chemical equations should be balanced so that the number of each kind of atom is the same on both the product and reactant sides of the equation. Favorable reactions involve favorable changes in energy and/or entropy. Fast reactions do not require much energy to reach the transition state; they have low activation energies. Fast reactions also have minimal order requirements in the transition state; that is, they have favorable activation entropies. Catalysts lower the energy or increase the entropy of the transition state so that the reaction speeds up, but the catalyst itself is not transformed by the reaction. Chemical equilibrium occurs when the forward and reverse rates of reaction are equal, and that equilibrium is the state of minimum energy and maximum entropy for the system. With these fundamental ideas in mind, we are now ready for a more detailed description of chemical bonding.

Chapter Framework

A. Brief Introduction to Chemical Bonding

1. New standing wave electron probability patterns when atoms bind to form molecules
2. If electrons in molecular orbitals are lower in energy than in orbitals of isolated atoms, bonds form
3. Molecular orbitals may be bonding (high electron probability between atoms) or antibonding (low electron probability between atoms)
4. Placement of electrons in molecular orbitals determines the nature of the bond

B. Predicting Chemical Bonding

1. Bonds form spontaneously when the energy of the system decreases and/or the entropy of the Universe increases
2. Types of bonding
   a. *Metallic*
   b. *Ionic*
   c. *Covalent*

C. Balancing Chemical Equations (Conservation of Matter)

1. Writing chemical reactions
2. Atoms are neither created nor destroyed in reactions; balancing the written reaction reflects this.

D. Rates of Chemical Reactions

1. Reactions occur at a wide variety of speeds
2. Rates increase with increasing temperature because collision rates and energies increase with temperature
3. Many reactions require activation energy to get started
4. Required orientation for reacting molecules is reflected in activation entropy
5. Catalysts decrease energy and/or entropy of activation
6. Enzymes are biological catalysts

E. Chemical Equilibrium

1. Reactions go both from reactants to products and from products to reactants
2. Equilibrium occurs when the forward and reverse rates of reaction are equal
3. Equilibrium is the state toward which all processes tend, because it is the lowest energy and highest entropy state

Comprehension

Matching

a. *Equilibrium*
b. *Bonding orbital*
c. *Antibonding orbital*
d. *Transition state*
e. *Activation energy*

1. ____ The low energy orbital of the pair of molecular orbitals (MO's) formed when two atomic orbitals combine.
2. ____ The point in a chemical reaction in which the forward and reverse reaction rates are equal.
3. ____ The point in a reaction that separates reactants from products on a potential energy surface.
4. ____ The high energy orbital of the pair of MO's formed when two atomic orbitals combine.
5. ____ The energy that must be put into a system before a reaction can take place.

True/False

1. ____ The probability waves (orbitals) that describe the possible locations for an electron in a molecule are exactly the same as those for an electron in an isolated atom.
2. ____ Electrons in a bonding molecular orbital are most likely to be found between the nuclei in a molecule.
3. ____ A reaction usually goes faster at higher temperatures.
4. ____ A catalyst is a chemical that is present at the beginning of a reaction but not at the end.
5. ____ A very fast reaction has a very high activation energy.

Fill in the blank

1. The _____ _____ in a reaction is usually the highest energy point on the path from reactants to products.
2. A _____ speeds up the reaction but is not itself consumed in the reaction.
3. Chemical equilibrium occurs when the forward and reverse rates of a reaction are _____.
4. Diamonds are, energetically speaking, _____ from graphite.
5. A chemical reaction that would _____ the disorder in the Universe will not occur.
6. Isolated systems achieve _____ when they reach their maximum entropy state.

Analysis

1. Which of the following equations are balanced?

   a) $2C + O_2 \rightarrow 2CO$
   b) $H_2 + F_2 \rightarrow HF$
   c) $Mg + F_2 \rightarrow MgF_2$
   d) $2H_2O_2 \rightarrow H_2O + O_2$
   e) $2 O_3 \rightarrow 3 O_2$
   f) $2Fe_3O_4 \rightarrow 3 Fe_2O_3 + O_2$
   g) $2 Al + 3 O_2 \rightarrow Al_2O_3$

2. Hydrogen is burned in oxygen to form water. The chemical equation representing the reaction can be given by

   $$2H_2 + O_2 = 2H_2O.$$

   On an exam, one student writes the equation as

   $$H_2 + O_2 = H_2O$$

   and the other as

   $$H_2 + O_2 = H_2O_2$$

Explain what is wrong with each of the student responses.

3. Atomic chlorine (Cl) is known to be a catalyst for some of the reactions that are responsible for the depletion of ozone (O_3) in the upper atmosphere (also known as the ozone hole). As a catalyst, Cl may

   a) be lowering the activation energy of some reaction involving ozone.

   b) be consumed in the reaction.

   c) form a transition state with O_3 in which O_3 bonds get weakened.

   d) a and c.

   e) a, b, and c.

4. Characterize the following reactions as occurring with a favorable energy change, a favorable entropy change, or both factors occurring with a favorable change.

   a) H_2(gas) + O_2(gas) = H_2O (liquid)
      Energy given off explosively

   b) C_3H_8(gas) + $5O_2$(gas) = $3CO_2$(gas) + $4H_2O$ (liquid)   Energy given off
      propane

   c) $C_6H_{12}O_6$ (solid) + $3O_2$(gas) = $3 CO_2$(gas) + $6 H_2O$ (liquid)   Energy given off
      glucose

   d) NH_4NO_3 (solid) + H_2O (liquid) = NH_4^+ + NO_3^- in water solution. Energy absorbed (ions are free to move throughout the solution).

      Reaction d is the reaction that occurs inside a *cold pack*, used by athletes to reduce swelling following an injury.

3. Sketch a potential energy diagram for a reaction in which the products are energetically downhill from the reactants but for which there is a high activation energy. Label the reactants, transition state, and the products. On the same diagram indicate how a catalyst affects the activation energy of the reaction.

Synthesis Questions

1. Why does food kept at room temperature spoil faster than food stored in the refrigerator or the freezer?

2. TNT is a well known explosive. It has the chemical formula $C_7H_5N_3O_6$. TNT explodes to form molecules of N_2 gas, CO gas and steam (water vapor) + soot (elemental carbon).

   a) Check to see if the decomposition reaction given below is balanced

   $2C_7H_5N_3O_6$ (solid) → $3N_2$(gas) + $7CO$(gas) + $5H_2O$(gas) + 7 C(solid)

   b) Discuss whether this reaction is favored from an energy perspective, an entropy perspective or both.

   c) As any viewer of old Westerns or Bugs Bunny cartoons can attest, TNT does not spontaneously explode. Often TNT is ignited by lighting a fuse. Explain this observation in terms of transition states and activation energies.

      Hint: The molecular shape of TNT is shown at right. Think about what must happen within the molecule to produce such species as CO.

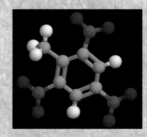

CHAPTER 21

BONDING IN METALS, ALLOYS, AND SEMICONDUCTORS

A theory is the more impressive the greater the simplicity of its premises, the more different are the kinds of things it relates, and the more extended its range of applicability.

~ Albert Einstein

In previous chapters (Chapter 12 and Chapter 17 especially) we have observed that different kinds of materials have widely different physical and chemical properties. In the next three chapters, we will see how the quantum model accounts for the characteristic properties of metallic, ionic, and molecular forms of matter. We begin in this chapter with metals.

Recall that metals fall into the category of network solids. We shall see that the quantum model, originally developed to explain the behavior of isolated atoms, can be extended to account for the strong interactions that result when many metallic atoms come together. The bonding in metals gives rise to the properties of metals that we have observed.

This quantum model also explains properties of elements that are found near the boundary on the Periodic Table between metals and non-metals. Materials like germanium (Ge), silicon (Si), and arsenic (As) are often referred to as **semiconductors** because they can be induced to conduct electricity. However, the characteristics of their electrical conductivity, as well as other properties, are markedly different from metals. The fundamental difference between metals and semiconductors can be traced to the different numbers and relative energies of valence electrons present in the two different types of materials.

21–1 A FEW MORE PROPERTIES OF METALS

Let's review the familiar metallic properties and add a few new ones. As you saw in Table 12.1, metals generally have very high melting and boiling temperatures. Only one metal, mercury, is a liquid at room temperature, and one other, cesium, melts at body temperature. In the solid state, metals have high densities. Lead and gold are two familiar metallic elements with especially high densities. Metals are good conductors of electricity.

Consider the answers to the following questions:

- If you hit a metal with a hammer will it shatter or flatten out?
- Can you see through a chunk of metal or is light blocked by it?
- Is a metal shiny and reflective?
- Does a metal heat up or cool down quickly?

Each of these questions points out additional common properties of metals.

Malleability: Metals can be hammered, pressed, or rolled into very thin sheets without shattering. Pure gold is especially known for its malleability. It can be rolled into sheets as thin

LEARNING OBJECTIVES

When you are finished with this chapter, you should be able to

- Use the quantum model of the atom to explain the bonding in metals and semiconductors.

- Discuss how the properties of metals and alloys (electrical conductivity, metallic luster, malleability, thermal conductivity, and chemical reactivity) can be explained by metallic bonding.

- Explain why the properties of semiconductors differ from those of metals.

as 0.000003 in. (0.1 micron). At this thickness, the gold foil is only a few atoms thick. Architects and interior designers take advantage of this fact and glue such thin gold foil, called gold leaf, on picture frames, furniture, vases, and other art décor. *Figure 21.1* shows two pictures of the Golden Pioneer atop the State Capitol Building in Salem, OR. The first photo shows the gold leaf being applied to the statue and the second shows the completed statue atop the building.

Opacity: How many times have you had to unwrap an aluminum-foil-covered bowl in your refrigerator looking for a particular leftover? Even relatively thin pieces of metal are opaque. A person can't see through the metal because light doesn't pass through it. Instead light is completely absorbed by the metal. Most metals absorb all colors in the light spectrum equally well.

b.

a.

Figure 21.1

a) Thin sheets of gold, called gold leaf, are applied to a statue known as the Golden Pioneer. b) The finished statue atop the Oregon State Capitol Building in Salem.

257

- **Semiconductors**

A solid crystalline substance, such as germanium or silicon, that conducts electricity better than insulators, but not as well as metals. Unlike metals, they become better conductors as their temperature increases.

- **Malleability**

The characteristic of substances that allows them to be worked into desirable shapes or drawn out into wires.

- **Opacity**

The opposite of being transparent. Visible light is absorbed by an opaque object.

- **Reflectivity**

The characteristic of being capable of or producing reflection.

- **Thermal Conductivity**

A measure of the degree to which a substance conducts heat. Metals have a high thermal conductivity.

Figure 21.2

The formation of molecular orbitals (MOs) from the combination of atomic orbitals. a) from two atoms, b) from three atoms, c) from a progression up to infinity.

Reflectivity: Every time you check your hair or makeup in front of a mirror, you take advantage of the high reflectivity of metals. Metals, in addition to being opaque to light, are also highly reflective. Light easily bounces back off the surface of metals.

Thermal conductivity: A cook stirring a pot of hot soup on the stove uses a wooden or plastic spoon rather than a metal one to avoid getting burned. Metals are good conductors of heat. They heat up much more quickly when they come in contact with something hot than do non-metallic materials.

21–2 BONDING IN METALS

Four key factors lead to the metallic bonding model. First, chemical bonding involves only an atom's valence electrons. Second, the valence electrons of metals have low ionization energies. Third, metals have few electrons compared to the total number allowed in their valence orbitals. Fourth, electrons want to be in the lowest energy orbitals available to them.

Figure 17.8 showed that, for a given period, an alkali metal (Group 1A) ionized most easily of the elements. The Group 1A elements have only one valence electron, but they have unfilled orbitals of comparable energy to accommodate up to seven more valence electrons. Transition metal atoms, which have low-energy d orbitals, have even more free orbitals. Titanium (Atomic number = 22) has four valence electrons but room for 14 more.

Molecular Orbitals or MOs

When isolated atoms approach each other, the electrons on one atom experience attractive

forces with the nucleus of the other atom. The orbital description that was appropriate for isolated atoms doesn't fit the new situation. The standing waves that describe electron states change to reflect the new interactions. The mathematical details of these new states are very complex, but we can give some general results for them. The new standing waves, which we call molecular orbitals (MO's), can be pictured pretty simply.

Figure 21.2a presents a simple illustration of what happens to the orbitals when two identical atoms come together. As a specific example, consider two sodium (Na) atoms, each with a single 3s electron. The two atomic orbitals (AOs) from the atoms combine to form two MOs. One MO is lower in energy than the starting atomic orbitals, while the other is higher in energy.

The two valence electrons from the atoms go into the lowest energy MO, called a bonding MO. This MO is lower in energy because there is a high probability that the electrons will be found between the two nuclei, where they experience strong attractive forces. An electron that found itself in the high energy MO would have a high probability of being on one side or the other of the molecule. There, it would experience an attractive force from only one nucleus. This interaction doesn't lead to bond formation, so the high-energy MO is sometimes called an anti-bonding orbital.

Now consider what happens if three identical atoms come together. The MOs shown in *Figure 21.2b* are the result of interactions amongst three identical atoms. Three MO's result: one is a bonding MO, one is an antibonding MO and the third has the same energy as the starting atomic orbitals. As more and more atoms come together, each contributing an AO,

a.

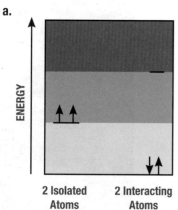

2 Isolated Atoms   2 Interacting Atoms

b.

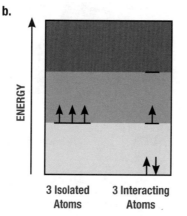

3 Isolated Atoms   3 Interacting Atoms

c.

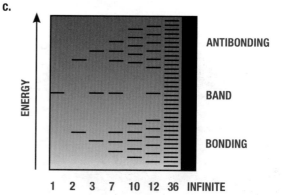

1   2   3   7   10 12 36 INFINITE

more and more MO orbitals form. Figure 21.c shows the progression in the pattern of MOs produced with increasing numbers of interacting atoms. The last column shows that when many atoms combine, the result is a series of closely molecular orbitals. If the number of atoms is very large—say 1023 or so—then the resulting MOs will be so close together in energy that they behave as a continuous band rather than a discrete set of levels.

For simplicity, *Figure 21.c* shows only the combination of one valence atomic orbital from each atom. In fact, all the valence orbitals of every atom may be able to combine with comparable AOs on other atoms, *even if the orbitals have no electrons in them.* The result follows the same general pattern described above. Combining some number, N, of atomic orbitals creates a set of bonding MOs, a set of antibonding MOs and perhaps some nonbonding MOs. A total of N MOs will result from the combination. For metals, the resulting MOs form a continuous band of energy levels.

Electrons in a solid piece of metal fill in the allowed energy levels starting at the lowest energy orbital, just like electrons in isolated atoms. Since individual metallic atoms have few valence electrons relative to valence orbitals, many of the MOs in the electronic band of the solid metal are empty.

Figure 21.3 represents the energy band of electrons in a metal. The energy levels filled with electrons are shown in blue, while the white areas represent empty orbitals. Because the levels are very closely spaced in energy, only small quantities of energy are needed to excite electrons up into unoccupied levels.

Just as with AOs, the MOs describe the probability of finding electrons somewhere in space. The MOs associated with metallic energy levels extend over large regions of space, large enough to include many nuclei. Let's pose an analogy. Consider the seats in a large basketball arena. An electron in an isolated atom could be thought of as being most likely to be found within a single seat in the bleachers. An electron in a metal has a high probability of being found in any of the seats in the arena.

Therefore, it is best to think of these electrons as being shared by all the nuclei, rather than belonging to any particular one. The term **delocalized electrons** is sometimes used to

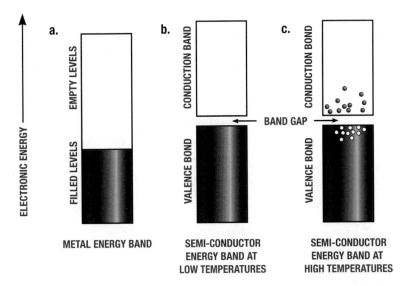

↗ Figure 21.3

The electronic band structure in metals and semiconductors. a) In metals there is a set of energy states so closely spaced that they can be regarded as continuous. b) In semiconductors, there is a gap between the filled and unfilled levels. At low temperatures all the electrons are below the gap. c) As the temperature increases, some electrons get thermally excited into the unfilled levels.

describe them because they are not localized around any one nucleus, but are free to move throughout the metal. Scientists reinforce this image by speaking of a "sea" of electrons that surround the nuclei. In *Figure 21.4* the sea of electrons is represented by the diffuse blue cloud surrounding the nuclei. This type of chemical bonding is called **metallic bonding.**

21–3 METALLIC BONDING MODEL EXPLAINS METAL PROPERTIES

The relatively simple picture in Figure 21.4 of a set of closely-spaced energy levels with delocalized, mobile electrons explains all the observations that you have collected about metals.

High melting temperature: In Chapter 12, the hypothesis was formulated that strong forces between atoms were present in materials that exhibited high melting temperatures. The metallic bonding model says that these strong forces come from the electrostatic attraction between the mobile electrons and the nuclei. The electrons serve as the glue that holds the metal nuclei together. The MOs extend over many nuclei, so these attractive forces keep many nuclei tightly bonded to each other. It takes a lot of kinetic energy in order to pull these nuclei away from each other to change the solid metal to a liquid.

• **Delocalized Electrons**

Electrons in metallic orbitals are not confined to be near a specific nucleus, but have comparable probabilities of being around many different nuclei.

• **Metallic Bond**

The chemical bond that binds metal atoms to other metal atoms in forming metal substances.

• **Electrical Conductivity**

A measure of the degree to which a substance conducts an electrical current.

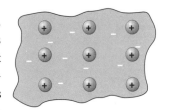

Figure 21.4

The distribution of electrons in the metallic-bonding model. The blue region represents the sea of electrons that surround the metallic nuclei. The electrons are said to be "delocalized" and free to move throughout the metal.

Electrical conductivity: An electrical current requires mobile charges that are free to move under the influence of an electric field. In a metal, the charge carriers are the mobile electrons. They are not bound tightly to any particular nucleus, so they are able to move relatively easily.

Thermal conductivity: The same mobile electrons responsible for electrical conductivity also cause the high thermal conductivity found in metals. When one end of a metal piece heats up, the mobile electrons carry the increased kinetic energy rapidly throughout the piece.

Malleability: Pounding a thick piece of metal into a thin foil requires that the metal nuclei pass over one another. The fluid-like electrons act like a lubricant between the layers of nuclei. They reduce the repulsive forces that would be generated when layers of nuclei, sliding over one another, come into direct contact.

Opacity: Given the almost infinite number of energy states and their close spacing, there are always going to be a pair of energy states that match the energy of photons throughout the electromagnetic spectrum. Metals are opaque because they can absorb radiation of the entire visible region of the spectrum, as well as in the infrared and the ultraviolet.

Reflectivity: This property is related to the explanation for opacity. The mobility of the electrons allows them to easily interact with the light waves. Absorption of light causes oscillations in the electrons. Those oscillations in turn radiate light energy. The reflection off a metal actually arises from this radiation. The different colors of copper, gold, and silver are related to subtle differences in their absorption and reflection properties in the visible region of the spectrum.

21–4 ALLOYS—METAL-METAL COMPOUNDS

Unlike the other types of bonding to be considered later, the requirements for metallic bonding are not too specific. Atoms with low ionization energies and few valence electrons satisfy the requirements. Since all metals fit this description, metallic bonding can occur between atoms from different kinds of metals. Therefore, it is possible to make metal-metal compounds,

called **alloys**, in which one or more types of metal atoms are incorporated into crystals of another kind of metal. White gold, for example, is an alloy of gold and platinum. Brass is an alloy of copper and zinc. Unlike most other kinds of compounds, however, the compositions of alloys are generally not fixed in simple ratios. For example, there are alloys of lead and tin that range from having a relatively few tin atoms, each one completely surrounded by lead atoms, to the reverse, a few lead atoms each completely surrounded by tin atoms.

Two different kinds of alloy structures can be formed, depending on the relative sizes of the different metal atoms (*Figure 21.5*). When the metal atoms are about the same size, one type of metal atom can substitute in the crystal for another. Think of a grocery display of red delicious apples and golden delicious apples. A red apple could occasionally be replaced with a green one and the stack would still be stable. Brass is an example of this type of alloy.

When the two types of metal atoms differ greatly in size, the smaller atoms can fit into the holes formed by layers of the bigger atoms. Returning to the grocery store fruit display analogy, think of the grocer placing cherries in the gaps formed by layers of oranges. Steel, which is an alloy of iron with a few percent of carbon, is an example of the second type. Which element is the orange and which is the cherry?

Whether an alloy forms at all, and which form it adopts if it does form, are governed by the principles of reactivity outlined in the previous chapter. Taking two pure metals and forming an alloy from them increases the entropy of the metallic system. The random positions of different metal atoms within the alloy lead to an increased disorder. If the two metals are very similar, then there is little energy change during mixing. Alloys formed from dissimilar metals do release or absorb energy from the surroundings. An alloy that releases energy on formation will be favored. For such a process, increased disorder appears in both the system and the surroundings and the overall entropy change of the Universe is large.

The properties of alloys are similar in character to those of metals, but they may differ in the actual magnitude. An alloy of two pure metals will conduct electricity, but either of the two pure metals will usually be found to be a better

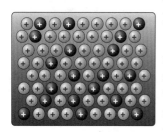

a.

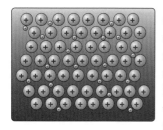

b.

Figure 21.5
The two types of alloys. a) Atoms from two different metals are the same size and can substitute for each other. b) Atoms from two different metal atoms of very different sizes. Small-sized atoms from one metal can can fit into spaces between the other metal's larger atoms.

• **Alloy**
A combination of two or more metals into a single homogeneous substance.

conductor. An alloy will often (but not always) melt at a lower temperature than either of the pure metals from which it has been made. The reduction in melting point can be very significant. Practical applications take advantage of that observation. Lead-tin alloys of certain compositions have much lower melting points than either pure lead or pure tin. These alloys are used as solders—low-melting-point materials that are used to connect metal pipes or wires together (*Figure 21.6*).

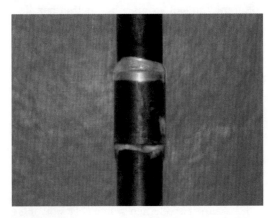

Figure 21.6
A photo of lead-tin solder (the silvery patches) holding pieces of copper pipe together. A plumber talks of "sweating" the pipe together.

The malleability of metals can often be a problem in many applications. Application of pressure to a piece of pure metal can cause the piece to thin or flatten. Most industrial uses for metal, such as in the construction of buildings, require hard, strong material. Adding another metal during the smelting process to form an alloy can produce a metal of the necessary hardness for a particular job. The irregularities introduced by the nuclei of different sizes make it harder for one layer to slip over another.

Magnesium and aluminum are two of the lightest metals. Alloys of both metals are used when reduction of weight is a design consideration. As the automotive and aerospace industries work to prepare lighter, stronger vehicles and planes, alloys based on magnesium or aluminum are becoming increasingly important.

21–5 SEMICONDUCTORS

Little has been said up to now in this text about semiconductors. Semiconductors are

those elements found around the black staircase drawn on the Periodic Table of Figure 17.6. Their properties are not exactly metallic in nature, nor are they the properties of the non-metals. Semiconductors are closer in most of their properties (e.g., being solids with high melting points and being electrically conductive under certain conditions), so they are sometimes called semi-metals.

Silicon and germanium are the most significant semiconductors for current technical use. Silicon Valley, a region in southern California, got its nickname from the many electronics and computer companies that sprung up there.

Semiconductors are at heart of all of the electronic devices that have revolutionized modern life. Computers, TV remotes, CD players, modern automobiles and the stop lights that direct traffic flow, all rely on semiconductor technology.

We introduce semiconductors in this chapter along with metals and alloys because an energy band model similar to that used to explain metallic properties also explains semiconductor properties. As the Einstein's quote at the opening of this chapter says, a model is more impressive when it can explain a wide range of properties and account for observed differences. In this regard, the quantum model of the atom and its offspring, the metallic bonding model, are both impressive and intriguing in their ability to explain semiconductors as well as metals.

Electrical Resistivity

Let's begin by looking first at the electrical conductivity of semiconductors. One way to characterize electrical conductivity is through a quantity called resistivity. The greater a material's resistivity, the less current will flow through it. As *Figure 21.7* shows, the resistivities of metals and semiconductors respond very differently to increases in temperature. Metals become slightly more resistive as the temperature is increased while semiconductors become much less resistive with increasing temperature.

The metallic behavior is due to the increased jiggling motion of metal nuclei with increasing temperature. Electrons get deflected as they flow through a circuit

- **Resistivity**
A measure of the resistance to the flow of electrical current.

Figure 21.7
The electrical resistivity measures resistance to the flow of electricity. The resitivity of metals increases slightly with temperature. That for semiconductors decreases greatly with temperatures. Unlike metals, semiconductors conduct electricity better at high temperatures.

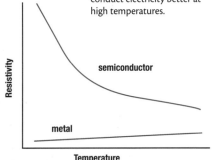

because of this motion. How can we understand the much more dramatic and opposite-trending behavior of semiconductors?

Band Gaps in Semiconductor MOs

The answer lies in the MOs that form in semiconductors. The central illustration in Figure 21.3 depicts the energy bands that arise when AOs on semiconductor atoms combine. The fundamental picture is the same as for metals: AOs on atoms combine to form sets of closely-spaced MOs. However, one key difference emerges. In metals, the bands associated with the bonding and antibonding MOs overlap, forming one continuous set of levels. In semiconductors, the bonding and antibonding MO's form distinct, separated bands. The energy spacing between the bands is called a band gap. Gap formation in semiconductors can be understood in terms of the different sizes and energies of valence orbitals in semiconductor atoms compared to those of metals. The details are beyond this text.

A semiconductor band gap is of relatively low energy. In pure silicon and germanium, the width of the band gap corresponds to photon energies in the infrared portion of the spectrum. That width can be altered somewhat by incorporating atoms of other elements into the crystalline arrangement of silicon or germanium atoms. That process is referred to as doping.

The band gap turns out be the reason for the different behavior with temperature of metallic and semiconductor resistivities. At very low temperatures, all of the valence electrons in a semiconductor reside in the lower energy band; this band, called the valence band, is completely or nearly filled. When the temperature is raised, electrons gain enough thermal energy to be excited into the upper band. Figure 21.3c represents this process by showing the excited electrons as blue circles in the upper band. The energies where electrons are missing are shown as holes in the valence band.

The excited electrons gain access to a large set of closely spaced energy levels once they jump up to the higher energy band. Remember that the existence of many empty, closely spaced energy levels was the origin of metallic properties, including electrical conductivity. Semiconductors become conducting when electrons occupy the upper band. For this reason, the

upper band is called the conduction band. Electrical conductivity is also helped by the creation of the holes down in the valence band. The electrons remaining in the valence band can now also begin to conduct, because there are now empty levels for them to move into. Movement of electrons into holes creates new holes, so electrical current, generally referred to as the "movement of electrons," can also be considered as the "movement of holes."

Semiconductors can also be formed from different kinds of atoms in a way that parallels the formation of alloys. The restrictions needed to maintain semiconductor behavior are a little stronger, so there are fewer binary semiconductors (two-element semiconductors) than there are alloys. Size and having a similar total number of valence electrons are two factors that favor the formation of a binary semiconductor.

For example, consider germanium (Ge, AN = 32) which we now to be a good semiconductor. Gallium (Ga, AN =31) and arsenic (As, AN = 33) are the two elements on either side of Ge on the Periodic Table. All three elements belong to the same row in the Periodic Table, so they are reasonably close in size. Ga has one fewer valence electron than Ge while As has one more valence electron. The combination, called GaAs, (and read as gallium arsenide) forms a semiconductor. What combination of two elements might be predicted to form a semiconductor like Si?

Optical Properties

Semiconductors will absorb photons whose energy matches or exceeds the band gap energy. For Ge and Si, whose band gaps are in the infrared, all colors of visible light can be absorbed, so the semiconductors appear black. GaAs has a larger band gap than pure Ge, but still one that corresponds to infrared photons, so GaAs also appears black. The band gap of the semiconductor formed from zinc (AN = 30) and selenium (AN = 34) corresponds to violet photons. ZnSe has a yellow color. Still other semiconductors can be created with band gaps in the low frequency end of the ultraviolet region. Such materials are white because all visible colors are reflected rather than being absorbed.

It doesn't take a lot of extra electrons up in the conduction band or a lot of holes in the valence bond to generate the important properties of a semiconductor. Electrons can be added into the valence band of silicon or germanium by inserting a few phosphorous atoms (P, AN=15) since P has one more valence electron than Si or Ge. Adding aluminum (Al, AN = 13), to Si or Ge creates holes in the conduction band, since Al has one fewer valence electron than the host material.

A semiconductor with "holes" is called a p-type semiconductor, while a semiconductor with extra electrons is called an n-type semiconductor. Doped semiconductors are still electrically neutral. They just have fewer or greater numbers of valence electrons than the pure semiconductor.

LED—a semiconductor device

Solid-state electronics (e.g., computers, radios, and CD players) all use semi-conductor based devices. A discussion of transistors, computer chips and circuit boards is beyond the scope of this textbook. But one increasingly important semiconductor device, a light emitting diode or LED, can be understood with the background established so far.

Ever used a TV remote? Then, you've used an LED that emits light in the infrared region. Increasingly, the traffic lights at the intersections you drive through consist of hundreds of red, green or yellow-emitting LEDs. The displays on those big, big, big TV screens seen in stadiums or basketball arenas are also made from clusters of LED's, each cluster acting like a pixel on a desktop computer. Examples of LED's are given in Figure 21.8.

A diode is created by bonding an n-type semi-conductor directly to a p-type semiconductor to form a single unit. The region where they join is called a junction. An electrical circuit can be created by attaching the N-type side of a diode to the negative terminal of a battery and the diode's P-type side to the battery's positive terminal as shown in Figure 21.9. If the battery supplies a large enough voltage, electrical current will flow. However, current will flow in only one direction. Electrons flow from the N-type region (the region with extra electrons) to the P-type region (the region with holes).

When an electron crosses the junction and falls into a hole, it gives up its extra electrical potential energy by emitting a photon. The color

of the photon is determined primarily by the band gap as shown on the right hand side of Figure 21.9. By choosing the proper semiconductor material, LED's that emit light from the infrared to the ultraviolet can be prepared.

21–6 CONCLUSION

The interactions of orbitals from many atoms give rise to bands of closely spaced molecular orbitals. In metals, the bonding and anti-bonding MOs overlap, while in semiconductors there is a small energy gap between the two of MOs. The band model explains many of the observed properties of both metals and semi-conductors. In the next chapter, the quantum model will be used again to explain *ionic bonding*, which is the bonding that takes place within compounds formed between metals and non-metals.

Figure 21.8
Several examples of applications using LEDs. A traffic light that uses a cluster of red, yellow, and green emitting LEDs is brighter and more economical than a lamp providing light based on gas-discharge tubes. The traffic light on the left is standard, and the one on the right uses LED.

* **Junction**

The interface between two different semiconductor regions in a semiconductor device.

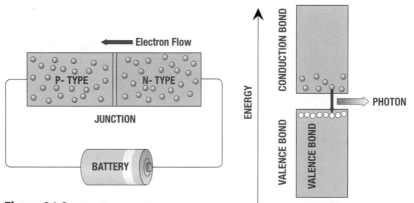

Figure 21.9
The figure on the left shows a diode, consisting of a p-type semiconductor (one that contains holes in the valence band) and an n-type semiconductor (one that has electrons in or near the bottom of the conduction band) in an electrical circuit with a battery. Electrons flow through the circuit as shown. The right hand side of the figure shows the relative energies of electrons in the conduction band and that of the holes in the valence band. When an electron falls down into a hole a photon is emitted. The photon color is governed mostly by the bandgap of the semiconductor.

Chapter Framework

A. Introduction

B. A Few Properties of Metal

C. Bonding in Metals

   1. MOs and AOs

D. Metallic Bonding Model Explains Metal Properties

E. Alloys—Metal-Metal Compounds

F. Semiconductors

   1. Resistivity

   2. Band Gaps and Conduction Bands

   3. LED and Diodes

Comprehension

True/False

1. _____ Light can only be seen through very thin metal.

2. _____ Generally, MOs are low in energy because their electrons will be found between two nuclei.

3. _____ Compositions of alloys are generally fixed in simple ratios.

4. _____ For an alloy to form, the atoms must be different sizes.

5. _____ Often alloys are better conductors than either of the metals, in their pure form, that make up the alloy.

6. _____ Semi-metals are electrically conductive and have high melting points.

7. _____ Semiconductors and metals are very similar in the way each forms alloys.

Matching

a. *Opacity*
b. *Reflectivity*
c. *Conduction band*
d. *Alloy*
e. *Delocalized electrons*
f. *Thermal conductivity*
g. *Metallic bonding*
h. *Semiconductors*
i. *Malleability*
j. *Resistivity*

1. _____ Metal-metal compound.

2. _____ Electrons act like a lubricant between layers of nuclei.

3. _____ "Movement of electrons."

4. _____ An electron which is not focused around any one nucleus.

5. _____ Property of absorbing photons throughout the electromagnetic spectrum.

6. _____ Substances that conduct electricity better than insulators but not as good as conductors.

7. _____ The degree to which a substance conducts heat.

8. _____ A measure for current flowing through a semiconductor.

9. _____ Nuclei surrounded by a "sea" of electrons.

10. ___ How easily light bounces off the surface of a substance.

Fill in the Blank

1. The _____ model helps answer questions about metals and semiconductors.

2. A difference between metals and semiconductors is caused by the different _____ and _____ of _____ electrons present in the two different types of materials.

3. The _____ electrons act like a _____ between the layers of nuclei when flattening metal with a mallet.

4. The source of differences between semiconductors and metal is caused by _____ _____.

5. In a diode, an n-type and a p-type semiconductor join at a _____.

Analysis

1. Which of the following pairs of metal is most likely to form alloys of all compositions?

   a) $_{56}$Ba and $_{31}$Ga

   b) $_{50}$Sn and $_{82}$Pb

   c) $_{3}$Li and $_{83}$Bi

2. Which of the following pairs of metals is most likely to form alloys of all proportions?

   a) $_{55}$Cs and $_{49}$In

   b) $_{82}$Pb and $_{19}$K

   c) $_{37}$Pt and $_{79}$Au

3. Which of the following is NOT why alloys are useful to us today? Alloys

   a) have lower melting temperatures.

   b) have a higher conductivity rate.

   c) are less malleable.

   d) reduce weight in objects.

4. How do metals and semiconductors change with increasing temperatures?

   a) Metals become less resistive and semiconductors more resistive.

   b) Metals and semiconductors become more resistive.

   c) Metals and semiconductors become less resistive.

   d) None of the above.

Synthesis

1. What combination of two elements might be predicted to form a semiconductor like $_{14}$Si?

2. What is responsible for all the properties of metals?

3. Why is metal not see-through?

4. What is the difference with electrons between isolated atoms and metal compounds?

5. Why would automotive industries build cars of out aluminum rather than iron? Than steel?

6. When gold and silver are mixed, the appearance is still that of pure gold. How could you distinguish the alloy from pure gold?

7. Why do metals have high melting points? How does this relate to metals?

8. Why would a sculptor use gold leafing to cover his statue? Answer in terms of malleability, opacity, and reflectivity.

9. What type of atomic particles are influenced in chemical bonding and why?

10. What is the difference between the anti-bonding and non-bonding molecular orbitals?

11. According to the metallic bonding model, how does power flow through a wire?

12. How are opacity and the properties of solids related?

13. Why do alloys have lower melting temperatures than the two metals that form the alloy?

14. Why do metals become less conductive as temperature raises? How is this related to heat conductivity?

15. Silicon has a band gap in the infrared region. What do you predict will be the color of a silicon crystal? Will visible photons be absorbed by a silicon crystal? If so, what color should you see?

16. The manufacturer's information sheet for an LED based upon the semiconductor gap says that the LED emits light at a wavelength of 525 nm (nanometer). What color light would this be?

17. An LED changes colors when it is dipped in liquid nitrogen. It shifts from being red to yellow. What is happening to the band gap of the semiconductor? Is it getting bigger or smaller? What might be causing this effect?

BONDING IN IONIC COMPOUNDS

In Chapter 21, we saw that the model of metallic bonding explained why metals have high melting points. The sea of mobile electrons acts like a sticky glue holding the metallic nuclei together in an extended structure. In chapter 19, we noted that two non-metallic substances in Table 12.1, our database of material properties, also have high melting and boiling temperatures. These two substances, sodium chloride (common table salt) and magnesium oxide, typify the compounds that metals form with non-metals. We call such compounds **ionic compounds** or **salts**, and we call the bonding in these compounds **ionic bonding**.

With respect to properties other than melting point, ionic compounds differ significantly from pure metals or alloys. This chapter will explain the model of ionic bonding that arises from the quantum model of the atom. You will see how this new model incorporates fundamental differences in metals and non-metals to account for all of the properties of ionic compounds.

As you study this chapter, take time to reflect back on Chapter 21 and the model of metallic bonding. Both Chapters 21 and 22 treat matter we have previously characterized

(Chapter 19) as having extended structures. Compare and contrast how the properties of metals and alloys differ from those of ionic compounds. Pay special attention to a) the fundamental differences in metals and non-metals that give rise to the two models; b) the key differences in the bonding models; and, c) how each model accounts for the physical properties of the respective type of material.

22–1 PROPERTIES OF IONIC COMPOUNDS

Ionic compounds have high melting temperatures and boiling temperatures, some so high that they have never been measured. Compounds formed by metals in the first two columns of the Periodic Table (1A and 2A) and non-metals in columns 6A and 7A are colorless. Large crystals of these compounds are transparent as shown in *Figure 22.1*. In fact, they are used as windows in some of the spectroscopy instruments described in Chapter 19. Salts that contain transition metals (elements in columns 1B–8B) may be highly colored. Figure 22.1c

LEARNING OBJECTIVES

When you finish this chapter, you should be able to

- Explain ionic bonding with the use of the quantum model of the atom.
- Discuss how ionic bonding explains the properties of salts (melting and boiling temperatures, electrical conductivity, transparency, and brittleness)
- Predict the most likely ion to form from metals at the far left of the Periodic Table and non-metals on the far right of the Periodic Table.
- Predict the formulas of simple salts based on ionic charges and name the salts.

shows the neon green color of a nickel salt and the brilliant blue of a copper salt. Figures 17.1, 17.2 and 19.10 show additional colored transition metal salts.

All salts are brittle; salt chunks cannot be easily reshaped. They shatter into many pieces when hit with a hammer. Chapter 12 stated that salts are ionic conductors. When molten

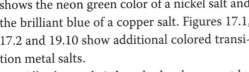

Figure 22.1

The transparency of ionic compounds.

a) Instrument windows made of sodium chloride (NaCl) and potassium bromide (KBr).

b) Ionic crystals with defects can appear white.

c) Salts that contain transition metal ions may be highly colored.

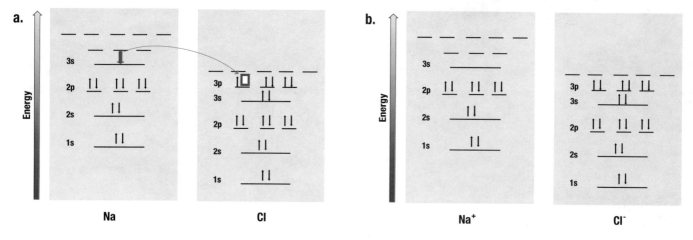

Na   **Cl**   **Na⁺**   **Cl⁻**

(liquid) or dissolved in water, salts conduct electricity, but dry solid salts do not.

22–2 WHY DO NON-METALS AND METALS REACT TO FORM SALTS?

Key Properties of Metals and Non-metals

To understand why ionic compounds form, consider the key differences between metal and non-metal atoms. You may wish to refer back to Figures 17.7 and 17.8 to remind yourself of those differences.

Metals have large atomic volumes, few valence electrons and low first ionization energies. They easily form positive ions by losing valence electrons. Non-metals, however, have small atomic volumes, many valence electrons and very high first ionization energies. From the high ionization energies, you can infer that non-metal atoms like to hold tightly onto their electrons. In fact, the situation goes farther than that. Non-metal atoms have such a strong affinity for electrons, that they can pull electrons away from other atoms.

One chemical reactivity principle described in Chapter 20 states that two chemical species are likely to react if the products have lower energy than the starting materials. Put another way, electrons, like falling balls, go to the lowest energy condition available to them. The formation of the ionic compound, sodium chloride (NaCl), from metallic sodium (Na element 11) and gaseous chlorine (Cl_2 element 17) illustrates this principle nicely.

Figure 22.2 presents the energy level diagrams of atomic Na and atomic Cl. Sodium has one valence electron in a 3s atomic orbital; chlorine has seven valence electrons and room for one more to fill its 3p set of orbitals. Notice that the Na orbitals are higher in energy than the comparable Cl orbitals.

Thinking like a scientist : Why should the Na atomic orbitals be higher in energy than their counterparts on Cl? What factors might explain this observation?

The classical electric force law that you studied in Chapter 4 helps to explain the relative energy orderings of comparable atomic orbitals in Figure 22.2. This law states that the force between two charged particles increases when the charge on one particle increases. The force also increases when the distance between the two particles gets smaller.

Both distance and charge influence the energy ordering of comparable atomic orbitals on Na and Cl. Compared to valence electrons on Na, the Cl valence electrons are closer to their nucleus than are those of Na. (Remember the large atomic size of metals.) Chlorine's valence electrons also experience a stronger attraction for their nucleus since the Cl nucleus has 17 protons compared to Na's 11.

These two factors have the same effect: the valence electrons in standing waves around chlorine have a lower electrical potential energy than Na's valence electron. So, when Na atoms and Cl atoms come together, the 3s electron of Na goes downhill energetically by jumping to the Cl atom; energy is given off in the process. Thus, the first principle of chemical reactivity is satisfied. What about the second principle, the one that has to do with increasing the disorder in the Universe?

The reaction of Na and Cl_2 actually produces an explosive amount of energy, much more than can be represented in Figure 22.2. This energy appears in the surroundings as heat and light. The energy heats up the surroundings around the reaction site. So much energy flows into the surroundings from the reaction that the surroundings' disorder increases significantly. The overall disorder in the Universe increases according to the second principle.

22-3 THE IONIC MODEL OF BONDING

Localized Electrons but Extended Structures

Metals easily lose electrons, and non-metals easily gain electrons. The combination of metals and non-metals that form salts can be understood simply as a marriage made in heaven: one likes to give, one likes to receive. Once formed, the positive and negative ions exert attractive electrostatic forces on each other. Ionic bonding gets its name because the interaction occurs between ions.

In contrast to the bonding in metals, the electrons in ionic compounds are in atomic-type orbitals localized on each ion. The orbitals do not extend beyond an ion for long distances. The extended, network structure that is found in salts arises from the strong, long-range nature of the electric force. One ion interacts with many neighboring ions. Each of those ions, in turn, interacts with its neighboring ions. Those ions interact with other ions, and before you know it, you have a chunk of salt.

Structures of Salts

The most energetically favorable arrangement of ions maximizes attractive interactions and minimizes repulsive ones. In the case of Na^+ and Cl^- ions, each ion type surrounds itself with ions of the opposite charge. Every ion experiences strong attractive interactions (+—+—) with its neighbors and is shielded from repulsive interactions (+ + + or———) with ions of its own type. *Figure 22.3a* shows the NaCl structure, where the green balls represent Cl^- ions and the yellow balls indicate Na^+ ions.

Many other salts adopt the NaCl structure. Magnesium oxide (salt made of Mg^{2+} and O^{2-} ions) and potassium bromide (salt made of K^+ and Br^- ions) both form in the NaCl structure of Figure 22.3a. Salts containing ions of the same charge (e.g., +1, −1 or +2, −2) and about the same size tend to take on this structure because it represents the most favorable energetic arrangement for these ions.

Because a salt must be electrically neutral, the total positive and negative charges must be equal. That neutrality is achieved in ionic compounds such as $CaCl_2$ (Ca^{2+} and Cl^-) or Na_2O (Na^+ and O^{2-}) by taking twice as many ions of one type as another. In Al_2O_3 it takes two ions of aluminum (Al^{3+}) for every three oxide (O^{2-}) ions to form a neutral aluminum oxide material. In a later section in this chapter, we will consider a simple picture to predict what combining ratios might be expected for different ionic materials.

Salts with combinations of positive and negative ions other than the 1:1 of NaCl adopt different arrangements of the positive and negative ions. Structures of representative 2:1 (Na_2O) and 2:3 (Al_2O_3) ionic compounds are shown in *Figure 22.3b* and *Figure 22.3c*, respectively. One common principle applies in all structures: each ion has ions of the opposite charge as its next-door neighbors.

22-4 HOW IONIC BONDING EXPLAINS IONIC COMPOUND PROPERTIES

The simple picture of charged ions held together by electrostatic interactions accounts for many of the properties described at the beginning of the chapter; the quantum model picture of atomic orbital energies explains the remaining ones.

High Melting and Boiling Temperatures

Electrostatic forces are long-range. An ion can feel the attractive force of oppositely charged ions several neighbors away. Also, the electrostatic force extends in all directions from an ion. Because of these two factors, individual ions interact strongly with many other ions. A great deal of thermal energy is required to pull indi-

a. NaCl

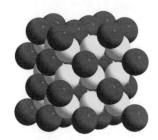

b. Na₂O

c. Al₂O₃

Figure 22.3

Structures of ionic compounds. Green balls represent chloride Cl^-, yellow balls represent Na^+, red ones represent the oxide ion O^{2-}, and blue ones represent Al^{+3} ions. The ball diameters reflect the relative sizes of ions.

a) The structure of sodium chloride, NaCl.

b) The structure of sodium oxide, Na_2O.

c) The structure of aluminum oxide, Al_2O_3 (corundum).

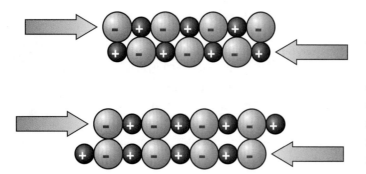

Figure 22.4

Hammering on an ionic compound forces ions of like charge to come in contact. The strong repulsive interactions cause the crystal to shatter.

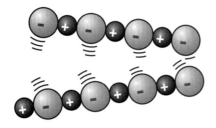

◆ **Electrolytes**

A chemical compound that ionizes when dissolved in water to produce an electrically conductive medium.

Figure 22.5

The conductivity of salts in different states. The blowup shows the arrangement of the ions in each state.

a) Solid
b) Molten (liquid) salt
c) Salt dissolved in water

vidual ions away from their neighbors, hence the high melting temperatures. Melting results in a loss of the ordered, fixed arrangement of ions, but interactions between clusters of ions are still strong. Boiling breaks down the clusters and that, too, requires high temperatures.

Brittleness

Salt crystals break and shatter when hit with a hammer. They do not bend, flatten, or easily change their shape. Bending, flattening, or shape changes would all require sliding layers of ions over each other. As shown in *Figure 22.4*, if one layer of ions moves a short distance, positive ions come in direct contact with other positive ions, and likewise for the negative ions. These strong repulsions force layers apart, shattering the crystal.

Electrical Conductivity Varies With State

Electrical conductivity requires mobile charge carriers. All the electrons in both ions of a salt are in low-energy closed shells. Their standing waves are localized on the individual ions. With no mobile electrons and ions fixed rigidly in place, solid salts have no way to conduct electricity. But when the salt melts, individual ions become free to move. Under the influence of the electric force applied through the battery, the mobile ions become the charge carriers in part of a circuit. However, ions are big and awkward compared to electrons. Thus, they conduct electricity more poorly than metallic electrons.

Likewise, when salt dissolves in water, its ions separate, become mobile, and conduct electricity. Materials that conduct electricity when dissolved in water are called **electrolytes**.

Figure 22.5 illustrates the ionic arrangement in the different physical states of salts responsible for conductivity behavior.

Transparency

The localization of electron orbitals on individual ions directly affects the electronic energy levels of those orbitals. Discrete energy levels, rather than the continuous levels of metallic electrons, occur for ions of main-group metals and non-metals (those found in columns of the Periodic Table with "A" designations). Gaps between successive energy levels in most salts correspond to high-energy photons in the ultraviolet part of the spectrum (*Figure 22.6a*). Because visible light photons don't excite an elec-

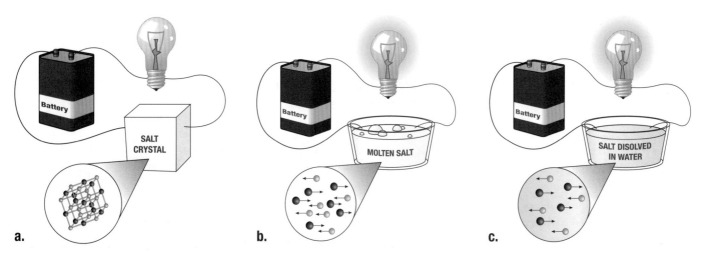

a.   b.   c.

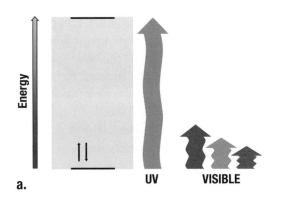

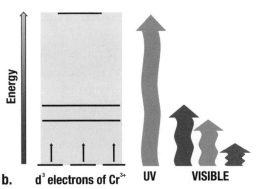

Figure 22.6

a) Most salts contain paired electrons and have energy states that are widely spaced apart, matching the energies of UV photons. They don't absorb visible light and are transparent.

b) Transition metal ions often contain unpaired electrons in d orbitals. These give rise to extra energy levels. Electrons can absorb visible light to be excited into these lower states. Cr^{3+} has levels that allow absorption of blue and green photons but not red ones. Rubies are red because of this.

tron to a higher level, these photons simply pass through an ionic material.

If a transparent salt crystal is ground to a fine powder, the small particles bend a light ray many times before it emerges from the powder. This means light no longer passes straight through as it did in a single crystal. Because photons scatter as they pass from particle to particle, a powder can appear white, when a large crystal of the same material would be transparent. A block of salt with many cracks or bubbles in it will also appear white. Many otherwise transparent minerals in nature appear opaque and white for this reason (see Figure 22.1b).

Some salts containing transition metal ions (the "B" type metals) have a few low-lying electronic states with spacing in the visible energy range. For example, Cr^{3+} has three unpaired electrons in *3d* orbitals. These electrons interact with each other and give rise to extra electronic states, as shown in *Figure 22.6b*. The 3d electrons of Cr^{3+} can absorb both blue and green photons, getting excited to upper levels in the process. Red photons can't be absorbed so they are reflected. This is what gives a ruby, a gemstone that contains Cr^{3+}, its distinctive rich red color. You can read more about rubies in the side bar text.

into its 3p orbitals. The Na^+ ion has a valence electron configuration given by $2s^2 2p^6$. Figure 17.10 shows that the noble gas, neon (Ne, element 10), has this same configuration. The Cl^- ion also has the same electron configuration as a noble gas, argon (Ar, element 18). Both Cl^- and Ar have the electron configuration $3s^2 3p^6$.

We have noted in Chapter 17 that noble gases with the $ns^2 np^6$ configuration are extraordinarily unreactive. The lack of chemical reactivity implies that this configuration corresponds to an especially low energy arrangement of electrons. Reactions of a noble gas atom with

22-5 FORMULAS OF IONIC COMPOUNDS: OXIDATION STATES

Formation of Ions with a Noble Gas Configuration: The Octet Rule

In the Na + Cl reaction, the Na atom loses its 3s electron and the Cl atom gains an electron

RUBIES AND SAPPHIRES

An observor might think that a ruby's chemistry differs greatly from the chemistry of a sapphire because of their quite different colors. In fact, from a chemical point of view, they are very similar. Both gems are based on aluminum oxide, Al_2O_3 (Figure 22.3c). In rubies, a small amount of chromium (Cr^{3+}) ions replaces Al^{3+} ions in the salt. This transition metal ion has several closely spaced energy levels that allow it to absorb blue and green light (Figure 22.6b). The red portion of the spectrum is reflected, giving the ruby its red color. The blue color in sapphires arises from a little more complicated source. Impurities of titanium (Ti^{4+}) and iron (Fe^{2+}) replace Al^{3+} ions. The two impurities, taken together, have a charge equivalent to two Al^{3+} ions. The pairs of ions can be incorporated together, but on different Al sites. Each ion has its own set of closely spaced energy levels, and the combined effect of their absorption of visible photons produces the sapphire's blue color. Other colors sometimes found in a sapphire are caused by different transition metal impurities in the gem.

Ruby

Sapphire

another atom do not lower electron energies so these reactions don't happen.

That Na and Cl atoms readily form ions having ns^2np^6 configurations to produce unreactive NaCl, further supports the conclusion that there is something "special" about this arrangement of electrons. In many other ionic compounds, the metallic and non-metallic elements form ions with the noble gas configuration. Scientists formulated a rule to predict ion formation based on this observation. Called the **octet rule** (for the 2+6 = 8 stable electron configuration), the rule states:

> **An atom will most likely form an ion that has the ns^2np^6 configuration of the closest noble gas atom.**

Metals follow the octet rule by becoming the positive ion in which all valence electrons are lost from the neutral atom. Thus, the ion acquires the electron configuration of the noble gas in the row *above* the metal in the Periodic Table. As seen above, Na in row 3 of the Periodic Table forms an ion whose electron configuration looks like Ne in row 2.

Non-metals have an affinity for electrons, so they satisfy the octet rule by gaining enough electrons to fill up their p orbitals and become negatively charged. Non-metals form negative ions with electron configurations of the noble gas in the same row as themselves. Cl, in row 3, forms a negative ion whose electron configuration looks like Ar, also in row 3.

The octet rule allows you to make accurate predictions of the most likely ion formed by elements at the two extreme ends of the Periodic Table. The metallic Group 1A, Group 2A and Group 3A elements form +1 ions, +2 ions and +3 ions, respectively. Non-metal atoms from Group 5A, 6A and Group 7A form -3 ions, -2 ions and -1 ions, respectively. For metals, the group number, that is, the column label on the Periodic Table, indicates the charge on the positive ion; for non-metals, the negative charge can be calculated from the formula: "group number" −8. The labeling of the Periodic Table's "A" columns thus provide visual clues about the most likely ion to be formed by an element.

For the transition metal elements in the B Columns of the Periodic Table, the d-type electrons invalidate the simple octet rule. Many of these elements form multiple ions with different charges. Manganese (Mn, element 25), for example, form ions with a +2 charge, a +3 charge, and a +4 charge. In one compound, Mn even appears to have an unlikely charge of +7. As the ionic charge on transition metal ions like Mn varies from compound to compound, properties such as color and magnetism can change as well (*Figure 22.7*). The details of what transition elements form which ions and their properties are fascinating but too complex to discuss at this point.

Figure 22.7
Three different manganese compounds.

The metalloid elements in the middle of the Periodic Table also behave in variable ways. Aluminum, in Column 3A, occurs below the dividing line; it generally behaves like a metal and loses three electrons. Boron, just above it, has more complicated behavior. B acts like a metal in its ionic compound with oxygen (B_2O_3), but it forms compounds with hydrogen that don't fit this pattern. Will an element like carbon (which has four valence electrons) lose its

Table 22.1 – *Formulas and Common Names of Salts*

NaCl	sodium chloride	PbS	lead sulfide
KBr	potassium bromide	Al_2O_3	aluminum oxide
MgF_2	magnesium fluoride	BaI_2	barium iodide
MnO	manganese oxide	$LaCl_3$	lanthanum chloride

SECTION 22-6 *Conclusion* **273**

four valence electrons (like a metal), or gain four to fill its shell (like a nonmetal)? We shall see in the next chapter that carbon prefers to take a different path altogether. Rather than gaining or losing electrons, it shares electrons with other atoms.

Thus, for elements in the middle of the chart, both transition metals and metalloid elements, there is a tendency for atoms to gain or lose different numbers of electrons in different chemical reactions, depending on the particular compound that is being formed. The important thing to understand and remember is that however these elements react, the driving force is to lower electronic energies.

Names of Salts

Writing down the formula for a salt can itself be reduced to something of a formula or recipe: The metal symbol is always written first and the nonmetal is written last. In speaking of a salt, or when naming a salt, the metal name is given first, leaving it unchanged, and the name of the non-metal is then given, but modified by replacing the last syllable of the non-metal name with the suffix "ide." Some examples are shown in *Table 22.1*. For salts in which the transition metal ion can have variable ionic charges, there is a formal protocol to specify the charge, but we shall not treat it here.

22-6 CONCLUSION

Back in Chapter 12, we offered a hypothesis regarding melting and boiling points that provides clues about the strength of forces holding matter together. In two cases, metals and salts, we have seen that hypothesis validated. High melting and boiling points are associated with strong forces. In metallic bonds the mobile sea of electrons acts like a glue tightly holding metallic nuclei together. Salts, composed of positive and negative ions, are held together by strong ionic bonds. Ionic bonds are strong because the electrostatic interactions between ions extend over long distances and in all directions.

In the next chapter, we will look at bonding in materials like nitrogen, ethanol, and water. These materials, unlike metals and salts, exist in the solid as discrete molecules. Knowing that those materials have relatively low melting and boiling points, you can probably conclude that the forces holding molecules of nitrogen, water, or ethanol together in their solid states must be pretty weak. However, other strong forces are also in action here. Those forces keep the atoms in individual molecules together. They are called "covalent bonds" and they form the subject of the next chapter.

Chapter Framework

A. Salts
    1. Ionic Bonding
B. Properties of Metals and Non-metals
    1. Atomic Volumes
    2. Ionization Energy
C. The Ionic Bonding Model
    1. Localized Electrons
    2. Extended Structures
D. Properties of Ionic Compounds
    1. Melting / Boiling Temperatures
    2. Electrical Conductivity
    3. Brittleness
    4. Transparency

Comprehension

True/False

1. _____ Salts can easily be flattened or reshaped.
2. _____ Ionic compounds have extremely low melting temperatures.
3. _____ Molten salts are ionic conductors.
4. _____ Metals easily lose electrons.
5. _____ A salt is electrically neutral.
6. _____ Electrons like to go to the highest energy condition available to them.

Matching

1. _____ A characteristic of ionic substances, such as salts, that readily shatter when struck a sharp blow.
2. _____ A characteristic of salts that readily transmit light. Opposite to opaqueness.
3. _____ The chemical bond that binds metallic ions to nonmetallic ions by electrical attraction.
4. _____ A charged object formed when an atom or molecule loses or gains electrons.
5. _____ A substance formed from the ionic bond of a metal with a nonmetal.
6. _____ A chemical compound that ionizes when dissolved or molten to produce an electrically conductive medium.

a. Salt
b. Ionic Bonding
c. Brittlessness
d. Electrolytes
e. Ion
f. Transparency

Fill in the Blank

1. _____ combine with non-metals to form highly-colored compounds.

2. Electrons go to the _____ energy condition available to them.

3. For a given period, metals have _____ atomic volumes, whereas non-metals have _____ atomic volumes.

4. Metals lose _____ to form positive ions.

5. The most energetically favorable arrangement of ions maximizes attractive _____ and minimizes repulsive ones.

6. Each ion of an ionic compound has the _____ charge as its next-door neighbors.

7. When writing down the chemical formula for a salt, the _____ symbol is written first and the _____ is written last.

Analysis

1. Why are sodium atomic orbitals higher in energy than their counterparts in chlorine?

2. Consider the compounds (salts formed by the following pairs of elements) held together in ionic bonds: (a) sodium, chlorine; (b) magnesium, chlorine. In each case:

    a. Determine the positive or negative charge on the ions that form.
    b. Write the chemical formula for the salt.
    c. Write and balance the chemical equation for the reaction.
    d. Sketch an energy diagram for each kind of atom in the compound. Draw a circle around each electron soon to be lost in one atom, and an empty circle at the location soon to be filled in the other atom.
    e. List the main parts of the quantum model of the atom.
    f. State the fundamental principle of wave-particle duality that the quantum model is based on.

3. Under what conditions do atoms form ionic bonds?

4. Why do ionic compounds have high melting temperatures?

5. Describe the interaction that occurs when hammering on an ionic compound.

6. The correct formula for sodium chloride is:

    a. Na_2O
    b. Al_2O
    c. NaCl
    d. AlO

7. Why does table salt appear white in color?

8. Why do rubies and sapphires differ in color?

Synthesis

1. Why do metals and non-metals react so easily to form ionic compounds?

2. Describe the types of forces present in an ionic compounds.

3. What are the properties of compounds held in

ionic bonds, and why do these compounds have such properties?

4. What procedure leads to the correct chemical formula for reactants formed in reactions involving compounds held together in ionic bonds?

5. Sketch a diagram showing a possible arrangement of the ions in a salt. Explain what would happen to this arrangement if shear forces were exerted on the salt. Why is the salt brittle? Also, using your understanding of ionic bonds, explain why table salt dissolved in water is an ionic conductor. Name and state the fundamental principle that explains the forces that are involved.

6. Describe the octet rule and its impact on the formation of ionic compounds.

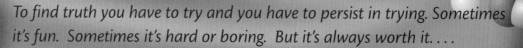

COVALENT BONDING AND INTERMOLECULAR INTERACTIONS

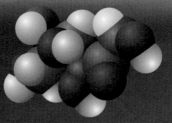

To find truth you have to try and you have to persist in trying. Sometimes it's fun. Sometimes it's hard or boring. But it's always worth it. . . .

The Creator of the universe has implanted a message in every created thing. Geology, astronomy, physics—all science is really nothing more than an effort to read those messages.

~ Henry Eyring

Up to this point this text has not discussed compounds between non-metallic elements. Materials consisting of non-metal atoms bound to each other are called **covalent** materials. From the point of view of living things, covalent materials are very common and important, because almost all living things are made of these kinds of compounds.

Chapter 12 offered the hypothesis that many of the bulk properties of matter, such as melting and boiling temperatures, can be understood in terms of the strengths of the forces involved in the interactions between atoms. The stronger the forces, it was suggested, the higher the melting and boiling points will be. We've seen that the wave, or quantum mechanical, model of the atom and of interactions between atoms is successful in predicting and understanding the interactions. We've seen that these ideas work well for metallic materials, which involve the metals on the left side of the periodic table, and for ionic materials, which involve interactions between metallic elements (from the left side of the periodic table) and non-metallic elements (from the right side of the table). Chemists have developed models for bonding in these cases that work very well to predict the properties of the materials.

What happens when non-metallic elements interact with each other? What model accounts for bonding in these materials? How can their properties be explained?

23–1 PROPERTIES OF COVALENT COMPOUNDS

Arriving at a rational answer to these questions begins by reviewing some of the properties of covalent materials. Table 12.1 lists two covalent, **organic molecules**, ethanol and sugar (sucrose). These substances have melting and boiling points in the intermediate range of all the substances listed on that table. This is generally true of covalent materials, and just means that relatively little energy is needed to separate the covalent molecules. There are some notable exceptions, such as diamond, which has a very high melting point, but most covalent compounds are relatively easy to melt or boil.

Another property that often tells much about a material is its electrical conductivity. Metals, with their mobile electrons, conduct electricity easily. Ionic materials do not conduct in the solid state but become conductors when they are melted, enabling the charged ions to become mobile. What about covalent materials?

Covalent materials generally either do not conduct electricity (i.e., they are insulators) or they are very weak conductors. This suggests either that, as in ionic materials, the charges in covalent materials are not mobile, or that individual covalent molecules are not charged. To understand the reasons behind these properties, a model is needed for covalent bonding.

23–2 A MODEL FOR COVALENT BONDING

The wave (quantum mechanical) model of matter predicts that certain ways of arranging electrons around nuclei (i.e., certain orbitals) are especially low in energy and are therefore especially favorable. Because all the lower energy shells are filled, only the outermost (valence) shell is important in interactions between atoms. For atoms, filling every orbital in the **valence shell** (or having the valence shell completely empty) is an especially favorable arrangement. This still holds true even when multiple nuclei are present and bonding is possible.

Metal atoms interacting with each other achieve filled valence shells by forming giant orbitals that are closely spaced in energy

LEARNING OBJECTIVES

After studying this chapter, you should clearly understand

- How covalent bonding forms molecules (using the quantum model of the atom), and be able to distinguish between metallic, ionic, and covalent bonding.

- What causes intermolecular forces.

- The relative strength of dispersion forces, polar interactions, hydrogen bonds, and covalent bonds.

- How to use these bonding concepts to understand trends in melting points, boiling points, and electrical conductivity.

(Chapter 21). Their electrons are only loosely held, meaning not much energy is required to remove electrons from metals. Nonmetals, on the other hand, tend to hold electrons well; large amounts of energy are required to remove electrons from non-metal atoms. In compounds that include both metals and non-metals, electrons are transferred from the metal to the non-metal so that the valence shell of the metal is empty and the valence shell of the non-metal is full (Chapter 22).

When nonmetals interact with each other,

277

• Organic Molecules

Molecules that have a central framework of carbon atoms. Originally, it was thought that organic molecules could only be produced in living organisms, hence the name. Now it is clear that the molecules can be produced abiologically.

• Covalent

Materials characterized by chemical bonds that involve sharing electrons. Typically, the bonds in covalent substances occur between non-metal atoms.

• Valence Shell

The outermost, highest-energy set of orbitals in an atom. The arrangement of electrons in the valence shell determines how the atom interacts chemically with other atoms.

• Single Bond

A covalent bond involving one pair of electrons shared between the two bound atoms. In chemical structure drawings, single bonds are represented by single lines.

• Double Bond

A covalent bond involving two pairs of electrons shared between the two bound atoms. In chemical structure drawings, double bonds are represented by double lines.

• Triple Bond

A covalent bond involving three pairs of electrons shared between the two bound atoms. In chemical structure drawings, triple bonds are represented by triple lines.

Figure 23.1

Singly-bound, doubly-bound and triply-bound carbon atoms in three covalent compounds of carbon and hydrogen (hydrocarbons). Carbon is represented by the gray balls.

neither nonmetal atom is likely to give up electrons because the energetic costs are too high. So how can nonmetal atoms achieve arrangements of electrons into the lowest energy orbitals? Rather than taking electrons from another atom (as in ionic materials), nonmetal atoms can put all their electrons in low energy orbitals, filling the valence shells, by *sharing* their electrons. We've already seen a nice example of this, in the formation of a bond between two H atoms to form the H_2 molecule (Chapter 20). When two H atoms come together, each supplies a single *s* electron to fill a bonding molecular orbital (which can accommodate up to two electrons), forming a bond between the two atoms. Each of the two electrons is shared between the two H atoms to form the bond. The hydrogen molecule is the simplest possible example of covalent bonding, but covalent bonding in more complicated molecules follows the same principles: electrons are shared so that every atom has a filled valence shell and all the electrons are placed in the lowest energy orbitals possible.

The strength of covalent bonds can be described in terms of the amount of energy required to separate the bound atoms. **Single covalent bonds** are typically fairly strong, which means that large amounts of energy are needed to break the bond and separate the atoms. In many molecules, more than one pair of electrons is involved in the sharing between a pair of atoms. This leads to stronger, multiple bonds; **double bonds** (i.e., two shared electron pairs) and **triple bonds** (three shared electron pairs) are common. Quadruple bonds are not common because there is insufficient room between atoms at bonding distance to accommodate four shared pairs of electrons. Triple covalent bonds, such as exist between the nitrogen atoms in N_2 or between the C and O atoms in carbon monoxide (CO) are among the strongest known chemical interactions.

Figure 23.1 shows an example of single, double, and triple bonding. All the compounds

in the figure involve two carbon atoms bound to each other, with hydrogen bound to fill the remaining sharing requirements. These kinds of compounds between hydrogen and carbon are called **hydrocarbons**. These are all examples of organic molecules, which are compounds that involve carbon atoms bound to each other. (It is a scientific convention in chemical structure illustrations to show single bonds as single lines, double bonds as double lines, and triple bonds as triple lines.)

23–3 MOLECULES

That brings us to one of the main differences between the metals and ionic materials that have already been discussed, and the covalent materials that are the subject of this chapter. Covalent materials, held together by strong covalent bonds, exist as discrete molecules, whereas metals and ionic materials do not. Metals are made up of groups of any number of metal atoms. The discrete units of ionic materials are the positively and negatively charged ions that make them up and can be arranged in ordered arrays in crystals. Covalent materials exist as molecules. For example, the smallest possible unit of water is a water molecule, H_2O, consisting of two hydrogen atoms and one oxygen atom covalently bound together, as indicated by the molecular formula. This idea is so important that another name for covalent materials is "molecular materials."

Each molecule of a covalent material has a well-defined shape and has the properties of the material. Typically, large amounts of energy are needed to take the molecules apart into their component atoms. A fairly simple (but powerful) theory allows us to predict when electron sharing will occur and what the shapes of the resulting molecules will be, but that is not germane to this discussion. (Take an introductory chemistry course to learn more about these fascinating ideas.)

Name	ethane		ethylene		acetylene	
Formula	C_2H_6		C_2H_4		C_2H_2	
CC bond type	single		double		triple	
Bond strength (kJ mol⁻¹)	348		614		839	

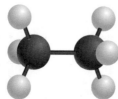

23-4 BOND POLARITY

Electron sharing is the hallmark of covalent bonding. However, the sharing of electrons is not always equal; sometimes the electrons in a bond tend to spend more time nearer one of the atoms than the other.

A range of situations is possible. If two identical atoms form a bond (as in the H_2 molecule), the sharing of electrons between the two atoms has to be equal (*Figure 23.2*). There is nothing special about one of the H atoms that makes it better able to attract electrons than the other H atom. However, if the two atoms differ in their

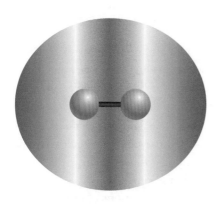

Figure 23.2

Charge distribution in the H_2 molecule. Blue = positive. Red = negative. The negative charge lies between the two nuclei, the ends of the molecule are positive and the charge is equally distributed between the two H atoms.

ability to attract electrons, the electron probability will be greater near one of the atoms than the other. Atoms that attract electrons well are said to be "electronegative," whereas atoms that do not are said to have low **electronegativity**. The relative ability of different kinds of atoms to attract electrons can be read from the Periodic Table. Electronegativity increases from left to right and from bottom to top. Therefore, atoms of fluorine (F) are especially good at attracting electrons, and atoms of cesium (Cs) are especially weak.

When a bond forms between two atoms with different electronegativities, the electrons will be attracted toward the more electronegative atom. The resulting increase of electron density around that atom gives it a small excess negative charge. At the same time, the electron density around the less electronegative atom decreases, while the positive charge on the

nucleus stays the same. The less electronegative atom is therefore left with a small excess of positive charge just balancing the excess negative charge on the more electronegative atom. Thus, overall, the molecule remains neutral. *Figure 23.3* shows one example, formaldehyde (CH_2O).

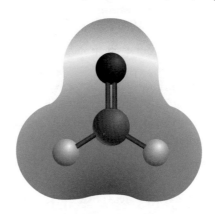

Oxygen is more electronegative than carbon, and the electron density in the molecule is strongly skewed toward the oxygen atom. Bonds that involve unequal electron sharing are said to be **polar**. Because the bond involves both a negative and a positive "pole," the resulting distribution of charge is called a **dipole**. The greater the charge separation between the poles, the stronger the dipole.

A wide range of bond polarities exists in nature. Bonds between two identical atoms, such as those in H_2, N_2, O_2, or F_2, are completely nonpolar. (Can you reason why?) Bonds between a low-electronegativity atom and a highly electronegative atom are highly polar, and in extreme cases the "sharing" covalent description of the bond is not accurate because the electron spends essentially all its time near the more electronegative atom; in such cases, the ionic model of bonding is more appropriate. This chapter will focus on the low end of the scale. (The high end was discussed in Chapter 22, where ionic materials were described.)

23-5 INTERMOLECULAR FORCES

The forces within covalently bound molecules are quite strong, but what about the forces *between* molecules? All the forces acting between nuclei and electrons (i.e., all the forces important to chemistry) are ultimately Coulombic forces. By way of review, the electrostatic force

- **Hydrocarbons**

Chemical compounds between the elements carbon and hydrogen. The compounds that make up gasoline are examples.

Figure 23.3

Charge distribution in the polar molecule formaldehyde (CH_2O). Blue = positive, red = negative. Oxygen is more electronegative than carbon. Consequently, the oxygen end of the molecule is quite negative, and the carbon end is correspondingly positive.

- **Electronegativity**

A measure of how strongly atoms attract electrons. Both ionization energy (the energy required to remove an electron from a neutral atom) and electron affinity (the energy gained when an electron is added to a neutral atom) contribute to electronegativity. Electronegativity increases from left to right across rows and decreases down columns of the Periodic Table.

- **Polar**

Bonds or molecules having an unequal distribution of charge (one end being positive, the other negative).

- **Dipole**

The separation of positive and negative charge in a polar bond or molecule.

• **Intermolecular**

Between molecules (as opposed to *intramolecular*, within molecules).

law says the force between two charges depends on the magnitude of the charges and is inversely dependent on the square of the separation between the charges. The forces between electrons and nuclei are therefore large, because the charges are large and the separation between them is very small in something as tiny as an atom.

Distances between molecules are much larger than distances within atoms, so the forces between molecules would be expected to be relatively small. Also, the charges contributing to forces between molecules are small. As a result, **intermolecular** forces are relatively weak.

How can a neutral molecule (charge = 0) be attracted to other neutral molecules by Coulombic forces? The polar bonds discussed in the section above are a good starting point to answer this question. We've already seen that bonds between non-identical atoms have regions of positive and negative charge, with the positive charge concentrated around the low electronegativity atom and the negative charge concentrated on the high electronegativity atom. For a molecule to be polar, it must have one or more polar bonds. For example, the O–H bonds in water are polar and so are the C=O bonds in carbon dioxide.

The existence of polar bonds in a molecule still does not guarantee that the molecule will be polar. Both water and carbon dioxide contain polar bonds, but while water molecules are highly polar, the carbon dioxide molecule is not. The crucial difference is the *arrangement* of the bond dipoles in the two kinds of molecule (*Figure 23.4*). In water, the two O–H bond dipoles are bent with respect to each other, so they can add together vectorially, yielding a net dipole for the molecule. In carbon dioxide, the

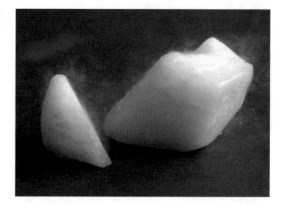

Figure 23.5

Because carbon dioxide has no net molecular dipole, its molecules do not stick together well, and consequently its melting point is lower than that of water. This is why dry ice (CO_2 in its solid form) is much colder than your average ice cube. This is also why CO_2 is difficult to liquefy—the molecules do not stick together well enough to easily form a liquid, but will crystallize into a solid if they are sufficiently cold.

two C=O dipoles point in opposite directions, effectively canceling each other out. Therefore, even though the bonds are polar, the net effect in the carbon dioxide molecule is zero.

Polarity has important chemical consequences. Because polar molecules have permanent regions of positive and negative charge, they can attract and repel the corresponding negative and positive regions of other polar molecules. Water is a great example of the influence of polarity on the interactions between molecules. The oxygen end of the molecule always has a small excess negative charge, so it can attract the slightly positive hydrogen atoms in neighboring molecules. Water molecules therefore stick together quite well. This makes the melting and boiling points of water much higher than for nonpolar molecules of similar size. Each water molecule has two regions of positive charge (the two hydrogen atoms) and one region of negative charge (the oxygen atom), so water forms extensive networked structures in both its liquid and its solid state. A picture of the arrangement of water molecules in ice is shown in *Figure 23.6*. Note how the hydrogen atoms of each molecule are pointed at oxygen atoms on neighboring molecules. The empty hexagonal spaces within the ice lead to its low density, relative to the more disordered liquid, which lacks the voids. The polarity of water, combined with the shapes of the molecules and their resulting arrangement in ice, is what makes ice float in water.

Another consequence of the polarity of

Figure 23.4

Water (a) has a net dipole and is polar, while carbon dioxide (b), despite having polar bonds, has no net dipole because the bond dipoles cancel. The oxygen end of the water molecule has a partial negative charge (red) and each hydrogen has a partial positive charge (blue). The oxygens in carbon dioxide have partial negative charges, but the molecule overall is not polar.

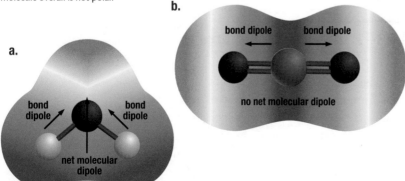

b.

bond dipole   bond dipole

no net molecular dipole

a.

bond dipole   bond dipole

net molecular dipole

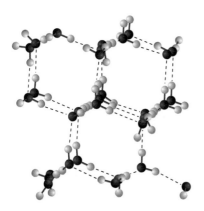

Figure 23.6

In this arrangement of water molecules in ice, note how the hydrogen atoms on one molecule point at oxygen atoms on adjacent molecules, leading to the open, hexagonal voids within the ice that contribute to its low density.

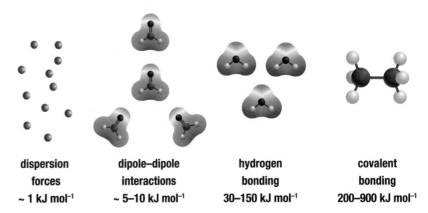

dispersion forces	dipole–dipole interactions	hydrogen bonding	covalent bonding
~ 1 kJ mol⁻¹	~ 5–10 kJ mol⁻¹	30–150 kJ mol⁻¹	200–900 kJ mol⁻¹

Figure 23.7
Relative strengths of molecular interactions.

water is the high solubility of ionic materials in water. Ionic materials consist of positive and negative ions. When a positive ion is placed in a polar liquid **solvent** such as water, the ion is immediately surrounded by the negative ends of the molecular dipoles of the solvent; the accompanying negative ions are surrounded by the positive ends of the solvent's molecular dipoles. Being able to place positive and negative charges close together is energetically favorable and helps to dissolve the ionic material. Similar effects account for the solubility of nonionic but polar materials like sugars in polar solvents like water.

Polar interactions involving hydrogen bound to oxygen or nitrogen are common and unusually strong for intermolecular forces, so they are given a name of their own: **hydrogen bonding**. Hydrogen bonding interactions are responsible for the high melting and boiling points of water and for the structure and density of ice. In addition, hydrogen bonding is very important in the way many large molecules fold and interact with solvents.

The intermolecular interactions described so far in this chapter involve permanent, relatively strong dipoles. However, experiments have shown that even non-polar atoms and molecules are attracted to each other. For example, even helium, the most non-polar material known, interacts with itself strongly enough so that at low temperatures the gas condenses and forms a liquid. What makes helium atoms "sticky" with respect to each other?

The answer lies in the nature of the electron distribution around atoms. So far, we have treated atoms as if the electron distribution were a con-

stant, frozen in time, so to speak. In reality, electron density constantly changes and fluctuates. This causes the formation of short-lived regions of excess or deficient electron density around each atom, leading to short-lived regions of negative or positive charge. When negative and positive regions on adjacent atoms match up, the two atoms are attracted to each other. Because this pairing is energetically favorable, +/- pairing occurs more often than does putting like charges next to each other. The result is that all atoms are "sticky" toward each other to some degree. Intermolecular forces arising from the formation of these temporary dipoles have a number of different names, including "van der Waals forces" and **dispersion forces**, but no matter how they are called, they tend to be very weak.

In summary, we can rank the relative amounts of energy required to separate atoms or molecules (*Figure 23.7*). Dispersion forces occur between nonpolar atoms or molecules and are very weak. These forces account for the low melting and boiling points in materials such as helium (He), nitrogen (N₂), and oxygen (O₂). Interactions between dipoles are stronger, and molecules in which dipoles are present (such as formaldehyde) tend to have higher melting and boiling points. Hydrogen bonding is a special case of dipole-dipole interaction, and is stronger still, but is weak compared to covalent bonding, which tends to be quite strong.

• **Solvent**
A material (typically a liquid) in which another material dissolves.

• **Hydrogen Bonding**
Interactions between hydrogen atoms bound to oxygen, nitrogen, or fluorine with other oxygen, nitrogen, or fluorine atoms. Hydrogen bonds are among the strongest intermolecular interactions.

• **Dispersion Forces**
Weak intermolecular attraction arising from the formation of temporary dipoles in non-polar molecules. Also known as van der Waals forces.

23–6 UNDERSTANDING PROPERTIES OF COVALENT MATERIALS

Knowledge of covalent bonding and of intermolecular forces helps us understand the properties of molecular materials. This section of the chapter will describe the properties of a few example materials. First, it will examine a few substances that exist as discrete molecules, but have very different properties. Then it will discuss two different covalent forms of carbon—diamond and graphite—and conclude by putting together ionic and covalent bonding by considering polyatomic ions.

Nitrogen

Nitrogen (N_2, *Figure 23.8*) is a typical covalent substance. It consists of molecules, each of which contains two nitrogen atoms bound together by a very strong triple covalent bond. This strong bond is difficult to break, so N_2 is chemically not very reactive. About 80% of Earth's air is nitrogen, which is fortunate for us because this unreactive gas dilutes the very reactive O_2 gas that makes up most of the remaining 20%; plainly stated, the nitrogen in the air keeps us from burning up.

The two nitrogen atoms in the N_2 molecule are identical, so the molecule has no dipole. This means that the forces between N_2 molecules are very weak dispersion forces. Because N_2 molecules are only weakly attracted to each other, low temperatures are required to liquefy or solidify nitrogen. At low temperatures the kinetic energy of the molecules does not overcome the weak attraction and the molecules can stick together to become liquid or, at even lower temperatures, solid.

Figure 23.8
Nitrogen is a purely covalent material and is therefore non-polar. Weak dispersion forces account for the attraction of N_2 molecules to each other. Because the intermolecular attraction is weak, low temperatures are required to liquify nitrogen (liquid nitrogen boils at 77 K or -321 °F).

Finally, the covalent electron sharing in the N_2 molecule allows all the valence electrons to be placed in low-energy orbitals without requiring the loss or gain of any electrons, so the molecules are neutral. This means that N_2 is a good electrical insulator.

Water

The water molecule (H_2O) has two polar O–H bonds arranged in a bent fashion so that the molecule has a net dipole (Figure 23.4). Because the H_2O molecule is polar, interactions between H_2O molecules are relatively strong, and because the polar interactions involve hydrogen bound to oxygen, these are hydrogen-bonding interactions. Water therefore has an extensive network of hydrogen bonds in both its liquid and solid states, and because of this extensive hydrogen bonding, the melting and boiling points of water are much higher than for molecules of similar size that lack hydrogen bonding.

The polarity of water also means H_2O interacts strongly with other polar molecules and with ions. This makes water an excellent solvent; it is sometimes called a "universal" solvent because so many other substances dissolve in water.

Hydrogen bonding in water is so extensive that there is even a weak tendency for water molecules to transfer H^+ in the reaction $2H_2O = OH^- + H_3O^+$ (about one molecule in every 10 million does this in pure water). As a result of this weak **self-ionization** reaction, a tiny fraction of water molecules become charged and pure water is a very weak electrical conductor. The ions that form from self-ionization of water, H_3O^+ and OH^- are called, respectively, hydronium and hydroxide ions.

The addition of compounds called acids to water increases the tendency to form hydronium ions, and in fact the concentration of hydronium ions in water can vary over many orders of magnitude. One of the most important ways of measuring hydronium ion concentration uses the **pH** scale, which expresses hydronium ion concentration logarithmically. Thus, a change of 1 in pH corresponds to a factor of 10 change in concentration, a change of 2 pH units corresponds to a 100-fold change in concentration, etc. Pure water has a pH of 7 and is said to be neutral. Lower values of pH have larger hydronium ion concentrations and are said to be **acidic**; pH values greater than 7 have lower hydronium ion concentrations and are said to be **basic**. The pH of water can have large effects on its chemical properties. For example, the solubilities of many compounds increase, sometimes dramatically, when the concentration of H_3O^+ increases. Biological processes are especially sensitive to pH. When sulfur oxide gases released during the combustion of coal dissolve in water, they can make the water quite acidic, resulting in "acid rain" that kills trees and fish and dissolves the rock in monuments.

Glucose

Glucose ($C_6H_{12}O_6$) is the main sugar that fuels the human body. A chain of carbon atoms covalently bound to each other forms the backbone of this organic molecule (*Figure 23.9*), with hydrogen or oxygen atoms attached to complete the filling of low-energy orbitals. A number of oxygen atoms, each with one hydrogen attached, are hung from the main carbon scaffold of the molecule. These oxygen-hydrogen combinations are polar (like they are in water), and their overall arrangement on the molecule makes the molecule, as a whole, polar. These polar, hydrogen-bonding groups of atoms make glucose molecules "sticky" toward each other (and also toward the proteins that make up human skin; this explains why pancake syrup is so sticky). Interactions between these polar molecules help make it energetically favorable to assemble the molecules into crystals (*Figure 23.10*).

Figure 23.10
Hydrogen bonding interactions in sugar cause the molecules to easily organize into large crystals. Table sugar is sucrose, which consists of a glucose molecule linked to another kind of sugar, fructose.

As you would expect with strongly interacting and polar molecules, the melting and boiling points of glucose are quite high compared to similar molecules that cannot hydrogen bond. Glucose, because it is polar, is among those molecules that are highly soluble in water. Glucose is less polar than water, so it has no tendency to self-ionize. Therefore, glucose is an electrical insulator.

Diamond

Next let's consider two pure forms of covalently bound carbon. Diamond and graphite are both made up of carbon atoms, but they differ in how the atoms are arranged. In diamond, each carbon atom has a single covalent bond to each of four neighboring carbon atoms. The result is a 3-dimensional network of strong covalent interactions (*Figure 23.11*).

Given this structure, it is not surprising that diamond has a very high melting point. The network of bonds makes the whole diamond crystal behave as one giant molecule. It can't be melted without breaking strong covalent bonds, so when heated it tends to decompose (react with surrounding materials), rather than melt.

Further, it is not surprising that diamond is one of the hardest known materials. Each of

- **Acidic**
Having a pH value less than 7, meaning that the hydronium ion concentration is greater than in pure water.

- **Basic**
Having a pH value greater than 7, meaning that the hydronium ion concentration is less than in pure water.

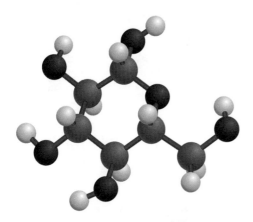

Figure 23.9
A glucose (sugar) molecule. The red balls represent oxygen atoms, the grey balls represent carbon, and the white balls represent hydrogen.

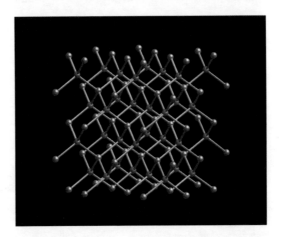

Figure 23.11
The arrangement of carbon atoms in diamond. Each atom is covalently bound to four other atoms.

the carbon atoms is held rigidly in place by four covalent bonds, so it is very hard to deform the structure.

Finally, the giant array of atoms that forms diamond holds all its electrons in low-energy orbitals with no need to add or lose electrons. Thus, the diamond "molecule" is neutral and cannot conduct electricity, making diamond an excellent insulator.

Graphite

Graphite, like diamond, is pure carbon. However, the arrangement of atoms is quite different, leading to big differences in structure and bulk properties. Graphite consists of 2-dimensional networks or planes of carbon atoms held together by strong covalent bonds (*Figure 23.12*).

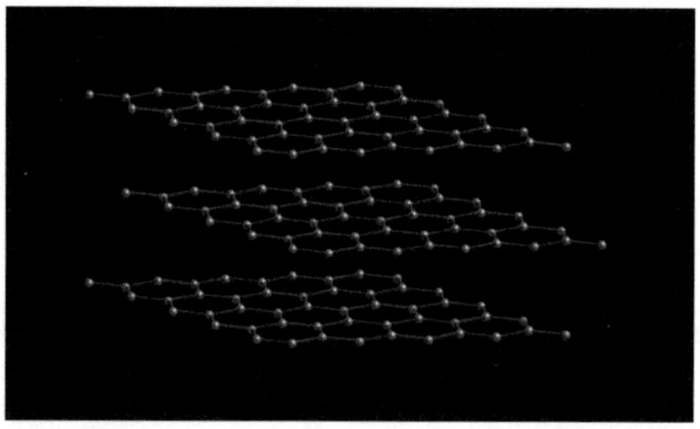

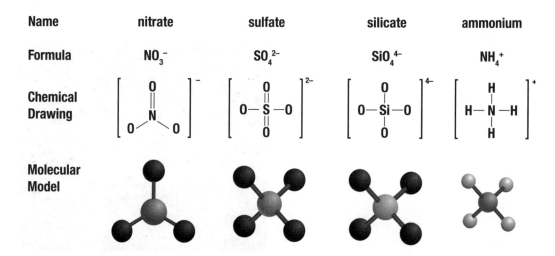

However, the various planes of atoms are held together by weak intermolecular forces.

The bonding arrangement in graphite gives this material several unique properties. Carbon atoms within the planes are held together by strong covalent bonds, so these planes of atoms behave as giant molecules and, graphite, like diamond, can't easily be melted; it tends to decompose at high temperatures rather than melt. On

the other hand, because the forces between the planes are weak, the planes of atoms can easily slip with respect to each other. This makes graphite soft. In fact, graphite is used commercially as an excellent lubricant. It is interesting that diamond and graphite are both forms of pure carbon, but that the arrangement of atoms gives them remarkably contrasting properties.

Molecular Ions

Frequently a group of non-metal atoms has too many or too few electrons to accommodate all the electrons in low-energy orbitals by electron sharing and covalent bond formation. For example, if a group of neutral atoms has an odd number of electrons, it is impossible to pair all of them in low-energy orbitals. At least one electron must remain unpaired, which is energetically unfavorable. For covalent bonding to work in such cases, electrons must be lost or gained so that placement of all the electrons in low-energy orbitals can occur. Often, the low energy achieved by sharing is enough to offset the energy cost of losing or gaining electrons. In these cases, a covalently bound group of atoms can have a positive or negative charge. Bonding *within* the resulting ion is covalent, but the ions can interact with each other just as other ionic materials do. We call the resulting ions *polyatomic* or **molecular ions**, because they are built from multiple atoms and behave as charged molecules.

Polyatomic ions are common in nature. A few important polyatomic ions (*Figure 23.13*) include nitrate (NO_3^-), sulfate (SO_4^{2-}), silicate (SiO_4^{4-}), and ammonium (NH_4^+). Bonding *within* polyatomic ions is covalent, but the ions inter-

• **Molecular Ions**
Groups of atoms covalently bound to each other that have a net charge because electrons have been lost or gained to facilitate formation of the covalent bonds. Also called polyatomic ions.

Figure 23.12
The arrangement of carbon atoms in graphite. Each carbon atom is bound to three neighboring carbon atoms, forming 2-dimensional covalent networks (planes) of atoms. Weak intermolecular forces hold the planes together.

Figure 23.13
A few important polyatomic ions.

Name	nitrate	sulfate	silicate	ammonium
Formula	NO_3^-	SO_4^{2-}	SiO_4^{4-}	NH_4^+
Chemical Drawing				
Molecular Model				

act with each other or with simple monoatomic ions (Na^+, K^+, F^-, Cl^-, etc.) via Coulombic forces, so the resulting material is ionic.

The minerals that make up the Earth are mostly formed from polyatomic ions, with silicate and related ions among the most important. Silicate has the ability to share its oxygen atoms with neighboring silicate groups. Thus, it can form chains and networks that occur commonly in minerals.

Ionic materials formed from polyatomic ions have the properties expected for ionic materials: they form crystals, they have high melting points, they conduct electricity when melted or in solution and they often will dissolve in polar solvents like water.

23-7 CONCLUSION

Covalent bonding occurs when nonmetal atoms can place all their electrons in lower-energy molecular orbitals by sharing electrons between the atoms, forming molecules. Covalent bonds tend to be quite strong, so it is usually fairly hard to break a molecule into its component atoms. This is evident in very hard molecular materials such as diamond. The forces *between* molecules, on the other hand, range from very weak dispersion forces to moderately strong interactions such as hydrogen bonding, accounting for the wide range of melting and boiling points observed in covalent materials. Details of how the atoms are arranged in covalent materials are often crucially important in determining the bulk properties of the materials, as in the examples of diamond and graphite.

We rarely deal with materials that exhibit only one type of bonding. This chapter has introduced polyatomic ions, which are assembled from atoms via covalent bonds but which interact with each other ionically.

With a basic understanding of metallic, ionic, and covalent bonding, and with an introduction to intermolecular interactions, you are now ready to put these ideas together to deal with more complex systems. That opportunity is just ahead, in Chapter 24.

Chapter Framework

A. Properties of Covalent Compounds
1. Wide range of melting and boiling points
2. Usually electrical insulators

B. A Model for Covalent Bonding
1. Nonmetals bond with each other by sharing valence electrons
2. Single, double, and triple bonds are possible, depending on the number of shared valence electrons in the bond

C. Molecules
1. Covalent materials exist as individual molecules
2. Each molecule has a shape and has the properties of the material

D. Bond Polarity
1. Electrons may not be shared equally in a bond
2. The electronegativities of the bound atoms determine which atom attracts the electrons more
3. Bonds with unequal sharing are polar

E. Intermolecular Forces
1. These forces between molecules are much weaker than chemical bonds within molecules
2. Types of intermolecular forces, from weakest to strongest
   a. *Dispersion forces*
   b. *Dipole-dipole interactions*
   c. *Hydrogen bonds*

F. Understanding Properties of Covalent Materials
1. Molecular substances (nitrogen, water, glucose)
   a. *pH as a measure of water self-ionization*
   b. *pH < 7: acidic*
   c. *pH > 7: basic*
2. Network solids
   a. *Diamond, graphite as examples*
   b. *Properties depend strongly on arrangement of atoms*
3. Molecular ions
   a. *Binding within the ion is covalent*
   b. *Binding between the ions is ionic*

Comprehension

Matching

1. _____ The chemical bond between two non-metals characterized by sharing of valence electrons.
2. _____ A polar bond.
3. _____ A material in which another material dissolves.
4. _____ Having a pH value less than 7, meaning that the hydronium ion concentration is greater than in pure water.
5. _____ Chemical compounds between the elements carbon and hydrogen. The compounds that make up gasoline are examples.

a. *Molecular ions*
b. *Intermolecular*
c. *Double bond*
d. *Polar*
e. *Covalent bond*
f. *Hydocarbons*
g. *Dipole*
h. *Solvent*
i. *Acidic*

6. _____ Ions composed of more than one covalently-bound atom.
7. _____ A covalent bond involving two pairs of electrons shared between the two bound atoms.
8. _____ Bonds or molecules having an unequal distribution of charge (one end being positive, the other negative).
9. _____ Forces between molecules.

True/False

1. _____ Covalent materials exist as molecules.
2. _____ Metal and non-metal substances combine to form covalent compounds.
3. _____ Covalent molecules do not have well-defined shapes.
4. _____ The triple covalent bond of carbon monoxide (CO) is a type of weak chemical interaction.

Fill in the Blank

1. Carbon atoms in diamond are held together by _____ _____.

2. Electrons in the outermost energy level are called _____ electrons.

3. An _____ is an atom that has lost or gained electrons

Analysis

1. What are molecular ions?

2. Why are H_2O and CO_2 by-products of a burning hydrocarbon?

3. Which type of bonding involves the sharing of electrons?

   a) Ionic bonding
   b) Covalent bonding
   c) Chemical bonding
   d) Physical bonding

4. Which of these substances consists of individual molecules?

   a) Diamond (C)
   b) Graphite (C)
   c) Water (H_2O)
   d) Sodium chloride (NaCl)
   e) Hydrogen (H_2)
   f) Chlorine (Cl_2)
   g) Ammonia (NH_3)

5. Which of the following pairs of elements would you expect to be covalently bonded (no ionic or metallic bonds):

   a) $_{27}Co$ and $_{28}Ni$
   b) $_{19}K$ and $_9F$

c) $_{15}P$ and $_8O$

d) $_{11}Na$ and $_{53}I$

Synthesis

1. What kind of bonding do you expect in a hydrocarbon? Why?

2. Classify the following bonds as polar or nonpolar. For the polar bonds, label which atom is more positive.

   a. The bond between two hydrogen atoms.
   b. The bond between hydrogen and chlorine.
   c. The bond between sodium and chlorine.
   d. The bond between carbon and hydrogen in a CH_4 molecule.
   e. The bond between carbon and oxygen in a carbon dioxide molecule.

3. Based on molecular polarities, predict:

   a. Will sodium chloride dissolve in a nonpolar solvent? Explain.
   b. How will the solubility of sodium chloride in very polar water compare to the solubility of sodium chloride in moderately polar ethanol? Explain.
   c. Glycerol is a moderately polar solute. In what type of solvent would you expect glycerol to have the higher solubility, in a polar solvent or in a nonpolar one? Explain.

4. Determine the metal or non-metal nature of C and O. If C and O form a compound, which of the following properties will it have?

   a. Metallic alloy, conducting
   b. Transparent gas
   c. Metallic alloy, nonconducting
   d. Brittle, transparent solid, nonconducting

5. Both graphite and diamond are forms of pure carbon. Explain why diamond is one of the hardest known substances, whereas graphite is a soft, lubricating material. If both are pure carbon, how can they be so different?

6. Very low temperatures are required to liquefy helium. Based on your understanding of intermolecular forces, explain why this is so.

CHAPTER 24

ANIMAL, VEGETABLE, MINERAL— IT'S ALL CHEMISTRY

Chemists like to call chemistry the "central science" because atoms and molecules are at the basis of all materials and most natural processes.

Do you know that molecules change in your eyes, your nervous system and your brain every time a photon strikes your retina and you "see" blue sky or red tulips.

Were you born brunette but are dying to be a blonde? Do you have straight hair but want curly locks? Hair dyes and the products for permanents and straighteners all have their roots (pun intended) in chemical principles.

Do you like to climb rocks? Do you know that differences at the atomic level make climbing on sandstone more dangerous than climbing on granite?

In this last chapter devoted to chemical principles, there isn't time to delve deeply into all the fascinating areas of biological chemistry, food science, cosmetology, pharmacology, atmospheric chemistry, or geochemistry. We have selected two areas to highlight; both areas involve families of naturally-occurring materials. Both have important applications in our every day life. The first presentation introduces a molecular family called fatty acids and their role in human health. The second focuses on extended network structures of geological mate-

rials. Taken together, these examples illustrate that chemical principles apply across diverse materials. Both also show that our understanding of these principles can lead to new products and better lives.

24–1 FATTY ACIDS

What are fatty acids and why should you care about them? Perhaps you or some member of your family counts calories and worries about the fat content in their diet. Reading the nutrition labels, like those shown in *Figure 24.1*, on your favorite butter, margarine, or cooking oil

Nutrition Facts
Serving Size 1 TBSP (14g)
Servings Per Container 32

Amount Per Serving

Calories 100	Calories from Fat 100
	% Daily Value*
Total Fat 11g	**17%**
Saturated Fat 2g	**10%**
Polyunsaturated Fat 4g	
Monounsaturated Fat 3g	
Cholesterol 0mg	**0%**
Sodium 160mg	**7%**
Total Carbohydrate 0g	**0%**
Protein 0g	

Vitamin A 10%
Not a significant source of cholesterol, dietary fiber, sugars, vitamin C, calcium, and iron.
* Percent Daily Values are based on a 2,000 calorie diet.

Nutrition Facts
Serving Size 1 Tbsp (15 ml)
Servings per Container 33

Amount Per Serving

Calories 120	Calories from Fat 120
	% Daily Value*
Total Fat 14g	**22%**
Saturated Fat 2g	**10%**
Polyunsaturated Fat 2g	
Monounsaturated Fat 10g	
Cholesterol 0mg	**0%**
Sodium 0mg	**0%**
Total Carbohydrate 0g	**0%**
Protein 0g	

Not a significant source of cholesterol dietary fiber sugars, vitamin A, vitamin C, calcium, and iron.
* Percent Daily Values are based on a 2,000 calorie diet.

Figure 24.1

Nutrition labels from margarine (left) and olive oil (right).

(corn oil, olive oil, etc.), you may encounter terms like "saturated fats," "unsaturated fats," and "trans-fats." You might also read that some fats are good, even essential, for your body to function. Advertisements you come across tout the absence of "trans-fats" or the presence of "omega"-fatty acids in products.

Can you make sense of all this? Yes, you now have the tools to get a molecular perspective on these materials. In addition, knowing how fats look and work on the molecular level will help you to see how molecular structures influence the behavior of matter on the human level.

Fats and Oils

Let's begin our study of fats and fatty acids as scientists would do. We will select a group of representative examples and observe them, categorizing their properties and relating those properties to structures.

Consider six samples of high-fat substances: shortening, butter, stick margarine, olive oil, canola oil, and a "buttery spread" shown in *Figure 24.2.* What observations can you make just from looking at them? How about starting with their physical state? Are they solids or liquids?

What other experiments can we do to characterize these materials? Back in Chapter 12, you considered the melting point and boiling points

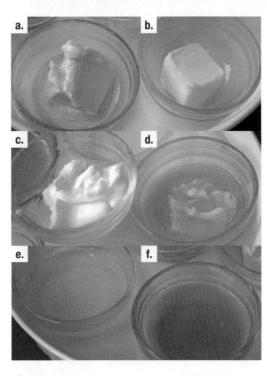

Figure 24.2

Six fatty substances as seen at room temperature: a) stick margarine, b) butter, c) shortening, d) a "buttery" spread, e) canola oil, and f) olive oil. Some are soft solids, others are liquid.

• Fats and Oils

Fats and oils are substances that do not dissolve in water, but can dissolve in hydrocarbon liquids. Fats are solid at room temperature; oils are liquid at room temperature.

as a way to consider forces between molecules. By cooling down the liquids and heating up the solids, we can get the temperatures at which these materials undergo the solid-liquid change of state.

Figure 24.3 shows what happens when these materials are cooled to the temperature of dry ice (−78° C). Similarly, *Figure 24.4* shows the physical state of each substance at 70° C. At the low temperature of dry ice, all six are solids. At the higher temperature, all are liquids.

If you were to monitor the state changes

ior tells something about the purity of a material. Pure substances change physical state at a single temperature; matter that is a mixture of multiple substances changes its physical state over a broad range of temperature. So, from our observations, we can conclude that each of these six substances is a mixture and not a pure compound.

Scientists have more fully characterized these foodstuffs than by just measuring melting points. They have identified the various components of each fat or oil by separating each mixture into its components and then using the instrumental techniques described in Chapter 19 to identify the components. We won't describe those additional experiments, but report later on their results.

Nutritionists and biochemists distinguish between fatty substances like our test materials on the basis of their melting points, using the terms **fats** and **oils** to categorize them. Fatty substances that are solid at room temperature are labeled fats; they melt to liquids at higher temperatures. Oils are liquids at room temperature but solidify somewhere below room temperature. Current thinking indicates that oils are better for your health than fats. Fats lead to artery-clogging deposits that cause heart attacks and strokes. Oils do not appear to be as much of a problem in this regard.

Figure 24.3

The state of these test substances when cooled to −78° C . All are solids at this temperature.

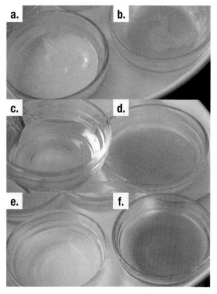

Figure 24.4

The state of these test substances when heated to 70° C. All substances are liquid at this temperature.

carefully, you would notice that the olive oil solidified before canola oil did. Upon heating, margarine, then butter, and finally shortening liquefied. Starting from the conditions of Figure 24.3, with all substances as cold solids, you would get the following ordering of melting temperatures as the substances heated up:

While measuring the melting points of these

| canola oil | olive oil | buttery spread | stick margarine | butter | shortening |

substances you would also notice something strange. We have noted earlier that water melts exactly at 0° C and copper melts sharply at 1083° C, but our test materials melt over a *range* of temperatures, not at a *single* temperature. Why is this?

Scientists know that melting point behav-

Triglycerides

At the molecular level, both fats and oils contain a small molecule called glycerol. *Figure 24.5* shows the structure of glycerol. Notice that glycerol is a small molecule, containing only three carbon atoms. Each carbon atom has one −OH group attached to it. These groups enable glycerol to react readily with molecules that belong to the family of organic acids. Remember

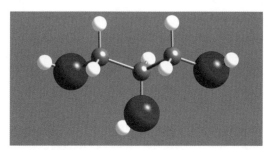

Figure 24.5

The molecular structure of glycerol, $C_3H_8O_3$, which lies at the base of all fats and oils. The atom colors are O red, C grey, and H white.

from Chapter 19 that an organic acid molecule contains the group:

$$O$$
$$\|$$
$$-C-OH$$

We shall use the notation –COOH group to represent this molecular group for conciseness.

One example of a glycerol + acid reaction is shown in *Figure 24.6*. Acetic acid (a simple organic acid found in vinegar) has been chosen to represent a typical organic acid. Each acid molecule "attacks" an –OH group on the glycerol molecule. During the reaction, the H atom on each OH group of glycerol and the entire –OH group on each acid are removed; bonds form between each organic acid and the glycerol molecule. The product, a molecule containing three acids hooked to glycerol, is called a **triglyceride**.

If you have ever had your blood analyzed by a doctor, you may have seen a value of the triglyceride level in your blood included in the report. The nature of the triglycerides found in your blood reflects your diet, especially your intake of fats and oils. Chemical analysis shows that the acid molecules found in fats differ from those found in oils, due to differences in the acids attached to glycerol.

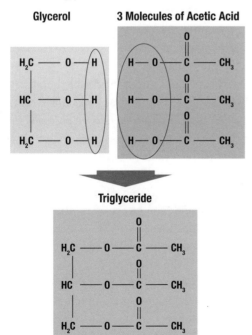

Figure 24.6

A simple example of the reaction of glycerol with three acid molecules. Acetic acid is a simple acid; the reaction with fatty acids is similar. The circled atoms are removed in the reaction, and bonds are formed that connect each acid molecule with glycerol.

Fatty Acids—Saturated and Unsaturated

SATURATED FATTY ACIDS

The acids most commonly found in fats and oils, called **fatty acids**, contain long hydrocarbon chains with a –COOH at the end. You have already seen two fatty acid molecules: Lauric acid (Figure 19.5m) and oleic acid (Figure 19.5n). Since the properties of fatty acids largely determine the properties of fats and oils, it is worthwhile to give these important molecules more study.

Thinking Like a Scientist: *Figure 24.7* presents names, melting points, molecular formulas, sources, and structures of fatty acids that are important in natural fats and oils. Look first at the molecular structures on the left under the heading of "Saturated fatty acids." What molecular grouping do all the molecules have in common? What makes one saturated fatty acid different from another? Describe the general trends in the melting points of the fatty acids. (Do molecules with long or short chains melt at higher temperatures?)

- **Triglyceride**
A large molecule created by reacting three fatty acids with glycerol.

- **Fatty Acids**
A molecule with a long hydrocarbon tail and an acid group –COOH at the other end.

Figure 24.7

Important saturated and unsaturated fats, their melting points, sources, molecular formulas, and structures. The number of double bonds are given in ( ) for unsaturated fatty acids. "NA" means not available.

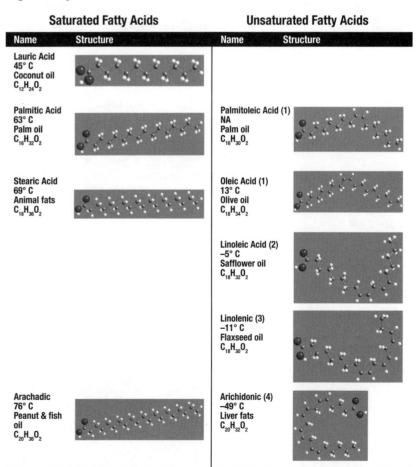

Saturated fatty acids contain long chains of C atoms linked together in a zig-zag fashion. The –COOH group sits at one end of every fatty acid molecule. Every carbon atom but the two at either end of the molecule contains 2 H atoms. One molecule differs from another by the number of –CH$_2$ groups. In general, the melting point of a saturated fatty acid increases with increasing chain length (or mass of the molecule).

Figure 24.8 represents in a simple way how saturated fatty acid molecules pack together in the solid state. The –C–C– chain is shown as a zig-zag line, the blue shape represents the acid group. Notice how the herringbone structure of each molecule allows for tight packing of molecules in the solid. The **van der Waals forces** (mentioned in Chapter 23) hold the molecules together in the solid. As the number of atoms in the molecule increase, more van der Waal interactions become possible. It takes more energy to break these interactions, and so the melting point increases as the number of –CH$_2$– units in the molecule increases.

Hydrogen bonds (also described in Chapter 23) provide additional bonding between pairs of molecules in the crystal. The enlargement of Figure 24.8 provides details of the hydrogen-bonding interactions between the fatty acid molecules.

UNSATURATED FATTY ACIDS

Thinking Like a Scientist: Now look at the unsaturated fatty acids on the right hand side of Figure 24.7. First, try and see if you can figure out where the names "saturated" and "unsaturated" came from. Look at saturated/unsaturated

pairs of molecules that contain the same number of carbon atoms (e.g., palmitic and palmitoleic, stearic and oleic, stearic and linoleic, arachidic and arachidonic). For each pair, which type of acid contains the most H atoms, the saturated or unsaturated one? How many more H atoms?

The saturated molecule in each pair contains two more H atoms than its simplest unsaturated partner. The term "saturated" indicates that the molecule contains the maximum possible number of H atoms. "Unsaturated" molecules have fewer H atoms than their saturated counterpart.

You saw earlier in Chapter 19 that C atoms like to make 4 bonds. If H atoms have been removed in unsaturated molecules, does each C atom still make four bonds? Look at the structures of the unsaturated acids to answer that question. Hint: Look carefully at the kink(s) in the molecules.

C atoms in unsaturated fatty acids make up for their missing H atoms by forming double bonds with the adjacent C atom. Each C atom in a double-bonded pair is bonded to three other atoms. C atoms that only form single bonds are connected to four other atoms. Remember that the geometry around a C atom with bonds to four atoms is different from the bonding geometry to only three atoms (Figure 19.6). The change in bonding geometry gives rise to kinks in the molecular structure.

What effects might the double bonds, and their associated structural kinks, have on the properties of unsaturated fatty acids? Look first at the melting temperatures of saturated/unsaturated pairs of molecules containing the same number of C atoms. Which melts at a lower temperature, the saturated or unsaturated acid? Then consider the effect of multiple double bonds. Which melts at the lowest temperature, oleic, linoleic, or linolenic acid?

Clearly, the effect of double bonds is to lower the melting point. All of the unsaturated fatty acids are liquids at room temperature. Is this observation consistent with the explanation of van der Waals interactions formulated earlier to explain the melting point trend of saturated fatty acids?

On going from stearic acid to oleic acid, the melting point decreases by 56° C. In terms of chemical composition, the molecules differ only

- **Van der Waals Forces**

Weak intermolecular attraction arising from the formation of temporary dipoles in non-polar molecules. Also known as dispersion forces.

- **Hydrogen Bonds**

The Interaction between hydrogen atoms bound to oxygen, nitrogen, or fluorine with other oxygen, nitrogen, or fluorine atoms. Hydrogen bonds are among the strongest intermolecular interactions.

Figure 24.8
The packing of saturated fatty acid molecules in the solid state. The zig-zag lines represent the hydrocarbon tails and the blue shapes represent the –COOH group. The dashed lines represent the hydrogen bonds that hold pairs of acid molecules together in the solid. Details of the hydrogen bonds are shown below. The close packing of the hydrocarbon tail leads to formation of many van der Waals interactions. These forces cause saturated fatty acids to be solids at room temperature.

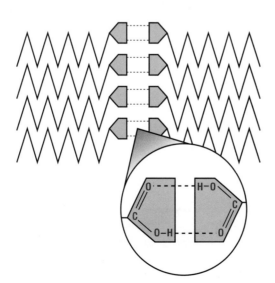

by two small H atoms. Since van der Waals interactions are weak, it seems somewhat surprising that removing only two H atoms can lead to such a huge reduction in melting points. Another factor must contribute. *Figure 24.9* identifies that factor—the inability of unsaturated fatty acids to pack tightly together in the solid.

The structural kink introduced at each double bond in an unsaturated fatty acid molecule makes tight packing impossible. As Figure 24.9 shows, trying to pack the left-hand side of the molecules closely together forces the right-hand side to either pack less efficiently or to have atoms trying to be in the same space. Overall, the van der Waals interactions decrease between adjacent unsaturated molecules. The reduction leads to the large difference in melting points of the saturated and unsaturated fats with a comparable carbon count.

Triglycerides and Your Health

All of the saturated fatty acids shown in Figure 24.7 are solid at body temperature. When these fatty acids combine with glycerol to form triglycerides, the triglycerides are also soft, sticky solids at body temperature. Such fats are called **saturated fats**.

Butter, shortening, and animal fats, all solids at room temperature, are triglycerides with a large proportion of saturated fatty acids. Shortening contains a high percentage of tristearin, the triglyceride formed from the reaction of three molecules of stearic acid (18 carbons) with glycerol. Animal fats contain mixed triglycerides with palmitic and stearic acids. Butter contains a mix of saturated fatty acid triglycerides and oleic-acid containing triglycerides.

Triglycerides formed from unsaturated fats are usually liquid at room temperature and make up the oils we have considered in the experiments of Figures 24.2 through 24.4. When the triglycerides contain acids with one double bond, they are called **monounsaturated fats;** those formed from acids with multiple double bonds are called **polyunsaturated fats**. Triolein, formed from glycerol and three oleic acid (18 carbons) molecules, is a monounsaturated fat found in olive oil. Other foods rich in monounsaturated fats include avocados and canola oil. Oils derived from plants (corn, peanut, sunflower) and some fish provide polyunsaturated fats.

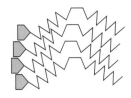

Saturated fats belong to the "bad guys" of nutrition. A diet rich in saturated fats leads to increased levels of cholesterol and increased tendencies toward heart disease, obesity, and diabetes. Monounsaturated fats like olive oil appear to have a neutral effect on cholesterol levels, while some polyunsaturated fats (those high in linoleic acid) have been shown to lower cholesterol levels.

Several polyunsaturated fats are considered essential parts of a healthy diet. Two from Figure 24.7, linoleic and linolenic, are important precursors to other essential molecules in human metabolism. Because the human body does not synthesize these acids, they must be obtained in our diet. Arachidonic acid, present in fish oils, is required for human brain development and function. Some research suggests that Alzheimer's disease and dementia may be tied to displacement in the brain of these natural acids with other acids.

This brief overview of fatty acids shows that the bonding principles explain molecular structures of even complex molecules. Molecular structures, in turn, give rise to properties that can have profound influence on our health and well-being. This case study has looked at a molecular-based family of materials. It is now time to turn our attention to look for similar insights in an extended, network-type family of materials. These materials occur in nature, produced by geological, earth-based processes.

24-2 SILICATE MATERIALS

Bonding in complex inorganic materials

The term mineral* describes a material that is a) naturally-occurring, b) an inorganic substance with a high melting temperature, and c)

---

*Nutritionists often refer to "minerals" as the inorganic materials necessary for biological functions. These include sources of calcium and magnesium and other metals.

Figure 24.9
The packing of unsaturated fatty acids in the solid state. Double bonds introduce kinks that prevent the neat, efficient packing found in saturated fatty acids. Because the unsaturated molecules cannot get as close to each other, van der Waals interactions decrease. Thus, the melting points decrease as well, making unsaturated fatty acids liquids at room temperature.

- **Saturated Fat**
  A triglyceride containing three saturated fatty acid molecules.

- **Monounsaturated Fats**
  Mono = 1 in Greek. Fats containing fatty acids with a single double bond, such as oleic acid.

- **Polyunsaturated Fats**
  Poly = many in Greek. Fats containing fatty acids with many double bonds, such as linolenic or arachidonic acid.

TRANS-FATTY ACIDS—A NEW HEALTH HAZARD?

While unsaturated fats appear to be more heart-healthy than saturated fats, they do have some downsides. The double bonds represent sites of high chemical reactivity, especially to oxygen. Butter left out on a warm kitchen counter goes rancid when the double bonds present in the oleic acid component react with oxygen in the air.

To increase shelf-life and prepare fats with a higher melting point, manufacturers can add hydrogen back into unsaturated fats turning them into saturated fats. A nutrition label on a food product that says "includes partially hydrogenated oil" indicates that these chemically altered fats are part of the product. Shortening, for example, starts out as a liquid oil that is hydrogenated to form a solid containing a high proportion of saturated fats.

Under the conditions in which the hydrogenation process takes place, a second reaction can occur simultaneously. This other reaction causes a change in the bonding geometry around double bonds. All naturally-occurring unsaturated fatty acids have both H atoms on the same side of the double bond (*Figure 24.10a*). During the hydrogenation process, unsaturated fatty acids can be transformed into molecules in which the H atoms are now on opposite sides of the double bond (*Figure 24.10b*).

The Greek words "cis" and "trans" are used to describe the two types of geometries around the double bond. "Cis" applies to the natural fats in which H atoms are on the same side; "trans" fats, produced during hydrogenation reactions, have H atoms across the double bond.

Trans-fatty acids resemble saturated fatty acids in their overall structure. The molecules are almost linear, with only small kinking at the double bond. *Figure 24.11* contrasts oleic acid (a), which is a cis-fatty acid, with its trans 18-carbon counterpart, elaidic acid (b). Current research suggests that these trans fatty acids cause even more problems than saturated fats. Trans fats are implicated in diabetes, obesity, cancer, and heart-disease. Some studies also suggest that trans fats may displace important polyunsaturated fats in the brain, leading to mental disorders, including dementia. In 2003, the U.S. Food and Drug Administration issued a regulation requiring food manufacturers to include the trans fat content in the nutrition labeling of all products by January 1, 2006.

Figure 24.10

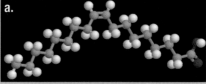

a. Cis   b. Trans

Figure 24.11

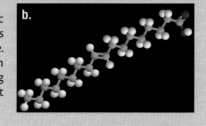

a.

b.

◆ **Trans-fatty Acids**

A non-natural form of unsaturated fatty acids in which H atoms are on opposite sides of the double bond.
Cis fatty acids are the natural form. H atoms are on the same side of the double bond.

● **Crystalline**

Crystalline matter is solid matter in which the constituent atoms or molecules are arranged in an orderly, repetitive pattern. For example, a crystal of sodium chloride has the regular pattern that every Na$^+$ ion is surrounded by six Cl$^-$ ions and every Cl$^-$ ion is surrounded by six Na$^+$ ions.

Figure 24.12

Three mineral specimens that illustrate different crystal morphologies.
a) An asbestos sample composed of fibers.
b) A mica sample composed of layers or sheets.
c) A quartz sample that breaks into irregular shaped pieces when shattered with a hammer.

crystalline with a defined chemical composition. A solid is said to be **crystalline** when its atoms or molecular units are arranged in a fixed, repetitive pattern.

The rock that you pick up on a mountain hike or the stone that you skip along the surface of a lake are generally not minerals but aggregates of different minerals. They may have formed together at the same time or come together in a later geological process. We will learn more about the origin of rocks and minerals in later chapters. For now, the focus will just be on a specific class of minerals called "sil-

icate minerals." Within the silicate mineral family occur a rich diversity of materials with very interesting structures and properties.

We shall see that with minerals, as with fatty acids, the underlying atomic structure gives rise to properties that we can observe with our naked eye. We will look at two minerals that have strong tendency to break apart or fracture in a very specific way and one that does not. Relatively weak forces, such as pulling with one's fingernails, are sufficient to break two of the minerals apart; the third requires whacking with a hammer to get smaller, irregularly

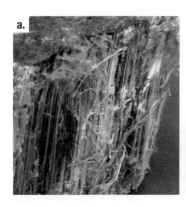

a.

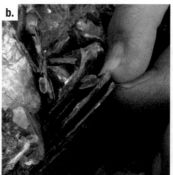

b.

c.

shaped chunks. *Figure 20.12* illustrates these three minerals and their external structure. The mineral shown in Figure 24.10a is one type of asbestos; this mineral is made up of thread-like fibers. These fibers are so strong that they can be woven into fabrics or matted into sheets that are fireproof and very poor heat conductors. Such properties make asbestos minerals useful for insulation and fireproofing. Unfortunately, very small bits of the fibers of some forms of asbestos can cause cancer if inhaled into the lungs and so their use has declined significantly. More details on the story of asbestos are given in the side box.

A different silicate mineral, known as a mica, is shown in Figure 24.12b. This mineral is composed of layer upon layer of material stuck together. The layers typically have a very uniform thickness and one layer separates easily from another. Simply picking at it with a fingernail can provide enough force to do it.

A third mineral, quartz, is shown in Figure 25.10c. Quartz cannot be pulled apart easily. To break a quartz crystal into smaller pieces requires much more force than pulling fibers or layers apart with tweezers or your fingernails. Hammers and chisels are required, and the resulting pieces have very irregular shapes.

These three minerals are said to have different morphologies. One is thread-like, the second layer-like, the third one is not well-defined. What gives rise to this property of a mineral, whether it can be easily pulled apart into fibers or sheets or can only be broken into irregular-shaped chunks by hitting with a hammer?

In the early 1800s, scientists hypothesized that the morphology (fiber, layers) of minerals was related to the underlying atomic structure and chemical bonding within the mineral. Now, using modern instrumentation based on the diffraction of crystalline materials by X-rays, geologists can determine the three-dimensional arrangement of atoms in even very complex minerals. They have verified that this hypothesis is correct. We will see how it applies to the three minerals of Figure 24.12.

ASBESTOS MATERIALS

The term asbestos refers to a group of six different minerals, all with a fibrous morphology. The fibers of five of these minerals reflect atomic-level structures like those described in the text. The sixth, chrysotile, also known as white asbestos, has an underlying structure that is layer-like, but the layers curl up to form fibers just like a flat carpet can be rolled up to form a tube. In all six minerals, bonding within each fiber is stronger than between adjacent fibers.

The fibers of these six minerals are strong and resistant to heat, light, and most chemicals and microbes. They are also electrical insulators and poor conductors of heat. These properties lend themselves to many important applications, including building materials such as heat insulation, flooring and ceiling tiles, and fire-resistant fabrics. Asbestos has also been used in clutches and brake linings of automobiles and to reinforce concrete on highways.

While the fiber structure of asbestos minerals led to its widespread use in building materials, that structure poses potential health problems. Very small fibers can be sloughed off, like dead skin, from surfaces subjected to repeated mechanical activity. Once in the air, the fibers can be inhaled into the lungs where they can be trapped. Chronic exposure to the fibers has been shown to cause lung cancer and other lung-related diseases. Asbestos miners and construction workers using building materials containing asbestos were found to be at increased risk.

The U.S. Environmental Protection Agency has banned the use of asbestos. Stringent regulations control the remodeling or demolition of building sites shown to be significantly contaminated by asbestos. You may have seen such buildings swathed in plastic wrap and inhabited by workers in protective suits and breathing respirators.

There is some debate amongst geologists and toxicologists about whether all forms of asbestos require such expensive measures. For example, chrysotile fibers, the most commonly used form of asbestos, are not as toxic as the other forms. They may still be safe for some applications and expensive removal of all types of asbestos may be unnecessary.

The story of asbestos provides a lesson in the care with which we should adopt new technologies. It also points out that we should thoroughly investigate problems with technology before taking drastic, expensive remedies.

Structure-Property Relationships in Silicate Minerals

The building block of all silicate minerals is a complex ion with formula SiO_4^{4-}, called the silicate ion. (Negative ions have names that end in "ate.") You can think of the silicate ion as a tightly-bound group (a single Si^{4+} ion surrounded by four O^{2-} ions) that has an overall negative charge of four units.

The lowest energy arrangement of four negative ions around a small positive ion is one that keeps the negative ions as far apart from each other as possible (to minimize the repulsive interactions), while still having each negative ion close to the positive ion (to maximize the attractive interactions). Is there a geometric shape that matches this description? *Figure 24.13* shows that the energetically favorable arrangement can be achieved by putting the Si^{4+} ion at the center of a tetrahedron, and an O^{2-} ion at each vertex.

You have seen this structure before: It is the same shape adopted by C atoms bonded to four other atoms. The same principle of minimizing electrostatic repulsions applies in both situations.

A silicate mineral is built up by stacking and packing silicate tetrahedra together in one pattern or another. Silicate ions are negatively charged, however, so positively-charged ions are also required for neutrality. Like the ionic crystal formed by sodium chloride (Figure 22.3a), positive and negative ions in silicate minerals arrange themselves in an orderly fashion so as to cancel out charges. The particular ionic arrangement depends upon the size and charge of the positive ions as well as the way in which the silicate ions string together.

Singly-charged positive ions found in naturally-occurring minerals include sodium or potassium ions (K^+ or Na^+). Commonly found ions with double positive charges include magnesium, calcium, and iron ions (Mg^{2+}, Ca^{2+}, Fe^{2+}); triply-charged aluminum ions (Al^{3+}) are also very common.

Whether and how silicate ions string together have profound influence on the morphological properties that we have introduced. So, let's start with a simple mineral that has silicate ions that do not connect with each other. Then we shall consider in turn a mineral in which the ions connect to form chains, a mineral in which the connections give rise to silicate layers, and finally one in which the connections are equal in all directions.

Minerals with Isolated Silicate Tetrahedra

One family of silicate minerals with individual silicate ions has the formula M_2SiO_4 where M can stand for positive ions with a +2 charge, including Mg^{2+} and Fe^{2+}. *Figure 24.14* a and b

COMPLEX IONS

A complex ion can be considered as a molecular entity from a chemical point of view. Some particular combinations of atoms with excess charge give rise to groupings which are so stable that changes like melting or dissolving in water leave the grouping intact. Much energy is needed to rip apart the bonds holding individual atoms.

Complex ions play an important role in the chemistry of living organisms. Some other important examples are

carbonate CO_3^{2-}

phosphate PO_4^{3-}

ammonium NH_4^+

Figure 24.13

Three representations of the silicate ion (SiO_4^{4-}).
a) In the ball and stick model, the red balls represent oxygen ions (O^{2-}) and the blue ball represents a silicon ion (Si^{4+}).
b) The tetrahedron, a four-sided figure made up of equilateral triangles, is a simple way to represent the structure of the complex ion.
c) The Si^{4+} ion is hidden in the center, and each vertex represents an oxygen ion.

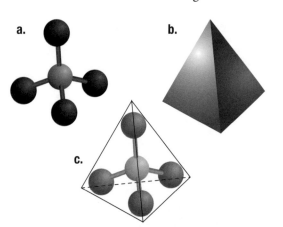

a.

b.

c.

Figure 24.14 ⇨

The arrangements of positive ions and silicate tetrahedra in one simple mineral shown as a projection. The three dimensional nature of the packing is not illustrated here.
a) Mg_2SiO_4, b) Fe_2SiO_4 and c) a mixed crystal containing both Mg^{2+} and Fe^{2+} ions. Pink spheres are Mg^{2+} ions, yellow ones are Fe^{2+} ions and triangles represent the flattened tetrahedra. The ions are drawn approximately to scale.

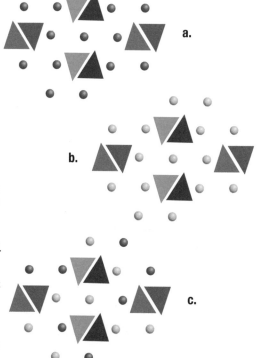

a.

b.

c.

shows the arrangement of positive ions and silicate tetrahedra in Mg_2SiO_4 and Fe_2SiO_4, respectively. The pink balls represent Mg^{2+} ions and the yellow ones represent Fe^{2+} ions, while the blue tetrahedra represent the SiO_4^{4-} ions. Notice that the arrangement of ions is very similar in the two structures. (The figures are drawn to reflect the actual sizes of ions.)

In nature, it is very common to find crystals that contain *both* Mg^{2+} and Fe^{2+} ions. Such a crystal would be described by the formula $Mg_xFe_{2-x}SiO_4$. The subscripts "x" and "2–x" indicate that the amounts of Mg and Fe can be variable. Notice that the sum of x and 2–x equals 2, so the atomic ratio of positive ions (Mg^{2+} and Fe^{2+}) to silicate ions (SiO_4^{4-}) is still 2 to 1. A representation of a mixed crystal is given in Figure 24.14c. In this figure the ratio of Mg^{2+}/Fe^{2+} is almost 1:1. You can see that in the mixed crystal one positive ion substitutes for the other; otherwise the structure looks very much the same. X-ray diffraction studies (Chapter 19) can reveal whether a given position is preferentially filled by a Mg^{2+} ion or an Fe^{2+} ion, or whether positions are occupied randomly.

The observation that nature prefers mixed crystals to pure ones is not limited to this M_2SiO_4 family of minerals. In more complicated mineral families, there may also be substitutions of Al^{3+} for Si^{4+} ions as well as in the "counterions," the positive ions that neutralize the charge of silicate ions. The common occurrence of "impure" or mixed crystals suggests that some important principle may be involved. In the accompanying box, we explore why nature often prefers mixed crystals. The question provides another illustration of the scientific method at work.

Minerals with Connected Silicate Tetrahedra

The silicate ion is very versatile. Silicate ions can form strong bonds with each other by sharing oxygen ions. Different families of silicate minerals arise from differences in the number of shared oxygen ions. Using the tetrahedral representation of silicate ions in which each vertex represents an oxygen ion, *Figure 24.15* shows how chains, double chains, and sheets can be formed. Two views are shown, one looking down on the tetrahedra, the other looking edge-on at them. How the tetrahedra are linked

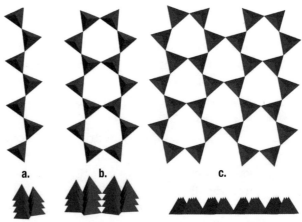

Figure 24.15
Silicate ions can link with each other by sharing oxygen ions.
a) Single chains form when two of the four oxygen ions of each tetrahedron are shared individually with two other silicate ions.
b) Double chains form when the single chains string together.
c) Sheets form when three corners of every tetrahedron are shared with three different tetrahedra.
For all three linkage patterns, two views are shown, one looking down on the tetrahedra, the other looking at them from the side.

together determines the mineral family and properties like stability, reactivity, and morphology.

The minerals shown in Figure 24.12 provide good examples of this last statement. A chunk of asbestos can easily be separated into long fibers, but breaking apart a fiber requires more force. A chunk of mica can easily be separated into sheets, but breaking a sheet requires more force. Hammering a piece of quartz leads to irregularly shaped bits.

How can these observations be related to the atomic-level structures of the three minerals? The most important structural difference among asbestos, mica, and quartz is in the linkage pattern of their silicate tetrahedra. The mica crystal is made up of stacked sheets with positive ions in the spaces between sheets, whereas asbestos crystal is made up of sandwiches of double chains held together by other positive ions. The bonds that hold the assembly of silicate tetrahedra together are much stronger than the ionic bonds between the cations and the tetrahedron assembly.

Figure 24.16 shows a simplified representation of a mica structure. The teal blue shapes represent Al^{3+} ions while the purple balls represent ions like K^+ or Na^+ Notice how the silicate sheets are separated by alternating layers of the two kinds of positive ions. Two silicate sheets are held tightly together by ionic

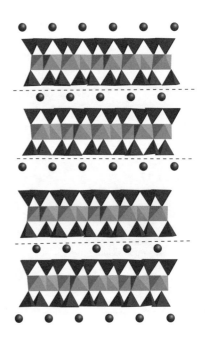

Figure 24.16
A simplified view of a mica structure, looking edge-on at the silicate tetrahedra. Two silicate layers (dark blue triangles) form a sandwich-like double layer around the aluminum ions (shown as the teal blue shapes). Purple balls are positive ions such as K^+ or Na^+.

The double layer sandwich is tightly-bonded together. Peeling off a mica layer corresponds to breaking the weak interactions of the K^+ or Na^+ ions, leaving the sandwich unit intact. Possible fracture lines are shown as dashed black lines.

Remember that only a portion of the crystal is shown here. The crystal extends backward through the page and out at each side.

bonding with the small, highly charged Al^{3+} ions, forming a sandwich-type structure. Adjacent sandwiches are held together by bonds with the larger +1 ions, but these interactions are relatively weak. Peeling off layers from a piece of mica corresponds to pulling off groups of layers of sandwiches.*

What about the asbestos structure? You can probably guess that it is either the chain or double chain structure that gives rise to filaments or thread-like materials. In fact, five of the six forms of asbestos get their tendency to form fibers from a double-chain silicate structure. A simplified view of one of the five arrangements is shown in *Figure 24.17*.

The pink and blue spheres represent positive ions, Mg^{2+} and Ca^{2+}, respectively.

Notice that pairs of double chains pack closely around a large number of the small Mg^{2+} ions while the larger Ca^{2+} ions sit outside, between pairs of double chains.

The double chains form tightly-bonded units with the small ions. Picture an extended foot-long sandwich held together by lots of sticky mayonnaise and you have an image of the unit. In the crystal, sandwich units are weakly linked together by the large Ca^{2+} ions. To continue on with the sandwich analogy, imagine packing lots of sandwiches into a cooler, stacking them in an orderly, organized fashion.

The black lines of Figure 24.17b show the weakest bonding interactions in this asbestos crystal. Parts held together by strong bonds stick together, separations occur along the surfaces where bonds are weak. If you remember that the chains extend backward into the figure, you can see why fibers or filaments are formed from this structure. It is easier to pull away a footlong sandwich than it is to cut the sandwich apart.*

There are also silicate minerals in which all of the bonding interactions are of the same strength. Olivine (Figure 24.14) and quartz (Figure 19.8a) are examples. What might you predict about the morphology or fracture pattern of such materials? Do you think there will be crystal direction that can be pulled apart more easily than another? No, these two crystals do not pull apart easily at all. When hit with a hammer, both types of material shatters into irregular shaped pieces.

24–3 CONCLUSION

In molecular materials such as the fatty acids and fats, the molecular structure determines properties like the physical state. Straight chain saturated fatty acids pack tightly together and are solid at room temperature. Unsaturated fatty acids have kinks because of their double bonds and don't pack as efficiently. The weaker interactions possible in this structure give rise to materials that are liquid at room temperature. The double bonds also make unsaturated fats susceptible to chemical deterioration.

In extended structures, differences in bonding strengths between repeating units in the structure can give rise to large-scale, easily observed features such as fibers and sheets.

The principles of ionic and covalent bonding enable us to understand why such features form.

These two case studies, fats and minerals, illustrate that a relatively few principles of bonding and reactivity can explain the properties of very diverse kinds of materials.

Figure 24.17

a) A simplified structure of one form of asbestos mineral showing the edges of double chains and the positive ions that hold them together. The small pink balls are small ions such as Mg^{2+}, the larger blue balls represent the large Ca^{2+} ions. Two sets of double chains form an extended sandwich around the set of small ions. These units are strongly bonded together. The larger Ca^{2+} ions hold sandwich units together, but only weakly.

b) The same structure, but the black lines mark the weak bonding interactions where the structure will pull apart most easily. Remember that these structures extend back into the page, so that the fracture forms fibers.

*Mica layers and asbestos fibers visible to the naked eye actually consist of many stacks of double-silicate layers and bundles of extended sandwiches, respectively. An individual double-silicate layer of Figure 24.16 or sandwich unit of Figure 24.17 would be too small to be seen.

ONE LAST CHANCE TO THINK LIKE A SCIENTIST

Why Does Nature Often Prefer Mixed Crystals?

What fundamental principles might be involved in answering this question? What model could be formulated to guide our thinking about it?

Below is one line of reasoning to propose an answer. The reasoning is based on principles and concepts you have seen before. Perhaps you may want to formulate your own answers.

Statement of the Problem:

Why does nature prefer mixed crystals containing both Mg^{2+} and Fe^{2+} ions in $Mg_xFe_{2-x}SiO_4$ minerals?

Relevant Background Information:

The principles of chemical reactivity suggest that a particular chemical product forms because it is lower in energy and/or higher in entropy than other possible products. The law of increasing disorder tells us that systems which are disordered have higher entropy than perfectly ordered ones. Since ions are involved, principles concerning electrostatic force laws and potential energy might be important.

Formulation of Two Hypotheses:

Hypothesis 1: Mixed crystals form because they are of lower energy than the pure crystals.
Hypothesis 2: Mixed crystals form because they have higher entropy than the pure crystals.

Building a Model to Test the Hypotheses:

Assume that pure crystals of Mg_2SiO_4, Fe_2SiO_4, and mixed crystals $Mg_xFe_{2-x}SiO_4$ are held together by ionic bonding interactions of +2 ions with the −4 silicate ion.

Assume that the Mg^{2+} ions and Fe^{2+} ions are about the same size. (Look at Figure 24.14 to see if this is a reasonable assumption.)

The Analysis:

Let's consider first whether there might be significant differences in energy between pure crystals and mixed crystals. The answer to the question boils down to whether there will be much difference in energy for the electrostatic interaction between Mg^{2+} ions and silicate ions from the interaction of Fe^{2+} ions with silicate ions. Energy is lowered when positive charges and negative charges approach each other. How much the energy is lowered depends on the same factors that determine the electrostatic force: charges on the ions and the distances between them. The charge on the two cations is the same, but is the distance between an Mg^{2+} ion and a silicate ion the same as that between a Fe^{2+} ion and its silicate ion? The structures in Figure 24.14 are drawn approximately to scale and you can see that the distances between ions are about the same in size. Thus, our model suggests that electrostatic energies in the pure crystals and the mixed crystals would be about the same. Therefore, the push to form mixed crystals does not come from energy considerations. Hypothesis 1 no longer seems reasonable.

What about Hypothesis 2? The law of increasing disorder tells us that nature prefers disordered materials. The mixed crystal has more disorder than the two pure crystals, each containing only one cation. (The situation is analogous to the mixing of gases depicted in Figure 18.6.) Since our first hypothesis was judged to be false, it seems that nature's preference for mixed crystals in this family of minerals is due to the higher entropy of the mixed crystals. Experimental tests measuring the relative energies and entropies support our conclusions.

Is this conclusion the same for other mineral families? In more complicated mineral families than the one described here, additional disorder is possible. For example, there can be substitution of aluminum within the silicate tetrahedra. For minerals that form in the presence of water, hydroxide ions (OH^-) can sometimes replace an oxide ion (O^{2-}). In these minerals, both energy and entropy factors are involved in the specific patterns and mixtures of cations that are formed.

Chapter Framework

A. Fatty Acids

1. Fats and Oils

2. Triglycerides

3. Saturated and Unsaturated Fatty Acids

4. Triglycerides and Your Health

    a. Saturated fats

    b. Monounsaturated fats

    c. Polyunsaturated fats

5. Trans Fatty Acids

B. Silicate Minerals

1. Bonding in Complex Inorganic Materials

2. Structure-Property Relationships in Silicate Minerals

3. Minerals with Isolated Silicate Tetrahedra

4. Minerals with Connected Silicate Tetrahedra

Comprehension

Matching

a. *Silicate ion (SiO$_4^{4-}$)*
b. *Saturated fatty acids*
c. *Asbestos*
d. *Quartz*
e. *Mica*
f. *Tetrahedron*
g. *Crystal*
h. *Unaturated fatty acids*

1. _____ Contains C=C double bonds.

2. _____ Contains only C–C single bonds.

3. _____ Best geometric arrangement of four bonds around a central atom.

4. _____ Building block of many minerals.

5. _____ State of matter in which atoms or ions are arranged in an orderly, repeating patterns.

6. _____ Silicate mineral in which all silicate tetrahedra are bonded with equal strength to four other tetrahedra.

7. _____ Silicate mineral that has a super "foot-long" structure.

8. _____ Silicate mineral that has a layer-like structure.

True or False

1. _____ The melting point of saturated fatty acids increases with increasing number of carbon atoms.

2. _____ An unsaturated fatty acid with the same number of carbon atoms as a saturated fatty acid will generally melt at a lower temperature than the saturated fatty acid.

3. _____ Ionic bonds hold fatty acid molecules together in the solid state

4. _____ The –COOH group is what makes an organic acid an acid.

5. _____ The silicate ion (SiO$_4$)$^{4-}$ is flat (planar) with the following structure:

$$ \begin{array}{c} O \\ | \\ O-Si-O \\ | \\ O \end{array} $$

6. _____ The underlying atomic structure of both fatty acids and minerals determines many properties such as melting point and crystal morphology.

7. _____ Most forms of asbestos form fibers.

8. _____ Crystals of quartz flake off in thin sheets.

9. _____ "Mixed" crystals like MgFeSiO$_4$ are more disordered than either pure Mg$_2$SiO$_4$ or pure Fe$_2$SiO$_4$.

10. _____ Fractures occur in crystals along lines or planes containing the strongest bonds.

11. _____ The term "saturated" in saturated fats refers to whether every C atom has as many H atoms as it can hold.

Fill in the Blank

1. A _____ contains three acids hooked to glycerol.

2. Fatty acids with the maximum number of H atoms are designated _____.

3. A solid is said to be _____ when its constituents are arranged in a definite, fixed pattern.

4. A silicate ion has the geometric shape of a _____.

5. _____ acids have H atoms on opposite sides of the double bond, whereas naturally occurring _____ acids have both H atoms on the same side of the double bond.

Analysis

1. A triglyceride is made by combining

    a) Glycerol and carbonate

    b) An organic acid and glycerol

    c) Glycerol and mica

    d) Asbestos and quartz

2. Which of the following is **not** a mineral?

    a) Quartz

    b) Mica

    c) Arachidic acid

    d) Asbestos

3. Which of the following is an unsaturated fat?

    a) Palmitic acid

    b) Oleic acid

    c) Lauric acid

    d) Stearic acid

4. Fatty acid molecules consist of a hydrocarbon tail attached to

    a) –SiO$_4$

    b) –MgFe

    c) –CO$_2$

    d) –COOH

5. Asbestos is both a poor conductor of heat and electricity. Which of the following are reasonable

conclusions. (More than one may be possible.)

a) The electrons in asbestos are delocalized like metals.

b) The electrons is asbestos are tightly bound to specific atoms or ions

c) The electronic energy levels are bandlike

d) The electronic energy levels are discrete.

Synthesis

1. Myristic acid is a saturated fatty acid with 14 carbon atoms. It is about 18 percent of the fat found in coconut oil. Looking at other fatty acids in Figure 24.7, in what temperature range might you expect this acid to melt?

2. These three labels have come from different sources of dietary fat.

   a. Predict the relative melting temperatures of the three substances.

   b. Discuss which one is likely to be more heart healthy from the perspective of the fat content.

4. This image is of a silicate mineral. Make a prediction of whether this mineral would appear as fibers, layers, or no regular pattern. Explain your answer.

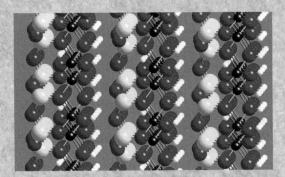

5. Human hair is made up mostly of large molecules called proteins. Based on the principles that you have learned in this chapter, describe what you think the protein molecular structure might look like.

a.

Nutrition Facts

Serving Size 1 Tablespoon (14g)
Servings Per Container 96

Amount Per Serving

Calories 120   Calories from Fat 120

% Daily Value*

Total Fat 14g	**22**%
Saturated Fat 1g	**5**%
Trans Fat 0g	
Polyunsaturated Fat 4g	
Monounsaturated Fat 9g	
Cholesterol 0mg	**0**%
Sodium 0mg	**0**%
Total Carbohydrate 0g	**0**%
Protein 0g	**0**%

Not a significant source of dietary fiber, sugars, vitamin A, vitamin C, calcium or iron.

*Percent Daily Values are based on a 2,000 calorie diet.

b.

Nutrition Facts

Serving Size 1 Tablespoon (12g)
Servings Per Container about 38

Amount Per Serving

Calories 110 Calories from Fat 110

% Daily Value*

Total Fat 12g	**18**%
Saturated Fat 3g	**15**%
Polyunsaturated Fat 3g	
Monounsaturated Fat 4g	
Cholesterol 0mg	**0**%
Sodium 0mg	**0**%
Total Carbohydrate 0g	**0**%
Protein 0g	

Vitamin E 15%

Not a significant source of dietary fiber, sugars, vitamin A, vitamin C, calcium and iron.

*Percent Daily Values are based on a 2,000 calorie diet.

c.

Nutrition Facts

Serving Size 1 TBSP (14g)
Servings Per Container 32

Amount Per Serving

Calories 80   Calories from Fat 80

% Daily Value*

Total Fat 9g	**14**%
Saturated Fat 2.5g	**13**%
Trans Fat 0g	
Polyunsaturate Fat 2.5g	
Monounsaturated Fat 3.5g	
Cholesterol 0mg	**0**%
Sodium 90mg	**4**%
Total Carbohydrate 0g	**0**%
Protein 0g	

Vitamin A 10% (10% as beta-carotene)

Vitamin E 10%

Not a significant source of dietary fiber, sugars, Vitamin C, calcium, and iron.

*Percent Daily Values (DV) are based on a 2,000 calorie diet.

3. Study the structures of saturated, cis-unsaturated and trans-unsaturated fatty acids and formulate a hypothesis about why trans-unsaturated fatty acids behave more like saturated fatty acids with respect to melting point and artery-clogging tendencies. What experiments might you do to test this hypothesis?

CHAPTER 25

RADIOACTIVITY, NUCLEAR PROCESSES, AND APPLICATIONS

The discovery of nuclear chain reactions need not bring about the destruction of mankind any more than did the discovery of matches. We only must do everything in our power to safeguard against its abuse.

~ Albert Einstein

Our working model of the atom describes the atom as a small, dense, positive nucleus surrounded by electrons, which are described by standing waves of probability. In preceding chapters, the behavior and inter-action of electrons have been described, and it has been shown how this governs chemical behavior. We have, until now, pretty much ignored the behavior of the nucleus, but as you've probably gathered from the title of the chapter, that is about to end.

Much of what has been explained thus far in this textbook about the behavior of electrons around atoms is quite similar to the behavior of protons and neutrons in a nucleus. Just as the electrons around atoms behave as standing waves of probability, protons and neutrons also have wave behavior. Because of this wave behavior, protons and neutrons will each obey the exclusion principle and occupy energy levels that are filled from lowest energy to highest energy. It is even possible to draw energy wells for a nucleus, one for protons and a separate one for neutrons, to depict all of the possible energy states in the nucleus. However, there is one rather large gap in our present ability to describe with assurance what happens inside the nucleus.

Very early in this course, four fundamental forces (gravitational, electromagnetic, nuclear strong, and nuclear weak) were explained in some detail. Chapters 4 and 5 were devoted to summarizing our understanding of gravitational force and electromagnetic force. Nuclear forces were not provided with their own explanatory chapter, but this wasn't because scientists consider nuclear forces to be unimportant. It is simply because scientists haven't yet determined what the laws (equations) that describe these forces look like.

Scientists are still actively working out the details of how nuclear processes work, so this provides an opportunity to examine the scientific process at work. In this chapter, you will not only be learning what we currently know about the nucleus and how we learned it, but the chapter will also discuss what science simply doesn't yet know about the nucleus, and what we are doing to fill the gaps in our understanding in this increasingly important area of research.

25–1 NUCLEAR FORCES AND ENERGY

Before Rutherford made his relatively recent discovery of the nucleus, no one knew that the **Nuclear Strong Force** existed. One of the rea-

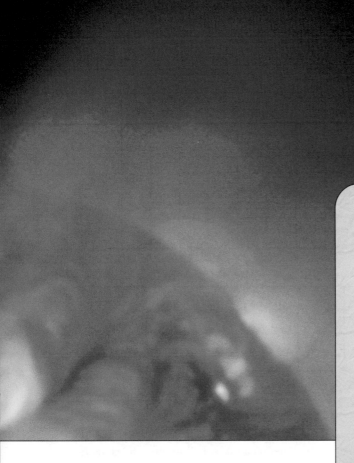

LEARNING OBJECTIVES

When you have studied this chapter you should be able to

- Understand the basic structure of a nucleus and nucleons.
- Identify the fundamental forces involved in forming a stable nucleus and describe how they influence nucleon mass.
- Work through the experimental data and reasoning process that lead to our current understanding of nuclear forces and structure.
- Describe the processes of fission and fusion.
- Describe how the two forces operating inside the nucleus interact to produce nuclear energy levels.
- Describe why only certain nuclei are stable, and how unstable nuclei decay.
- Understand the role of mass-energy conservation, as well as the other conservation laws, in nuclear processes.
- Understand the probabilistic nature of nuclear decay.

sons Rutherford was so astonished to discover that all of the positive charge was concentrated in a small positive nucleus was that up until that point scientists only knew of two fundamental forces: gravitational forces and electromagnetic forces. The existence of a small positive nucleus meant that there had to be some previously unknown force, stronger than the electric repulsion of like-charges, holding the nucleus together. No one had observed any evidence of the force until the discovery of the nucleus, so its effects had to be extremely short range—confined to the nucleus, in fact. Therefore, in a burst of creativity, this strong force whose range only extends to the nucleus was dubbed the "Nuclear Strong Force."

The discovery of something truly new in science is extremely rare and exciting, and many scientists began working on determining the behavior of the nucleus and its forces. Scientists studying the atom and those studying the nucleus worked during the same time period. However, the nuclear scientists were at a distinct disadvantage, compared to the atomic scientists. Atomic scientists were trying to determine the behavior of a single particle (electrons) under the influence of a single, well-understood force (the electromagnetic force), and successfully developed the quantum model of the atom to

help them advance their research. Nuclear scientists were faced with the challenge of describing two different particles (protons and neutrons) under the influence of two forces (the strong and electromagnetic), one of which was newly discovered and not at all understood. Needless to say, they haven't made much headway in this complex area, compared to what has been done in atomic research. Nuclear scientists haven't yet worked out the equation for the strong force, so to date no one has developed a model of the nucleus that allows the calculation of nuclear energy levels in the same way that we can accurately calculate electron energies using the quantum model of the atom.

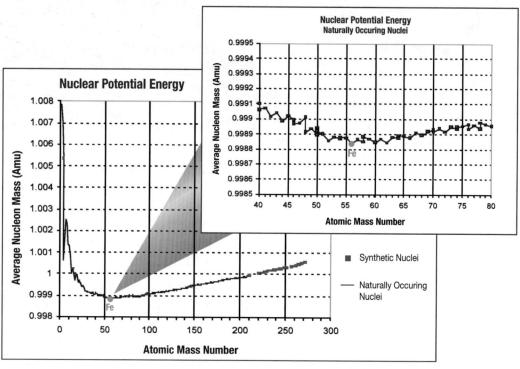

Nuclear Potential Energy

Figure 25.1

Graph of average nuclear mass versus atomic mass number. The graph is based on isotope masses from the National Institute of Standards and Technology (http://physics.nist.gov) .

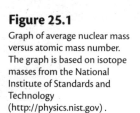

• **Nuclear Strong Force Law**

F = ?

Scientists are still trying to figure out what the equation for the strong force looks like. Compare this with the Electric Force Law equation: $F = kqQ/d^2$. The electromagnetic force pushes the protons in the nucleus apart.

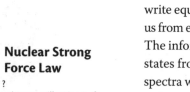

• **Amu**

The abbreviation for atomic mass unit. One atomic mass unit = 1.660559×10^{-27}kg. This is the average mass of the protons and neutrons in a 12C atom. Because protons and neutrons are so small, it is more convenient to measure their mass in units of comparable size.

The fact that scientists are not yet able to write equations for energy states doesn't prevent us from experimentally measuring those energies. The information gleaned about electron energy states from measurements of discrete emission spectra was important in the development of the Bohr and quantum models of the atom. Similarly, we have been able to figure out quite a bit about both the strong force and the energy levels in nuclei by experimentally measuring how tightly bound nucleons are in different nuclei. While scientists can and have measured energy levels in nuclei by exciting the protons and neutron, doing so is difficult. There is an extremely large amount of energy separating one energy level from the next, so it requires huge amounts of energy to excite a nucleon to a higher energy level to produce a nuclear emission spectrum. It turns out that the easiest way to measure nuclear energies is by measuring the mass of the nuclei.

In our discussion of energy in Chapter 9–5, it was shown how mass and energy are related by the equation $E=mc^2$. Just as *increasing* the energy of an object increases its mass, *decreasing* the energy decreases the mass. The mass changes associated with changes in electrical or gravitational potential energy are not large enough to be detected, but the strong nuclear force is large enough to allow measurement of the changes in mass associated with changes in nuclear potential energy. A proton by itself has

a mass of 1.007276 **amu**. A neutron has a mass of 1.008665 amu. A helium nucleus is made of two protons and two neutrons which have a combined mass of 4.031882 amu. However, the actual mass of a helium nucleus is 4.0022603 amu. This means that protons and neutrons held together in a helium atom have about 0.7% less mass than unbound protons and neutrons. Breaking the nucleus apart would need the addition of enough energy to increase their combined mass to the unbound level.

In *Figure 25.1*, the average mass of protons and neutrons in a nucleus is plotted versus the total mass number for all naturally occurring nuclei. Charting out atomic behaviors lead the development of the periodic table and provided a foundation for the understanding of the structure of atoms. Similarly looking at the trends in nuclear mass has provided a lot of information about nuclear structure.

One careful look at the graph should make three facts immediately obvious.

Overall shape: The average mass of nucleons initially decreases and then increases again. Nucleons have the least amount of mass in iron atoms. This tells us that the strong force reaches its maximum range at a distance about the same size as an iron atom's nucleus. How do you know the strong force reaches its limit at this size?

Abrupt end: The graph ends fairly abruptly. There are no naturally occurring nuclei with mass numbers larger than 238, and no nuclei at all with masses larger than 281. This tells us that when enough protons are gathered together, the increase in the size of electromagnetic repulsion couples with the limited range of the strong force, allowing the electromagnetic force to exceed the strong force.

Multiple stable isotopes: There are several dots illustrated in the chart, rather than just one above many of the atomic mass numbers. This happens because mass number is the total number of protons and neutrons, and there are several different combinations of protons and neutrons that will provide the same total. For example, nuclei consisting of three protons, two protons and one neutron, one proton and two neutrons, and three neutrons all would have a mass number of 3. For each **element** there are several possible numbers of neutrons. Each different mass number for an element is a different **isotope** of the element. Returning to the example above, in nature we find only two, not four, nuclei with a mass number of 3. Combinations of three protons or three neutrons don't occur. The fact that only some nuclei naturally occur turns out to be quite important in an overall understanding of this subject. The circumstances that limit the number of stable isotopes of nuclei will be discussed later.

25-2 FUSION AND FISSION

Nuclear energy is of course one of the most widely recognized applications of our present understanding of the behavior of the nucleus. Protons and neutrons have less mass in the nuclei of medium-sized atoms than they do in either very small or very large atoms. Mass can be turned into energy, according to the equation $E=mc^2$. This means that if you either combine the smallest nuclei to make a larger nucleus or split the largest nuclei to make smaller ones, the mass that the protons and neutrons lose will be turned into energy.

Fusion

The largest nucleon masses are found in the smallest atoms, and the mass drops off very quickly. (This makes sense because nuclear potential energy, and hence mass, is lost when

the strong force binds nucleons together.) The biggest changes in nucleon mass happen, and the most energy is released, if isotopes of hydrogen that have one or two neutrons are combined to make helium.

There is just one problem with this. The strong force is extremely short range. The electromagnetic force is long range. In order to get the nuclei of two small atoms close enough for the strong force to pull them together, a way must be devised to overcome the electromagnetic repulsion that is keeping the two small atoms apart.

There are several ways to make **fusion** work (*Figure 25.2*). One method is to find an attractive force larger than the electromagnetic repulsion. There are only four forces. The strong and weak are short range and the electric force is repulsive, which leaves gravity. The gravitational force is attractive, but gravity is the weakest of the four forces. In order to have a gravitational force large enough to overcome the electromagnetic repulsion, a huge amount of mass must be gathered. Stars are lumps of hydrogen gas with enough mass to overcome the electromagnetic repulsion and fuse hydrogen nuclei together to make helium. Obviously, this works well in nature, and solar energy is really nuclear power, but it would not be practical for humans to try to copy this particular fusion reactor design.

A second way to make fusion work is simply to sufficiently increase the speed of the atoms. This works almost exactly the same way that energy influences chemical reaction rates. If the atoms have enough speed to start with, the electric force will only slow them down, rather than stop them, before they get close enough for the strong force to take over. Just like the roller-

• **Element**

An element is determined by the number of protons, the atomic number.

• **Isotope**

An isotope is determined by the number of neutrons: the atomic mass number minus the atomic number.

• **Fusion**

A nuclear reaction in which nuclei combine to form more massive nuclei with the simultaneous release of energy.

Typical fusion reactions:
$^2H + {}^3H \rightarrow {}^4He + neutron$
$^2H + {}^2H \rightarrow {}^4He$
$^2H + {}^2H \rightarrow {}^3He + neutron$

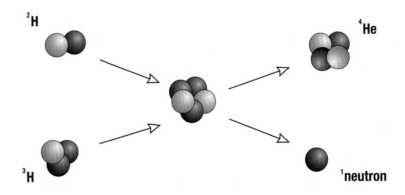

Figure 25.2
The fusion reaction: $^2H + {}^3H \rightarrow {}^4He + neutron$. Note that the total number of protons and neutrons doesn't change.

If you're not moving fast enough here

You won't make it over the hill here...

...and so you won't get rid of all remaining gravitational potential energy and finish the ride

Figure 25.3

For a rollercoaster to get back to its starting position, it needs to move fast enough to make it out of the valley and over the hill. Atoms need to be moving fast enough to overcome the electric force before they can fuse.

• **Fission**

A nuclear reaction in which an atomic nucleus, especially a heavy nucleus such as an isotope of uranium, splits into two fragments of comparable mass, releasing energy.

Typical fission reactions:

$^{235}U + {}^1neutron \rightarrow {}^{140}Xe + {}^{94}Sr + 2\,{}^1neutron$
$^{235}U + {}^1neutron \rightarrow {}^{138}I + {}^{95}Y + 3\,{}^1neutron$

• **Critical Mass**

The minimum amount of material necessary for each fission to result in one additional fission.

• **Chain Reaction**

A chain reaction is one that is self sustaining or increasing once it has started. Dominoes knocking each other over is a classic example of a chain reaction.

coaster in the photo, if the nuclei are moving fast enough to make it over the electromagnetic hill, they'll release a lot of energy (see *Figure 25.3*).

Kinetic energy of atoms corresponds to heat, so fusion can be made to happen simply by heating the atoms. Unfortunately, this seemingly simple plan requires temperatures of several million degrees. It is difficult to maintain and control material at temperatures this hot. Several countries have developed working fusion devices that achieve the necessary temperatures for a very short period of time, releasing extremely large amounts of fusion energy all at once. (The name for such a device is "hydrogen bomb.") However, no one has come up with a way of sustaining fusion temperatures in a controlled way that doesn't require more energy than the fusion produces. To date there are no fusion reactors that produce more energy than they use.

Fission

The other way to release nuclear energy is to start with very large atoms and split them into smaller atoms. With **fission**, all of the problems with fusion work in our favor. The electric repulsion between protons is helping to split the nucleus apart, and the largest atoms have larger nucleon masses as well as the biggest electric repulsion. The short range of the strong force limits its size, allowing the electric repulsion to eventually catch up with the strong force as nuclei get larger. The maximum size of a nucleus is determined by the point where the two forces are equal.

In the largest naturally occurring nuclei, the electromagnetic force is nearly as large as the strong force. Only a small amount of additional energy is needed in order to break the nucleus apart. Once again it's like that roller coaster, but in this case its sitting stopped in a very shallow dip high on the track, just waiting for any little push to get it moving. When the nucleus is given the necessary energy it will split into two pieces of approximately equal size, plus a few extra neutrons (*Figure 25.4*).

In a nuclear power plant operation, the energy needed to split the nucleus is provided by a free, slow-moving neutron released by a previous fission. When the nucleus of a fuel atom, typically uranium, absorbs the neutron, the neutron's mass decreases, the lost mass is turned into energy, and the energy is enough to destabilize the uranium atom, splitting it and releasing more neutrons that can be absorbed by other atoms. This makes the reaction self-sustaining as long as at least one neutron from each fission is absorbed by another uranium atom, making it split. When enough atoms are close enough together and configured so that on average each fission triggers one more fission, the result is the **critical mass** for a **chain reaction**.

The reaction can be slowed down by allowing inert material to absorb more of the released neutrons. It will speed up if more than one neutron is hitting another uranium atom. This allows control of the amount of energy being released simply by changing the ratio of fuel to inert material present inside the reactor.

While the fission process used in nuclear reactions is fairly easy to control, there is one significant problem. Comparison of the atomic masses of the byproducts of fission with the

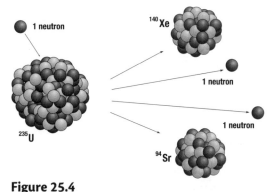

1 neutron

^{140}Xe

1 neutron

1 neutron

^{235}U

^{94}Sr

Figure 25.4

A fission reaction. A uranium atom absorbs a neutron and splits into 2 medium-sized atoms and some free neutrons. Note that the total number of nucleons remains the same.

atomic masses found on the periodic table will show that the fission byproducts have substantially larger masses than the masses that occur in nature. This fact brings us back to two unanswered questions from our graph of nucleon masses.

1. Why don't all possible combinations of protons and neutrons occur naturally?

2. What happens if a nucleus that doesn't occur naturally is made?

25-3 UNSTABLE NUCLEI AND RADIOACTIVE DECAY

In science there is typically one answer as to why something that looks like it should be possible doesn't happen. One of the consequences of the Second Law of Thermodynamics is that everything in nature tends to occupy the lowest available energy state. Any time something doesn't occur naturally, it is usually because there are lower available energy configurations. In chemical reactions, electrons drop into the lowest available orbital. Protons and neutrons in a nucleus behave the same way inside the nucleus. If there are any possible configurations of the nucleons that are lower in energy, the nucleus will tend to change so that it is in the lower-energy state, as long as it can get there without violating any fundamental laws.

Any process that changes a nucleus from a high-energy state to a lower-energy state is called **radioactive decay**. The changes in nuclei typically involve emitting photons and charged particles, and the original parent nucleus turns into a daughter nucleus with less mass. Because the nuclear force is so large, the emitted particles typically have extremely high energies and can cause damage to anything they hit. It is these emitted particles that make radioactive decay so dangerous.

The short answer to both the questions posed in the previous section is that only the lowest-energy configurations of protons and neutrons occur naturally. If a researcher happens to make a nucleus that wouldn't normally exist, it will decay, emitting energetic particles, and change into something that is lower in energy and hence more stable. There are several distinct ways that atoms can change.

Spontaneous fission and alpha decay

As we discussed above, one very large atom has more energy than the same number of protons and neutrons in two medium-sized atoms, so big atoms can undergo fission and split into two medium-sized atoms. Returning to the roller coaster analogy, if nuclei really behaved like parked roller coasters, nuclei would never split unless they were given enough energy to push them out of the dips they're sitting in. Unlike the stalled roller coaster, however, nucleons exhibit wave behavior. If a roller coaster gets stuck in a valley, it's obvious to all observers that it is really in the valley. If a small particle like a proton or neutron is placed in a "strong force hole" the locations of the protons and neutrons are not certain. While it is most probable that they will be found somewhere in the "hole," there is a small but real probability that a person looking for them can find groups of protons and neutrons far enough away from the nucleus that they are effectively out of the hole. There is a small probability that a nucleus will split by itself as long as charge and mass-energy are conserved in the process.

The probability of finding a group of atoms outside of the range of the strong force depends on the size of the group and the mass-energy of the group. Groups of atoms with the lowest energies (masses) are most likely to be found together outside of the range of the strong force. Medium-sized atoms have the lowest overall energies, so large atoms will occasionally undergo spontaneous fission, splitting without absorbing a free neutron. However, the odds are small that 100 or so protons and neutrons could be located together outside the nucleus, so spontaneous fission is fairly rare.*

Referring back to the graph showing nucleon masses, there is one small nucleus that has substantially less mass-energy than any of its neighbors. Helium-4 nuclei are particularly

• **Radioactive Decay**
Spontaneous disintegration of a radionuclide accompanied by the emission of ionizing radiation in the form of alpha or beta particles or gamma rays.

---

* Nuclear bombs count on spontaneous fission as their trigger. The uranium or plutonium is kept in segments that are far enough apart that the free neutrons from a spontaneous fission are very unlikely to be absorbed by other fuel atoms, and a chain reaction is impossible. When the bomb is detonated, the segments are pushed together. Neutrons released by any subsequent spontaneous fission will trigger more fissions in a runaway chain reaction.

ALPHA PARTICLES AND SMOKE DETECTORS

Because alpha particles have a large charge, they can't travel very far through matter before they steal a few electrons, lose their energy, and become normal helium atoms. This is the technology behind most smoke detectors. A tiny sample of americium emits alpha particles. These particles travel through the air and hit an electrode where they combine with electrons from a battery, causing a small current. As long as there is a current, all is well.

However, if there is smoke in the room, the alpha particles absorb electrons from the smoke, the current stops and an alarm sounds.

• **Alpha Decay**

The radioactive decay of an atomic nucleus by emission of an alpha particle.

Two alpha decays:
$^{226}Ra \rightarrow + ^{222}Rn + ^{4}He$
$^{238}U \rightarrow + ^{236}Th + ^{4}He$

stable. The odds of finding two protons and neutrons together fairly far from the nucleus is relatively high. As long as the total mass of the original nucleus is greater than the mass of the helium nucleus plus the mass of the nucleus made of the remaining protons and neutrons, energy will be released that will enable the helium nucleus to escape permanently. Any nucleus larger than Bi-209 has enough mass-energy to emit helium nuclei. This is why very few nuclei larger than bismuth occur naturally.

Helium nuclei are relatively large and highly charged, so they are easy to detect. This was the first radioactive decay process discovered and was called **alpha decay** for the first letter in the Greek alphabet.

Beta decay

We now know why large atoms aren't found naturally, but further explanation is needed to answer the question of why only certain specific isotopes occur. The answer to this question led to the discovery of the weak nuclear force and

our modern understanding of the fundamental particles that make up matter.

A quick glance at the periodic table shows that stable isotopes of atoms with small atomic numbers have about the same number of protons and neutrons, but this changes as atomic numbers increase. Medium-sized atoms have a few more neutrons than protons and large nuclei have substantially more neutrons than protons (see *Table 25.1*)

Earlier in this chapter we learned that protons and neutrons within the nucleus behave similarly to electrons, and each type of particle will fill up separate energy wells. If only the strong force, which is the same for protons and neutrons, is considered, you would expect the energy wells to be identically shaped. When the electromagnetic force is taken into account, you would expect that the energy levels for protons would be pushed higher. As the number of protons increases so does the electromagnetic force pushing them apart. Therefore, the proton energy levels (when there are many protons) should be substantially higher than the energy levels for a comparable number of neutrons.

The pattern we see for the numbers of protons and neutrons in stable atoms only makes sense if there is a rule in nature that requires proton and neutron energy wells to be full to approximately the same level. Then in small nuclei, while the electromagnetic force between protons is small, the difference between the energy wells is not large enough so that there are any extra neutron energy levels below the corresponding proton levels, and atoms will have the same number of protons and neutrons.

Table 25.1 – Neutrons and Protons in Stable Atoms

Atom	Atomic Number	Atomic Mass Number	Number of Protons/Neutrons
O	8	16	8/8
Fe	26	56	26/30
U	92	238	92/146

THE STANDARD MODEL

Our current understanding of matter is that the fundamental building blocks of normal matter are two types of quarks (up and down) and two types of electron-like particles (electrons and neutrinos), collectively called leptons (from the Greek for light). Quarks combine in groups of three to make protons and neutrons. For each of these fundamental particles there is a matching antimatter particle that has exactly the same mass, but all other characteristics, like charge, are completely opposite. If a matter particle comes together with its antimatter counterpart, they will "cancel out" and their combined mass will be converted into energy. Similarly, when energy turns into mass, it always produces a particle-antiparticle pair.

In addition to normal matter, there are types of unstable, exotic matter made up of two more massive quarks, (strange and charm) and two more leptons (muons and mu-neutrinos). There is also a third pair of quarks (top and bottom) and a third pair of leptons (tauons and tau-neutrinos). These heavier particles tend to rapidly decay into their lighter, normal matter counterparts. While a few of these particles occur naturally (muons, for example, are produced in the Earth's atmosphere), matter made of these heavier particles is typically created from energy released in collisions in particle accelerators.

Each of the four fundamental forces are related to a specific characteristic of matter. Each force is conveyed between the two objects involved in the interaction by the exchange of small particles called "bosons."

- Gravitational force depends on mass. It occurs because of the exchange of particles called "gravitons." Because there is only one type of mass, the gravitational force is always attractive.
- Electromagnetic force depends on charge. It acts because of the exchange of photons. There are two types of charge, positive and negative. The electromagnetic force can be either attractive or repulsive.
- The strong force is the force that causes quarks to combine in groups of three. It acts because of the exchange of gluons. Because quarks combine in groups of three, there must be three different types of "strong force charge." This characteristic is called "color charge" because it is somewhat analogous to the three primary colors. The nuclear strong force is actually a residual effect similar to an electric contact force. When two nucleons get so close together that the quarks that make up the first nucleon are nearly as strongly affected by the quarks that make up the second nucleon as they are by each other, they will attract each other. This is why the nuclear strong force is so short range.
- The weak nuclear force allows one type of quark or lepton to turn into another type. Charge is typically transferred when the type of particle changes, so this force is currently thought to be closely related to (if it isn't just another manifestation of) electromagnetic force. Theoreticians are currently trying to find a single set of equations that combines both effects.

For more information see: http://www.pbs.org/wgbh/nova/elegant/part-nf.html

Figure 25.5
Calvin and Hobbes
(reprinted with permission of Andrews and McMeel, a Universal Press Syndicate Company)

With medium-sized atoms the difference is large enough so that most atoms will need a few more neutrons than protons in order to fill the energy wells to the same energies. In large atoms the electric force is larger, pushing the proton energy levels much higher than the energies for the corresponding number of neutrons. In order to fill the energy wells up to the same energy, there will be a lot more full neutron levels.

Spontaneous fission occurs naturally and produces medium-sized nuclei with far more neutrons than protons. None of these nuclei are found in nature so there has to be a way for a neutron to change into a proton to fill empty, lower-energy proton levels and vice versa. Processes that change neutrons into protons or protons into neutrons are known as **beta decay**. Note the following:

- The fact that protons and neutrons can change into one another is important evidence showing that they are made of smaller particles.

- There must be some previously unidentified force that causes the particles to change. This force is called the weak nuclear force.

- Charge must be conserved, so a reaction that changes a neutron into a proton must also either absorb a positively charged particle or produce a negatively charged particle. Likewise, a reaction that turns a proton into a neutron must either absorb a negatively charged particle or produce a positively charged particle.

Since the lowest-mass charged particles are matter and anti-matter electrons, beta decay involves emitting and absorbing electrons and positrons. In order for a nucleus to produce an electron or a positron during beta decay, the difference in mass-energy between the old and new nucleus must be large enough to provide the mass of the extra particle. This limits the number of nuclei that can decay by either of these two processes.

The electron-capture process doesn't require any minimum difference in energy because it relies on absorbing an electron that is already there. However, the probability of finding an electron, even an atom's 1s electrons, within the bounds of the nucleus is extremely small. If the probability of having an electron in the nucleus where it could be absorbed is small, there is also a very low probability of such atoms decaying in any given time period. So nuclei that are only slightly higher in energy than the minimum energy for that mass number are typically stable.

Gamma decay

Just as collisions and chemical reactions can excite electrons into higher energy levels, extremely high-energy collisions and nuclear-decay processes can excite protons and neutrons into high-energy levels. Any time protons and neutrons shift from one energy level to a lower level, a photon of light is emitted just as it is when electrons change energy levels. These photons have extremely high energies and are called gamma rays.

25–4 RADIOMETRIC DATING

Decay processes depend on the wave behavior of the nucleons, so they are probabilistic in nature. With the double-slit experiments using photons and electrons it was impossible to predict where any one particle would hit the screen. With nuclei it is impossible to predict whether or not any one nucleus will decay. The researcher can only determine the odds that the nucleus will decay within a given time period.

However, when a large number of electrons or photons passed through a pair of slits they would always produce an interference pattern with the same shape. Similarly, a large group of a specific type of radioactive nuclei will always follow the same pattern as they decay.

To determine the decay pattern of a particular radioactive isotope, a large sample of the isotope is monitored for an extended period of time, several days or even a couple of weeks. The number of decay particles (helium nuclei, electrons, positrons, or photons) emitted by the sample is measured. By knowing what fraction of the nuclei decayed over the known measurement period, the researcher can predict what fraction of any large sample of the same material would decay in any given time period.

Decay rates are typically measured in terms of **half-life**. One half-life is the time it takes for 1/2 of all the nuclei in a large sample of that radioactive isotope to decay. As long as there is a reasonably large number of atoms left, in each half-life, half of the remaining radioactive nuclei will decay.

Radioactive nuclei decay at a fixed rate, so radioactive isotopes can be used as a clock. If it is known how many particles a sample started with, and a measurement is made of how many are left, the number of half-lives that have passed can be calculated. Multiplying the number of half-lives by the length of the half-life allows the researcher to determine how much time has gone by since the initial measurement was made. In other words, radioactive decay can be used to measure how much time has passed, as long as you know starting and ending amounts of radioactive material.

Many radioactive clocks run slowly, so they are particularly well suited to measuring geologic processes. In the next chapter you will see exactly how this and other tools have been used to determine time scales for events in the Earth's past.

Chapter Framework

A. Nuclear Forces and Energy
1. Nuclear Strong Force Law
2. Elements and Isotopes

B. Fusion and Fission
1. Critical Mass
2. Chain Reaction

C. Unstable Nuclei and Radioactive Decay
1. Spontaneous Fission and Alpha Decay
2. Beta Decay
3. Gamma Decay

D. Radiometric Dating

Comprehension

True/ False
1. _____ The strong force between two protons is always stronger than the electric repulsion between two protons.
2. _____ The electromagnetic force extends over a longer distance than the strong nuclear force.
3. _____ Charge is always conserved in any nuclear process.
4. _____ Mass changes in nuclear processes.
5. _____ If two large nuclei were to combine, the process would release energy.

Fill in the Blank
1. Protons and neutrons bound in a nucleus have _____ mass than free protons and neutrons.
2. Oxygen-15, oxygen-16, and oxygen-18 are 3 different _____ of the element oxygen.
3. When an unstable isotope changes into a more stable daughter nucleus and releases energetic particles, the process is called _____ _____.
4. When two nuclei combine to make a larger one, the process is called _____.
5. When a large nucleus splits into two nearly equal parts, the process is called _____.
6. A group of atoms that all have the same number of protons is called an _____.

a. Alpha decay
b. Fission
c. Chain reaction
d. Critical mass
e. Beta decay
f. Fusion
g. Gamma decay
h. Half-life

Matching
1. _____ The minimum amount of mass necessary for one fission to trigger another.
2. _____ A nucleus changes one of its protons into a neutron, or one of its neutrons into a proton.
3. _____ A uranium atom splits into thorium and helium.
4. _____ A nucleon jumps from a high energy level to a lower one and emits a photon
5. _____ Two hydrogen atoms combine to make a helium atom.
6. _____ A uranium atom splits into xenon and strontium plus a few neutrons.

7. _____ The amount of time required for 1/2 of the remaining radioactive nuclei to decay.
8. _____ A process where one event always triggers one or more additional events.

Analysis

1. In which of the following nuclear reactions is total charge conserved?

   a) $^{198}_{79}Au \rightarrow ^{198}_{80}Hg + ^{0}_{+1}positron + ^{0}_{0}neutrino$

   b) $^{60}_{27}Co \rightarrow ^{60}_{26}Fe + ^{0}_{-1}electron + ^{0}_{0}neutrino$

   c) $^{212}_{84}Po \rightarrow ^{208}_{82}Pb + ^{4}_{2}He$

   d) $^{198}_{80}Hg + ^{0}_{-1}electron \rightarrow ^{198}_{80}Hg + ^{0}_{0}gamma\ ray$

   e) $^{11}_{6}C \rightarrow ^{11}_{5}B + ^{0}_{-1}electron + ^{0}_{0}neutrino$

2. Carbon-14 is a radioactive isotope of carbon. Nitrogen-14 is naturally occurring. If you compare the two, what would you expect to find?

   a) A C-14 nucleus has more mass.

   b) An N-14 nucleus has more mass.

   c) The masses of the two are equal.

3. Which of the following nuclear reactions has a proton changed into a neutron?

   a) $^{198}_{79}Au \rightarrow ^{198}_{80}Hg + ^{0}_{-1}electron + ^{0}_{0}neutrino$

   b) $^{212}_{84}Po \rightarrow ^{208}_{82}Pb + ^{4}_{2}He$

   c) $^{198}_{80}Hg \rightarrow ^{198}_{80}Hg + ^{0}_{0}gamma\ ray$

   d) $^{11}_{6}C \rightarrow ^{11}_{5}B + ^{0}_{+1}positron + ^{0}_{0}neutrino$

4. Which of the following is true regarding forces in nuclei?

   a) The electromagnetic force is weaker than the strong force, and therefore has no important effects that need to be taken into account in studying nuclei or nuclear energy.

   b) The electromagnetic force, though weaker than the strong force, helps to bind nucleons together into nuclei.

   c) The electromagnetic force acts as a disruptive force in large nuclei, creating repulsions which help in fission.

   d) The electromagnetic force, although disruptive at long range, is attractive at short range and helps keep small nuclei together.

   e) The strong force is short-range, and therefore of no major importance in nuclear energy considerations. The electromagnetic force, on the other hand, is very important in fission and fusion reactions.

5. Which of the following would be the best fuel for a fission reaction?

   a) Hydrogen

   b) Iron

   c) Plutonium

6. Which of the following is the biggest problem with using fusion as a source of energy?

    a) The scarcity of fuel (deuterium).

    b) The danger of long-lived radioactive wastes.

    c) The danger of a runaway reaction.

    d) Overcoming the electromagnetic repulsion of particles with like charges.

    e) The scarcity of suitable material for control rods.

Synthesis

1. Uranium has an atomic number of 92. If a uranium atom emits a helium nucleus, what will the atomic number of the daughter nucleus be? What element is that?

2. If you were to combine two carbon-12 atoms in a fusion process, what element would you get? Would this process absorb or release energy?

3. Oxygen-15 is a radioactive nucleus commonly used as a medical dye. Why isn't Oxygen-15 stable? How is it likely to decay?

4. In a fission reaction, Uranium-235 absorbs a neutron and splits into Barium-144, 3 neutrons, and another atom. Use conservation of mass-number and conservation of charge to figure out what that other atom must be.

5. Iodine-123 is often used in medical scans. It has a half life of 13 hours. Approximately what percent of the total amount is left one day after you receive a scan?

6. Explain what evidence led scientists to the conclusion that there were two additional forces, a nuclear strong and weak force, responsible for nuclear processes.

7. Explain how scientists arrived at the conclusion that the strong force is short range.

8. Explain how both splitting atoms apart (fission) and putting atoms together (fusion) can release energy.

9. Why do only certain isotopes occur naturally?

10. Why are there no elements with atomic numbers much larger than 100?

11. What are some of the drawbacks and advantages of fission and fusion as sources of energy? Why is fusion generally considered a preferable potential energy source? Since fusion is preferred, why are all commercial nuclear power plants using energy from fission?

12. Describe the process of beta decay. What roles do conservation of charge and mass-energy play in beta-decay?

CHAPTER 26

GEOLOGIC TIME

"But first, what is a day?

It is a specified time period; it is an eon, a division of eternity; it is the time between two identifiable events. And each day, of whatever length, has the duration needed for its purposes. . . . There is no revealed recitation specifying that each of the 'six days' involved in the Creation was of the same duration. . . . It seems clear that the 'six days' are one continuing period and that there is no one place where the dividing lines between successive events must of necessity be placed."

~ Bruce R. McConkie

When scientists speak of the time since the formation of Earth or of the universe, they often describe it as "deep time." It is deep time because the span of time is enormous—almost incomprehensible. Understanding, visualizing, and conceptualizing the whole idea of deep time is one of the most difficult things to learn. Our own lives seem to be a long period of time to us. Our own grandparents and great grandparents appear to have lived in a different age, a time beyond our reckoning.

The ancient Greeks and Sumerians lived in a time so very distant, so remote, that it is difficult to relate to them. Looking even farther back in the history of mankind, it is difficult for many of us to think of the people of the Stone Age as even being human, because they existed so long ago, in such a different world. Yet the entire span of man's time, from when the first members of our species sat around, marveling at fire, until the present day, as we sit around, marveling at flat-screen televisions, is just a brief moment in the long span of Earth's history.

Our best estimate of Earth's age at present is 4.6 billion years. If you made a movie of the Earth's history and viewed one year of this history every second, how long would it take to see the entire movie? If you didn't pause to go out for popcorn, and kept watching 24 hours a day, you would be able to view all Earth's history in just over 145 years!

The 4,000 years of written history, from its beginnings in the "fertile crescent" of Mesopotamia, all the way down to the present day, would take up only about the last hour of this 145 year-long movie. One hour for all of human history on Earth! Because of this great expanse of time, the record of early Earth history is difficult to read. It is like an ancient manuscript written in a different language, with most of the pages damaged or missing.

To the credit of many persevering scientists, some of this early history has been deciphered, but there is still much to learn. The last one billion years (1,000,000,000) of Earth's history can be read and understood more clearly than the first 3.6 billion years. Over this last billion years, fewer of Earth's rocky pages are missing and the language seems more familiar. We find in the rocks signs and structures that are similar to features we find forming in rocks today.

LEARNING OBJECTIVES

- Understand what uniformitarianism means
- Learn the techniques used by scientists to determine the relative ages of events in Earth's history:
    - Original horizontality
    - Superposition
    - Inclusions
    - Cross-cutting relationships
    - Faunal Succession
- Learn how scientists use radioactivity to determine the quantitative or absolute ages of events in Earth's history.
- Gain an understanding of the vastness of geologic time.

26–1 UNDERSTANDING TIME

We cannot understand Earth's history without understanding time, and how time affects the laws of nature. The concept of "time symmetry" has been discussed earlier in this book. Time symmetry is a fundamental scientific assumption. Scientists assume that the passage of time does not affect the laws of nature, but operate in the same way today as they did in the past. Geologists call this concept "**uniformitarianism.**" We apply the principle of time symmetry to the study of our Earth as we learn about its past and hope to predict its future.

One other important principle that helps us interpret past events in Earth's history is **Occam's Razor**. This principle tells us that if more than one explanation is possible, then we should choose the simplest one that satisfies all of the evidence. For example, suppose that you have returned home from school to find that the bed you made earlier is now a mess. You live in an apartment with just one roommate who likes to come home for a brief nap every day. You have the following additional bits of information to

help you determine how the bed became unmade:

- The door was locked when you returned home.
- There is no evidence of any forced entry into the apartment.
- You discover one of your roommate's socks under the sheets in your messed-up bed.
- The sheets from your roommate's bed are in the dryer.
- Your roommate has, at best, a vague conception of personal space.

Now, what is the simplest explanation for the mess? Could it be that aliens beamed into your room while you were out, slept in your bed, placed one of your roommate's socks in your bed

• **Uniformitarianism**

The idea that the laws of nature do not change with time. This idea is also called the principle of "Time Symmetry."

• **Occam's Razor**

The rule that where two or more explanations exist for the same physical phenomenon, we should choose the simplest one that satisfies all of the observations.

• **Relative Time**

The determination of the sequence in which events occurred, relative to each other.

• **Absolute Time**

A numeric or quantitative measure of time.

to deceive you, and left before you came home? Maybe while you were gone a temporary malfunction of your air conditioning system created a blast of air from the vent over your bed and blew the covers around. It could be that there is some undiscovered law of nature that beds made too early in the morning will always mess themselves up before late afternoon. Your roommate may even offer one of those explanations as a plausible solution.

None of those explanations would fit Occam's Razor as the simplest explanation that satisfies all the facts. It is more probable that your roommate came home for a short nap and remembered that the sheets were being washed. Not wanting to nap on a bed without sheets, your roommate took a nap in your bed. Even though alternative explanations may be possible, that does not make them the most plausible or simplest explanation. With distant events in Earth's past history, we do not have the luxury of doing the experiment again, and so we must rely on Occam's Razor to help us choose the best explanation.

With Occam's Razor in mind, let us now look at Earth and see if we can come up with some simple ways to determine the origin and sequence of events that have occurred in the past and are now recorded in the rocks. When we try to place events in their proper sequence, we can either position them in relation to other events, or we can determine a numeric age.

For example, suppose you are setting up a date with a friend. You might say, "Let's get

together after our Physical Science class tomorrow." You might instead say, "Why don't we get together at 12:15 PM tomorrow." In the first example, you have given your friend a relative time frame (get together after class), while in the second example you have given a numeric value (get together at 12:15 PM). Scientists who study past events in the history of Earth use both of these measures of time. The first we call **Relative Time** and the second **Absolute Time** (although a better name might be quantitative or numeric time, because it is really just a good estimate of time, not the exact or absolute time). Both of these measures of time are extremely valuable in understanding the history of our planet.

26–2 RELATIVE TIME

In determining the relative ages of events, we will use simple but very powerful tools called the "Principles of Relative Dating." They all rely heavily on Occam's Razor, and they help us to pick the simplest explanation for a sometimes complex series of events. Five of these principles will be included in our discussion here:

1. Principle of Original Horizontality
2. Principle of Superposition
3. Principle of Inclusions
4. Principle of Cross-cutting Relationships
5. Principle of Faunal Succession

Principle of Original Horizontality

Much of what we can learn about Earth's past comes from sedimentary rocks. Sedimentary rocks form on Earth's surface and they often hold clues—pieces of stone, bones, and other evidence that help us understand past events. We can use time symmetry to observe how and where sedimentary rocks are forming today and apply this knowledge to our study of sedimentary rocks that formed in the past. Our observations of sedimentary rocks today have shown us that these rocks are almost always deposited in layers that are nearly horizontal. This is the Principle of Original Horizontality:

Sedimentary rocks are deposited in horizontal layers.

How can we apply this to understanding events in the geologic past? Let's take an

Figure 26.1
Folded limestones in Rock Canyon near Provo, Utah.

example from the mountains east of Provo, Utah. One of the scenic trails used by local college students and other hikers winds through Rock Canyon. Rock Canyon's walls are composed mostly of layers of sandstone and limestone that are no longer horizontal (*Figure 26.1*).

What must we conclude about the non-horizontal layers of these rocks, if we apply the Principle of Original Horizontality? We must conclude that something happened after the sedimentary layers were deposited that disturbed them and rotated them from their original horizontal position.

"What forces could have done this?" might be the next question we ask. We need to gather more information before coming to a firm conclusion. However, we can confidently identify at least two events and place each event in its correct order. First, the rocks were deposited horizontally. Secondly, they were later tilted so that they are now no longer horizontal. Here we have the beginnings of a geologic history of Rock Canyon.

Principle of Superposition

Observing the formation of sedimentary rocks in modern lakes and ocean basins has also taught us that layering in sedimentary rocks is caused by variations in the sediment that is deposited. Changes in the composition or size of the grains being deposited, or even in the type of cement (binding material) holding the grains together, can create layering.

An experiment in the laboratory, using a "stream table" (*Figure 26.2*), can confirm this observation. A stream table is designed to mimic the actions of a small stream or creek. We make a pile of sand on one end of the table. The sand mixture should include both fine sand and coarse sand. When we spray a strong stream of water over our sand pile, the sand particles are washed down the table and into the transparent basin built into the end of the table. We can then look through the side of the basin to observe the way the fine and course sands were deposited into layers.

This is the same type of sedimentary layering that occurs naturally in oceans and lakes, where fine sand, coarse sand, rocks, and other materials are brought in by streams and rivers. We can also observe that the oldest layers, the

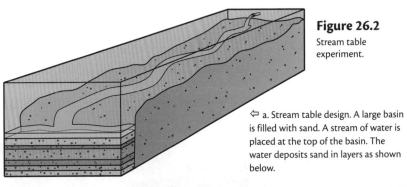

Figure 26.2
Stream table experiment.

⇦ a. Stream table design. A large basin is filled with sand. A stream of water is placed at the top of the basin. The water deposits sand in layers as shown below.

b. Layers created by the stream table.

ones that formed first, are always on the bottom of a stack of layers, and that the layers that were more recently deposited are found closer to Earth's surface.

This is the Principle of Superposition:

In a stack of sedimentary layers, the oldest layer will be on the bottom and the youngest on the top.

In *Figure 26.3*, two prominent sedimentary units in Rock Canyon, a dark brown one and a lighter rusty orange one, are shown. The brown

Figure 26.3
Layers of tan Tintic Quartzite atop brown Mineral Fork Tillite in Rock Canyon near Provo, Utah.

rock unit is called the Mineral Fork Tillite, and the rusty orange unit is called the Tintic Quartzite. Which of these two do you think is the oldest? If you use the principle of superposition, you will choose the brown Mineral Fork Tillite because it is underneath the Tintic Quartzite.

Figure 26.4
Layering within the Tintic Quartzite.

In fact, the Mineral Fork Tillite is, indeed, the older of the two units. If we look closer, we can see that each of these two major units is made up of smaller layers (*Figure 26.4*). Again, the principle of superposition tells us that these layers get progressively older from the top of the stack to the bottom.

Can you think of any reason to be cautious about applying this principle in our study of Earth? How accurate would we be if we applied the Principle of Superposition to our study of a rock formation in which the sedimentary layers had been completely overturned by some later event? This would place the oldest rock layers on top, closest to the surface, and the youngest rocks on the bottom. This does occur in some rock sequences, but other clues within the rock layers tell us which way was originally up. We will not discuss these additional features in this text, but you can find them discussed in any good introductory geology textbook, and you

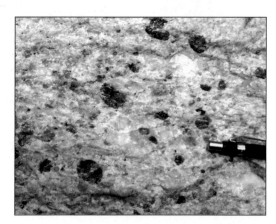

Figure 26.5
Small dark pebbles and white grains of sand can be seen in this close-up of the Tintic Quartzite.

can find many examples of this type of rock layering throughout the Rocky Mountains.

Principle of Inclusions

If you were to carefully examine a piece of the Tintic Quartzite from the outcrops in Rock Canyon, you would easily see that the quartzite is made up of small, rounded grains and pebbles of quartz held together by some kind of natural glue or cementing material (*Figure 26.5*). Where did these pebbles and grains come from? How did they become cemented together? To answer these questions, we must rely on Occam's Razor.

The simplest explanation for their origin is that they came from the places where rounded pebbles and sand grains are found forming today. And where is that? We find them forming along beaches, and in rivers and deserts. But the pebbles and grains of sand in these modern environments are not cemented or glued together: they are just loose sand and gravel, not rock.

However, if we go to the coast of Louisiana or Texas and drill down through soil, loose sand, and gravel, and into solid rock, we will find that the deeper we go into the subsurface, the more solid and better cemented the rocks become. How does this happen?

Cementing happens when loose sediment made up of fine sand and coarser material is saturated with water. The water carries material that precipitates into the grains' pore spaces, gradually binding the grains together. The pebbles and grains of sand that make up the rock, however, are older than the rock itself. They did not grow in the rock, but are tiny inclusions within it. We may not be able to tell where these inclusions came from without further study, but we can be sure that they are older and bring with them an earlier history. This is the Principle of Inclusions:

> **Solid materials (like the pebbles and grains of sand) enclosed within another solid (like the quartzite from Rock Canyon) are older than the rock that encloses them.**

In our brief study thus far of the geology of Rock Canyon, the scientific principles we have used allow us to identify the following events:

1. Deposition of the Mineral Fork Tillite
2. Formation of the sand grains found in the Tintic Quartzite
3. Deposition of the sand grains found in the Tintic Quartzite

Figure 26.6
Fossil ammonites that once lived in a shallow sea near what is now the town of Schliefhausen, Germany, during the Jurassic Period approximately 180 million years ago.

4. Cementing of the sand grains into rock
5. Tilting of the rock layers to their present position

Another example proving the principle of inclusions can be seen in *Figure 26.6*, which shows fossil **ammonites** found in a limestone formation. The fossils must be older than the rock because they are included in it. *Figure 26.7* shows yet another example of this principle. This figure shows dark inclusions in granite found near Yosemite National Park in California. Granite forms from "magma," which is molten rock deep in the Earth that occasionally spurts through volcanoes and other types of cracks in the surface. The dark inclusions are pieces of older rock that were entrapped in the magma before it cooled into the solid granite.

Figure 26.7
Dark inclusions in a lighter gray granite in the Merced River Gorge near Yosemite National Park, California.

Principle of Crosscutting Relationships

We will now wash the fine sand, the coarse sand, and the cooled magma off our hands and sit down at an imaginary dinner table, where a beautiful, but equally imaginary pumpkin pie has just been placed in front of us. Now, for purposes of understanding the next scientific principle, imagine that the pie has been cut into six sections. We all have had experience with pie, so we can easily deduce that someone has cut the pie after it was baked. The marks left by the knife that cut the pie can easily be seen in the otherwise smooth surface of the pie. The same kinds of marks can be found in nature. *Figure*

26.8 shows a small **fault** cutting through the Mineral Fork Tillite and the Tintic Quartzite in Rock Canyon. Sedimentary rock layers form horizontally, and if those horizontal layers are disrupted or cut across by something like a fault, then the fault must have happened after the rock layers were formed. This is the Principle of Crosscutting Relationships:

Rocks are older than the features (such as faults) or rocks that crosscut them.

Let's go back and look more closely at the dark inclusions found in the granites discussed earlier. Figure 26.9 shows a close-up of one of the dark inclusions. Can you see the crack cutting across the dark inclusion and how it has been filled with lighter-colored granite? Now we have two evidences that the darker inclusions are older than the granite. First, the dark inclusions are surrounded by the granite and second, the dark inclusions are crosscut by fractures filled with the granite.

• **Ammonite**
The name given to the fossil-shell remains of animals that lived in the oceans millions of years ago, but are now extinct. They were squid-like animals whose closest modern-day relatives are the nautilus.

Figure 26.8
Small faults (blue) displacing the layering between the Tintic Quartzite and darker Mineral Fork Tillite in Rock Canyon near Provo, Utah.

• **Fault**
A break in the Earth where rocks on one side of the break have slipped past the rocks on the other side. Faults are created by earthquakes.

Figure 26.9
Close-up of dark inclusions in granite shown in Figure 26.7. Note the camera lens cap for scale. In this photo you can see a crack in the dark inclusion (upper right) that is filled with lighter granite. You can also see the "ghosts" of some dark inclusions that have almost been completely assimilated into the granite.

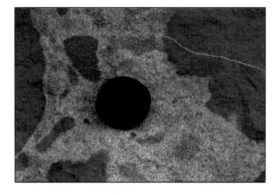

Principle of Faunal Succession

In some landfills and garbage dumps, trash accumulates, layer upon layer, year after year, until the location is completely full. The landfill is then covered over, landscaped, and turned into a golf course or park. Suppose at some later time that you want to study the old landfill-turned-golf course. Perhaps you work for the Environmental Protection Agency (EPA) and need to know where in the landfill toxic materials were dumped, or maybe you are a historian studying the living conditions of the people who lived in that area many years ago. You do not want to uncover the entire landfill in your study, but you need to be sure that in any trench you excavate, you can correlate the layers of garbage you find to layers of the same age in trenches you have dug in other parts of the former landfill.

How can you do this in the most reliable and inexpensive way possible? As you excavate the first trench, you discover that the upper layers include certain kinds of trash that you don't find as you dig deeper. Each of the deeper layers, however, has its own unique kinds of trash.

For example, in the upper layers you find plastic soda bottles and aluminum soda cans that open by pushing a part of the top into the can. As you dig deeper, the pop-top cans are replaced by soda cans that have peel-off tops, and plastic bottles are not as common, but a few twist-top glass soda bottles appear. Even deeper, plastic bottles and aluminum cans disappear altogether and the only kinds of soda containers you find are glass bottles of various sizes that were opened with a bottle opener. In the lowest layers, there are no soda containers at all. In every trench you

• **Trilobites**
A common animal that lived in the Earth's oceans during the Paleozoic Era. They are most closely related to the modern Horseshoe Crab.

Figure 26.11
Fossil trilobite collected from the Wheeler Shale near Delta, Utah.

dig in this landfill, you find this same succession of discarded materials. This allows you to easily determine how each layer of material relates to layers of similar materials found throughout the landfill.

This same kind of layering happens in sedimentary basins, except the material is the remains of animals and plants, called fossils, instead of soda cans and plastic bottles. We know, from other scientific studies over many years, that animals and plants have changed, or evolved, through eons of time, and so we also know that the kinds of fossils that we will find in rock layers will differ, depending on the age of the rock.

Let's look at the rocks in Rock Canyon and find out what fossils they contain. *Figure 26.10* (right) is a geologic map of the Rock Canyon area, showing both the Mineral Fork Tillite and the Tintic Quartzite. The Mineral Fork Tillite does not contain any fossils and the Tintic Quartzite contains only traces of fossil life.

Deposited on top of the Tintic Quartzite are the Ophir Shale and Maxfield Limestone. Within these formations we can find fossil **trilobites** and trilobite fragments (*Figure 26.11*). Trilobites, like pop-top soda cans, changed their shapes through time and therefore, the ones we find imbedded in the Ophir Shale and Maxfield Limestone formations differ in shape from trilobite fossils found in younger layers. It is interesting to note that we do not find trilobites of any kind in sedimentary rock layers that are younger than about 250 million years old.

If we continue up through the sedimentary layers we find that each rock layer has its own unique fossil assemblage. South of Rock Canyon is Slide Canyon (see if you can find this canyon on the geologic map) where we will find the same trilobite fossil types in the same order as they are found a few miles away in Rock Canyon. Even when we go several hundred miles out into western Utah, these same patterns can be found. This is the Principle of Faunal Succession:

Within stacks of sedimentary rocks, there is a predictable pattern of change in the types of fossils the layers contain. The fossils can therefore help us determine the relative age of different layers.

Figure 26.10
Geologic map of the Rock Canyon and Y Mountain areas near Provo, Utah.

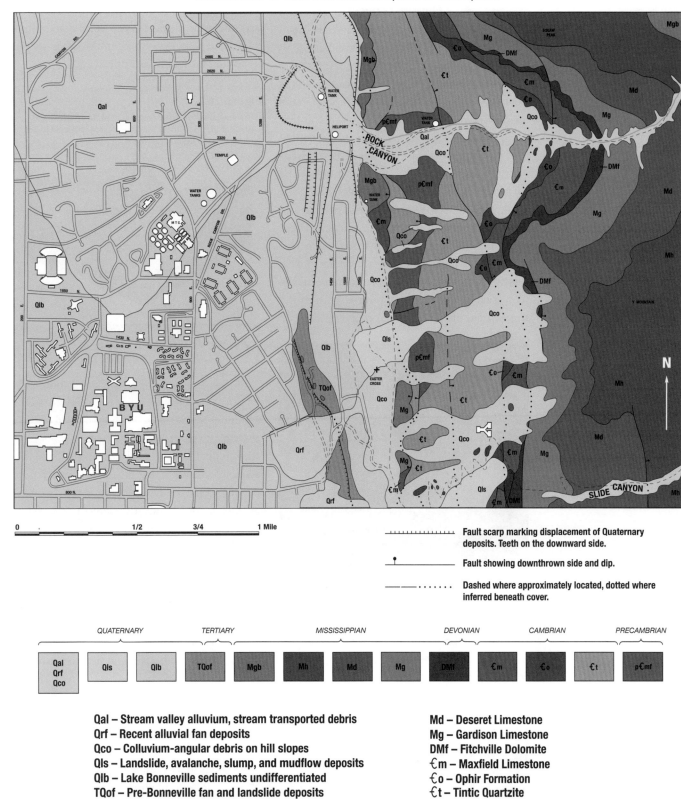

GEOLOGIC MAP OF THE Y MOUNTAIN AREA, EAST OF PROVO, UTAH

Fault scarp marking displacement of Quaternary deposits. Teeth on the downward side.

Fault showing downthrown side and dip.

Dashed where approximately located, dotted where inferred beneath cover.

	QUATERNARY			TERTIARY	MISSISSIPPIAN				DEVONIAN	CAMBRIAN			PRECAMBRIAN
Qal Qrf Qco	Qls	Qlb		TQof	Mgb	Mh	Md	Mg	DMf	€m	€o	€t	p€mf

Qal – Stream valley alluvium, stream transported debris
Qrf – Recent alluvial fan deposits
Qco – Colluvium-angular debris on hill slopes
Qls – Landslide, avalanche, slump, and mudflow deposits
Qlb – Lake Bonneville sediments undifferentiated
TQof – Pre-Bonneville fan and landslide deposits
Mgb – Great Blue Limestone
Mh – Humbug Formation

Md – Deseret Limestone
Mg – Gardison Limestone
DMf – Fitchville Dolomite
€m – Maxfield Limestone
€o – Ophir Formation
€t – Tintic Quartzite
p€mf – Big Cottonwood Formation

26–3 UNCONFORMITIES

One of the challenges in reading Earth's history, as it is recorded in the rocks, is that the record is incomplete. It's a little like trying to make sense of a novel after someone has ripped out every third page. You might still be able to follow the general trend of the story, but you would miss many important details. This is exactly what it is like for scientists trying to read the history of Earth. We find in some places that sedimentation stopped, so nothing was recorded for a particular interval. In other places the sedimentary layers forming many feet below the surface of the ocean were lifted high above sea level, and then erosion or some other natural event destroyed all or part of the layers. These gaps in the geologic record are marked by features we call **unconformities**. In a novel with missing pages, the unconformities would be identified by missing page numbers, or by the frayed remains of a torn out page. In the rock

• **Unconformity**
A break or gap in the geologic record.

Figure 26.12
The "Great Unconformity" in the Grand Canyon between the Cambrian Tapeats Sandstone (top) and the Precambrian Vishnu Schist (deformed, metamorphosed sediments at bottom). Note the finger pointing at the layer of pebbles along the unconformity. These pebbles are pieces of eroded and broken Vishnu schist.

record unconformities are recognized by noticing that certain fossils are missing, or by the worn off edges of rock layers (*Figure 26.12*). It is important to be able to recognize these unconformities so that we know how complete the rock record is at any given location.

26–4 USING THE PRINCIPLES OF RELATIVE TIME

Now that you have been introduced to scientific principles that help us place events in a proper age sequence, let's apply the principles

to a world-famous geological landmark, the Grand Canyon. *Figure 26.13* is a cross-sectional view (a vertical slice) down through the rocks of the Grand Canyon. How many events can you recognize? Can you determine a relative sequence for these events? Can you recognize any unconformities? Do you think that it is possible to explain everything in the cross-section as having formed in just one event?

Figure 26.13
Block diagram showing the rocks that make up the Grand Canyon. To see how these rocks came to be arranged in this way, look at the sequence of events in Figure 26.14.

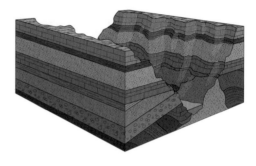

26–5 ABSOLUTE TIME

The simple principles explained above show us how we can determine the relative ages of events in Earth's past fairly easily and without any expensive equipment. However, sometimes we would like to know not just the relative sequence of events, but the times at which those events occurred. The study of absolute time is at the core of our quest to determine a quantitative measure of when events occurred in the geologic past.

Earth's Age

One important event that has always interested scientists is the formation of Earth and the Solar System. How long ago did these events occur? What methods might be used to give us an age for these events?

James Ussher (1581–1656), an Anglican Bishop in Ireland, believed that the days of creation mentioned in the Bible were periods of 24 hours each. He used the Biblical genealogies and chronology to determine that the Earth was created in 4004 BC (a short time later a Biblical scholar at Cambridge, Dr. John Lightfoot, identified the exact time of creation as 9:00 a.m. on October 26 in that same year!) If their calcula-

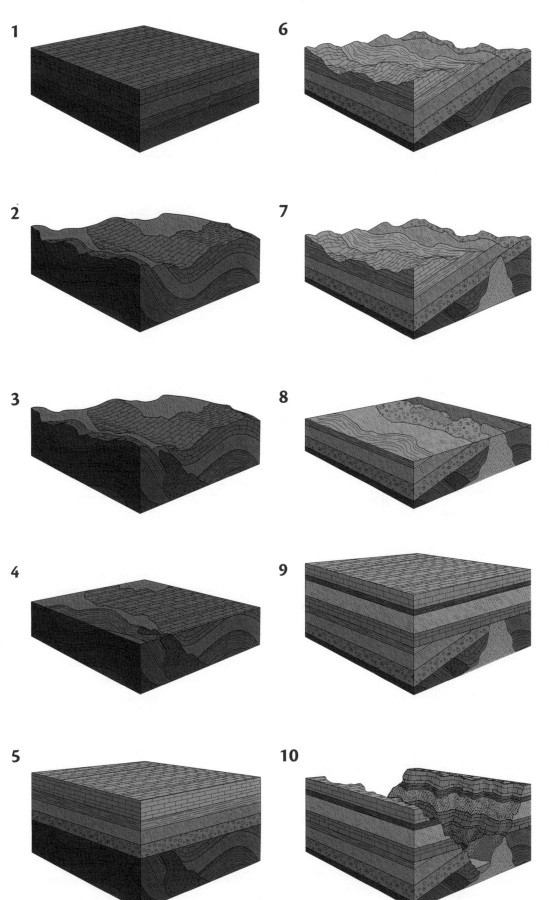

Figure 26.14
Sequence of events that created the Grand Canyon in Arizona.

1–Deposition of layers of sediment (shown in brown shades) in an ocean about 1.8 billion years ago.

2–Folding, metamorphism, and uplift of sediments to create a mountainous region and form the Vishnu Schist from the sediments about 1.7 to 1.6 billion years ago.

3–Intrusion of Zoroaster Granite (red) between 1.6 and 1.4 billion years ago.

4–Erosion of the region back to sea level between 1.4 and 1.2 billion years ago.

5–Deposition of new set of sedimentary layers in an ocean between 1.2 and 1.0 billion years ago. These layers are now called the Grand Canyon Supergroup (shown in green shades).

6–Tilting and uplift of the region creating a new highland or mountainous area about 1billion and 740 million years ago.

7–Intrusion of the Cardenas Basalt (purple) about 1 billion years ago.

8–Erosion of the region back to sea level and formation of the "Great Unconformity" between 740 and 550 million years ago.

9–Deposition of Paleozoic, Mesozoic, and Cenozoic sedimentary rocks (orange shades) between 550 and 20 million years ago.

10–Uplift of the region and cutting of the Grand Canyon by the Colorado River since 20 million years ago to produce the canyon we see today.

tions are correct, the Earth today would be about 6,000 years old.

Even though 6,000 years is a long period in terms of human events and lives, this seemed much too short a period of time since the creation to other people also curious about the actual age of Earth. One of the most prominent of these was James Hutton (1726–1797). He studied the rocks around his home in Scotland, finally coming to a much different conclusion than Usher regarding the actual age of Earth. Hutton proposed the radical idea that the age of Earth was essentially infinite. He stated that he could see "no vestige of a beginning, no prospect of an end."

Attempts to measure the age of Earth were made by a number of scientists and naturalists using the principle of time symmetry (also called "uniformitarianism") discussed at the start of this chapter. Each of these attempts used the rates of current processes to estimate Earth's age. Georges Leclerc, Count of Buffon (1749), calculated the age to be about 100,000 years, based on experiments with the cooling rates of cannonballs. In 1846, Lord Kelvin also used cooling rates for Earth to estimate that the age was somewhere between 10 million and 100 million years old, although he personally favored the lower end of that estimate, between 20–30 million years.

These estimates seemed too young for many researchers who were literally breaking new ground in their studies of the rocks and fossils they found deep under the surface and high on the mountains. By the late 1800s, additional estimates of Earth's age had been produced by calculating the amount of salt that had accumulated in the oceans (about 100 million years) and by estimating the time it would take to deposit all of the accumulated thickness of sedimentary rock layers found around the world (between 3 million and 1,500 million years).

All of these estimates were based on cal-

culations developed from basic ideas which themselves had problems. The cooling age calculated by Lord Kelvin was only accurate if the Earth had no internal sources of heat to keep it warm. We know today that radioactive decay at Earth's core creates considerable heat. The calculation of the saltiness of the ocean did not consider how much salt had precipitated out of the ocean. We now know that a considerable amount of salt has precipitated. Finally, even the thickest piles of sedimentary rocks contain numerous unconformities, so they only represent a portion of the total time that has passed.

A major scientific breakthrough took place in the late 1800s and early 1900s, when the phenomenon of radioactivity was discovered by Henri Bequerel and Pierre and Marie Curie. Although they did not apply their discovery to a study of the age of Earth, other scientists soon did. It was the start of a new age of accurate and reliable estimates for Earth's age and for events that had occurred during Earth's long history.

Radioactivity, which is described in detail in Chapter 25, is the spontaneous decay of unstable nuclei by any of several processes. It takes place at a rate that is unique but constant for each radioactive isotope. As experiment and observation revealed the nature of radioactive decay, it became apparent that it could be used as a geologic clock—a way to measure the age of any rock that contained radioactive isotopes.

Consider the uranium isotope ^{238}U, often written as uranium-238. It is called a **parent isotope** and it decays to a **daughter isotope** that is also radioactive. This isotope then decays to yet another radioactive isotope, and so on through a complex series of alpha and beta decays that finally cause the original uranium-238 to become lead-206, which is a stable isotope, meaning that it undergoes no further decay. The entire ^{238}U to ^{206}Pb decay sequence has a **half-life** of 4.5 billion years. Given that a half-life is the time required for one-half of the amount of parent isotope to decay to the daughter product, it is a simple exercise to construct the decay curve of *Figure 26.15*. This graph would work for any radioactive isotope by changing only the time period corresponding to its half-life.

The vertical axis of the decay curve shows the fraction remaining of the original parent isotope. At "time zero" there is no daughter product yet, so the fraction is 1. After one half-

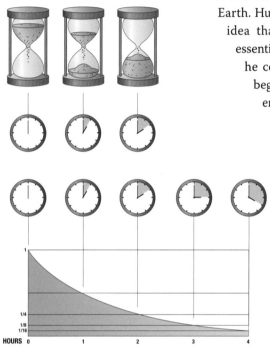

Figure 26.15

Decay curve for radioactive isotopes. Unlike some other "clocks," radioactive decay is not linear but exponential. Sand grains fall through an hourglass in a linear fashion. This means that if it takes 1 hour for 1000 grains to fall, then it will take two hours for 2000 grains. With radioactive decay this is not the case. For example, suppose you have 1000 radioactive atoms. You leave them and come back in one hour and find that 500 of them have decayed. You might think that in another hour all of the atoms will have decayed. Instead, when you return in another hour, you still have 250 of the original atoms left. Only one-half of the 500 atoms that remained after the first hour decayed in the second hour. Each hour that passes produces a similar result with one-half of the radioactive atoms that remained decaying. For this hypothetical example, one hour would be the half-life of the radioactive atoms.

life, the fraction is 1/2 because half of the original parent is left. Likewise, after two half-lives, the fraction is 1/4, and so on. If we had some way of determining how much uranium-238 there was in a rock originally and how much is left at present, we could divide the latter by the former to obtain the fraction. We could then draw a horizontal line from that value on the vertical axis, intersect the decay curve, and draw a vertical line from that intersection to the horizontal axis, where we would read the age of the rock.

All the information needed to perform this task can be obtained by experiment. The various isotopes of an element all behave identically in chemical reactions, so a chemical analysis for uranium and for lead would be insufficient. But we could analyze for each isotope by using a mass spectrometer (see Chapter 15), and that is exactly what is done. The total amount of parent isotope (uranium-238 in this example) originally present is determined by adding the amount of decayed uranium-238 (represented by its daughter product, lead-206) to the amount of uranium-238 currently in the rock.

You may have recognized that this procedure requires the assumption that the rock, as originally formed, had no lead-206, so that all of that isotope now present can be ascribed to uranium decay. This assumption is not always valid, but there are ways (which are beyond the scope of this textbook) to determine how much of the lead-206 is "original" and to correct for that.

A radioactive isotope, if it is to be useful as a geologic clock, must meet certain requirements. First, it must have a half-life that is long enough so that there will still be a measurable amount of parent isotope in the rock being examined. Second, the parent isotope must be relatively abundant in common minerals so that

the rocks will contain enough of it to be useful. Several qualifying isotopes exist, and the most commonly used parents and daughters are listed, along with their half-lives, in *Table 26.1*. The experimental procedures required to measure minute quantities of isotopes are demanding and difficult, and whenever possible, two or more isotopic systems, often called "isotopic clocks," are used on the same rock to verify the results.

You will observe that carbon-14 has a very short half-life, compared to the other parent isotopes (*see Table 26.1*). It is different from the other clocks in other ways, too. It only works for dating objects that have once been alive. Carbon-14 is produced naturally in the atmosphere, and is part of every living organism. While it is alive, an animal or plant continuously replaces carbon-14 as that element decays. When the organism dies, however, the carbon-14 in the dead animal's body is no longer replaced. If we analyze a dead organism, the amount of carbon-14 remaining reveals how long ago the organism died. After a few half-lives, there is not enough carbon-14 left to measure accurately, so that method is limited to the study of organisms that died within the last 70,000 years or so. This method is thus not universally useful in geology (and certainly not for determining the age of the Earth), but it is well suited to archaeology and recent Cenozoic (65 million years to present) geology.

One widespread misconception about isotopic dating is that the ages obtained by these methods represent the ages of the elements that make up rocks or minerals. This is not the case. The ages obtained by these methods represent **events**, not the age of the elements. We can illustrate this by briefly discussing an isotopic dating method called "**fission-track dating**." Like

• **Parent & Daughter Isotopes**
The result of radioactive decay, in which one element decays to form another element. The element we start with is called the parent and the new element formed in the decay process is called the daughter.

• **Half-life**
The time required for half the nuclei in a sample of a specific isotopic species to undergo radioactive decay.

Table 26.1 – *Radioactive isotopes used in absolute dating of rocks.*

Parent Isotope	Daughter Isotope	Half-life (years)
rubidium-87	strontium-87	47.0 billion
thorium-232	lead-208	14.1 billion
uranium-238	lead-206	4.5 billion
potassium-40	argon-40	1.3 billion
uranium-235	lead-207	713 million
carbon-14	nitrogen-14	5,730

all isotopic dating methods, fission-track dating relies on the decay of radioactive isotopes. In the case of fission-track dating, the isotope of interest is uranium-238. When certain minerals (e.g. zircon and apatite) crystallize from liquid magma, they contain trace amounts of uranium-238. With the passage of time, uranium-238 (the parent isotope) decays to produce a new isotope (the daughter), usually by emitting an alpha particle, but occasionally by spontaneous fission. The rates (half-lives) of alpha decay and of spontaneous fission for uranium-238 have been measured independently in many laboratories around the world. When a uranium-238 atom decays by spontaneous fission, the atom breaks into two positively charged, highly energetic fragments. These fragments crash through the mineral that contained the uranium-238 atom and leave a trail of ionized atoms (atoms where some of the electrons have been knocked off). These trails are called fission tracks. It is these tracks that are used in fission-track dating.

So how do we date a rock or mineral using fission tracks? And what does the age mean when we have obtained it? Let us use, as an example, granite from Little Cottonwood Canyon located in the Wasatch Mountains east of Salt Lake City. This granite was quarried by the first settlers of Salt Lake City and used to build the LDS Salt Lake Temple. The granite is composed mostly of quartz, feldspar, and biotite, with small amounts of zircon, sphene, and apatite, minerals that contain enough uranium-238 to be useful in isotopic age determinations. In the laboratory, a sample of granite is crushed and processed through a series of mineral separation techniques to obtain a concentrate of the uranium-bearing minerals. The minerals are then glued to a glass slide, carefully polished, and the fission tracks are revealed by etching the mineral with acids or bases. The tracks found in a mineral grain are counted and this number is used, along with data on the amount of uranium-238 in the grain and the isotopic decay rate, to calculate the age of that rock specimen. The fission tracks tell us how much daughter product was created by the decay process, the amount of uranium-238 represents the amount of parent isotope remaining, and the decay rate (or half-life) allows us to link these two pieces of information into an age.

The fission-track ages we obtained from apatite grains in the Little Cottonwood granite ranged from about 6.5 million years (MYR) to about 11 MYR. This range in age for the granite is substantial and may appear to be evidence of the failure of isotopic dating systems. These differences in age obtained on the same rock body have been used by some to attempt to discredit the whole idea of geologic time and the science behind it. As students of the scientific method, how then do we explain the discovery of such widely differing ages on the same rock body? Which age is right?

Simply put, all the ages measured as described above are "right." They are each telling us something about the cooling history of the granite. The apatite fission-track ages on the temple granite change systematically from 6.5 MYR near the base of the Wasatch Mountains (at about the 5000 ft. elevation) to 8 MYR at about the 7000 ft. elevation, to 11 MYR at the 11,000 ft. elevation. This change in age with elevation reflects the fact that the Wasatch Mountains have been pushing upward along the Wasatch fault for millions of years. As the mountains are uplifted, the granite has been brought to the surface of the Earth. Temperatures deeper inside the Earth are warmer, and so as the granite was uplifted it cooled. When the apatite grains in the granite cooled below about 100°C, they began to preserve fission-tracks. This temperature is called the "closure temperature." It is different for each mineral and each type of isotopic decay. Before the apatites cooled below 100°C, uranium atoms were still decaying and producing tracks, but the tracks were not stable because the temperature was too high. Only when the mineral cooled below 100°C did tracks begin to accumulate in the apatite grains. The reason the apatite fission-track ages are older at the top of the mountain than they are at the bottom of the mountain is because the top of the mountain. It cooled below 100°C about 11 MYR ago, while the rocks at the bottom of the mountain cooled below that temperature only 6.5 MYR ago.

All isotopic dating systems are sensitive to temperature, some (like the apatites in the example above) to fairly low temperatures, and others only to much higher temperatures. It is important to remember, however, that the ages obtained are not the ages of the elements themselves, nor necessarily of the time the rock first formed. The ages obtained by using these isotopic clocks are ages of thermal events, ages of the last time the rock or mineral was heated above and then cooled below its closure temperature. Every isotopic dating system has its limitations, but once we understand them they can provide a wealth of information about Earth's history.

26–6 GEOLOGIC COLUMN

As the science of geology developed in the early 19th century, it became possible to define various divisions of rocks by the fossils they contained. Often these divisions were given names based on geographic or historical features of the areas in which they were described. The Cambrian, Ordovician, Silurian, and Devonian rocks were named after the Roman name for Wales, two ancient British tribes, and the English county of Devonshire, respectively. Cambrian rocks were identified as those in which the earliest, very abundant fossils of marine invertebrates were found; the presence of certain key fossils identified other rocks as Ordovician, or Silurian, or Devonian, and so forth. In this way the **Geologic Column** as shown in *Figure 26.16*, evolved.

Note that the Geologic Column is divided into **periods**, which are grouped into four **eras**—the Cenozoic, the Mesozoic, the Paleozoic, and the Precambrian. The first three literally mean recent life, middle life, and ancient life, the names referring to the similarity (or dissimilarity) between modern life forms and the fossils in rocks of those ages. The Precambrian Era is characterized by very rare fossils—mostly impressions of soft-bodied creatures, single-celled organisms, and other very primitive life forms. The Paleozoic Era is characterized by abundant marine invertebrates (trilobites, sponges, corals, mollusks, etc.). However, fish, amphibians, and reptiles, as well as land plants, also appear in the fossil record of that era. Reptiles of an astonishing variety flourished during the Mesozoic Era (it was the age of the dinosaurs), and that era also saw the emergence of birds, small mammals, and flowering plants. We live in the Cenozoic Era, and the fossils found in Cenozoic Era sedimentary stone layers (which are still being formed), and the many living

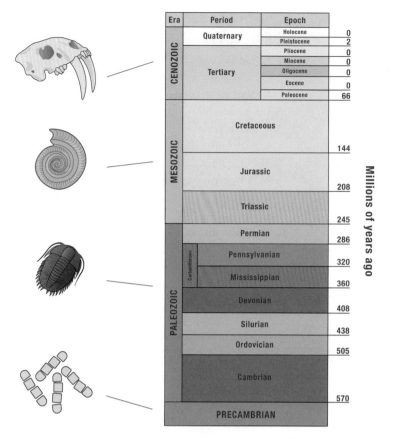

organisms around us, testify that we, and animals with many of our same characteristics, dominate this period of geologic history, thus making it the age of the mammal.

The Geologic Column evolved conceptually over many years, before there were any techniques for determining the absolute ages of rocks, so none of its developers knew how long any of the periods were or even whether they were all of the same length. Even so, the use of fossils (and the principle of faunal succession) enabled geologists to identify rocks as belonging to a particular period of geologic time, say for example, the Mississippian. Further, they knew that the Mississippian rocks were therefore younger than Devonian rocks, even if there were no crosscutting relationships or other relative-dating indicators visible in the area. With the ability to determine absolute ages of rocks, the Geologic Column has now become a quantitative tool with known ages for the major divisions and many of the minor subdivisions. It is used in many aspects of geology and it has become the foundation upon which the history of the Earth is laid.

Figure 26.16
Geologic Column showing the main subdivisions of geologic time into "eras" and "periods". Each of the periods are characterized by different assemblages of fossils.

- **Geologic Column**

A chart that shows the subdivisions of geologic time.

- **Period**

A subdivision of geologic time. Smaller than an era, but still several 10's of millions of years long.

- **Eras**

The largest subdivision of geologic time.

Chapter Framework

A. Introduction
1. "Deep Time"
2. Earth's estimated age
3. Time symmetry, or uniformitarianism
4. Occam's razor

B. Relative Time
1. Principle of Original Horizontality
2. Principle of Superposition
3. Principle of Inclusions
4. Principle of Cross-Cutting Relationships
5. Principle of Faunal Succession

C. Unconformities

D. Absolute Time and Age of Earth
1. Various historical methods
2. Radioactive isotopes and half-life
3. Carbon-14
4. Fission-track dating

E. Geological Column
1. Eras and periods
   a. Cenozoic
   b. Mesozoic
   c. Paleozoic
   d. Precambrian

Comprehension

True/False
1. _____ Our best estimate for the age of the Earth is 4.6 million years.
2. _____ The principle of superposition lets us determine the absolute ages of layers of in a stack of sedimentary rocks.
3. _____ Daughter isotopes are the products of decay of radioactive elements.
4. _____ Half-life is the time it takes for one-half of the radioactive parent isotope to decay.
5. _____ An era is a smaller subdivision of geologic time than a period.

Matching
a. Relative time
b. Absolute time
c. Era
d. Unconformity
e. Half-life
f. Period
g. Fault
h. Trilobite
i. Fission-track dating
j. Event
k. Ammonites
l. Geologic column
m. Uniformitarianism

1. _____ A subdivision of geologic time. Smaller than an era, usually several 10's of millions of years long.
2. _____ A type of radioactive decay clock that uses the trails or tracks created by uranium fission decay to determine the age of geologic events.
3. _____ Determining the sequence in which events occurred relative to each other.
4. _____ The largest subdivision of geologic time.
5. _____ A chart that shows the subdivisions of geologic time.
6. _____ A break in the Earth where rocks on one side of the break have slipped past the rocks on the other side.
7. _____ A numeric or quantitative measure of time.

8. _____ The idea that the laws of nature do not change with time.
9. _____ The time required for half of the parent isotope to decay to the daughter isotope.
10. _____ A common animal that lived in the Earth's oceans during the Paleozoic Era.
11. _____ Fossil shells of animals that lived in the oceans millions of years ago, but are now extinct.
12. _____ A break or gap in the geologic record.
13. _____ Something that has happened in the Earth's history.

Fill in the blank
1. Time symmetry or _____ is the idea that the laws of nature do not change with time.
2. The _____ teaches us that when one solid is enclosed within another solid, the enclosed or included solid must be older.
3. An _____ is a gap or break in the rock record.
4. The divisions in the geologic column are based upon the _____ they contain.
5. The pattern of fossils found in rocks can help us to determine their ages according to the principle of _____.

Analysis

1. Which of the following principles is not used in relative dating?

   a) Principle of Inclusions
   b) Principle of Faunal Succession
   c) Principle of Superposition
   d) Principle of Isotopic Decay
   e) Principle of Cross-cutting Relationships

2. A sedimentary rock layer lies on top of a lava flow. The lava flow has been dated at 44 million years. Both the sedimentary rock layer and the lava flow are cross-cut by a dike of igneous rock that has been dated at 27 million years. The layer of sedimentary rock has an age of

   a) more than 44 million years.
   b) somewhere between 44 and 27 million years.
   c) less than 27 million years.
   d) halfway between 44 and 27 million years at 35.5 million years.

3. To be useful as geologic clocks, radioactive isotopes must occur in

   a) very few rocks and have long half-lives.
   b) very few rocks and have short half-lives.
   c) many rocks and have long half-lives.
   d) many rocks and have short half-lives.

4. A fault that cuts through a group of sedimentary rock layers is

   a) younger than the layers.
   b) older than the layers.
   c) either younger or older than the layers depending on its absolute age.

5. Uranium-238 has a half-life of 4.5 billion years. If a mineral has 200 uranium atoms when it is forms, about how many of these atoms would be left after 9 billion years?

   a) 200
   b) 100
   c) 50
   d) 25
   e) impossible to determine from the information given

6. A moon rock contains equal amounts of uranium-238 and its decay products. How many half-lives have gone buy since the rock solidified?

   a) ½ of a half-life
   b) 1 half-life
   c) 2 half-lives
   d) 3 half-lives
   e) Impossible to determine from the information given.

7. What can you conclude from this cross section?

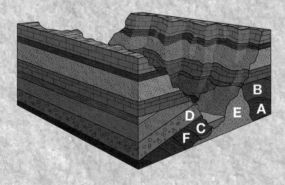

   a) E must be the oldest since it is at the bottom of the other rocks
   b) It is impossible to know whether F is older or younger than E
   c) E is cross-cutting A, B, C and D; therefore it is younger than all of them
   d) D must be an igneous rock since they are almost always deposited in horizontal layers
   e) None of the above

8. Why are the periods in the geologic column not equal in length?

9. What two factors limit the usefulness of carbon-14 dating?

10. How are relative dating and absolute dating different in concept?

11. Describe why the same decay curve can be used for any radioactive isotope, regardless of the length of its half-life.

12. Explain why the principle of uniformitarianism is critical in geology and how we use it to understand the history of Earth.

13. Name and state the five principles of relative dating.

14. Create your own Geological Column showing the four eras and representative life forms found in the rocks of each era. Indicate on your Geologic Column the absolute dates of the beginning of each era as determined from radiometric dating.

15. Describe two early methods for dating Earth. List a weakness of each method. What was Earth's age according to these methods?

Synthesis

1. Describe the general process of radiometric dating. What makes radiometric dating the most reliable method of dating? What limitations are there to radiometric dating techniques?

2. Explain what unconformities are and provide examples of the geologic processes that cause them.

3. Create a sequence of events that describes the geologic history you can determine from the cross-section below. Your sequence should include the deposition of rock layers, tilting and erosion of said layers, and formation of faults in their proper order. Explain which methods of relative dating you used to arrive at your conclusions. A and B are both sedimentary rocks. C is a fault.

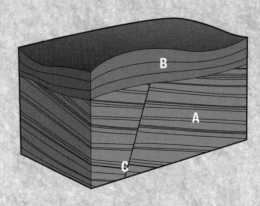

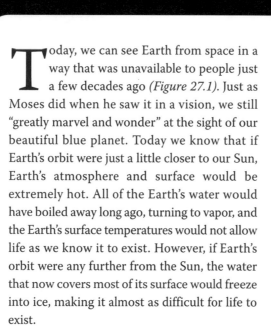

PLANET EARTH

"And it came to pass that Moses looked, and beheld the world upon which he was created . . . of the same he greatly marveled and wondered"

~ Moses 1:8

Today, we can see Earth from space in a way that was unavailable to people just a few decades ago *(Figure 27.1)*. Just as Moses did when he saw it in a vision, we still "greatly marvel and wonder" at the sight of our beautiful blue planet. Today we know that if Earth's orbit were just a little closer to our Sun, Earth's atmosphere and surface would be extremely hot. All of the Earth's water would have boiled away long ago, turning to vapor, and the Earth's surface temperatures would not allow life as we know it to exist. However, if Earth's orbit were any further from the Sun, the water that now covers most of its surface would freeze into ice, making it almost as difficult for life to exist.

It is water, found mostly in liquid form on Earth, that makes our planet so unique among all the planets of our solar system. Movement of

water on Earth's surface, in what is called our planet's "hydrologic system," wears down enormous mountains, drop by drop. Water erodes and changes all of Earth's surfaces, sometimes quickly, in great natural cataclysms, sometimes more slowly, dissolving some materials, holding some tiny particles in suspension, and grinding stone against stone, constantly, and over enormous spans of geologic time. A high mountain of solid rock on Earth's surface may be dramatically changed over eons of time simply by rainwater seeping into tiny holes in that mountain's rocks. When Earth's surface temperature falls sufficiently, water freezes and expands to flake and gradually split even the densest stone. The broken rocks may then be carried down the side of the mountain by more rainwater, which causes the jagged pieces to grind against one another, gradually creating smaller rocks and a material

LEARNING OBJECTIVES

- Understand the importance of the hydrologic and tectonic systems in shaping the surface features on Earth.
- Know the major geologic features of the continents, including continental shield, stable platform, mountain belt, continental shelf, and continental slope.
- Know the major geologic features of the ocean basins, including ridges, trenches, abyssal plains, abyssal hills, volcanic island arcs, seamounts, atolls, and guyots.
- Understand how the three broad classes of rocks (igneous, sedimentary, and metamorphic) can provide valuable clues to Earth's geological history.

called sediment. This sediment—tiny particles of stone—is carried by the water into streams, rivers, and glaciers down to lakes and oceans where this material it is deposited.

As was already mentioned, Earth, in its orbit around the Sun, is at exactly the right distance to allow water to exist in fluid, solid, and vapor forms, on, above, and below Earth's surface. Earth's fortunate position in the solar system is only one reason for the great differences between Earth and the other planets orbiting our Sun. Earth is of the right size and composition to maintain a very hot interior. This heat is not uniform throughout the Earth's core. The slight difference between the core's extremely hot, dense center and less-hot, slightly less-dense mantle, which is a little closer to Earth's surface, creates movement in this dense mass. Convection cells in both the liquid and solid (but plastic, like

modeling clay) rocks at Earth's core are in constant motion, and this motion is an important factor in the formation of Earth's surface features.

Floating on top of Earth's liquid-rock core, like a dry leaf on a mud puddle, is a second major Earth system, our planet's unique "plate tectonic system." The convection at Earth's center pushes upward against these cooler, solid (brittle) rocks at the surface, which have been broken into fragments we call "tectonic plates." The movement of these plates against each other, some rising to create vast mountain ranges (which erosion then wears away over eons) and some diving under

331

- **Igneous Rock**

Rocks that have been formed by solidification from a molten state.

- **Sedimentary Rock**

Rocks formed by the deposition of sediment.

- **Metamorphic Rock**

Rocks that have been subjected to intense heat and pressure that cause the minerals in them to undergo chemical reactions, forming a "new" rock.

- **Mineral**

A naturally occurring, inorganic solid that has a specific chemical formula.

- **Quartz**

A common mineral that has a chemical formula of SiO_2.

- **Feldspar**

The name of a family of silicate minerals that are the most abundant minerals in the Earth's crust.

- **Magma**

Hot, liquid rock. It is called lava when it erupts onto the Earth's surface.

- **Plutonic Rocks**

Igneous rocks that solidify underground.

- **Volcanic Rocks**

Igneous rocks that cool and solidify at the Earth's surface.

- **Granite**

An igneous plutonic rock that is made mostly of quartz along with sodium and potassium-rich feldspar.

- **Basalt**

An igneous volcanic rock that is composed of calcium-rich feldspar and other iron-rich minerals.

- **Gabbro**

An igneous plutonic rock made of the same minerals as basalt, but, because the minerals cooled slowly underground, they are coarse-grained.

Figure 27.1

View of Earth from space as see by the Apollo 17 astronauts. Photo shows Africa and Antarctica, as well as water in vapor form (as swirling white clouds), liquid form (the blue oceans), and solid form (the Antarctic ice sheet).

other plates, is usually so slow it cannot be detected without precise scientific instruments. But such movement of these plates is relentless because of the constant movement of the convection cells far below, and without the constant activity of both the hydrologic and plate tectonic systems, Earth would be a much different planet. In this chapter you will be introduced to the major features of planet Earth and the basic types of rock that we find on its surface.

27–1 ROCKS AND MINERALS

Every rock, regardless of its size, or whether it came from a deep excavation, a nearby beach or stream, or high on a mountain top, is classified as **igneous, sedimentary,** or **metamorphic**. Each of these rock types is made up of smaller parts called **minerals**. A mineral is a naturally occurring chemical compound that has a specific chemical formula. For example, **quartz** is a common mineral made of silicon and oxygen with a chemical formula of SiO_2. It is important to remember that minerals are *not* rocks! Minerals are what rocks are made of, just as you and I are made of cells. The most abundant type of mineral found in rocks on the surface of Earth is **feldspar**. Feldspar is also made mostly of silicon and oxygen, but, unlike quartz, its chemical composition includes aluminum, sodium, potassium, and calcium.

Igneous Rocks

Igneous rocks form when hot liquid rock (called **magma**) cools to a solid state either below or at Earth's surface. When magma solidifies beneath the surface of Earth, it forms "**plutonic rocks**" (named after the ancient Roman god of the underworld, Pluto). When magma erupts through Earth's surface and cools in the atmosphere, the rocks formed there are called "**volcanic rocks**" (after Vulcan, the Roman god of fire).

Classification of the common types of igneous rocks is based on their composition (what minerals they contain) and their texture. If the igneous specimen is plutonic, or coarse-grained, it cooled slowly underground. If it is volcanic, or fine-grained, it cooled quickly at the surface. Most people are familiar with the igneous rocks called **granite** and **basalt** (*Figures 27.2a & 27.2b*), but some of the other kinds of igneous rocks are less well known. You can review the chart of igneous rock names to see how composition and texture relate to the rock type (*Figure 27.3*). For example, basalt and **gabbro** both came from magma that is low in silica, high in iron, but gabbro is a plutonic rock that cooled slowly underground, while basalt is a volcanic rock that cooled quickly at the surface.

Sedimentary Rocks

Sedimentary rocks were formed from sediment that resulted from the weathering and erosion of other sedimentary rocks, igneous rocks, and metamorphic rocks. As rocks weather, the minerals they contain are altered by the gases and fluids that are present at Earth's surface. In

Figure 27.2a

Coarse-grained granite from New England. This granite is composed of several minerals that can easily be seen, including: salmon-colored potassium feldspar, white plagioclase feldspar, gray quartz, and black biotite mica. The photographed specimen is about 20 cm across.

Figure 27.2b ⇨
Fine-grained, black basalt lava flows on the island of Hawaii. The basalt cooled quickly as it poured out onto the surface of the Earth. The Hawaiians called this type of lava "pahoehoe."

Figure 27.3 ⇩
This chart shows the main types of igneous rocks and their relationship to composition and texture. The fine-grained rocks erupted onto Earth's surface and cooled quickly. They are called volcanic rocks. The coarse-grained rocks cooled more slowly underground and are called plutonic rocks.

TEXTURE			
Fine Grained (Extrusive) Rhyolite	Andesite	Basalt	Komatiite
Course Grained (Intrusive) Granite	Diorite	Gabbro	Peridotite

High Silica Low Iron Low Density ————————————————→ Low Silica High Iron High Density

• **Shale**
A sedimentary rock made up of fine particles of clay and mud.

• **Calcite**
A mineral that is usually the main component of limestone. Calcite has the chemical formula $CaCO_3$.

• **Limestone**
A sedimentary rock usually formed from the precipitation of the mineral calcite in the ocean.

some cases, chemical reactions occur and new minerals are produced. For example, when feldspar minerals come into contact with water and carbon dioxide, clay minerals are formed. These clay minerals are more stable at Earth's surface and can be carried by rivers and streams, eventually to be deposited in layers of sedimentary rock called **shale** *(Figure 27.4)*.

The same fluids that react with feldspar as described above affect other minerals differently. The mineral **calcite** (an ionic solid with a chemical formula of $CaCO_3$), when it comes into prolonged contact with water, does not react to form another solid, but simply dissolves, producing a solution with Ca^{+2} ions and CO_3^{-2} ions. These ions are easily carried by rivers and streams out to the ocean. When the concentrations of these ions become high enough, they begin to precipitate out of the ocean to form layers of **limestone**.

Some minerals rising up through the layers at Earth's core are unaffected by chemical processes encountered at Earth's surface. Quartz, for example, does not react easily with most of the fluids found on the surface; instead, pieces of quartz carried along in moving water may grind against each other, becoming rounded and abraded. The tiny quartz particles broken off the larger pieces thus become grains of sand and silt that will eventually be carried away by streams

a. Shale

b. Limestone

c. Sandstone

Figure 27.4
Three common types of sedimentary rocks.

and rivers, deposited in lakes or oceans to form layers of **sandstone** and **siltstone** .

Metamorphic Rocks

Metamorphic rocks form when igneous or sedimentary rocks are changed (metamorphosed) by some combination of heat, pressure, and fluids to become different rocks made up of new mineral combinations. These changes take place in the solid state without melting the rock. A piece

• **Sandstone**
A sedimentary rock made up mostly of grains of sand.

• **Siltstone**
A sedimentary rock made up mostly of grains of silt (smaller than sand size particles, but still gritty, not smooth like clay or mud).

a. Marble

b. Gneiss

c. Slate

Figure 27.5

Photos of (a) marble, (b) gneiss, and (c) slate, three common metamorphic rocks.

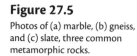

♦ **Gneiss**

A banded or foliated metamorphic rock, usually of the same composition as granite.

♦ **Quartzite**

A metamorphic rock composed of sand grains that have been welded tightly together, unlike sandstone where the sand grains rub off in your hand.

♦ **Marble**

Metamorphosed limestone.

♦ **Slate**

Metamorphosed shale. It still breaks into thin layers like shale, but the layers are much harder and more durable. In fact, slate is hard enough to use for roofing tile.

♦ **Continent**

The granite part of the earth's crust. The continent is divided into three major structural parts: shield, stable platform, and folded mountain belts.

of granite can be transformed into a metamorphic rock called **gneiss**. A piece of sandstone can be changed into a **quartzite**, a limestone into a **marble**, and a shale into a **slate**, all by a variety of metamorphic processes *(Figure 27.5)*.

Why Do We Study Rocks?

Rocks fascinate geologists and other scientists, not just because they are often beautiful, but also because they are the keys to unraveling Earth's history. For example, the processes that form igneous and metamorphic rocks are most active where the plates in the plate tectonic system are interacting with each other, bumping and grinding against one another with enormous pressure over long periods of time. These rocks, therefore, help us to unravel the history of plate interactions through geologic time. Likewise, sedimentary rocks form where there are large basins or oceans in which the sediment can accumulate. Sedimentary rocks collected many miles from the nearest salt water bay tell us where ancient oceans lay and ancient rivers once flowed; they tell us about the animals that lived and died in these oceans and rivers; and they have even recorded ancient changes in climate and environment for careful researchers who can recognize the clues in the sample sedimentary rocks.

27–2 THE CONTINENTS

One of the most unusual things about Earth is the existence of continents. Continents may

not seem unusual to you, but they are not found on any of the other planets in our solar system. We can see this because on Earth the continents are at much higher elevations than the ocean basins. A graph of elevation plotted against the percentage of the Earth at each elevation gives a bimodal (double humped) curve, while the elevation distributions on the other planets are all unimodal *(Figure 27.6)*. Why is it that the continents on the Earth are so much higher than the ocean basins? And why do we have continents on the Earth at all? Before we answer these questions, let's look at the composition, age, and major features of Earth's continents.

Composition and Age of the Continents

The surfaces of Earth's **continents** are mostly covered by sedimentary rocks. As we drill holes in the center of a continent, however, we find that in most places that layer of sedimentary rock is thin, usually only a few hundred feet thick. But when we drill holes closer to the edge of the continent, the sedimentary cover increases, and can be several thousand feet thick. Under the cover of sedimentary rock we find a "**basement**" of igneous and metamorphic rocks that have an average composition of granite. (Actually, the composition falls between granite and diorite, but sometimes even the most

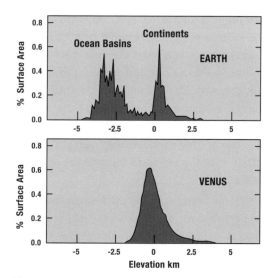

Figure 27.6

Graphs comparing the distribution of topography on Earth and Venus. Earth has a distinctly bimodal distribution, one mode for the continents and one for the ocean basins, while Venus has only a single mode. This is accepted as evidence by many scientists that Venus did not have, nor does it currently have, an active tectonic system.

exacting scientist-instructor may get lazy and just casually say it has a granite composition. See *Figure 27.3*.) This does not mean that all of the rocks that form the basement of the continents are granites and diorites. Indeed, many types of rocks can be found, but the average composition of this layer deep below Earth's surface is granite.

From this average composition, we can determine an average density for the continents, which turns out to be about 2.7 g/cm³. The rocks of the ocean basins are denser, averaging about 3.0 g/cm³. It is this difference in the average densities of the rocks forming the continents and ocean basins that cause the continents to be high and the ocean basins low. This difference in the density creates the bimodal distribution of topography we find on Earth. The fact that other planets circling our Sun do not have this bimodal distribution of topography indicates that they do not have two distinct types of crustal rocks. Earth's hydrologic and plate tectonic systems have worked together over the 4.6 billion years of Earth's history to produce these two separate regions (continents and ocean basins); without them our planet would look much more like Venus and Mars.

The rocks that make up the continents range widely in age from the oldest rocks found anywhere on Earth (over 4 billion years old) to rocks that are still forming today. What do you suppose the average age would be for continental rocks? It turns out to be about 3 billion years, indicating that most of the rocks that make up the continents are extremely ancient.

Features of the Continents

Each of Earth's continents has a unique geologic history and each continent differs from the other continents in the amounts and types of rocks it contains. However, each continent also has several features that are common to all of them *(Figure 27.7)*. First, all of the continents have a fairly flat region where the sedimentary cover has been completely removed by erosion, exposing the basement of igneous and metamorphic rocks beneath. These areas are the **continental shields**, a name that comes from the fact that they have profiles that somewhat resemble the rounded shape of a warrior's shield—high in the center and sloping toward the edges. On

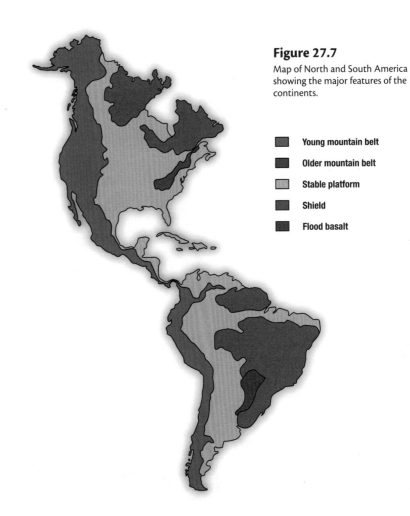

Figure 27.7
Map of North and South America showing the major features of the continents.

- Young mountain belt
- Older mountain belt
- Stable platform
- Shield
- Flood basalt

the North American continent this geological feature is called the Canadian Shield, because it lies mostly in eastern Canada. The igneous and metamorphic rocks which make up the continental shields are the oldest rocks found anywhere on Earth, and many of them are highly deformed, having once resided in the roots of ancient mountain ranges which have long since worn away. These rocks now form vast lowland areas of the continents, most areas being less than 200 feet above sea level.

Surrounding the continental shields is a region where the basement of igneous and metamorphic rock is covered by a few hundred feet of sedimentary rock. This sedimentary rock layer is a reminder to us that at times in the distant geologic past oceans have covered much of each continent, either because the sea level was at one time higher than it is now, or because the continents themselves were somewhat lower. It does not take much of a change in sea level to affect broad areas of most of the continents. Because the old basement rocks of the shield are covered

- **Basement**

  What geologists call the igneous and metamorphic rock found in the continental shields and under the sedimentary rock cover in the stable platforms.

- **Continental Shields**

  The oldest parts of the continents. They represent the roots of very ancient mountains, long since eroded away.

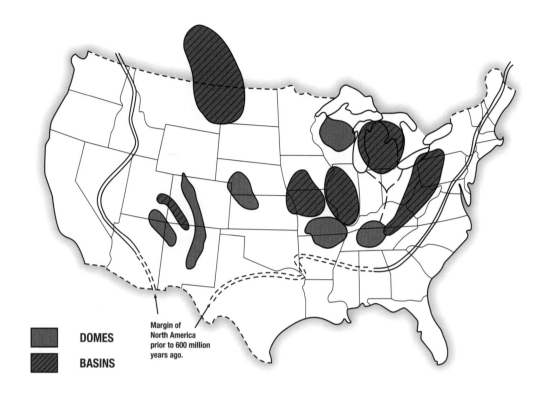

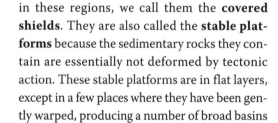

Figure 27.8

Map of the central United States showing the extent of the stable platform and the broad domes and basins within this region. The lower diagram shows a cross section through a dome and basin. The sedimentary layers are folded very gently, and they lie on top of the igneous and metamorphic rocks of Earth's continental basement.

♦ **Stable Platform or Covered Shield**

An area of the continent where the old rocks of the shield have been covered by relatively flat-lying sedimentary rocks.

♦ **Mountain Belts**

Regions of the continents where the rocks have been highly deformed by enormous forces. These belts usually lie along the edges of the continents.

in these regions, we call them the **covered shields**. They are also called the **stable platforms** because the sedimentary rocks they contain are essentially not deformed by tectonic action. These stable platforms are in flat layers, except in a few places where they have been gently warped, producing a number of broad basins and domes *(Figure 27.8)*.

Bordering the stable platforms are **mountain belts**. The term "belt" is used because this feature on a continent is generally long and narrow, like a belt. Mountain belts are composed of a combination of folded, deformed sedimentary rocks, intermediate composition volcanic rocks (called "andesite"), and plutonic rocks ranging in composition between granite and diorite. As water, wind, gravity and other natural factors work together to erode a mountain belt, its "roots" become exposed. There we find a wide variety of highly deformed metamorphic rocks that are similar to the rocks found in the continental shields. In North America, we have one old mountain belt, the Appalachian Mountains

(Figure 27.9), positioned north-south along the eastern margin of the continent and one fairly young mountain belt, the Rocky Mountains, also positioned north-south, along the western margin. The Rocky Mountains are actually a composite mountain belt made up of an eastern part (in Colorado, Utah, Wyoming), which is older and composed mostly of folded and faulted sedimentary and metamorphic rocks, and a younger western part (the Sierra Nevada and Cascade Range), which is composed of mostly volcanic and plutonic rocks.

The modern-day coastlines of the continents might be a convenient place to end this discussion of the geology of the continents. However, this would be a mistake. A continent does not end where the ocean surrounding it begins. Each continent's mass actually continues for some distance out under the oceans bordering it. (Refer back to *Figure 27.7*.) This broad, flat surface is called the **continental shelf** because is sits like a shelf above the floor of the deep ocean basin below. The continental shelf

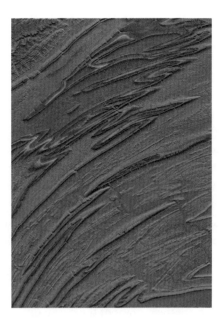

Figure 27.9
Digital relief map of a portion of the Appalachian mountain belt. Layers of sedimentary rock have been folded by enormous forces within Earth. Here we see them exposed at the surface after this old mountain belt has been eroded down nearly to its roots.

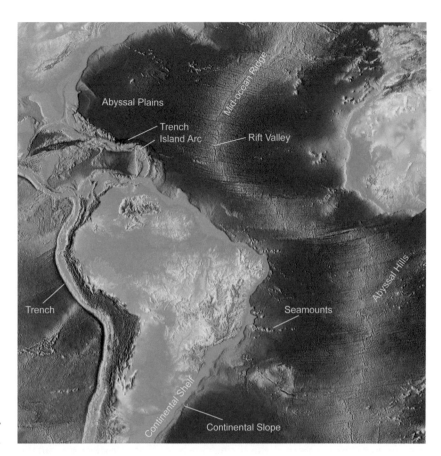

Figure 27.10
A geological view of the Atlantic Ocean basin, showing the major features discussed in the text. These same features are common to all the world's ocean basins.

◆ **Continental Shelf**
Part of the continent that is under a shallow cover of water.

◆ **Continental Slope**
The boundary between the continents and the ocean basins. It marks a distinct change in the composition of the rocks near Earth's surface.

is cut in many places by huge underwater canyons, which provide passageways for sediment, in the form of dense underwater debris flows, to move down from the shelf into the deep ocean. During past ice ages, when more water was frozen into continental ice sheets, large areas of the continental shelf were exposed because of a drop in sea level. The continental shelves are rich in resources; the best fisheries and some of the world's largest oil fields are found there. The rocks that comprise these shelves are similar to those found on the stable platform, except that the sedimentary layers may accumulate here in much greater thicknesses, up to several thousands of meters.

A steep slope, called the **continental slope**, runs from the continental shelf down into the deep ocean basin. This slope is considered to be the true edge of each continent, and it also marks a distinct change in the character of the rocks as well.

27–3 OCEAN BASINS

The Atlantic and Pacific Oceans each have an average depth of 400 feet on their continental shelves and an average overall depth of about 12,000 feet. Obviously, the drop from the flat top of a continental shelf to the deepest parts of an ocean is significant. In places the ocean is over 36,000 feet deep. The deepest parts are not found in the middle of the ocean basins, as one might logically think, but instead, close to the edge of the continents. The middle of the ocean basins often tend to be elevated higher than the rest of the basin *(Figure 27.10)*. We will look at this phenomenon as we examine the composition and major features of the ocean basins and come up with questions about them and about the features of the continents as well.

Composition and Age of the Ocean Basins

Beyond the edge of the continental slope is where the "geologic" ocean basin begins. Here is where we find a significant change in the character of the underlying rocks. The continents, remember, are made of a basement of igneous and metamorphic rocks that have an average composition between granite and diorite, which is covered in most places by a few hundred meters of sedimentary rocks. The deep ocean basins also have a cover of sedimentary rocks, but the sediments are quite different in character from those we find on the continents and

- **Turbidity Flow**

A mass of water and sediment that flows down off of the continental shelf into the deep ocean. Because the sediment mixed with water is denser than plain water, these flows move along the bottom of the ocean.

- **Oceanic Ridge**

Mountain ranges that are under the oceans. They form very long mountain chains that essentially encircle Earth.

- **Rift Valley**

A valley bounded by faults or breaks in the crust of Earth. These valleys are formed as the plates of Earth pull apart.

- **Abyssal Hills**

Mounds of basalt on the deep ocean floor.

- **Abyssal Plains**

Broad, flat areas on the ocean floor.

- **Seamounts**

An underwater mountain rising from the ocean floor and having a peaked or flat-topped summit below the surface of the sea.

- **Guyots**

Flat-topped seamounts that once were above the surface of the ocean, but have now subsided below it.

- **Trenches**

Long, narrow, deep places on the ocean floor. They are usually found near or next to continents.

- **Island Arcs**

Arc-shaped chains of volcanoes that are always found associated with an ocean trench.

continental shelves. Sediments in the deepest areas of the ocean floor are very fine-grained, silica-rich mud, which accumulates slowly in fairly thin layers. The ocean bottom near the continental slopes is covered with coarser sediments that have been carried down into the deep ocean by **turbidity flows**; these flows are underwater debris flows that flow down the continental slope as dense currents composed of water and sediment.

Under the ocean floor's relatively thin blankets of fine-grained or coarse sediments, there is another layer, this one composed entirely of dense basalt. This is entirely different from the materials that make up the continental basement, which is a wide variety of igneous and metamorphic rock types. Even when we drill down into the basalt below the ocean, the composition remains basaltic.

The ages of the basalts on the ocean floor have been determined by the isotopic dating methods we discussed in Chapter 26. Several surprising discoveries have been made, using this dating, one being that no rocks found on the ocean floor are older than 200 million years, and 200 million years, in geologic terms, is very young, just the last 5 percent of Earth's history. The average age of rocks found on the ocean floor is about 100 million years, which is much less than the 3 billion year average age for the continents. Geologically speaking, we can summarize the age of the continents as being old and the ocean basins as being young.

Features of the Ocean Basins

Winding around the globe like a giant snake is a range of mountains called the **oceanic ridge**. This mountain formation is often called the "mid-ocean ridge" (although it is not always located in the middle of the ocean) because it was originally discovered in the Atlantic Ocean (refer back to *Figure 27.10*), where the ridge *is* in the middle. This ridge is actually the longest mountain chain on Earth, and it is certainly one of the most important geologic features on our planet. The oceanic ridge is much wider than it is tall (about 850 miles wide and at most, only 2 miles tall). Also, a central valley, called a **rift valley**, runs lengthwise down its center. In addition, the ridge is cut by many fractures that are approximately perpendicular to its length.

Large portions of Earth's ocean basins are covered by small hills that are only a few hundred meters higher than the surrounding seafloor. These hills are known as the **abyssal hills** (meaning "very deep"), and they are actually the most common landform on Earth. The height of individual hills diminishes, the further away they are from the oceanic ridges because the low areas between them are gradually filled with sediment. Where the cover of sediment becomes thick enough, far from the oceanic ridge, these hills give way to vast flat areas called **abyssal plains**. Scattered on the ocean floor, sometimes as solitary formations and sometimes in long chains, are higher hills called **seamounts**. These seamounts are volcanoes that either never rose above the surface of the ocean or were at one time above the surface but are now submerged beneath it. Flat-topped seamounts, which are thought to have been above sea level at some distant time and then were eroded flat, are called **guyots**.

Long, narrow, arc-shaped deeps in the ocean basins are called **trenches**. The trenches are much deeper than the 12,000 foot average ocean depth, reaching down as far as 36,000 feet below sea level. The deepest of the trenches, the Marianas Trench, is so deep that you could place Mount Everest, Earth's highest mountain, into this trench and the mountain's peak would still be more than one mile below the ocean's surface. Two other interesting facts about ocean basin trenches are: First, a trench tends to be near to the edge of a continent, not out in the middle of a basin, and second, trenches are always associated with chains of extremely dangerous and explosive volcanoes that run parallel to the trench. These chains of volcanoes are called **island arcs** because the chains usually are arc-shaped. The Aleutian Islands off of Alaska, the islands of Indonesia, the islands of Japan, and the Marianas islands are all examples of island arcs (*Figure 27.11*).

A second type of volcanic island chain is also found in the ocean basins. These volcanic chains tend to be straight, not arc-shaped; they tend to have only a single active volcano, instead of the several active volcanoes found near island arcs. Their eruptions are relatively quiet, with lava (molten rock) flowing from vents, as compared to volcanoes in arc-shaped chains, which are spectacularly explosive, hurling huge chunks of

Figure 27.11
Digital relief map of the Aleutian Islands arc and trench.

rock, lava, and ash thousands of feet into the air. The Hawaiian Islands formation is one of the best examples of a straight-line volcanic island chain (*Figure 27.12*).

27-4 QUESTIONS ABOUT THE CONTINENTS AND OCEAN BASINS

The fact that all of the continents have the same basic components suggests some sort of common and perhaps predictable history for their formation. Likewise, the ocean basins all have common features, again suggesting common modes of formation. These observations of continental and ocean basin anatomy raise several important questions: How do continents and ocean basins form? In fact, why are there any continents at all? We know that similar features are not found on Mars and Venus, two planets that have many other things in common with Earth. Why are mountains distributed in belts instead of randomly all over the surfaces of the continents? Why are trenches, the deepest

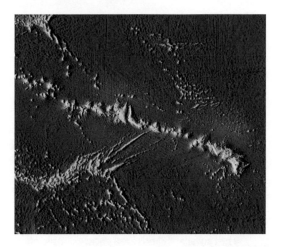

Figure 27.12
Digital relief map of the Hawaiian Islands chain. Notice that the chain is fairly straight and is not associated with a trench. In addition, the only active volcanoes are on the island of Hawaii, which is on the southeast end of the chain.

parts of the ocean basins, so narrow and found next to the continents, rather than in the middle of their nearby ocean basins? Why are there underwater mountain belts, called ocean ridges? Where can we find forces large enough to fold solid rock and create the pressures required for the formation of the metamorphic rocks that we find in continental shields? Why are volcanoes concentrated near trenches and oceanic ridges? These questions, as well as other questions regarding our fascinating planet, will be addressed in succeeding chapters of this book.

Chapter Framework

A. The hydrologic and tectonic systems

B. Rocks and Minerals
1. Igneous
2. Sedimentary
3. Metamorphic

C. The Continents
1. Basement
2. Continental shields
3. Covered shields/Stable platforms
4. Mountain belts
5. Continental shelf/Continental slope

D. Ocean Basins
1. Turbidity flows
2. Oceanic ridge
3. Rift valley
4. Abyssal hills/Abyssal plains
5. Seamounts/Guyots
6. Trenches
7. Island Arcs

Comprehension

True/False

1. _____ The ocean basin is less dense than the continents.

2. _____ The Hawaiian Islands are a good example of an island arc.

3. _____ Continental shield is a flat region where the basement of igneous and metamorphic rock is exposed.

4. _____ Earth is the only planet in our solar system with plates and continents.

5. _____ Plutonic rocks form above the Earth's surface.

Matching

1. _____ An igneous plutonic rock made of the same minerals as basalt, but, because the minerals cooled slowly underground, they are coarse-grained.

2. _____ Metamorphosed shale. It still breaks into thin layers like shale, but the layers are much harder and more durable.

3. _____ A valley bounded by faults or breaks in the crust of the Earth.

4. _____ A mass of water and sediment that flows down off of the continental shelf into the deep ocean.

5. _____ The oldest parts of the continents composed of the roots of very ancient mountains, long since eroded away.

6. _____ The area of the continent where the old rocks of the shield have been covered by relatively flat-lying sedimentary rocks.

a. *Volcanic rocks*
b. *Mineral*
c. *Stable platform*
d. *Continental slope*
e. *Magma*
f. *Slate*
g. *Turbidity flow*
h. *Seamounts*
i. *Abyssal hills*
j. *Continental shields*
k. *Feldspar*
l. *Mountain belts*
m. *Continental shelf*
n. *Gabbro*
o. *Rift valley*

7. _____ Underwater volcanoes that are mostly extinct and usually have never been above the surface of the ocean.

8. _____ Mounds of basalt on the deep ocean floor.

9. _____ Regions of the continents where the rocks have been highly deformed by enormous forces. These belts usually lie along the edges of the continents.

10. _____ Family of silicate minerals that are the most abundant minerals in the Earth's crust.

11. _____ Igneous rocks that cool and solidify at the Earth's surface.

12. _____ Hot, liquid rock. It is called lava when it erupts onto the Earth's surface.

13. _____ A naturally occurring, inorganic solid that has a specific chemical formula.

14. _____ Part of the continent that is under a shallow cover of water.

15. _____ The boundary between the continents and the ocean basins. It marks a distinct change in the composition of the rocks making up the near surface rocks of the Earth.

Fill in the Blank

1. _____ are long, narrow, subduction zones on the ocean floor. They are usually found near or next to continents.

2. The _____ is what wears down and erodes mountains away over long periods of geologic time.

3. Sedimentary and igneous rock changed by pressure, heat, or fluids form _____ rocks.

4. Marble is metamorphosed _____.

5. Sandstone, siltstone, and limestone are examples of _____ rocks.

Analysis

1. Which of the following lists contains a feature not found in the oceans?

   a) Trenches, abyssal hills, ocean ridges
   b) Ocean ridges, island arcs, trenches
   c) Abyssal plains, stable platforms, ocean ridges
   d) Island arcs, trenches, linear island chains

2. Which of the following is not a correct metamorphic process?

   a) Calcite turns into limestone
   b) Shale turns into slate
   c) Granite turns into gneiss
   d) Sandstone turns in quartzite
   e) All of the above are correct

3. Continents contain:

   a) Granitic rocks   b) Folded rocks
   c) Stable platforms   d) All of the above

4. How do the origins of igneous, sedimentary, and metamorphic rocks differ?

5. Compare the composition of ocean basins to the continents.

6. Describe the relationship among the major features of the ocean floor.

7. What two criteria largely determine how geologists classify igneous rocks?

8. How are the tectonic system and hydrologic system predominantly responsible for Earth's appearance today?

9. What is the difference between a seamount and an island?

10. What are the similarities between basalt and gabbro? If they both hold these similarities, why do geologists name them differently?

11. What difference(s) exist between magma and lava?

12. What is metamorphism? What agents change the rocks?

13. Describe the three main rock types found on Earth and give an example of each.

Synthesis

1. What features make Earth a unique planet in our solar system and explain why these features are important?

2. Describe the main features of both the continents and the ocean basin.

3. Which type of rock is missing at most unconformities? Explain why this rock may be particularly susceptible to creating unconformities.

4. How does the rate of cooling influence the crystallization process (the size of the rock's grains)?

5. Compare and contrast the following pairs of rocks:

   a. Basalt and gabbro
   b. Limestone and marble
   c. Granite and gneiss

EARTH'S INTERIOR

"Now faith is the substance of things hoped for, the evidence of things not seen."

~ Hebrews 11:1

The Apostle Paul's definition of faith as the "evidence of things not seen" is the perfect starting point for much of science, but particularly for this chapter, which discusses Earth's interior. No one has ever seen the interior of Earth. Modern scientists, however, believe they know what Earth's deepest interior is like by studying physical clues found on the Earth's surface. The evidence is so compelling that we can eliminate all but a few possibilities for the interior of Earth. We can be certain, for example, that the center of Earth is nothing like the fanciful description offered by Jules Verne in his 19th century novel, *Journey to the Center of the Earth*. Furthermore, Earth's center bears only a passing resemblance to the interior as pictured by Hollywood in the 2003 movie, *The Core*.

So how do we learn about Earth's interior? What are the evidences that give us confidence in our understanding of this unseen part of our world? Such evidences can be divided into five categories:

- Direct observation of rocks from the interior
- Relationships to rocks from space (meteorites)
- Inferences from Earth's density
- Evidence from seismic (earthquake) waves
- Requirements for producing Earth's magnetic field

28–1 EVIDENCES FROM DIRECT OBSERVATION

When you were a child, you may have ambitiously started to dig a hole in the ground with the intention of digging all the way through to Earth's other side. Sooner or later (probably sooner) you became tired or bored with your project, abandoning it for some other activity. You may never have become aware of how impossible your plan was. Even with the best equipment, latest techniques, and modern methods, scientists have only been able to penetrate a fraction of one percent of Earth's thickness. The deepest man-made hole is on the Kola Peninsula in Russia. This hole reached a depth of 7.6 miles—not very deep, compared to the 3,975 miles to Earth's center! Nonetheless, the information gathered from such boreholes helps us to better understand the interior of our Earth.

In addition to rock samples extracted by drilling, there are places where rocks that were formed deep within Earth are now exposed on the surface. By "deep," however, we mean that those rocks were formed 15 or 20 miles down, still only a fraction of the distance to Earth's center. Occasionally rocks that may have formed at depths of as much as 150 miles are carried

upward by ascending magmas and blasted from volcanoes out onto the surface. These rocks give us a glimpse into deeper parts of Earth that can't be reached by drilling or in some other way. Examination of these samples, as well as those collected by drilling, has shown that Earth is not of a uniform composition. The continents are made up of fairly low-density rock, such as andesite, granite, and gneiss (which have average densities of about 2.7 g/cm³). Earth's oceans float on basins of basalt and gabbro that have a somewhat greater density (3.0 g/cm³ average). The rock foundations of our continents and oceans are part of Earth's uppermost layer, similar to the peel of an orange. We call this layer Earth's **crust**.

Rock fragments brought to the surface in volcanic eruptions, like the one shown in *Figure 28.1*, are denser (up to 3.3 g/cm³) than even the basalts on the ocean floor. They come from a

layer below Earth's crust, which is called the **mantle**. Rocks formed in this lower layer, when found on the surface, are called **peridotite**. Peridotite contains more iron and magnesium and less silicon and aluminum than are found in the rocks of the crust.

Rock samples from the crust and mantle give us important information, but they do not provide us with a complete picture of the interior, because the samples are sparsely distributed over the surface. We will need to look elsewhere for some additional evidences.

28–2 EVIDENCES FROM METEORITES

Every day about 100 tons of material is added to Earth's mass by the fall of debris that is picked up during Earth's orbit around the Sun.

Figure 28.1
Photo of mantle peridotite inclusions in basalt from Australia.

◆ Crust

The uppermost compositional layer of Earth. It is very thin and composed of two parts: granitic continental crust and basaltic oceanic crust.

◆ Mantle

The middle compositional layer of Earth. It is a thick layer made up of peridotite in the upper part and higher density rocks of peridotite composition in the lower part.

◆ Peridotite

A rock made up mostly silicon, oxygen, iron, and magnesium that is denser than the basalt and granite that make up Earth's crust.

◆ Stony Chondrites

Meteorites thought to represent the primitive material from which the planets were made.

◆ Stony Achondrites

Meteorites thought to represent material from small planetary bodies that had differentiated into layers and then were broken up.

◆ Iron Meteorites

Meteorites thought to represent the type of material found in Earth's core.

◆ Core

The deepest or central compositional layer of Earth. It is composed mostly of iron.

Most of the material consists of dust particles that burn up quickly on their way down through Earth's atmosphere. Occasionally larger pieces, called meteorites, make it through the atmosphere and land on the surface or in a body of water. There are several types of meteorites, some of which are seen in *Figure 28.2*.

About 85% of all meteorites that have been found are of the type called **stony chondrites**. These are composed of materials that suggest they are of the same basic material from which Earth and other planets in our solar system were originally made.

A second group of meteorites, making up about 7–8%, are called **stony achondrites**. They appear to be from the upper portions of small planetary bodies (perhaps as big as the Moon or even the planet Mars) that had differentiated into layers and were then broken up by collisions with other small planetary bodies.

In fact, some of these achondritic meteorites have chemical fingerprints that identify them as rocks that were somehow ejected from the Moon or Mars. **Iron meteorites** (about 6% of all meteorites) also come from differentiated, layered planetary bodies that were later broken and scattered.

All these meteorite types help us understand the interior of Earth. Stony chondrites show us the raw material from which Earth was made, while the achondrite and iron meteorites represent the major layers into which a planetary body, like Earth, may differentiate. Therefore, the very dense iron meteorites are similar in composition to Earth's central layer, called the **core**, and the stony achondrites are similar to the peridotite found in Earth's mantle.

28–3 EVIDENCES FROM THE EARTH'S MASS AND DENSITY

Earth's mass can be found by observing the acceleration of any object falling toward Earth. We need to remember Newton's Second Law of Motion and the Universal Law of Gravitation discussed earlier in this book. These laws can be written as simple equations:

Second Law of Motion

$$F = ma$$

Figure 28.2
Photos of the three main types of meteorites.

a. Iron

b. Stony Chondrite

c. Stony Achondrite

Universal Law of Gravitation

$$F = GmM/d^2$$

In these equations, **F** indicates the force of Earth's gravity, and **G** is the universal constant of gravitation. The letter **a** is the acceleration caused by Earth's gravitational force on some object with mass **m**, and **d** is the distance between Earth and the object. M is Earth's mass. By rearranging the terms in these two equations, we can determine Earth's mass, which will be given by this equation:

Earth's mass

$$M = ad^2/G$$

Notice that to find Earth's mass, all we need to know is the acceleration of the object, its distance from Earth, and the Universal Constant of Gravitation. We do not need to know the force of Earth's gravity or the mass of the falling object. Earth's mass turns out to be a fairly large number, 5.973×10^{24} kilograms. This may be nice to know, but why do we care what the mass of Earth is? We care because if we know Earth's mass then we can calculate its density, and the density in turn will tell us about the rocks that compose Earth.

Earth's average overall density is about 5.5 grams per cubic centimeter. As we noted earlier in this chapter, the rocks that make up Earth's crust have much lower densities; the continental crust averages about 2.7 g/cm³ and the oceanic crust averages about 3.0 g/cm³. Even the rocks brought up through volcanic action from Earth's upper mantle have densities of only about 3.3 g/cm³.

We can conclude from these observations that rocks in layers lower in the Earth's mantle will have even greater densities. But where is this denser material and how is it distributed? *Figure 28.3* shows two possible models for Earth's interior; either (a) the density could increase relatively continuously with depth, or (b) Earth's layers, in addition to the crust and the mantle, could consist of separate, discrete layers whose densities increase with depth discontinuously.

Our determination of the average density does not discriminate between the two models. There are many other models that could perhaps be imagined for the Earth's interior, but most of these do not follow Occam's Razor of selecting the simplest explanation that satisfies the observations. If we are to determine which of these two models for Earth's interior is most probable, we will need to find some additional evidences.

28–4 EVIDENCES FROM SEISMOLOGY

Earth seems hard and brittle to us, but it is actually somewhat elastic. When Earth's brittle, upper most layer (called the **lithosphere**) is subjected to enormous stress (pressure), that layer changes its shape—just like a balloon will become deformed when it is pressed between two hands, and a rubber band will become deformed when it is stretched. However, when the stress on the lithosphere is greater than Earth's limited flexing ability, the lithosphere will rupture. This is similar to stretching a rubber band until it breaks. After the rubber band breaks it snaps back to its original length and width, even though it is now broken. When Earth's lithosphere experiences a rupture, the resulting return of the lithosphere to its normal form is called **elastic rebound**. This phenomenon is illustrated in *Figure 28.4*. The break along which the failure of the lithosphere occurs is called a **fault.** The natural elasticity of Earth's upper layers generally prevents a fault from being more than a few dozen kilometers in length, and such faults have not been found to extend down through the lithosphere's entire thickness.

Stress on Earth's lithosphere can be almost undetectable, as when the natural gravitational pull of the Moon acts like a magnet on one side of Earth, or it can cause great natural catastro-

- **Lithosphere**
  The rigid outer shell of Earth, which consists of the crust and the outermost part of the mantle that is too cool to be partially molten.

- **Elastic Rebound**
  The point at which stress in Earth's lithosphere is strained to a point where it can bend no further and the lithosphere ruptures and rebounds somewhat like a rubber band that has just been pulled apart.

- **Fault**
  A break in Earth's lithosphere along which earthquakes have occurred.

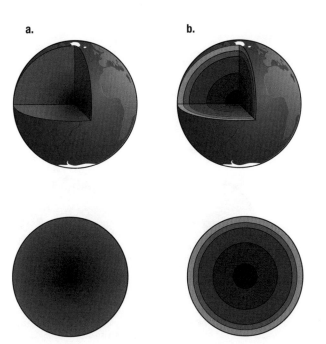

a. b.

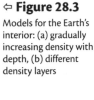

⇦ **Figure 28.3**
Models for the Earth's interior: (a) gradually increasing density with depth, (b) different density layers

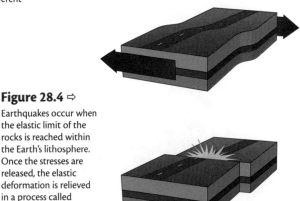

Figure 28.4 ⇨
Earthquakes occur when the elastic limit of the rocks is reached within the Earth's lithosphere. Once the stresses are released, the elastic deformation is relieved in a process called "elastic rebound."

phes when the stress is caused by the movements of the **tectonic plates**. When the edge of one enormous tectonic plate grinds up against another plate, deep under the surface, tremendous pressures are placed on the rock formations that comprise each tectonic plate. When mounting pressure finally snaps a section of a plate's dense, brittle rock formation, shock waves are generated. These waves are called **seismic waves** (*seismos* is Greek for earthquake); earthquakes simultaneously produce three different types of shock wave—compressional, shear, and surface. (Remember these wave types from Chapter 12).

Early seismologists observed that three kinds of waves, each with its own identifiable characteristics, arrived at earthquake-recording stations after an earthquake. Compression waves arrived first. They were called "primary" waves, a term that has been shortened to **P-waves**. The next to arrive (shear waves) were called "secondary" waves, or **S-waves**. The slowest and last to arrive were the surface waves. Surface waves can actually cause concrete highways and hard ground to visibly ripple. Surface waves generated by seismic events in the ocean can cause devastating **tsunamis** (sometimes erroneously called "tidal waves"). Surface waves, whether far inland or in the ocean, are responsible for most of the damage caused by an earthquake. They travel only near the surface, and therefore, they tell us little about the interior of Earth. It is important to remember that all three types of seismic waves are produced at the moment an earthquake occurs and travel in all directions outward from the source of the earthquake.

The source of an earthquake is called its **focus**. This is the point deep in Earth's lithosphere where the disturbance actually takes place. The location of an earthquake referred to in a news account is the point on Earth's surface directly above the focus; this is called the **epicenter** (see *Figure 28.5*). The speeds of P-waves

and S-waves not only differ from each other but they also change with the properties of the rocks through which they travel. Essentially, the stiffer and/or denser the rocks, the faster the waves travel through them. That fact makes it possible for us to gain knowledge about Earth's interior by analyzing the speeds of waves that pass through different parts of it.

As long as seismic waves stay within a medium whose elastic properties are the same in all directions, they will travel in straight lines. However, if seismic waves travel through media with different elastic properties (that is, from rocks of one elasticity to rocks of another, or through rocks with elasticity that is gradually changing with depth), they experience refraction—a phenomenon we recall from our previous discussion of wave behavior.

The difference is suggested by *Figure 28.6*. Studies of seismic waves detected by wave detectors (called **seismographs** or **seismometers**) set up at varying distances from a natural or artificially induced seismic event showed that the waves arriving at detectors farther and farther from an earthquake arrived progressively earlier and earlier than expected (if we assumed that Earth is a uniform-density sphere). The waves that traveled farther must have traveled through greater depths than those that traveled lesser distances (by either model in *Figure 28.6*), so they must have traveled faster as they went deeper. Therefore, the rock layers must be denser, the deeper they are, and the waves there-

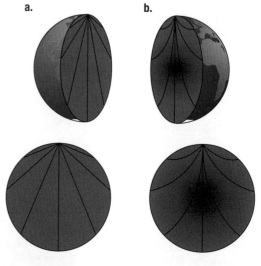

a.   b.

Figure 28.6
Paths for seismic waves in (a) a uniform-density Earth and (b) an Earth where the density increases with depth

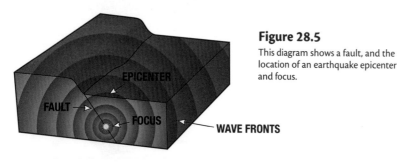

Figure 28.5
This diagram shows a fault, and the location of an earthquake epicenter and focus.

fore followed the curved paths shown in *Figure 28.6b*.

But there is more evidence that must be considered, before we flatly state that there is a uniform, gradual increase in rock layer density the deeper we probe into Earth's layers. In the early 1900s, Croatian seismologist Adrija Mohorovicic (1857–1936) compared the travel times of seismic waves arriving at seismometer stations less than 125 miles and more than 125 miles from earthquakes in eastern Europe.

He discovered in the resulting data a discontinuity in the seismic wave velocities that was related to some abrupt change in the rock layers only a few tens of kilometers below the surface. A **seismic discontinuity** is a distinct and abrupt change in the velocities of seismic waves (which signals a different hardness and density exist in part of a particular rock layer).

This requires modification of the idea that all rock layers in Earth's lithosphere show smooth and gradual change, from lighter, near Earth's surface, to denser, at deeper levels. Mohorovicic had discovered the base of Earth's crust, a thin rock layer that "floats" on top of a layer of measurably different properties, called Earth's mantle. The boundary between crust and mantle is now known as the "Mohorovicic discontinuity," generally shortened (for obvious reasons) to the **Moho**. The continental crust is fairly thick (18 to 35 miles), while the oceanic crust is thin (only about 3 to 6 miles thick).

About this same time, Beno Gutenberg (a German-American seismologist, 1889–1960) was puzzling over different data. Observations of seismograph records for strong earthquakes occurring long distances from seismometer stations showed an even more interesting behavior: In a broad band 103° to 143° from any earthquake epicenter, *no seismic waves at all were detected*. Beyond 143°, only P-waves were recorded.

Figure 28.7 depicts the observation and the interpretation. The band of seismic non-response is called the **shadow zone**. The P-waves that would have emerged within it have been refracted away by some very significant discontinuity, to emerge beyond 143° from the epicenter. The complete absence of S-waves beyond 103° from the epicenter indicates that the discontinuity is a boundary between the solid mantle and a liquid layer below, called the **outer core**. (Remember that S-waves are shear waves, and shear waves can travel only in a solid.)

As early as 1936, examination of seismograph records for earthquakes around the world showed that a few weak P-waves arrive within the shadow zone by reflection from a discontinuity within the liquid outer core. In addition, unusual early arrivals of P-waves traveling through Earth's center revealed that this discontinuity was the boundary between the liquid outer core and a solid **inner core**, at a depth of about 3200 miles. Seismic data have shown us

- **Seismic Discontinuity**
  A place where the velocities of seismic waves change abruptly.

- **Moho**
  The seismic discontinuity at the base of the Earth's crust.

- **Shadow Zone**
  A region of the Earth where seismic waves cannot be detected by seismometers.

- **Outer Core**
  The upper part of the core that is made of liquid iron.

- **Inner Core**
  The lower part of the core that is made of solid iron.

Figure 28.7
Earthquake shadow zones (a) S-wave and (b) P-wave shown for a quake occurring at the North Pole.

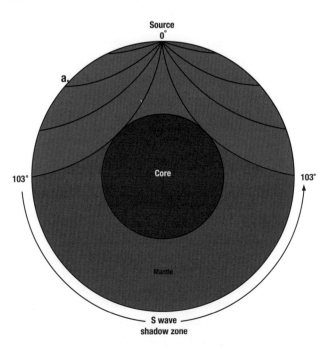

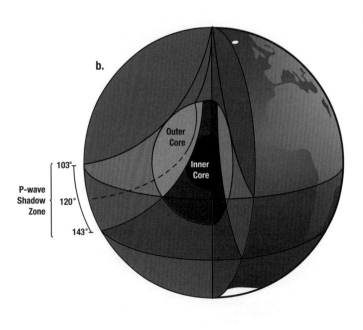

that Earth is, indeed, a layered planet with a very thin crust, a thick mantle (about 84 percent of Earth's total volume), and a core that is liquid on the outside and solid in the center.

28–5 EVIDENCES FROM THE EARTH'S MAGNETIC FIELD

Earth possesses a magnetic field that behaves as if the planet has a large permanent magnet within its core. We might hypothesize that a large, permanently magnetized body of iron is present deep inside Earth. However, a piece of magnetized iron that is heated to 760°C loses its magnetism. (The temperature at which iron loses its magnetism is called the **Curie temperature**.) The problem is that Earth's temperature reaches 760°C less than 50 km below the surface; that vertical subterranean distance is about the same as the horizontal distance between Salt Lake City and Provo, Utah. A distance of 50 km is only a fraction of Earth's surface-to-core distance (approximately 3000 km. Earth's core temperature is currently thought to be several thousand degrees centigrade.

So, if we must discard the once-popular idea of a magnetized core at the center of Earth, how then is Earth's magnetic field produced, and what is it trying to tell us about Earth's interior? We know that an electrical current in a wire also creates a magnetic field, so perhaps electrical currents could generate Earth's field. But how could such currents exist in Earth's core? The answer is that Earth's outer core (the area closest to Earth's surface) is liquid iron with relatively cooler temperatures at the core's surface (about 6,000°C) and increasingly hotter temperatures

towards the center of the core (where the temperature is about 6,500°C).

Therefore, the outer part of the core must experience convection, as the iron atoms move in great cylindrical cells driven by the temperature difference between the top and bottom of the upper core, and by Earth's rotation. When this liquid iron (an electrical conductor) is moved in the presence of pre-existing magnetic field (in this case, the sun's magnetic field) electrical currents result. These electrical currents in Earth's outer core then generate Earth's magnetic field. This would not happen without the sun's magnetic field to get it started, and it would not happen if the outer core of Earth was not liquid. The easily demonstrated fact that Earth has a magnetic field, therefore, when combined with what we also know about how electrical currents are generated, means that Earth's outer core must be liquid and composed of iron, just as was supposed by the evidence from seismology and from meteorites.

28–6 COMPOSITIONAL LAYERS OF THE EARTH

All the evidences we have examined so far show that Earth we know as a place of great oceans, snow-capped mountains, and generally temperate climate, is much different deep down inside of it.

Indeed, our planet is layered both compositionally and mechanically. First, let's look at the three distinct compositional layers, crust, mantle and core, that we have already identified as Earth's interior (refer to *Figure 28.8*).

The Crust

We live on Earth's crust, so we know quite a bit about its composition. In Chapter 27 we learned that continental crust and oceanic crust are significantly different. The continental crust consists of a wide variety of rock types—igneous, sedimentary, and metamorphic rocks of all sorts—but on average it has a granite composition. These rocks consist, in general, of fewer than 20 common minerals, most of which are **silicates**, compounds whose major components are silicon and oxygen, bonded together. The oceanic crust also consists largely of silicates,

• **Curie Temperature**
The temperature at which a material loses its magnetism.

• **Silicates**
Minerals that contain silicon and oxygen bonded together.

Figure 28.8
The Earth's interior compositional layers: the crust, mantle, and core.

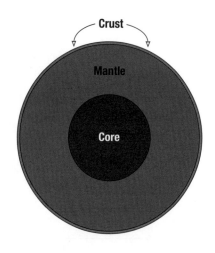

but with somewhat less silicon. In contrasting with the numerous different rock types found in the continental crust, the oceanic crust is virtually all basalt—a single specific type of rock. The average rock density of the continental crust is around 2.7 g/cm³, while the oceanic crust is about 3.0 g/cm³ as previously mentioned.

The Mantle

Most of Earth's mantle is a compound of silicate minerals called peridotite. This formation is high in silicon, oxygen, iron, and magnesium. Some chunks of the mantle, you will remember, have been brought to Earth's surface in volcanic eruptions, and pieces of some achondritic meteorites are also thought to be similar to Earth's mantle.

Laboratory experiments subjecting minerals found in peridotite to very high pressures and temperatures show those minerals to be unstable under the conditions present in the mantle's lower depths; these minerals must undergo chemical reactions and structural changes that produce denser minerals, at two depths in particular, at about 175 miles down, and also at about 425 miles down. In fact, seismic evidence reveals two zones of rapid change, from lower to higher seismic velocities at these same depths. It is thought that these represent the two sets of reactions predicted by laboratory experiments. Below those zones, the seismic velocities simply increase gradually, all the way to the base of the mantle. The chemical composition of the lower mantle is probably nearly the same as that of the upper mantle, but the atoms have rearranged themselves because of these chemical reactions to form denser, more stable compounds called **dense oxides**.

The Core

From seismic data and current understanding of Earth's magnetic field, scientists have determined that Earth's core is mostly iron. This idea is supported by research on iron meteorites, which are thought to be the remains of the cores of disrupted planet-size bodies. Earth's average density is about 5.5 g/cm³, and we have already concluded that the densities of Earth's crust and mantle are less than this value. It therefore follows that the core must be denser than the surface rocks. The density of liquid iron at the

extreme pressures that exist at the depth of the core would be 10 or 11 g/cm³, and the density of the solid iron within that core would be 12 to 14 g/cm³. These figures turn out to be about the values needed to provide the observed average density of our planet.

28-7 MECHANICAL LAYERS OF THE EARTH

In addition to Earth's compositional layers (crust, mantle, and core), it can also be categorized for study in terms of the mechanical behavior of the rocks in those layers. Mechanical behavior identifies how the rocks deform when forces are applied to them. Do they behave like solids or liquids? Are they brittle or plastic? We use the word *plastic* here to mean non-rigid, deformable, and capable of flowing in response to pressure, whether that pressure is mechanical or gravitational. Think back to Chapter 12 and the discussion on how Silly Putty® easily forms into a ball (mechanical pressure), and yet can deform and flow on its own. Leave the ball on a table overnight, and it will slowly sag and flatten by morning (force of gravity). The lithosphere's low velocity zone is certainly not like Silly Putty in any other way, but it *is* plastic.

From the study of earthquake waves, we can determine these properties of Earth's interior and map its mechanical layers (Refer to *Figure 28.9*).

The Lithosphere

Earth's outermost mechanical layer is a rigid, brittle layer called the **lithosphere**. The litho-

• **Dense Oxides**

Minerals that form deep in the Earth's mantle due to the enormous pressures.

• **Lithosphere**

The uppermost mechanical layer of Earth. It is brittle and is the only layer in which earthquakes can occur.

Figure 28.9

Earth's interior mechanical layers: The lithosphere, the asthenosphere, the mesosphere, the outer core, and the inner core.

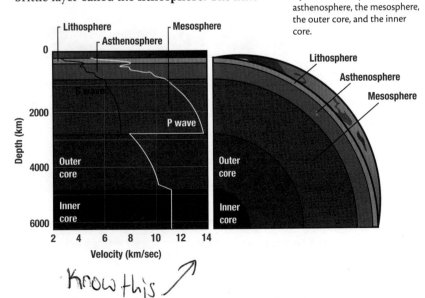

Know this ↗

sphere includes the relatively thin oceanic crust and somewhat thicker continental crust as well as the uppermost part of the mantle. The lithosphere has, therefore, a quite diverse mineral composition. It is composed of granite in the continental crust, basalt in the oceanic crust, and peridotite in the mantle. The lithosphere is usually about 45 to 60 miles thick. The continents and ocean basins are part of the lithosphere, and this crust is divided into several large segments, briefly described previously in this chapter, called tectonic plates. These enormous plates are not stationary, but "float" on the softer, partially molten rock layer of the mantle beneath them. As they move, they collide with and rub against one another.

The Asthenosphere

Scientists studying seismic waves traveling through Earth's subterranean rock formations have found that those waves encounter a layer through which they suddenly travel more slowly than in either the rocks above or those below. This layer extends to a depth of approximately 150 miles and is sometimes called the **low velocity zone**. The top of the low velocity zone is in the upper mantle and is not a boundary between different types of rock (such as, for example, the Mohorovicic discontinuity between the crust and the mantle). Rather, it is a boundary between solid peridotite and peridotite that is partially molten—perhaps only 1% to 10% liquid, but enough to make the rock plastic and able to flow.

Because the low velocity zone is a relatively soft layer in the lithosphere, it is called the **asthenosphere** (from the Greek *astheneia*, meaning weak), and *Figure 28.10* shows why it exists. The curve in this figure shows how temperature increases inside Earth. As we go deeper, the temperature tends not to increase quite so sharply below about 150 miles. At depths between about 45 and 150 miles below the surface, the temperature curve crosses into the shaded area, which represents the range of temperatures and pressures at which solid peridotite begins to soften, and become more pliable or plastic. We call this "partial melting." Peridotite, like most rocks, consists of more than one mineral. Each of the minerals in peridotite has its own melting point at any given pressure, and that is why the boundary between solid and liquid peridotite is a band, rather than a sharp line. When the temperature curve crosses below that band with further increase in depth, peridotite is again completely solid, owing to the higher pressure, even though the temperature in Earth continues to climb higher as we go down.

The Mesosphere

Below the asthenosphere is a layer (the lower part of the mantle) that has not been given a formal name, although scientists studying the mechanical aspects of Earth's layers sometime called it the **mesosphere**. This layer extends all the way down to the core. This layer is solid, not even partially molten, and yet because of the great pressures and temperatures in this part of Earth, the rocks are still plastic, not brittle like the lithosphere. Here the rock still has a peridotite composition, but the high pressures in this part of Earth's interior have recrystallized the minerals that make up peridotite into more dense silicates and oxides. The high pressures also allow the solid rock to flow (very slowly, at a rate of no more than a few centimeters a year). This flow is caused by temperature and density differences within the mesosphere. Over time

- **Low Velocity Zone**
A region of the upper mantle where seismic waves travel slower than expected.

- **Asthenosphere**
A soft, plastic, partially-molten mechanical layer in Earth located below the lithosphere.

- **Mesosphere**
A term we use here to describe the mechanical layer between the asthenosphere and the outer core. It is solid, but still plastic and able to flow.

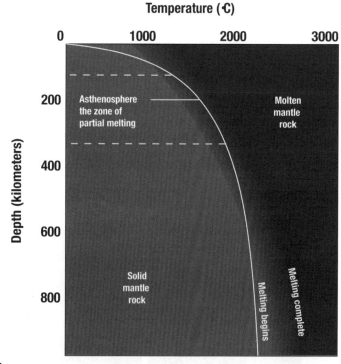

Figure 28.10
The white curve shows how Earth's internal temperature and pressures are related. The shaded band is the range of temperatures and pressures within which peridotite begins to melt. Between depths of about 70 and 250 kilometers, the temperature is within the region of partial melting of peridotite. This identifies the lithosphere's low velocity zone, or asthenosphere.

this flow has helped the Earth to mix and stir itself, allowing the layers we now observe to form.

The Outer Core and Inner Core

The base of the mesosphere is also the base of the mantle, the level where Earth's core begins. Here is the one place inside the Earth where there is both a change in composition and in mechanical properties. The outer core is made of iron, not a peridotite-like material. It is not solid, but liquid. The liquid nature of the outer core has several important effects. First, it allows the Earth to have a strong magnetic field. Second, it prevents earthquake S-waves from penetrating through the Earth, strongly refract-ing P-waves and creating a large seismic shadow zone for both wave types. Lastly, the continuing solidification of iron onto the solid inner core releases an enormous amount of heat, helping to keep the interior of Earth warm.

Summary

Earth is made of layers. The layers can be identified in two ways: 1) based upon composi-tion, or (2) based upon physical properties. The layers are different depending on which of the two ways we choose. Earth's compositional lay-ers are: (1) crust, (2) mantle, and (3) core, while its physical property layers are: (1) lithosphere, (2) asthenosphere, (3) mesosphere, (4) outer core, and (5) inner core.

Chapter Framework

A. Earth's Interior—Evidence
1. Direct Observation
2. Meteorites
3. Earth's Mass and Density
4. Seismology
5. Composition of Earth's Layers

B. Composition of Earth's Layers
1. The Crust
2. The Mantle
3. The Core

C. Mechanical Structure of Earth's Interior
1. Lithosphere
2. Asthenosphere
3. Mesosphere
4. Outer and Inner Core

Comprehension

True/False
1. _____ The crust is mainly made up of peridotite.
2. _____ The lithosphere is a rigid outer shell of the Earth, which consists of the crust and the outer most part of the mantle.
3. _____ The outer core is made up of solid iron rock.
4. _____ The deeper into Earth's center one goes, the more dense rock becomes.

Matching
1. _____ The middle compositional layer of the Earth. A thick layer made up of peridotite in the upper part and higher density rocks of peridotite composition in the lower part.
2. _____ A break in the lithosphere of the Earth along which earthquakes have occurred.
3. _____ The point at which earthquakes originate.
4. _____ A term we use here to describe the mechanical layer between the Asthenosphere and the outer core. It is solid, but still plastic and able to flow.
5. _____ Compression waves that arrive before shear waves at the seismic wave detectors.
6. _____ A region of the upper mantle where seismic waves travel slower than expected.
7. _____ Rock made of mostly silicon, oxygen, iron, and magnesium that is denser than the basalt and granite that make up Earth's crust.
8. _____ The _____ of an earthquake is the point on the Earth's surface directly above the focus.
9. _____ These are thought to represent the type of material found in Earth's core.
10. _____ Meteorites that are believed to be similar to the material that formed Earth and other planets in the solar system.
11. _____ The lower part of the core that is made of solid iron.

a. *Curie temperature*
b. *Mesosphere*
c. *Stony achondrites*
d. *Iron meteorites*
e. *Inner core*
f. *Silicates*
g. *P-Waves*
h. *Mantle*
i. *Epicenter*
j. *Shadow zone*
k. *Low velocity zone*
l. *Fault*
m. *Peridotite*
n. *Focus*
o. *Asthenosphere*

12. _____ Minerals that contain silicon and oxygen bonded together.
13. _____ The temperature at which a material loses its magnetism.
14. _____ Layer composed of partially molten peridotite.
15. _____ A region of where seismic waves cannot be detected by seismometers.

Fill in the Blank
1. Scientists measure seismic waves using a _____.
2. When the temperature of iron reaches 760°, known as the _____, it loses its magnetism.
3. An earthquake occurs at the _____, and the spot directly above this location, on the surface, is called the _____.
4. The core consists of a _____ iron and nickel outer core layer and a _____ iron and nickel inner layer.
5. The _____ is the seismic discontinuity at the base of the Earth's crust.

Analysis

1. From Earth's average density, we know that:
   a) The Earth's interior is of uniform density.
   b) Density increases as the depth increases.
   c) Earth is a layered planet.
   d) Density decreases as the depth increases.

2. What causes the S-wave shadow zone?
   a) The distance is too far to sustain any amplitude.
   b) The waves refract and are directed away.
   c) The waves reflect back to the epicenter.
   d) Shear waves cannot pass through the liquid outer core.

3. From the center to surface, the chemically distinct layers Earth are:
   a) Inner core, outer core, mantle, crust.
   b) Core, mantle, lithosphere.
   c) Inner core, outer core, lower mantle, upper mantle, crust.
   d) Core, mantle, crust.

4. Which of the following is one of the important sources of information about the interior structure of Earth?
   a) Sedimentation rates.
   b) Exploration of deep caves.
   c) X-rays.
   d) Earth's magnetic field.
   e) Chemical analysis of rocks from the interior.

5. What causes the P-wave shadow zone?
   a) The distance is too far to sustain any amplitude.

b) The waves refract and are directed away.

c) The waves reflect back to the epicenter.

d) Shear waves cannot pass through the liquid outer core.

6. How do we know the composition of the asthenosphere?

7. What are Earth's five mechanical layers called?

8. What evidence do meteorites give us concerning the composition of Earth's interior?

9. When we refer to "plastic" in describing the low velocity zone, what does it stand for?

10. Explain the difference between the mechanical layers and the compositional layers.

11. If the outer core and inner core are both composed of iron, why is the inner core solid and the outer core liquid?

12. Briefly describe the differentiation of Earth's interior and what this means.

13. Why do seismic waves make abrupt changes in direction and speed when traveling through Earth? Why do the waves travel in curved paths?

14. Describe the differences between S-waves and P-waves.

15. How are the focus and epicenter related?

16. What does *elastic rebound* mean?

Synthesis

1. What creates a shadow zone? What are the ranges of the shadow zones for S-waves and P-waves? Sketch an example of an earthquake with the different shadow zones generated. Also show in the sketch the curves of each seismic wave according to the layers and density of Earth.

2. List the five sources of information about the Earth's interior discussed in the chapter and briefly describe what information is obtained from each source.

3. Draw a picture of showing both the mechanical and chemical layers of the Earth. Label the drawing and describe each layer of the picture. Explain the relationship between the two types of layers.

4. Figure 28.9 uses the mechanical classification of Earth's interior instead of the compositional classification of Earth's interior when describing seismic waves. Explain why.

5. What is an earthquake? Under what circumstances do earthquakes occur?

6. List the major seismic discontinuities and explain what causes each of them to occur.

7. Look at Figure 28.9. Notice that besides the major discontinuities the waves increase in speed as they increase in depth. After the waves travel through the outer core, does their wave speed continue to increase or decrease as they approach the side of the lithosphere opposite the epicenter? Explain the reasoning behind your answer. Consider the following additional question to aid you in formulating the correct solution.

   a. What is a wave?

   b. What happens to density as depth increases?

   c. How does density play a key role in the waves' speed?

FROM CONTINENTAL DRIFT TO PLATE TECTONICS: THE EVIDENCE

"And unto Eber were born two sons: the name of one was Peleg; for in his days was the earth divided...."

~ Genesis 10:25

One of the most incredible ideas to surface in man's relatively recent scientific studies of our planet Earth is the theory of continental drift. How could an entire continent, so enormous, hard and unchanging, actually be floating on Earth's surface? This idea was so outrageous that when it was first formally proposed it was openly ridiculed by the scientific establishment of the time. The only type of division of lands they believed could occur on Earth was the type spoken of in Genesis: a political division of land among peoples.

In this chapter we will learn about the theories of Continental Drift and Plate Tectonics and review the evidences that led to these theories, including:

- Jigsaw fit of the continents
- Matching cross-continent structural trends
- Fossil (paleontological) evidence
- Paleoclimatic evidence
- Paleomagnetic evidence
- Sea-floor magnetic reversal stripes
- World-wide earthquake patterns
- Sea-floor topography
- Seafloor age
- Seafloor sediments thickness

29–1 A BRIEF HISTORY

In 1620, Sir Francis Bacon (1561–1626) noted in his book *Novum Organum* that the coasts on either side of the Atlantic Ocean appeared to parallel one another. He may not have been the first to make this observation, for it was readily apparent even on the crude maps of that day. During the succeeding three centuries such observations multiplied. To Benjamin Franklin the apparent relationship of the coastlines was so striking that he speculated, far ahead of his time, that the surface of Earth might be a cracked shell whose fragments were driven about by the movements of a dense fluid upon which they floated. Near the end of the 19th century, Eduard Suess, an Austrian geologist, noted many geologic similarities between Africa, South America and India. To him, those geological clues suggested the fragmentation of a supercontinent. He also proposed that Earth's oceans had formed when blocks of crust between the present landmasses sank.

This set the stage for Dr. Alfred Wegener, a German meteorologist who championed an idea that would eventually revolutionize the way we look at Earth. He theorized that Earth's continents are mobile blocks of crust, capable of

LEARNING OBJECTIVES

- Understand the development of the theories of continental drift and Plate Tectonics.
- Be able to discuss the evidences for the theory of Continental Drift and understand the reasons why this theory was not widely accepted.
- Learn the new evidences that emerged after World War II that led to the theory of Plate Tectonics.
- Be able to explain why the theory of Plate Tectonics is such a good theory.

moving thousands of kilometers around the globe. This is the "Theory of Continental Drift," The story behind Wegener's then-radical ideas about the movements of Earth's surface shows how scientific curiosity, inquiry and testing moves, often ponderously, toward the truths it is capable of seeking, sometimes taking wrong turns but slowly correcting its own errors as it goes. And the story of how this theory developed is one of the best examples of how science works, and how the true scientist hopes that newer, revised theories growing from his or her original concept will eventually result in a deeper understanding of the complexities of our physical reality.

Wegener, born and raised in Germany, was educated in German schools, which at that time provided the best higher education available in the sciences. His interests in meteorology and geology developed as he studied astronomy at his university, and after receiving his degree in 1905, he took a position as a lecturer in meteorology at the University of Marburg. He recorded that he first began thinking about a concept that he called "continental displacement" in 1910 when he, like others before him, considered the parallelism of the coastlines across the Atlantic Ocean. At first, he felt the whole idea of continents actually moving was improbable. However,

he ran across an old scientific paper that suggested strong similarities between fossils on opposite sides of the Atlantic Ocean. This similarity had been used by the author of the paper to suggest an ancient land bridge between South America and Africa that had foundered and sunk. Wegener knew that the sinking of large blocks of continental crust was not likely, but the fossil correlations intrigued him. He began to gather data concerning geologic similarities between unconnected continents, and in 1912 he first outlined his ideas about "continental displacement" in a lecture. He followed that in 1915 with a book, *The Origin of Continents and Oceans*, in which the comprehensive theory was described.

During his lifetime, Wegener was highly respected for his work in climatology and paleo-climatology (ancient climates), but his theory of continental drift was given a cool reception by his scientist colleagues. Nevertheless, despite the rejection of his original theory and the outright ridicule he received from most of that period's scientific establishment, it is for his ideas about the movements of the continents that he is remembered today. Wegener didn't live to see his theory widely accepted; he died in an ill-fated climatological expedition to Greenland in 1930, and it was not until the 1970s that the theory finally gained wide acceptance.

29-2 EVIDENCES FOR CONTINENTAL DRIFT

How did Wegener come up with his theory of continental drift? We need to look at the geological observations that he was trying to explain. Remember that a theory is an explanation that ties together all the available observations and all of the pieces of evidence. Just as a detective uses pieces of evidence to solve a crime, so a scientist uses evidences to compose a theory that tries to solve some mystery about the physical world. Each of the evidences that support a particular theory gives us increased confidence that the theory is good.

Jigsaw Fit of the Continents

The most obvious evidence for continental drift, and certainly one of the most compelling, is the shape of the continental margins.

The jigsaw puzzle-like fit of some continents is obvious on a world map, but it is even more striking when the continents are cut from the map and juxtaposed. *Figure 29.1* shows how well South America and Africa match at the edges of their continental shelves (which, you will remember from Chapter 27, are the actual edges of the continents). There are only few minor regions where the two continents overlap. This might be of some concern if those areas were not generally where major rivers empty into the sea and deposit their sediment. Because such sediment has been deposited during relatively recent times, the "overlaps" did not exist before the continents separated. In addition, it is probable that some deformation would have occurred along the continental margins when these huge landmasses started drifting apart.

South America and Africa are not the only continents that fit together remarkably well at their shelf boundaries. As later figures in this chapter will show, India, Antarctica, and Australia join them in the south, with North America and Eurasia to the north, to strongly suggest all those continents were once part of a massive supercontinent. Wegener named this large landmass **Pangaea**, a word derived from Greek, meaning "all earth." *Figure 29.2* shows Pangaea as he envisioned it seventy years ago. The efforts since then of many researchers using sophisticated modern scientific devices to refine

• **Pangaea**

Pangaea is the name Alfred Wegener gave to the supercontinent that broke up at the start of the Mesozoic Era to form the continents we have today.

Figure 29.1

The fit of the continental shelf margins of South America and Africa. Continents are shown in brown, continental shelves in blue, and the mismatched areas are shown in red. The major mismatch areas are located where large rivers flow into the ocean from one of the two continents. The deltas of these rivers have built up since the time the continents drifted apart.

Figure 29.2

The supercontinent of Pangaea as Wegener thought it would have looked near the end of the Paleozoic Era, just prior to its breakup.

or add to Wegener's proposed map of Pangaea have produced remarkably few major changes.

Continental Structure

In our discussion in Chapter 27 of the major structural features of the continents we learned that all continents have one or more shields, stable platforms, and mountain belts. The shields are the ancient geological (although not necessarily geographical) cores of the continents. Each continent's shield or shields are surrounded by stable platforms. There are some shields, however, that end abruptly at continental margins. *Figure 29.3* shows the shield areas of South America and Africa, with the continents arranged as in *Figure 29.1*. The shield regions that end at the margin of one continent appear to continue on the adjacent continent, despite the fact that the continents were arranged according to continental shelf margins rather than according to the locations of shields.

The curved lines adjacent to the shields represent **structural trends**. These are the directions of major geologic structures, such as zones of deformed rocks and mountain belts. They appear to be continuous across the continental boundaries, as if they had once been connected. Not only that but, across these boundaries, the ages of the rocks also match, as do localities of economic mineral resources such as tin, iron, and diamond deposits.

We have used South America and Africa to demonstrate the geologic continuity across continental boundaries because we first used those continental examples to discuss the way continental shelf margins fit. Had we chosen to examine other continental boundaries, the results would have been similar. For example, on a map, the Appalachian Mountains of eastern North America continue across into the British Isles and Scandinavia when the North Atlantic Ocean is cut away and North America, Greenland and Europe are brought together.

Paleontological (Fossil) Evidence

Could the continuity of structural trends, as well as the jigsaw fit of the continental margins, all be coincidence? Other scientists of the time were convinced that they were, despite Wegener's claims. Additional evidence for Wegener's theory piled up as **paleontologists**

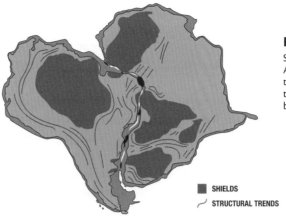

Figure 29.3
Structural features of South America and Africa, with the two continents arranged so that the continental shelves match best.

■ SHIELDS
╱ STRUCTURAL TRENDS

started turning up fossils in rocks of the similar ages across these continental boundaries, particularly in the five southern continents (South America, Africa, India, Australia, and Antarctica). Some of the fossils discovered were the remains of ancient land plants, and others represented land-dwelling animals of various species. Neither the plants nor animals that Wegener studied in the fossil record could have survived the long swim across the oceans, nor could they have survived in the widely different climates we find today on these continents.

One of the most well-known is a group of plants called the **Glossopteris flora**. We should understand here that the biological term "flora" consists of the plants of a particular area, environment, or time period. This particular group, therefore, is made up of fossil plants that are typically found in association with one another, and the genus Glossopteris is the characteristic fossil for which the flora is named (*Figure 29.4*).

During Wegener's lifetime this flora was known from rocks of the Permian Period in South America, Africa, India, Australia, and Madagascar; it has since been found in Permian rock formations in Antarctica and the Falkland Islands. Seeds of those plants could not have been spread across thousands of kilometers of

• **Structural trends**
Structural trends are the orientations of major geologic features such as mountain belts, continental shields, stable platforms, and areas of folded and deformed rocks.

• **Paleontologists**
Scientists who study ancient life preserved as fossils in the rocks.

• **Glossopteris Flora**
The Glossopteridales are an extinct group of seed plants that arose during the Permian Period. These plants went on to become a dominant part of the flora on the southern part of the supercontinent Pangaea through the rest of the Permian, though they dwindled to extinction by the end of the Triassic Period.

Figure 29.4
Fossil leaves from plants that constitute the Glossopteris flora. A fossil of Glossopteris itself is on the left and is about 20 centimeters long.

• **Mesosaurus**

Mesosaurus was a fresh-water dwelling reptile that lived from the late Pennsylvanian Period to the early Permian Period. It had an elongated head and snout with nostrils near its eyes and a flattened tail used for swimming. Typically it would have been about 1.5 feet long.

• **Lystrosaurus**

Lystrosaurus was a sturdily built, plant-eating reptile (not a dinosaur). Scientists disagree on whether it spent most of its time in water browsing on plants like a modern hippo, or whether it lived mostly on land. An adult would have been about 3 feet long and weighed about 200 pounds.

• **Paleoclimatology**

Paleoclimatology is the study of ancient climates.

Figure 29.5

The present distribution of rocks glaciated by the Permian Ice Age is shown on the left, while their distribution, when restored to the continents pre-drift positions, is shown on the right. Arrows show the directions of ice movement.

open ocean by natural methods, so Wegener reasoned that these southern landmasses must not have been separated by oceans during the Permian Period.

Fossils of some freshwater and land animals are also found in common on landmasses that are currently widely separated. During the Permian Period, a small freshwater reptile called a **mesosaurus** lived in what today is South Africa and also in Brazil. Somewhat later, during the early Triassic Period, a medium-sized land-dwelling reptile called a **lystrosaurus** left its remains in what are now Brazil, South Africa, India, Antarctica, and China. Neither mesosaurus nor lystrosaurus were capable of crossing large bodies of water, yet their fossils are now separated by oceans.

Many more examples could be cited, but these demonstrate why Wegener was so impressed with the paleontological evidence for continental drift.

Paleoclimatic Evidence

Rocks contain clues about the climatic or environmental conditions under which they formed. For example, fossil plants in sedimentary rocks can often be identified as typical of tropical, subtropical, or temperate climates; coal beds are the remains of plants that flourished in warm, swampy, coastal environments; coral reefs only flourish in warm shallow seas found near the equator; some rocks consist of chemical precipitates (such as rock salt), suggesting the evaporation of poorly circulating bodies of water such as lakes or landlocked seas; thick deposits of windblown sand may be preserved as sandstones and record the positions of ancient deserts.

Among the most distinctive indicators of

ancient climates are the deposits left by continental glaciers, great sheets of ice that covered thousands of square kilometers. Glaciers can form and exist only in a cold climate and as they move forward (during cold weather) and recede (i.e. melt during warm weather) they leave characteristic deposits of sediment that can be recognized as glacial in origin. The Great Ice Age of the northern hemisphere—the one we often associate with woolly mammoths and saber-toothed tigers—was a very recent event (geologically speaking), ending only a few thousand years ago. Another ice age occurred much earlier in Earth's history. Evidence for it is found in Permian age rocks of the southern hemisphere, distributed as shown in *Figure 29.5a*. Consider the arrangement of these glaciated areas as they appear on a present-day world map. It seems to make no sense. Why was eastern South America cold enough to support glaciers, but the much higher and therefore colder Andes Mountains on the continent's west coast had no glaciers during this period? How could India, sitting across the Equator, have had glaciers? And if India had glaciers, then why did they not form in the higher and colder Himalayas?

Such questions as these bothered Wegener. He felt that continental drift provided the best solution to these mysteries. *Figure 29.5b* shows Pangaea again, with the continents arranged so that their continental shelf margins fit best. The areas affected by the Permian glaciation now form one single region. Not only that, but the directions in which the ice moved (which can be determined by deep grooves left in the glaciated rocks) are now consistent. Wegener viewed this as a remarkable confirmation of continental drift and believed that this **paleoclimatic** evidence could hardly be coincidence.

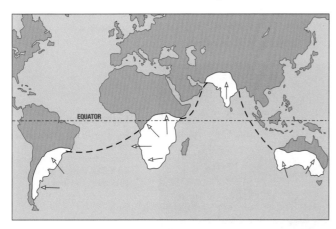

a.

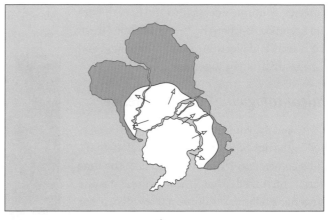

b.

Figure 29.6 shows the overall climatic conditions of Earth during the late Paleozoic Era (Permian Period), as determined from the rocks of that age. This climatic distribution can only be explained by moving the continents back into their pre-drift positions. It cannot be explained on the basis of their present positions.

Paleomagnetic Evidence

When volcanoes erupt basaltic lava (that is, lava that will cool to form the black volcanic rock we call basalt), one of the minerals found in the rock is called **magnetite,** an iron oxide that can be magnetized. As basalt cools at the surface of Earth, the grains of magnetite become tiny recorders. They record the orientation of Earth's magnetic field in a process similar to the recording of music onto a cassette tape. When the basalt has completely cooled, this magnetic orientation is "frozen" into the rock. A basalt can lose its magnetic record only if it is heated above the Curie temperature (refer back to Chapter 28 for a discussion of the Curie temperature).

Figure 29.7 depicts schematically what is found when the magnetic fields of late Paleozoic lava flows are measured in South America, Africa, and India. The magnetic records do not give a consistent orientation for the direction to the North Magnetic Pole. The nature of Earth's magnetic field requires that there be only one North Pole at a time; therefore, these results do not make sense. But if these landmasses are placed together in the way that Wegener believed

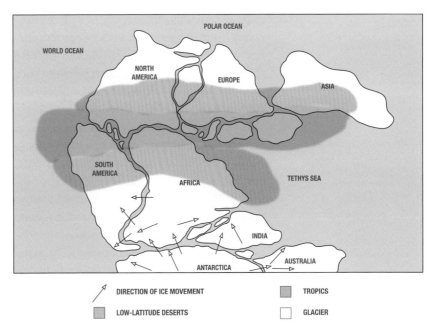

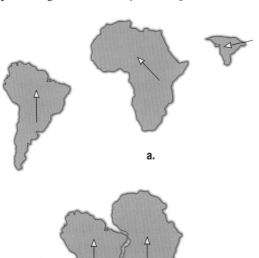

a.

b.

they existed during the late Paleozoic, then the north arrows frozen in the basalt of each continent all point to a single location. Again, Wegener felt that this was a strong indication that the continents had drifted from locations that were quite different from the positions they currently have.

29–3 A COLD RECEPTION FOR A NEW THEORY

The evidences outlined above became main points Alfred Wegener cited in support of his theory of continental drift. It connected some puzzling observations and gave them a single, common explanation, which is what good theories are supposed to do. Why then was this theory given such a cold reception by the scientific establishment in the early 1900s? It was a problem of mechanics, for even though the theory could explain many things, Wegener's theory offered nothing to explain how the continents could have moved. Unfortunately for Wegener, he was an empiricist rather than a theoretician—that is, he was best at building theories out of observations but not particularly

Figure 29.6

Earth's overall climate picture, covering the supercontinent of Pangaea during the late Paleozoic Era (Permian Period), as determined from the rocks of that age. This distribution of climates is unexplainable on the basis of the present arrangement of landmasses in the world.

♦ **Paleomagnetism**

Magnetism preserved or fossilized in rocks. It can often tell us about changes in the orientation of rock bodies after their formation.

♦ **Magnetite**

An iron oxide mineral found in basalt. The magnetic field of the magnetite aligns with Earth's magnetic field as molten basalt cools to solid form and makes a permanent record of the direction of Earth's magnetic field when the rock formed.

Figure 29.7

(a) Orientations of the magnetic fields recorded in lava flows of late Paleozoic Age in South America, Africa, and India, with the present orientation of continents; (b) The same magnetic records, with the continents assembled in their pre-drift orientations.

good at supporting those theories with the necessary mathematics and physics. Wegener's theory wasn't helped when Sir Harold Jeffreys (1891–1989), an eminent British physicist with a formidable scientific reputation, made some elementary calculations to show beyond doubt that Earth's ocean floor is much too rigid for continents to be shoved through it by any imaginable force. Jeffreys' math was beyond dispute, and not even the few scientists who felt continental drift was the best explanation for the growing body of fossil, geological, and magnetic evidence could offer a more reasonable mechanism for separating the continents. To many geologists and scientists of other fields, it seemed almost as though the very validity of the evidence itself rested on the need for an acceptable mechanism, and there didn't seem to be one.

Jeffreys spent years in the face of mounting evidence trying to disprove the concept of continental drift, and for a long time his efforts were largely successful. He was joined by a host of geologists and other scientists who considered the whole idea, to quote one of them, "utter damned rot." Most of the evidence that came forth early in the debate was found in the southern hemisphere. Therefore, some South African geologists (notably Alexander Du Toit) who were active in the first half of the 20th century accepted and continued to foster Wegener's ideas.

For a time, Wegener's theory was considered acceptable south of the Equator but heresy in the north. However, the great majority of geologists were European and North American, so continental drift fell into disfavor with the bulk of the scientific community. Despite its general rejection, the theory was far from forgotten, and heated debates about the evidence went on for decades.

29-4 A THEORY REBORN: EVIDENCES FROM THE SEAFLOOR

From the moment Wegener had proposed that Earth's continents were once a single supercontinent, and right up to the mid-20th century, a minority of advocates and the majority of crit-

ics of continental drift had both concentrated their attention on the continents. This was not because they were not interested in the ocean basins, but because little was then known about the seafloor.

During and after World War II, the U.S. government and other countries with oceanic coastlines became interested in the character of the sea floor. Submarines had been critical to the success (and perhaps to the near failure) of the Allies' war effort. Scientists were interested in the ocean floor for pure research. Industries and businesses of the U.S. and many other nations were interested in the natural-resources potential of the ocean floor, and it was important for our Armed Services to know what the seafloor looked like so that we would better know where to hide our submarines and where the enemy might be hiding theirs.

The 1950s and 1960s saw considerable effort expended to map the ocean floor in great detail. Among the surprising features found during the mapping was a great sinuous ridge that girdled the globe, only rarely poking above sea level at places like Iceland and in a few other locations.

In the Atlantic Ocean, the ridge was located almost exactly in the center, equally distant from North America and Europe, and from Africa and South America. The newly discovered undersea ridge's shape was strikingly similar to the continental shelf margins of the continents on either side. Not only did the continents fit together as Wegener had proposed more than one-half century earlier, but this mid-Atlantic ridgeline mimicked the same shape. This could not be just another coincidence. Scientists who had earlier rejected the theory of continental drift, began to look at it again. What they found were many new evidences to support the theory, and they found the mechanism for moving the continents.

Sir Harold Jeffreys and others who opposed the theory had less and less to say. By the late 1960s and early 1970s the shift of scientists away from Jeffreys and towards continental drift as a fact was in full swing. The "**Theory of Plate Tectonics**," a new theory that included all of Wegener's observations as well as many new ones, and which offered for the first time a mechanism for explaining how enormous continental masses can drift, was born.

♦ **Theory of Plate Tectonics**
The model of Earth in which the rigid outer layer of the Earth (lithosphere) is fractured into separate pieces (plates) that move relative to one another carried by convection currents originating in the mantle and driven by heat released by radioactivity. The plates move on a partially molten layer (asthenosphere) underneath them and may push against one another (convergent boundary), move away from one another (divergent boundary), or slide past one another (transform boundry). The model unifies the ideas of continental drift and seafloor spreading.

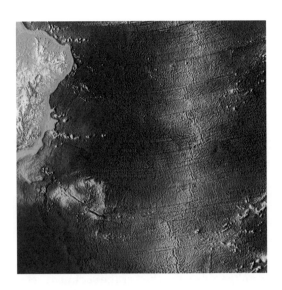

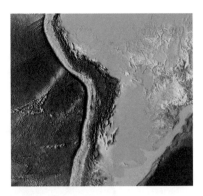

Figure 29.8a
Topography of the ocean floor off the coast of Brazil. Notice the Mid-Atlantic Ridge with its central rift valley.

Figure 29.8b
Ocean topography off the western coast of South America. Note the lines of underwater volcanoes (seamounts) and the location of the Peru Trench right next to the continent.

Topography of the Seafloor

When the first maps of the ocean floor became available, several new features were discovered that needed to be explained (*Figure 29.8*). Detailed investigation of the long, winding Mid-Atlantic Ridge revealed that it has a central valley running along its length. What could be the cause of this valley?

Another feature that was hard to explain was a type of seamount (underwater hills or mountains), called a **guyot**. Guyots all have perfectly flat tops. Research vessels sent to collect samples by dredging from the tops of these seamounts found dead coral in the sediments dredged up. This was an amazing discovery because most of the tiny life forms that produce coral need filtered sunlight to survive, so almost all coral in the ocean only grows a few feet below the surface of the ocean. Yet the tops of the guyots were hundreds of feet below the ocean's surface. Either sea level had been much, much lower in the past, or else these seamounts had sunk deeply into the ocean. Whichever was the case, this new finding needed to be addressed in any plausible theory about the formation of the ocean basins.

Unexpected also was the discovery of a third major feature of the ocean floor: deep trenches—long, narrow, and much deeper than the rest of the ocean basin. In addition, these deep features were not located in the central parts of the ocean basins, but were generally found along the edges. How did these trenches form and why were the deepest places in the oceans located near their margins and not farther out in the basin? Research continued as theories were developed.

Composition and Age of the Ocean Floor

In addition to collecting data on the topography of the ocean floor, scientists working in this post-war era also collected samples from the bottom of the ocean. They found some interesting patterns in the composition of the ocean floor, the age of the ocean floor, and the thickness of sediments on the ocean floor.

First, the ocean floor was compositionally simple. It was made up everywhere of basalt, covered in places by sediment. This is unlike the continents, which are composed of a wide variety of rock types. Second, the ages of rocks on the ocean floor were found to be very young near the ridges, and rocks dredged up farther from the ridges were found to be progressively older (*Figure 29.9*). The oldest rocks, however, were still quite young when compared to rocks on the

- ◆ **Guyots**

Flat-topped seamounts (underwater mountains usually of volcanic origin) that are the submerged equivalent of modern atolls.

Figure 29.9

Ages of the rocks on the ocean floor. Note how the ages get progressively younger farther away from the mid-ocean ridges. Also, note that the oldest ocean floor rocks are less than 200 million years old.

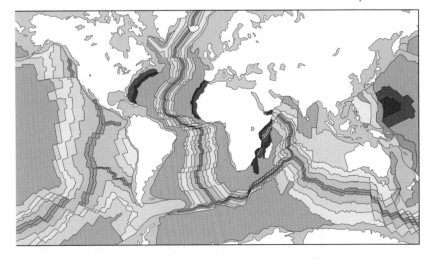

	(0-5 MY)		(23-35 MY)		(56-65 MY)		(146-157 MY)
	(5-23 MY)		(35-56 MY)		(65-146 MY)		(157-178 MY)

continents; the oldest rocks on the ocean floor were Jurassic (about 200 million years old), while the oldest rocks thus far discovered on any continent are nearly 4 billion years old. Third, no sediment covered the basalts right at the mid-ocean ridges, but the thickness of sediment became greater and greater when examined farther and farther from the ridges.

29–5 SEAFLOOR SPREADING

A breakthrough came with an idea proposed in 1960 by Harry Hess of Princeton University. He called this idea "**seafloor spreading**." Hess reasoned that the central rift of the ocean ridge had to be a tensional feature, indicating that the seafloor was being pulled apart. He proposed that convection currents in the soft and partially molten upper mantle were rising near the mid-ocean ridges and then flowing horizontally away from the ridge, pulling the overlying oceanic crust with it. The ridge, he said, is high because of hot, buoyant magma rising underneath it. The

• **Seafloor Spreading**
The theory that the ocean floor grows on either side as the mid-ocean ridge moves apart. The rift created in this process is filled in with basalt as magma squeezes up into the fractures created by rifting.

Figure 29.10
Formation of a guyot from an oceanic volcano.

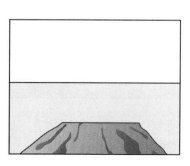

• **Atoll**
An ocean island that has no remaining central volcanic edifice, but exists only as a coral reef almost completely at or below sea level.

rift valley along the middle of the ridge is created as the ridge is pulled apart. In this process, magma erupts along fractures in the rift, creating new oceanic crust. This new oceanic crust moves slowly away from the oceanic ridge toward the deep ocean trenches, where it descends into the upper mantle to be melted and recycled. He reasoned that because the seafloor was created at the ridges and consumed at the trenches, all old oceanic crust had been destroyed. This was the reason the ocean floor was so young. It also explained why the sediments got progressively thicker away from the ocean ridges; the farther the samples are taken from the ridge, the thicker the sediment gets, because it has had longer to accumulate. At the ridge itself, the rocks are so young that no sediment has yet built up on top of the basalt. Today scientists use "asthenosphere" and "lithosphere," respectively, to describe "mantle" and "crust." Chapter 28 explains that the lithosphere is made up of the crust and upper mantle; it is the lithosphere that moves in this process of sea-floor spreading over the softer, partially molten asthenosphere beneath.

But how do guyots fit into this theory? Could Hess's theory of seafloor spreading explain these flat-topped seamounts? He believed it could, and guyots were one of the central evidences he used to support his theory (*Figure 29.10*). He explained that guyots were formed near the mid-ocean ridges as volcanic islands. They initially protruded above the surface of the ocean where coral reefs grew around their shores, just as is taking place right now around many islands in the Pacific Ocean. However, as seafloor spreading continued, these islands moved farther and farther from the mid-ocean ridge. While the guyots were located on the ridge, they protruded above the ocean level because the ridge is high, supported by the warm magma rising under it. Farther from the ridge, as the ocean lithosphere cooled and became denser (a process that is continuous, but very slow), those formerly above-surface islands sank deeper into the underlying asthenosphere and the islands became guyots. They are flat-topped because as they slowly subside, the coral around their fringes continues to grow upward, trying to stay near the surface of the ocean. Eventually, the island becomes an "**atoll**." If for some reason the coral dies or cannot grow as fast as the island is subsiding, then it completely sinks beneath the ocean to become a guyot.

29–6 THE THEORY OF PLATE TECTONICS: BRINGING IT ALL TOGETHER

Hess's theory of seafloor spreading provided the mechanism that was missing from Alfred Wegener's theory of continental drift. Nevertheless, when Hess first presented it in 1960, the evidence was still so tenuous that Hess called it "geopoetry." Certainly, more scientists were converted to the idea of drifting continents because of these new ideas, but the acceptance was still not universal. It would take some additional evidences from scientists studying the magnetism of the seafloor and earthquakes to bring these theories the universal acceptance they have today.

Magnetic Reversals and Stripes on the Seafloor

Early in this century, geologists who were measuring the "frozen" magnetic fields in basalts in France discovered that some were oriented in a direction opposite of present-day north; that is, the magnetic fields of the tiny magnetite minerals in the basalts pointed toward the south. As other old lavas were investigated, it became increasingly clear that Earth's magnetic field has experienced many reversals in the past—there have been times when it has been oriented in its present direction (normal polarity) and intervening times when it has been oriented in exactly the opposite direction (reverse polarity). The reason for such reversals is still not fully understood, but there is no doubt that they have occurred. By studying stacks of basalt flows, the sequence of reversals was worked out, complete with absolute dates. It was discovered that reversals during the Cenozoic Era have taken place irregularly but on an average of every half-million years.

Independently of all of this research on global magnetics accumulated by geologists studying the continents, seafloor geologists were mapping the magnetism in rocks at the bottom of the North Atlantic Ocean. What they were measuring is the magnetism recorded in the basalts. Once again, the findings were amazing. What they found were stripes—long, narrow bands running parallel to the Mid-Atlantic Ridge that alternated symmetrically on either side of the ridge as bands of strong and weak magnetism. Not only was this result completely unexpected, but it also seemed inexplicable, which is a word no scientist likes to have to use. Not until 1963 did an explanation emerge, when two Cambridge (Great Britain) scholars, F. J. Vine, a graduate student, and D. H. Matthews, Vine's supervisor, combined Hess's ideas about seafloor spreading, the discoveries of magnetic reversals on the continents, and the magnetic stripes of the seafloor into one grand theory we now call the "Theory of Plate Tectonics."

Vine and Matthews proposed that the stripes of strong magnetism are those for which Earth's magnetic field and the magnetism frozen in the rocks of the seafloor add together (that is, the rocks have normal polarity magnetism) and that the other stripes, in which the magnetism is weaker, are those in which the magnetic field of the basalts subtracts from Earth's field (the rocks have reverse polarity). What had really been revealed by the magnetometer surveys were bands of normal polarity and reverse polarity in the seafloor basalts. As the basalt lavas were extruded and erupted at the oceanic ridge, they became magnetized by the Earth's magnetic field. As the process continues, these rocks migrate away from the ridge, allowing newer rock to form that also records Earth's magnetic field. At some time the polarity of Earth changes, and then the subsequent lavas record the opposite polarity. The process is diagramed in *Figure 29.11*.

Patterns of Earthquakes

It had been known for many years that earthquakes did not occur randomly across the surface of Earth. The constant increase of data about the topography of the ocean floor helped seismologists, scientists who study earthquakes, realize that most of the world's earthquakes occur along ocean trenches and ridges. This fit nicely with the seafloor-spreading ideas of Harry Hess. At the ridges, earthquakes occur as the brittle lithosphere is pulled apart and at the trenches as the lithosphere is bent and sinks back into the asthenosphere.

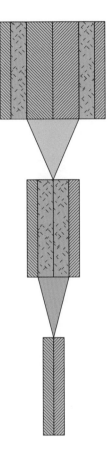

Figure 29.11
The development of magnetic stripes of alternating normal and reverse polarity on the seafloor as basaltic lava is extruded at the oceanic ridge and then is pulled to either side as the seafloor spreads. The actual boundaries between adjacent stripes are more complex than can be shown in this generalization.

◆ **Focus**

(plural–foci) The focus of an earthquake is the point within Earth where earthquake starts. The focal depth is the depth from the surface of Earth down to the focus.

But it was a study of the **foci** of earthquakes that provided one of the most important evidences for the new theory of plate tectonics. Hugo Benioff, an American seismologist, studied the pattern of trench-based earthquake foci and showed that the focal depths for earthquakes get progressively deeper in a systematic way when moving away from the trench to the associated island arc. Earthquakes occurring near a trench have shallow focal depths (less than a mile deep) but he found that the focal depths increase to moderately deep (only a few dozen miles from the trench, and then to very deep (foci up to 400 miles deep) at distances of about 100 miles from the trench. Benioff believed that this zone of increasing focal depths (now called a Benioff Zone) show the old oceanic lithosphere sinking into the mantle and confirmed Hess's idea that the trenches are places where old oceanic crust is destroyed (*Figure 29.12*).

The Breakup of Pangaea

We return now to Wegener's Pangaea—not "the beginning" of Earth nor even the "original" continent, but a landmass that came together by the process of plate tectonics as a discrete event in the long history of Earth. The same forces that brought Pangaea together during the late Paleozoic Era shifted directions and ripped it apart during the Mesozoic.

Like nearly all things scientific, the final chapter on science's reconstruction of ancient plate motions has not yet been written. Much work is still being done on pre-Pangaea plate motions. There are many unanswered questions

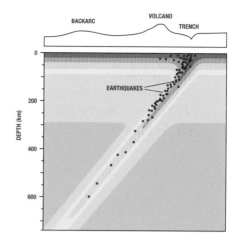

Figure 29.12

Earthquake foci (shown in red) are shallow near the trench and get progressively deeper under the volcanic arc in this diagram of a Benioff Zone.

that remain for researchers of this and future generations to answer. However, these lingering questions do not invalidate the broad aspects of the theory. They may require some revisions or adjustments—fine-tuning—in years to come. For example, the fossil remains of a dinosaur called titanosaurus are found in South America, Africa, and India. No problem, right? Wrong. The age of the rocks in which this fossil is found is late Cretaceous, and our current estimates of continental movements indicate that by that time the landmasses were too far apart to allow titanosaurs to migrate. Could these fossils be very similar but not actually identical? Possibly. Or perhaps there is another answer that will bring more surprises—and possibly offer new puzzles—when we discover it.

POSTSCRIPT: A COMMENT ON THE WAY SCIENCE WORKS

All the evidence that accumulated during the first half of the 20th century in favor of the idea of continental drift is pretty impressive. Any individual observation might be accepted as merely coincidence, but all the data, when considered as support for a specific idea, is indeed imposing. Yet for half a century after Wegener proposed Pangaea and its breakup, the theory met with open opposition from most scientists, all of them trained in good scientific research methods and some of them considered especially eminent in the their disciplines. Hindsight is always available and crystal clear to those of a later generation, so it is easy for us to be critical of the scientists who rejected continental drift. That judgment may cause us to overlook some of the important strengths inherent in the methods of science.

Wegener's treatment at the hands of the scientific establishment is reminiscent of Galileo's treatment at the hands of the religious establishment. It is clear that some of the opposition was not necessarily about Wegener's theory, but was instead aimed at the presumption of Wegener, a well-trained meteorologist who had wandered well beyond the perimeter of his own field, to propose radical ideas in a discipline for which his formal educational credentials did not qualify him. On the other hand, Jeffreys was, in fact, absolutely correct when he announced that continental movement through the oceanic rocks could not possibly have occurred. Had he or someone else not challenged this proposed mechanism, and if it had been widely accepted, it would still have been incorrect; truth is, after all, not determined by majority vote. Thus, sending the proponents of continental drift "back to the drawing board" to come up with a more convincing mechanism was not a penalty, but a reasonable scientific requirement.

Despite occasional statements that science and scientists are not always completely objective, science is an intensely personal endeavor to those engaged in it. Each scientific issue of any consequence is represented by a number of differing viewpoints, each with its own group of proponents. New developments or proposals put forth by one group are scrutinized and tested by the other groups, and weaknesses are exposed while strengths are admitted. Instead of tearing

Alfred Wegener

Sir Harold Jeffreys

science down, this process builds it by preserving only the theories and ideas that are most consistent with observation. Eventually, those theories that can withstand the most rigorous testing come to be accepted even by those who initially disagreed.

Even then, it is recognized that good theories are no more than close approximations to the truth, needing constant testing and additional study for possible refinement. (Consider, for example, that Newtonian mechanics and gravitation were considered accurate descriptions of nature for nearly three centuries, until quantum mechanics and relativity revealed them to be only very good approximations.) Thus, if the methods of science are often painstakingly slow, they are at least self-correcting, and serious errors are eliminated, as long as old ideas are honestly questioned and those found lacking are replaced by better ones.

Chapter Framework

A. Historical context
1. Sir Francis Bacon, Ben Franklin, and Eduard Suess
2. Alfred Wegener and the "Theory of Continental Drift"

B. Evidences for Continental Drift
1. Jigsaw fit of the continent
2. Continental structure
3. Paleontological (fossil) evidence
4. Paleoclimatic evidence
5. Paleomagnetic evidence

C. A Cold Reception for a New Theory
1. Sir Harold Jeffreys
2. Lack of viable mechanism

D. Evidences from the Seafloor
1. Topography
   a. *A mid-ocean ridge with a central valley*
   b. *Guyots*
   c. *Deep ocean trenches*
2. Composition and age
   a. *Seafloor is sediment-covered basalt*
   b. *Sediment buildup greater at edges*
   c. *Seafloor is older at edges*
   d. *Seafloor rock is relatively young*

E. Seafloor Spreading
1. Harry Hess
   a. *Convection in upper mantle*
   b. *Guyots*

F. The Theory of Plate Tectonics
1. Vine and Matthews
2. Magnetic reversals and stripes on the seafloor
3. Patterns of earthquakes
4. Hugo Benioff

Comprehension

True/ False
1. _____ Scientists widely accepted the theory of continental drift when Wegener proposed it.
2. _____ Opposition to scientific theories can make theories more concrete.
3. _____ All questions about the breakup of Pangaea have been answered.
4. _____ Basalt can lose its magnetic orientation if it is heated above the Curie temperature.
5. _____ Guyots are rounded seamounts found on the ocean floor.

Matching

a. *Pangaea*
b. *Seafloor spreading*
c. *Glossopteridales*
d. *Paleomagnetism*
e. *Paleontology*
f. *Structural trends*
g. *Lystrosaurus*
h. *Atoll*
i. *Guyots*
j. *Mesosaurus*
k. *Paleoclimatology*
l. *Focus*

1. _____ An ocean island that has no remaining central volcanic edifice, but exists only as a coral reef almost completely at or below sea level.
2. _____ The study of ancient life preserved as fossils in the rocks.
3. _____ A fresh-water dwelling reptile with an elongated head and snout with nostrils near its eyes and a flattened tail used for swimming.
4. _____ The term used to identify the point within Earth where an earthquake starts.
5. _____ The supercontinent that broke up at the start of the Mesozoic Era to form the continents we have today.
6. _____ Flat-topped seamounts that are the submerged equivalent of modern atolls.
7. _____ A sturdily built, plant eating reptile (not a dinosaur).
8. _____ The theory that the ocean floor moves as the mid-ocean ridge separates.
9. _____ The orientations of major geologic features such as mountain belts, continental shields, stable platforms, and areas of folded and deformed rocks.
10. _____ The study of ancient climates.
11. _____ An extinct group of seed plants that arose during the Permian through the Triassic Period.
12. _____ Magnetism preserved or fossilized in rocks. It can often tell us about changes in the orientation of rock bodies after their formation.

Fill in the Blank
1. _____ evidence, from the pre-drift era, indicates that certain areas of the world supported cold, arctic environments.
2. The Polarity of Earth switches every half-million years from _____ polarity to _____ polarity.
3. The ocean floor is mostly composed of _____, with some deposits of _____ .
4. The ocean floor is found to be deepest at the _____ .
5. The coasts on either side of the Atlantic Oceans appear to _____ one another.

Analysis

1. The occurrences of the Glossopteris flora in Permian rocks of South America, Africa, Antarctica, India, and Australia is evidence that:

   a) these plants lived in the southern hemisphere since the Permian Period.
   b) these plants can survive in a wide variety of climates.
   c) the southern landmasses have separated since the Permian period.
   d) the southern landmasses have become closer since the Permian period.

2. Which of the following is not evidence for continental drift?

   a) Changes in Paleozoic trilobites in North America and Europe.

b) The presence of glossopteris on several continents.

c) Glaciated Permian rocks on several continents.

d) The geometrical fit of North America and Australia.

3. The alternating stripes of strong and weak magnetism found in rocks of the seafloor

a) parallel the oceanic ridges.

b) are perpendicular to the ocean ridges.

c) are oblique (at an angle to, other than perpendicular) to the ocean ridges.

d) are too far for the oceanic ridges to judge their relationship.

4. When attempting to fit the continents together, we use the continental shelves rather than the coastline, Why?

5. How does paleomagnetism support the theory of continental drift?

6. What first led scientists like Alfred Wegner to believe that the continents once formed one large continent?

7. What two evidences indicate that the seafloor is spreading at the oceanic ridges?

8. What was Pangaea?

9. What evidence did Wegner and his supporters gather to strengthen their claim about continental drift?

10. How did evidence of glaciation in the Southern Hemisphere support the continental drift hypothesis?

Synthesis

1. You stumble across a time travel device and find yourself stuck in a debate between Alfred Wegener and Sir Harold Jeffreys, with a large audience attending the debate. They ask you the following questions, how would you answer them?

a. What is meant by continental drift?

b. What evidences and observations do you have to support the idea of continental drift? (Name and describe five.)

c. Are there any major problems with the idea of continental drift? Is so, what are they?

d. What does seafloor spreading mean and how is it different from continental drift?

e. What evidences and observations do you have to support the idea of seafloor spreading? (Name and describe two.)

f. How can the seafloor spread when Earth maintains a constant size?

2. Where does the lithosphere form? Where is the lithosphere destroyed? Why must the creation and demolition of the lithosphere occur at the same rate?

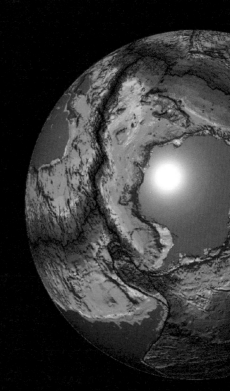

CHAPTER 30

PLATE TECTONICS: A WORKING MODEL FOR THE EARTH

"You may take geology, for instance, and it is a true science; not that I would say for a moment that all the conclusions and deductions of its professors are true, but its leading principles are; they are facts—they are eternal. . . ."

~ Brigham Young

The theory of plate tectonics is not just "one" of the leading principles of geology. It is "the" leading principle. This explanation of (among other things) why the surface of Earth is in constant—if extremely slow—movement has revolutionized the science of geology. Plate tectonics permeates every aspect of geologic science. It has become the keystone in understanding how our planet works and in establishing its history.

So far we have established that seafloors spread and that continents move about like passengers on great plates of the lithosphere (*Figure 30.1*). If Earth's diameter is not expanding like a giant balloon, and there are places where the seafloor is separating as new oceanic crust is created, shouldn't there also be places where things are coming together and old crust is being destroyed? What is it that moves the plates? Why are earthquakes so much more abundant and severe along some plate boundaries than along others? In this chapter we will try to answer these questions and learn how the plate tectonic system works.

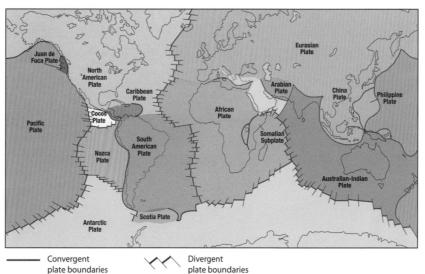

Figure 30.1
World map of the major plates and plate boundaries.

30–1 WHY DO THE PLATES MOVE?

LEARNING OBJECTIVES

- Learn the basic forces that drive the Plate Tectonic System.
- Know the basic types of plate interactions and their characteristics.
  - Spreading Zones
  - Collision Zones
  - Transform Boundaries
- Understand the occurrence and value of Hot Spots to the Plate Tectonic Theory.
- Be able to explain how continents evolve.

You may remember that in the early years of the 20th century, German geophysicist Alfred Wegener's then-radical new theory of continental drift was rejected by the scientific establishment because he was unable to satisfactorily explain how the continents moved. Wegener thought that it might have something to do with the rotation of the planet or with tides, but such forces were long ago shown to be inadequate. He couldn't come up with a mechanism for moving the plates, so his theory was rejected by most other scientists of his era. Scientists are in general a skeptical lot and new theories, particularly ones that go against traditional ideas, are not easily accepted. It often takes years of work to gather evidence and sometimes revise the original theory before it becomes accepted as part of mainstream science. Such was certainly the case with continental drift.

So what could move the large plates of the Earth? Some forces can be easily eliminated. The strong force and the weak force are effective only at very small distances (within the nucleus of atoms) and, thus, cannot be responsible for moving tectonic plates. Long-range electromagnetic forces act only between charged objects, and the plates are electrically neutral. This leaves only gravity and short-range (contact) electromagnetic forces to drive plate motion. Currently, scientists have identified three main locations where forces generated by gravity and contact forces push and pull on the tectonic plates (*Figure 30.2*).

First, along the mid-ocean ridges the plates are higher than the surrounding ocean floor. They are higher because the lithosphere is young and warm and because hot, low-density asthenosphere is welling up beneath them. Remember from the chapter explaining buoyancy that when a fluid is heated, it expands, thus increasing the buoyant force and causing it to rise in a process called "convection." It turns out that even though the Earth's asthenosphere is mostly solid (with perhaps 1–5% being liquid), it behaves over long

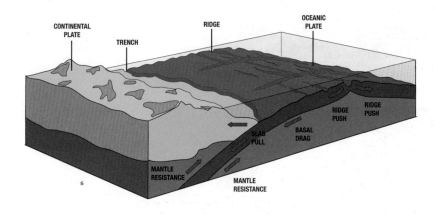

Figure 30.2
Forces driving and resisting plate motion.

• **Ridge Push**

Helps move the Earth's plates. The ridge is high and has gravitational potential energy which is converted into kinetic energy as the plate moves.

• **Slab Pull**

Helps move the tectonic plates. As an oceanic plate becomes old, cold, and dense, it sinks back into the mantle, pulling the rest of the plate along with it.

• **Basal Drive**

May help the plates to move. As the asthenosphere flows along under a plate, it may help to pull the plate along like a conveyor belt.

• **Mantle Resistance, Plate Collision, and Transform Fault Friction**

Forces that resist plate motion.

periods of time like a very viscous fluid. It may seem strange to think of solid materials flowing like fluids, but given enough time (thousands or millions of years) and the right temperature and pressure conditions, solid rocks will flow. This upwelling of the asthenosphere at the ridges gives the plates extra gravitational potential energy. As the force of gravity pulls on these high areas of the plates, the gravitational potential energy is converted into kinetic energy and the plates slowly move away from the ridges, sliding down toward the trenches over the weaker asthenosphere. This force is called **ridge push**.

A second force acts on the plates at the oceanic trenches. The trenches are formed where old oceanic lithosphere is being destroyed. Old oceanic lithosphere is cold and dense, unlike the warm, young lithosphere at the ridges. As warm lithosphere moves away from the ridge, it cools and contracts. The contraction of the lithosphere reduces the volume of the plate, making it denser and lowering the buoyant force pushing upward. At first, this drop in the buoyant force just makes the oceanic lithosphere sink lower into the underlying asthenosphere, even though it continues to float. But when the gravitational force on the lithosphere exceeds the buoyant force, the plate then founders and sinks. As it sinks it pulls the rest of the plate down with it. We call this force **slab pull.**

The third force that may help the plates to move is a contact force created by convection of the asthenosphere as it flows away from the ridges toward the trenches along the base of the plates. This flowing asthenosphere pulls the overlying lithosphere along with it, much like the action of a conveyor belt. This force has been called **basal drive** and for many years it was

thought to be the main force moving the plates. However, as scientists have observed plate motions more carefully and examined the magnitudes (sizes) of each of the forces involved, it has become clear that basal drive may not be a significant force at all. In fact, it appears that convection in the asthenosphere is probably a result of motion of the plates, not the other way around.

Figure 30.2 also shows the forces that are resisting plate motion. The main forces resisting plate motion are contact forces: **mantle resistance** (friction with the mantle along the subducting plate), **plate collision** (running into another plate), and **transform fault friction** (friction between two plates sliding past each other). As long as the forces driving plate motion are greater than or equal to the forces resisting plate motion, they will continue to move.

30–2 HOW FAST ARE THE PLATES MOVING?

Over time, the tectonic plates may speed up, slow down, or even change direction. Despite this non-uniform motion of the plates, we usually find it unnecessary to hold onto something to keep from falling down! All Earth's plates move *very* slowly, but the velocity of each plate differs. The North American continent and the European continent are each riding on a different plate and the distance between the east coast of the United States and the west coast of France increases by about one inch every year. The African plate seems not to be moving at all, but the Indian-Australian plate sprints along (geologically speaking) at about five inches per year. These speeds may not sound very impressive, but in terms of geologic time, the North American continent could eventually slam, one inch at a time, into Asia, somewhere on the other side of the globe.

30–3 PARTS OF THE TECTONIC SYSTEM

The plate tectonic system can be subdivided into three main subsystems, based on how adjacent plates are interacting: divergent plate boundaries (also called spreading zones), convergent plate boundaries (or collision zones), and transform boundaries. Spreading zones are places where plates are pulling apart, collision zones are places where they are pushing against each other, and transforms are places where adjacent plates are sliding past each other.

Divergent Plate Boundaries (Spreading Zones)

Divergent plate boundaries are places two plates pull away from each other. The most common type of divergent boundary is found in the ocean basins. Here the great oceanic ridges form. As two oceanic plates move apart, they open up a great rift or crack in Earth's ocean floor, allowing room for liquid magma from the asthenosphere to flow in and solidify. The magma cools into basalt and in the process creates new oceanic crust. Volcanoes are common along the oceanic rift, but because most of them erupt under water, we rarely see such volcanic activity. Occasionally, enough material erupts under the ocean surface to produce an island that rises, hot and steaming, above that ocean surface. The island of Iceland sits astride the Mid-Atlantic ridge and is the site of frequent eruptions of basalt. It is also a place where we can see the great cracks created as two plates pull apart (*Figure 30.3*). Volcanic eruptions occurring along the oceanic ridges can produce spectacular displays of fireworks, but in general such eruptions are relatively quiet, producing fountains of red-hot lava and flows of red basaltic magma.

The oceanic ridges are also the sites of frequent earthquakes. However, because the lithosphere at the ridge is thin and warm (making it weak), and because the plates are pulling apart rather than colliding, earthquakes tend to be small, ranking of about 5 on the **magnitude scale** devised by Charles Richter, with shallow focal depths. These earthquakes do not produce **tsunamis** (commonly but erroneously also called tidal waves) and are generally not dangerous.

Divergent boundaries also occur on the continents in areas where a continent is splitting apart. One of the best examples of a continental spreading zone is in eastern Africa (*Figure 30.4*). Here we find a long **rift valley**, filled in places by lakes (Lake Malawi, Lake Tanganyika) and connecting to a narrow arm of the Red Sea.

Arabia and part of eastern Africa are perched on a tectonic plate that is slowly moving away from the rest of the African continent. Eruptions of both basalt and **rhyolite** occur along the rift valley and some of the eruptions can be quite violent and dangerous. In addition, earthquakes, with magnitudes up to about 7.5 on the Richter Scale, occur in what is now known as Africa's Rift Valley. Earthquakes are stronger in continental spreading because continental lithosphere is thicker, colder, and more brittle than the young, warm lithosphere found in oceanic spreading zones.

As spreading continues along a continental rift, eventually the continent is completely ripped apart and a new ocean basin forms. In east Africa this has already started where the Red Sea now fills part of the rift and the crust beneath the sea is new oceanic crust. Given enough time, a new ocean basin can develop in just this way. In fact, we believe that the Atlantic Ocean started as a continental spreading zone about 200 million years ago as North and South America drifted away from Europe and Africa (*Figure 30.5*).

Convergent Plate Boundaries (Collision Zones)

Because Earth's size has remained about the same since very early in its history, the creation of new oceanic lithosphere at divergent boundaries requires that somewhere else older oceanic

Figure 30.3
The visible result of plates pulling apart in Iceland.

- **Magnitude Scale**
A measure of the size of an earthquake. The first widely used magnitude scale was developed by Richter and was called the "Richter Scale." Today the most widely used scale is called the "moment magnitude scale." All of these scales have one thing in common: they are non-linear logarithmic scales. As you increase the magnitude from, for example, a 7.0 to an 8.0, the amount of energy released goes up by 30 times.

- **Tsunami**
A water wave produced by an earthquake. They can be extremely dangerous for people living near the coast.

- **Rift Valley**
A long, linear depression that commonly forms along a divergent plate boundary as two plates pull apart.

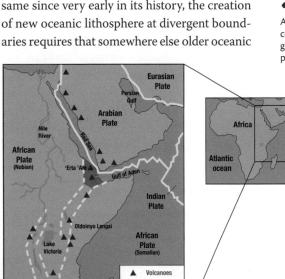

Figure 30.4
A continental divergent plate boundary in eastern Africa.

- **Rhyolite**
A volcanic rock that has the same composition as a granite, but has erupted and cooled at the surface, rather than underground.

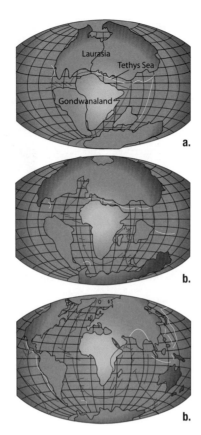

a.

b.

b.

lithosphere be destroyed. The places where this destruction occurs are called convergent plate boundaries, or places where two plates are colliding. These collision zones are often beautiful, but also exciting and dangerous places to live. Rugged, spectacular mountains, explosive volcanoes and huge earthquakes are common along these boundaries. In nature, out of destruction or devastation new life emerges. This is the case at convergent boundaries. Even though old ocean lithosphere is destroyed, in the process material is created from which continents are born, and continents, once created, do not easily disappear. We will divide our discussion of convergent plate boundaries into three boundary sub-types: ocean-ocean collisions, ocean-continent collisions, and continent-continent collisions.

• **Subduction**

What geologists call the process that occurs at the trenches where old oceanic lithosphere is sinking back into the mantle. The trench area is also called a "subduction zone" and as the plates sink, they are said to be subducting.

• **Volcanic Arc**

A chain of volcanoes, shaped like an arc, that form at some convergent plate boundaries.

Figure 30.6

A diagram of an ocean-ocean plate collision.

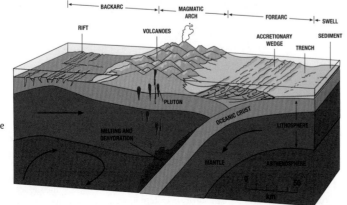

OCEAN-OCEAN PLATE COLLISIONS

The collision of two oceanic plates causes one plate to dive under the other and sink into the asthenosphere. This process is called "**subduction**." The plate that is sinking is said to be subducting. In general, the plate that sinks is older, colder, and, therefore, denser than the plate that does not sink. As a plate subducts, it rubs against the overlying plate sometimes causing enormous earthquakes (magnitudes as high as 8.5 to 9.5) that often produce tsunamis. The plate must also bend and crack as it sinks. This causes earthquakes in a narrow zone directly above the plate that is plunging deep into the Earth. This is what we identified in the previous chapter as a Benioff Zone.

A massive earthquake (magnitude 9.0) occurred in December 2004 along the collision zone between the Indian-Australian plate and the Asian plate, near the northern end of the island of Sumatra. The quake generated a tsunami with waves up to 50 feet high, smashing against the low-lying coasts of Indonesia, Sri Lanka, India, Thailand, and other countries as far away as the east coast of Africa. Scientists monitoring various earthquake early-warning systems had adequate time to send out warnings of the coming of the waves, but systems to pass on such warnings locally were not in place in this part of the world at the time, so an estimated 300,000 people were killed in one of the worst natural disasters in recorded history.

Over the millions of years that it takes a plate to travel from a divergent boundary, where it was created, to a convergent boundary, where it is destroyed, it lies beneath the ocean soaking up water. During subduction the sinking plate heats up and this water is released into the overlying wedge of mantle where it lowers the melting temperature until it begins to melt (*Figure 30.6*). The part that melts is warm and buoyant, rising to the surface and creating a chain of volcanoes along the collision zone. These chains are usually arc-shaped and have come to be called "**volcanic arcs**." The Aleutian Islands, the West Indies, the islands of Indonesia, Tonga and the Marianas are all volcanic arcs formed above a subducting plate. The volcanic rock that forms these island arcs is less dense than the basalt of the ocean crust. It has a composition that is more like the rocks in the continents. In fact, we

THE AWESOME POWER OF VOLCANIC ERUPTIONS

Ivan Orloff, an Alaskan Eskimo, wrote the following to his wife during the 1912 eruption of Katmai volcano in the Aleutian Islands:

We are awaiting death at any moment. A mountain has burst near here. We are covered with ash, in some places ten feet and six feet deep. All this began on June sixth. Night and day we light lanterns. We cannot see daylight. We have no water, the rivers are just ashes mixed with water. Here are darkness and hell, thunder and noise. I do not know whether it is day or night. The earth is trembling . . . It is terrible. We are praying.

In 1902, Mt. Pelée on the West Indies island of Martinique erupted (*Figure 30.7*). A Mr. Thompson, assistant pursor on board a ship which was approaching the harbor when Mt. Pelée exploded, later wrote down what he had observed and experienced on shipboard well out at sea:

I saw St. Pierre destroyed. It was blotted out by one great flash of fire. Nearly 40,000 people were killed at once. Of eighteen vessels lying in the Roads, only one, the British steamship Roddam escaped and she, I hear, lost more than half on board. It was a dying crew that took her out. Our boat, the Roraima, arrived at St. Pierre early Thursday morning. For hours before we entered the roadstead, we could see flames and smoke rising from Mt. Pelée. No one on board had any idea of danger. Capt. G. T. Muggah was on bridge and all hands got on deck to see the show. The spectacle was magnificent. As we approached St. Pierre, we could distinguish the rolling and leaping red flames that belched from the mountain in huge volumes and gushed high into the sky. Enormous clouds of black smoke hung over the volcano. The flames were then spurting straight up in the air, now and then waving to one side or the other a moment, and again leaping suddenly higher up. There was a constant muffled roar. It was like the biggest oil refinery in the world burning up on the mountaintop. There was a tremendous explosion about 7:45 soon after we got in. The mountain was blown to pieces. There was no warning. The side of the volcano was ripped out, and there hurled straight towards us a solid wall of flame. It sounded like a thousand cannon.

The wave of fire was on us and over us like a lightning flash. It was like a hurricane of fire. I saw it strike the cable steamship Grappler broadside on, and capsize her. From end to end she burst into flames and then sank.

Figure 30.7
Harbor of St. Pierre, Martinique prior to (above) and after (below) the eruption of Mt. Pelée.

The fire rolled in mass straight down on St. Pierre and the shipping. The town vanished before our eyes.

The air grew stifling hot and we were in the thick of it. Wherever the mass of fire struck the sea, the water boiled and sent up great clouds of steam. The sea was torn into huge whirlpools that careened toward the open sea. One of these horrible, hot whirlpools swung under the Roraima and pulled her down on her beam end with the suction. She careened way over to port, and then the fire hurricane from the volcano smashed her, and over she went on the opposite side. The fire wave swept off the masts and smokestacks as if they were cut by a knife.

I saved my life by running to my stateroom and burying myself in the bedding. The blast of fire from the volcano lasted only for a few minutes. It shriveled and set fire to everything it touched. Thousands of casks of rum were stored in St. Pierre, and these were exploded by the terrific heat. Burning rum ran in streams down every street and out into the sea.

Before the volcano burst, the landings at St. Pierre were crowded with people. After the explosion, not one living being was seen on land. Only twenty-five of those on board [out of 68] were left after the first blast."

believe that these island arcs are the material from which continents are built over many millions of years.

Unlike the volcanoes that form at divergent boundaries, these volcanoes are extremely violent and explosive when they erupt, largely because the erupting magma contains more water and is more viscous than magma erupted at divergent boundaries. Eruptions of volcanoes at collision zones have produced some of the world's most deadly natural disasters. They often include earthquakes, tornadoes, tsunamis, spectacular lightning, complete darkness over wide areas and thick deposits of volcanic ash. Those who have witnessed the awesome power of these eruptions do not easily forget them.

OCEAN-CONTINENT PLATE COLLISIONS

When an oceanic plate collides with a continental plate, it is always the oceanic plate that subducts. The continents are made of low-density rock that will not sink. Sometimes slices of the down-going oceanic lithosphere are scraped off onto the continent, leaving a folded and deformed record above sea level of what the oceanic plate had been like.

Large earthquakes and explosive volcanoes are characteristic of these ocean-continent plate collisions, just as they are at ocean-ocean plate collisions. The main difference is that the volcanoes come up through the edge of the continent rather than form a volcanic island arc (*Figure 30.8*). This material that is erupted onto the continents is unlikely to ever be subducted, but it adds new continental material to the continent. The volcanoes of the Andes in South America and the Cascade volcanoes in North America are good examples of this type of collision zone. During the eruption of Mount St. Helens in Washington State on May 18, 1980, the blast was described as "almost beyond com-

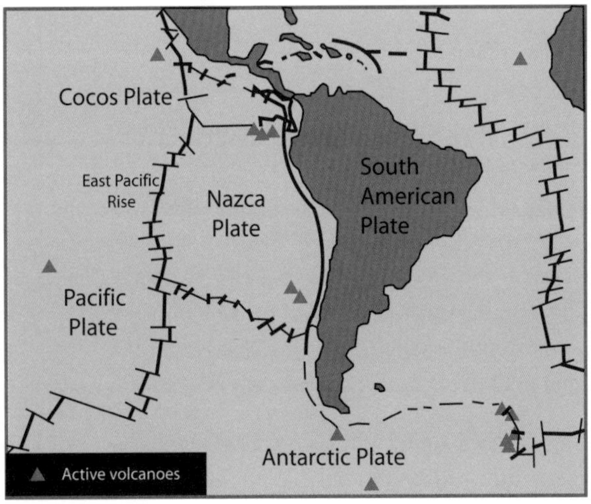

Figure 30.8
Active volcanoes, plate tectonics, and South America.

prehension, 500 times greater than the 20-kiloton atomic bomb that fell on Hiroshima and moving outward at velocities of over 300 miles per hour." An eyewitness who viewed the blast reported the following:

I looked east toward Hanaford Lake and Fawn Lake and that area—it looked like that whole mountain range had just exploded. As the blast cloud approached it looked like a boiling mass of rock—and just as high as you could see. Trees were picked up and thrown into the air at the leading edge of the cloud… The cloud approached with a roaring noise. As it passed overhead, a tree began to fall and within seconds there were no trees left.

CONTINENT-CONTINENT PLATE COLLISIONS

What happens when two unsinkable objects collide? Continents are made of low-density rocks that are so buoyant they will not sink into the mantle. Continents are moved along by the movement of the plates on which they ride. When a continent reaches a subduction zone and collides with another continent, the process of subduction ceases. The continent will begin to subduct, but because of its low density it cannot sink. Instead, the plates plow more directly into each, more like two cars in a head-on collision. The edges of the plates and anything in between crumples into a huge mass, creating the highest mountain ranges on Earth. Continents that were once separate land masses become welded together. The best modern example of this type of collision is the Himalaya Mountains, which have formed as India collides with Asia (*Figure 30.9*). The Appalachian Mountains in the

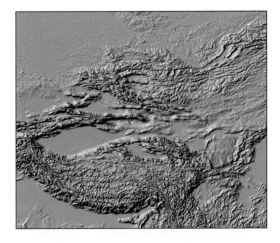

Figure 30.9
Digital relief map of Eastern Himalayas.

eastern United States are an example of an ancient collision zone, now mostly eroded away.

In the deeper parts of a continent-continent collision, the rocks are changed by heat and pressure to metamorphic rocks, sometimes folding and shearing the rocks. In the upper parts of these collision zones the rocks are less metamorphosed and remain brittle. During deformation they may crack along faults, producing large earthquakes. The impact of India into Asia has affected a large part of the Asian continent and has produced some of the world's most destructive earthquakes. In July, 1976, a large earthquake (magnitude 7.8) struck the Tangshan area of China. Even though the earthquake only lasted for about 15 seconds, it killed over 250,000 people.

The one striking difference between continent-continent collisions and the other collision types is that there are no volcanoes. Because no plate is sinking into the mantle and melting, no volcanoes form.

Transform Plate Boundaries

The oceanic ridges are not smooth continuous ridges but instead are formed from relatively straight, short segments that are offset from one another by what appear to be cracks or faults (Refer back to Figure 30.1). These are transform faults and they constitute the third major type of plate boundary. Along these boundaries the plates are neither colliding nor diverging. Rather, they are simply sliding past one another (Figure 30.10). Volcanoes do not form along transform boundaries, because nothing is being subducted and no rifting is occurring.

Not all transform faults are short. The famous San Andreas fault in California connects a segment of oceanic ridge in the Gulf of California with a segment at the south end of the Juan de Fuca plate. In doing so, it slices off a sliver of California that is several hundred kilometers in length. While most of the state is part of the North American plate, that sliver rides on the Pacific plate. As the two plates move past one another, strain builds up wherever the fault binds and is released in the earthquakes that are so common in California. Some of these earthquakes can be fairly large and destructive (up to magnitude 8.0).

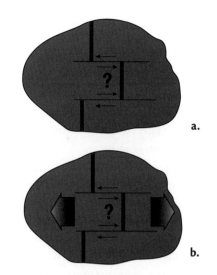

Figure 30.10

a) At first it may appear that segments of oceanic ridge separate from each other along a transform fault.

b) Actually, a transform fault is a boundary that separates two plates that are moving laterally past one another.

30–4 PLATE MOTIONS—HOT SPOT TRAILS

The Hawaiian Islands are one of several linear island chains in the Pacific that do not seem to fit anywhere in the plate tectonic picture. Although they are volcanic in origin, none of them has a deep ocean trench or a Benioff zone nearby. In fact, they are nowhere near any plate boundaries.

The only currently active volcanoes in the Hawaiian Islands are on the island of Hawaii, at the southeast end of the chain. As one proceeds up the chain to the northwest, successive islands are progressively older and all inactive (*Figure 30.11*). How did this chain of islands form? It turns out that the same heat source has produced all the volcanoes in the chain. The heat source is a **mantle plume** rising from deep in the Earth, perhaps from near the core-mantle boundary, which has remained almost stationary while the Pacific plate moves over the top of it. We call these rising plumes of hot rock **hot spots**. As the plate moves over the hot spot a

• **Transform Fault**
The break in the Earth's lithosphere that connects segments of ridges or trenches together. These are plate boundaries where the plates are sliding past each other.

• **Mantle Plume**
A buoyant mass of hot rock rising through the Earth's mantle. As it nears the surface of the Earth some of the plume melts and erupts at the surface forming a "hot spot."

• **Hot Spots**
Volcanoes that result from the lithosphere moving over a mantle plume. Hawaii is an example of an island-formed hot spot. As the plate moves over the mantle, a line of volcanic structures (such as the Hawaiian chain of islands) marks the passage. The trail of volcanism is called a hot-spot trail.

Figure 30.11
A linear chain of hot-spot volcanoes is formed as a plate moves over a mantle plume.

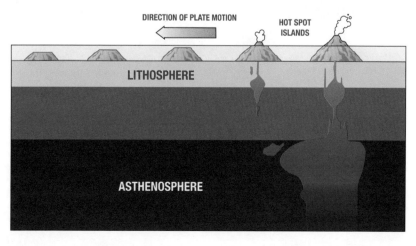

♦ **Pangaea**

The name Alfred Wegner gave to the large continental mass that existed before the continents began to drift apart about 200 million years ago.

♦ **Continental Accretion**

The process by which continents grow. When continents collide with island arcs or with other continents, new material may be added and the continent grows.

volcano is created and remains active for a period of time. Then, because the volcano is moving along with the plate, it passes beyond the hot spot and becomes extinct. However, a new volcano arises over the hot spot to replace it. In this manner a chain of volcanoes is created on top of the plate, but only the volcano that sits over the hot spot is active.

The trails of volcanism left on a plate as it moves over a mantle plume (linear island chains) provide us with information that would be very difficult to get in any other way—the absolute motion of that plate. As we stand on one plate and make any sort of observations or measurements to determine the motion of another plate, all we get is the relative motion between the two. It is as if we were stationary and only the other plate moved. What we need is a frame of reference that is stationary with respect to *all* of the plates, and the worldwide collection of mantle plumes appears to provide just that. Thus, hot-spot trails show the direction of absolute plate motion. Geologists can use the absolute ages obtained from dating of the volcanic rocks to determine the rates of plate motion over the lifetime of the mantle plume.

30–5 PLATE TECTONIC EVOLUTION OF A CONTINENT

When Wegener proposed the idea of continental drift, he offered a name for the "super-

continent" that he believed existed prior to the time when the continents drifted apart. He called this continent **Pangaea** meaning "all earth." However, the construction of Pangaea was a relatively recent major event (happening only about 300 million years ago). All the features we see on the ocean floors, as well as the present plate configuration, are a result of events that have occurred since Pangaea broke apart, about 200 million years ago. But how did the continents first come to be, and can we determine their histories? Each continent has followed a unique and complex course of development, but the broad outlines of the general evolution of a continent can be understood by focusing on North America. *Figure 30.12* is a map of North America showing generalized ranges of isotopic dates (absolute ages) found for basement rocks in various parts of the continent. Basement rocks are those that underlie the younger sedimentary cover and are mostly Precambrian. A consistent pattern is clear: The most ancient rocks are in the shield, and the ages become younger toward the margins of the continent.

This age distribution suggests the following general history: The continent originated as a small landmass during Precambrian times. The first mini-continental areas were probably just volcanic island arcs produced at subduction zones. Over time, some of these island arcs collided together forming larger land masses. Other continents were, of course, in their own formative stages, and so continental collisions would likely have occurred. These would have welded onto North America "foreign" rocks—rocks that might have remained even after continental rifting. For instance, there is good geologic evidence that much of the southeastern United States was part of the African continent before the assembly of Pangaea. When the supercontinent rifted apart in the early Mesozoic Era, it did not break apart along the same suture, but left part of the African continent attached to North America. This idea that continents have grown by addition of material at convergent boundaries is called **continental accretion** and it is by this process that we believe the continents have reached their current shapes and sizes. The wonder of the theory of plate tectonics is that it has provided the way for us to look deep into the past history of the Earth, and, conversely, to look into its future.

Figure 30.12

A map of North America showing *generalized* ranges of ages for the continental "basement" rocks. Notice that the ages become younger from the shield toward the margins of the continent.

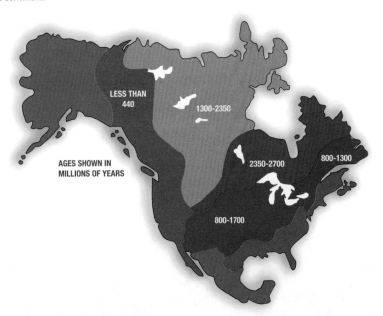

LESS THAN 440

1300-2350

2350-2700

800-1300

800-1700

AGES SHOWN IN MILLIONS OF YEARS

Chapter Framework

A. Why Do the Plates Move?
1. Contact electromagnetic forces and gravity
   a. *Ridge Push*
   b. *Slab pull*
   c. *Basal drive*
2. Plates move slowly

B. Parts of the Tectonic System
1. Divergent Plate Boundaries (Spreading Zones)
2. Convergent Plate Boundaries (Collision Zones)
   a. *Ocean-Ocean Plate Collisions*
   b. *Ocean-Continent Plate Collision*
   c. *Continent-Continent Plate Collisions*
3. Transform Plate Boundaries or Transform Faults

C. Plate Motions—Hot Spot Trails
1. Rising mantle plumes
2. Reference points for absolute motion

d. Evolution of a Continent
1. Accumulation of smaller plates over time
2. Continental accretion

Comprehension

True/False
1. _____ When two continents collide, the denser continent is subducted.
2. _____ Faults, like the San Andreas, form when two continents diverge.
3. _____ Island arcs colliding together form into continents overtime.

Fill in the Blank
1. _____ rise through Earth's crust creating hot spots.
2. The most deadly volcanoes and earthquakes are a result of _____ boundaries.
3. A colder, older, _____ ocean plate is subducted under a warmer, younger ocean plate.

Analysis

1. Convergent plate boundaries do not involve
   a) subduction zones.
   b) mountain-building events.
   c) creation of new oceanic lithosphere
   d) creation of linear island chains.

2. Among the following choices, an earthquake would least likely occur
   a) in a young fold mountain belt.
   b) in a continental shield.
   c) at a transform fault.
   d) along the ocean ridge system.

3. The least amount of plate tectonic activity would be found in which of these locations?
   a) The California coastline area
   b) The Canadian shield
   c) Iceland
   d) Japan

4. How does a study of earthquakes and seismic waves provide evidence in favor of the plate tectonic theory?
   a) The pattern of earthquake activity corresponds to plate boundaries.
   b) Wave velocities are related to plate motion.
   c) Seismic studies have determined the boundary between the mantle and the core.
   d) Seismic waves power continental drift.
   e) Earthquakes are regarded as the energy source for tectonic plate motion.

5. A converging plate margin bisects the Mediterranean Sea. What will be the probable outcome of this situation.
   a) The Mediterranean will shrink.
   b) A mid-ocean ridge will soon begin to emerge within this area.
   c) The water body will grow longer as a result of shear transform faulting.
   d) The water body will grow wider.
   e) A rift valley will appear in the middle of the Mediterranean.

6. Why are fold mountains belts long, narrow features?

7. Explain how an ocean plate moves.

8. Why do island arcs tend to be larger than islands in island chains?

9. What causes the elevated position of the oceanic ridges?

Synthesis

1. What are the basic elements of the plate tectonic model? How does it resolve the problems unexplained by earlier ideas of continental drift and seafloor spreading?

2. Describe the differences in the type and duration of volcanic activity in island chains and island arcs? Explain these differences

3. Explain how a continent like North America may have formed.

4. What natural disasters are associated with plate tectonics? Why?

CHAPTER 31

THE CHANGING FACE OF THE EARTH

> *"Know what's weird?*
> *Day by day, nothing seems to change, but pretty*
> *soon . . . everything's different."*
>
> ~ Calvin, from the *Calvin and Hobbes*
> cartoon series drawn by Bill Watterson

Calvin got it exactly right. Day by day, if we just sit and watch, nothing much seems to change in the world around us. Occasionally we get a big earthquake or landslide or flood that causes some obvious changes, but mostly the world seems pretty static. However, when we view the small changes that occur every day on the Earth over the vast expanse of geologic time we find, as Calvin did, that "everything's different." The Earth is not a static, unchanging place, but, rather, a dynamic, constantly changing world.

Many of Earth's changes are related to the movements of Earth's tectonic plates , but the tectonic system is only half of the story when it comes to our changing Earth. Changes are also caused by the movement of water. Earth's hydrologic system carves, shapes, and erodes the features created by the tectonic system. The hydrologic system is held in a delicate balance by many factors. Changes in the system occur both naturally and because of human activities. In this chapter we will study Earth's hydrologic system to better understand how it works and what future changes we might expect in this system caused by both natural events and human efforts.

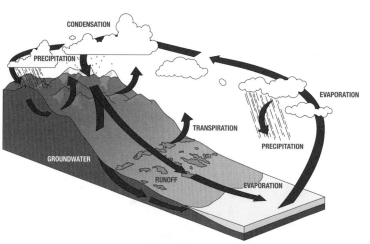

Figure 31.1
The hydrologic system showing the main pathways for movement of water. Evaporating water rises because of buoyancy forces and returns to the Earth because of gravity. On Earth's surface, gravity acts on both ice and water creating flowing glaciers, rivers, and movement of groundwater.

LEARNING OBJECTIVES

- Understand the movement of water the Hydrologic System.
- Know the basic sub-systems of the Hydrologic System and their characteristics.
    - River systems
    - Glacial systems
    - Groundwater systems
    - Shoreline systems
    - Eolian systems
- Be able to discuss the evidences and causes of climate change.
- Learn what our best forecasts for future climate are based on and understand the consequences of human activity.

31-1 THE HYDROLOGIC SYSTEM

The hydrologic system is driven by gravity and buoyancy forces (*Figure 31.1*). Warm, moisture-laden air rises from the oceans and continents because it is more buoyant. As it rises it cools, causing the water vapor to condense into rain or snow that gravity then pulls back to the Earth. Much of this precipitation falls directly back into the oceans, but some falls on the continents. It is precipitation, either rain or snow, that falls on the continents, along with the ocean water that moves against and along the margins of the continents, that is of particular interest to geologists. This is the water that shapes the continents and produces the many different landforms we see. It is also this water, which interacts with the continents, that is most important to us. Modern man depends on fresh water for life itself. Fresh water from lakes, rivers, reservoirs, and underground aquifers is used in enormous quantities daily for drinking, washing, crop irrigation, and industry. Water also may cause natural disasters (floods, landslides, storm waves, tsunamis) that can destroy property and take lives.

The hydrologic system includes so many dif-ferent aspects that we often divide it into smaller subsystems for easier study and reference.

River Systems

The most important part of the hydrologic system for shaping the continents is the system of flowing water found in rivers, streams, and rivulets that cover almost the entire surfaces of the continents (*Figure 31.2*). Gravity drives this flowing water. It always moves from areas of higher gravitational potential energy to areas of lower gravitational potential energy. In less sci-entific, but still accurate words, water always flows downhill. In mountainous regions where slopes are steep the water flows swiftly as grav-itational potential energy is converted quickly into kinetic energy. In places where slopes are

Figure 31.2
This satellite photo taken of part of the Hindu Kush mountains in Afghanistan shows the intricate drainage system developed on the surface of the Earth by water flowing in rivers and streams.

♦ **Floodplain**
A relatively flat region around a river where rich sediment has been deposited by the river's floods.

Figure 31.3
Flooding along the Santa Clara River in southern Utah in January of 2005 destroyed a number of expensive homes that were built on the river's floodplain.

more horizontal than vertical, the rivers flow slowly and with less kinetic energy. Wherever water flows, some of its kinetic energy is lost as it rubs against and pushes on Earth's rocks and sediments. This continual rubbing and pushing on the rocks causes them to erode, sometimes slowly, but sometimes quite quickly. The flowing water picks up the eroded rock particles and carries or pushes them on down the slope until the water loses all its kinetic energy by flowing into an ocean or lake. Here the sediment is deposited in layers that will eventually become sedimentary rock.

Rivers often offer scenic, beautiful views to the human eye and because of this attract developers and homeowners. However, rivers, aesthetically pleasing or not, are dynamic systems that naturally change and move their courses over time. Under certain conditions, a river that may be just a trickle of water most of the time can become a raging torrent (*Figure 31.3*). What kinds of conditions can produce the natural process of flooding that occurs along a river? Rivers flood when there is more water coming down the slope than the river channel can contain. This might be caused by an unusual amount

of rain, by rapid snowmelt, by man's activity upstream (e.g., by removing trees that would normally hold much of the precipitation in the ground), or by some combination of these factors. When such excessive water flow happens, the water spreads out beyond the banks of the river onto a region called the **floodplain**. Floodplains were discovered long ago to be excellent places to farm because the soil is enriched each time the river floods, sometimes as often as every year. However, a floodplain is not the best place to build a home, for exactly the same reason that it's good farmland. This is a fact of life that residents of many farming communities on both sides of the Mississippi River rediscover as Spring approaches each year.

Around the world, humans have tried a number of methods to prevent rivers from flooding, while also developing new ways of harnessing the power of moving water to produce electric power (and before that, water-wheel power), for recreation and agriculture. These efforts have produced both great benefits and additional problems.

One major change humans have made to control river systems is with the construction of dams. Dams help to control flooding by maintaining a more consistent flow of water downstream throughout the year. Dams with water turbines and generators installed also provide inexpensive electricity. The reservoirs they impound provide water for individual homes, cities, and large tracts of otherwise much less productive agricultural land. They also create scenic recreational destinations for boaters, fishing enthusiasts, and campers. What could be bad about that? Research over the years shows that dams also create many problems. A dam catches all the sediment that the river carries, which would normally pass on downstream. This sediment is no longer available to enrich farmland on lower-level floodplains, nor to provide the sand supply that would otherwise build deltas and beaches.

Since construction of the Aswan High Dam in Egypt, for example, much of the rich farmland along the river and in the Nile Delta has disappeared. Those changes also affected wildlife and their habitats along the river, helping push some species to extinction and driving others out of the river system. What has happened to the Nile Valley because of the Aswan High Dam

Figure 31.4
This relatively small continental type glacier in Iceland shows the zone of accumulation (white central region) of ice and snow and the zone of ablation (gray areas around margin of glacial mass).

has also happened, in greater or lesser form, to many other areas around the world where dams have been constructed.

In other places, usually on low-lying areas, people have attempted to control the movement of large rivers over inhabited floodplains by building embankments (called artificial **levees**) along riverbanks to keep the water moving in the same channel. Much of the city of New Orleans was built on the lowest point of the Mississippi floodplain, right where this great river empties into the Gulf of Mexico. Much of the city is actually several feet *below* sea level, while the river flows through it in a channel 10 to 15 feet *above* sea level. This is a disaster waiting to happen. At some point in the future, the system of levees and dikes that protect New Orleans will be unable to hold back the pressures of a particularly large Springtime flow, or perhaps a wave surge caused by a hurricane will overwhelm the city's levees. Whatever the natural event, if New Orleans' river-controls are overcome, an enormous amount of damage and perhaps even some loss of life will occur.*

Glacial Systems

Glaciers are not currently as abundant as rivers on the surface of Earth, but glaciers are still an important agent of change. The ice in glaciers, although solid, flows just like the water in a river, only much less rapidly; glacial ice

---

* This part of the text was written five months prior to the devastation of Hurricanes Katrina and Rita in August and September of 2005. To date (Oct. 2005) Hurricane Katrina is on record as the costliest storm in US history, in large part due to the flooding of New Orleans when the city's levees broke.

behaves like a very thick, viscous liquid. Snow builds up on a glacier surface called the "**zone of accumulation**," which is usually the highest end of the glacier. That snow packs down as more snow is deposited, and the pressure of the increasing weight of this glacial snow pack, plus the pull of gravity, causes the glacier to slowly "flow" downstream. The snow that was deposited high on a mountain glacier's zone of accumulation hundreds of years before flows downstream as hard-pressed ice, eventually reaching the face of the glacier where it comes into contact with the slightly warmer lake or sea. At this point the ice leaves the glacier, either as spectacular "calves," huge chunks of ice that drop off to become icebergs or, less spectacularly, as melt water in a part of the glacier called the "**zone of ablation**" (*Figure 31.4*). Glaciers may be either continental in scale, such as those in Antarctica or Greenland, or they may be small glaciers found in mountainous regions, called "valley glaciers" (*Figure 31.5*).

Figure 31.5
Valley glaciers flowing off of high mountains carry a significant load of rock and debris with them, eroding and carving the mountains and valleys they touch.

Glaciers are powerful agents of erosion, reshaping the land and carving spectacular, rugged mountain peaks (called horns) and beautiful U-shaped valleys. These valleys are quite different from the typical V-shaped valleys carved by rivers (*Figure 31.6*). Several of our National Parks are situated in regions that were previously glaciated or where there are still active glaciers. Yosemite, Rocky Mountain, Glacier, Grand

- **Levees**
Broad embankments built up along the banks of a river channel. These may be naturally created by floods or they can be artificially constructed to keep a river in its banks.

- **Zone of Accumulation**
The part of a glacial system where snow and ice are accumulating faster than they are melting away.

- **Zone of Ablation**
The part of a glacial system where melting of snow and ice occurs faster than accumulation.

Figure 31.6
U-shaped valley along the coast of Alaska carved by a valley glacier.

Figure 31.7
This photo shows a thin slice through a sandstone from 12,000 feet deep in the Gulf of Mexico. The clear grains of sand are quartz, while the darker grains are mostly clay. The violet-colored regions are the open pores in the rock. It is through these pores where groundwater flows.

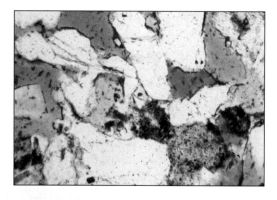

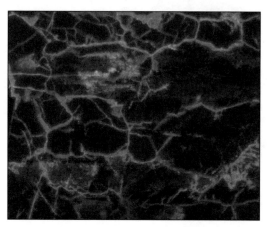

Figure 31.8
This is a photo of a piece of granite taken in ultraviolet light after it has been stained with a dye that soaked into the cracks. This interconnected network of cracks provides pathways for groundwater to flow.

- **Ice Age**
A time in Earth's history when conditions are such that large continental glaciers can form and grow.

- **Porosity**
The amount of open space found in a rock.

- **Permeability**
A measure of the connectedness of the porosity in a rock.

- **Water Table**
An underground surface that marks the level at which the rocks become saturated with water.

Teton, Mount Rainier, Great Basin, Yellowstone, and Olympic National Parks in the lower 48 states, and several more National Parks in Alaska would be included among the parks where valley glaciers played a major role in developing the beautiful scenery we find today. Continental glaciers, on the other hand, played a major role in shaping the features we find in Voyageurs, Isle Royal, and Acadia National Parks. Pilots and tourists flying at 30,000 feet over vast areas south of Canada's Hudson's Bay can easily see the remarkable effects of continental glaciers that scoured the soils from the area's granite subsurface many thousands of years ago. The southward flow of those long-gone glaciers pushed huge boulders over less-dense stone, grinding the boulders down as they created long, deep striations in the bare rock.

Glaciers also play a major role in Earth's climate, expanding during cooler periods and melting during warmer periods. During an **"ice age"** enough ocean water can be frozen in continental glaciers to lower sea level by up to a few hundred feet, exposing large portions of the continental shelf that were previously under water. Conversely, when these continental glaciers melt during warmer climatic periods, the sea level may go up by a several hundred feet,

drowning coastal areas. (Later in this chapter we will examine the causes and effects of climate change.)

Groundwater Systems

The oceans contain about 97% of Earth's water, while another 2.2% is found in glaciers. Groundwater is the third most abundant supply of water on Earth, accounting for 0.7%. Even though this may seem like a small amount, it is an extremely important reservoir to mankind because it is widely used for irrigation and culinary water. One of the common misconceptions about groundwater is that it occurs mostly in large underground pools, rivers, and lakes. In reality, only a small percentage of all groundwater is found in large open cavities or caves. Most groundwater occurs in tiny pores and cracks found in "solid" rocks (*Figure 31.7* and *Figure 31.8*). The amount of pore space in a rock is called its **porosity**. Water moves through a rock's subsurface because most of the pores and cracks in rocks are interconnected. **Permeability** is a measure of the interconnectedness of the pores and cracks in a rock. If permeability is high, then the pores and cracks are well connected and water can flow freely through the rock. If the permeability is low, then water does not easily flow through the rock.

The pores and cracks in rocks near Earth's surface contain a mixture of air and water, but deeper below the surface, the rocks at some point become saturated with water, even in desert regions. The **water table** is the point in the subsurface where the rocks become saturated with water (*Figure 31.9*). Good wells are found at sites where the subsurface rocks are

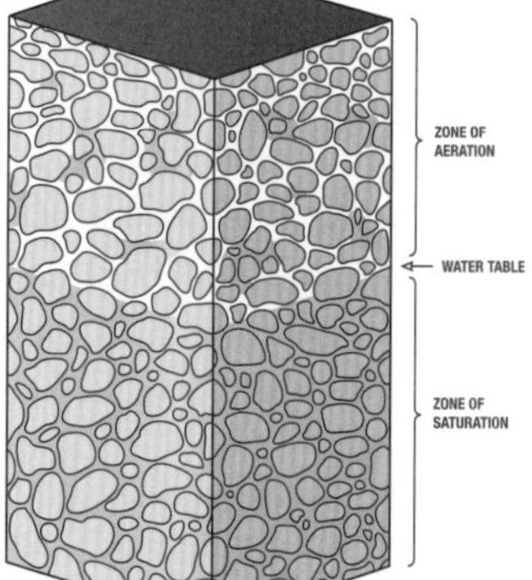

Figure 31.9
In the subsurface, rocks near the surface have pores that are only partially filled with water; this is called the zone of aeration. Lower down, the pores are completely filled with water in what is called the zone of saturation. The boundary between these two zones is called the water table.

permeable and within range of the well-digger's shovel or drill, close enough to the surface to allow the digger to reach the water table in the saturated rock formation.

Some rocks in the subsurface dissolve slowly in water; limestone is one rock type that is particularly susceptible to dissolution, especially if the groundwater is slightly acidic. When limestone is dissolved away, it leaves behind open cavities that we call caves or caverns. Not only does limestone dissolve but it also will precipitate when the ground water becomes saturated. Most of this material precipitates in the tiny pores and cracks where groundwater flows, forming a strong cement that holds rocks together. However, some of the dissolved limestone may precipitate back into larger caves, creating the beautiful cave decorations (*Figure 31.10*) seen in some of our National Parks and Monuments (e.g., Carlsbad Cavern, Mammoth Cave, Timpanogos Cave, Lehmann Cave).

When underground caverns form too close to the Earth's surface, they have a tendency to collapse, forming a depression called a "**sink hole**." In Florida new sinkholes form almost every year and almost immediately fill with

Figure 31.10
Cave decorations (stalagmites, stalactites, etc.) are created when groundwater contains more dissolved limestone than it can carry. The limestone is precipitated out of the water to form these beautiful cave features.

Figure 31.11
Sinkhole that formed in December of 2004 along Howland Blvd. in Volusia County, Florida.

water, because of that low-lying state's shallow water table. Occasionally, a home or street will be swallowed by a sinkhole as it forms (*Figure 31.11*).

Shoreline Systems

Ocean coastlines have become favorite places to build homes. However, those who build on the edge of an ocean coast don't always understand that shorelines are active, dynamic systems, constantly changing. Most of the daily

changes along a shoreline are small and relatively unimpressive. But every so often, a shoreline will undergo a major change when it is battered by a storm, hurricane, or tsunami. These major events may happen only once every 100 to 200 years, but when they do occur they can be devastating not only to property, but also to life. During the fall of 2004, the U.S. Atlantic coast was hit by four major hurricanes (Jeanne, Ivan, Francis, and Charley). Estimates of the damage costs from these storms range from 25 to 35 billion dollars, with more than 150 lives lost. The tsunami that struck Southeast Asia in December, 2004, killed an estimated 280,000 people and cost over 20 billion dollars in lost property. Even with these types of disasters, people continue to rebuild and move back into these coastal areas, apparently assuming they are somehow going to be more fortunate than the people who lived there before.

♦ **Sink Hole**
A depression created at the Earth's surface when an underground cavern collapses.

Figure 31.12
Sea stacks, cliffs and very narrow beaches along the south coast of Australia are an indication that this coastline is mostly the product of erosion.

Figure 31.13

The Atlantic coast of North Carolina and surrounding states is broad and relatively flat with wide beaches. Here transportation and deposition of sediment are the main geologic processes at work. In this satellite photo you can see the movement of sand along the coast; the water near the coast is a lighter color because of the sand it is carrying.

These events affect more that just those who live along the coast. In the United States, disaster relief funds provided to those who are affected come from all of those who pay taxes. Taxpayers are thus subsidizing the lifestyle of those who choose to live along the shore.

The processes of erosion, transportation of sediment, and deposition take place on a shoreline just as they do in river systems. Where wave energy is high, erosion predominates (*Figure 31.12*) and where wave energy is low, deposition of sediment is the major process (*Figure 31.13*). Sand and mud are moved along a shoreline by the constant action of waves. In fact, a shoreline can be thought of as a river of sand, always in constant motion. Incoming waves push sand up the beach and receding waves tumble grains of sand back down the beach towards the water because of the pull of gravity (*Figure 31.14*). When humans build barriers across a beach, the barrier will trap sand on one side, but starve the other side of its normal supply of sand. The supply of sand to the shore can also be disrupted when we build dams on nearby rivers. Rivers that remain free of dams provide a fresh supply of sediment to the shoreline, but when a dam is built on a river the supply of sediment is trapped behind the dam and no longer makes it to the sea. The Aswan Dam in Egypt now traps most of the sediment that used to be deposited on the Nile Delta. Because of this, the delta has started to erode and subside beneath the sea. Changes to a shoreline system which are caused by human activity may be

viewed as either good or bad, depending somewhat on individual perspective. However, we should always be aware that our actions can and do change these environments and may have more far-reaching effects than we can foresee.

Eolian Systems

The Eolian system is the system of wind that blows across Earth's surface. It takes its name from Aeolus, the Greek god who was the "Keeper of the Winds." Wind is a poor agent of erosion, meaning that it is not nearly as effective at erosion as ice and water. However, wind is very effective at transporting sediment and depositing it. In desert areas of the world where water is scarce, wind is the primary agent of sediment transport and deposition, forming large fields of sand dunes (*Figure 31.15*) and producing large plumes of dust during storms (*Figure 31.16*). Fine dust picked up by desert winds in North Africa can blow all the way across the

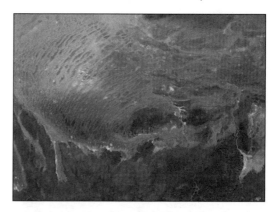

Figure 31.15

This satellite photo is of part of the central Sahara Desert. Tan colored sand blankets the darker rocks beneath. Beneath the dunes in many places we can find old stream and river channels, evidence that the Sahara was once a wetter place.

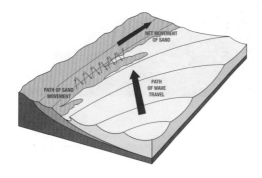

Figure 31.14

Sand moves along the beach because in most places the waves hit the shoreline at angle. The waves move sand grains up the beach and then gravity pulls them back down. This constant pushing and pulling slowly moves the sand along the shore.

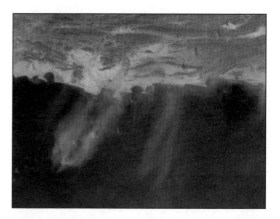

Figure 31.16

Dust carried offshore by winds blowing along the south coast of Pakistan.

Atlantic Ocean and be deposited in North America.

Wind is selective in the size of particles it will carry. Sand grains and smaller particles can easily be moved by wind. Particles larger than dust, silt, and sand, however, cannot be carried by wind and are left behind, often creating a surface consisting only of small pebbles and larger stones. These surfaces are called "**desert pavements**" (*Figure 31.17*).

Areas on the edge of deserts are susceptible to a process called "**desertification**." In these regions, sand and loose sediment are held in place by plants. However, if cattle and other livestock are allowed to overgraze in those areas, the plants may be killed when they are cropped too close to the ground, or eaten so often that they can't produce sufficient seed. Such overgrazing causes the plants eventually to disappear from the area, leaving only loose soil and rocks. The wind blowing across the area picks up the sediment and moves it to areas where existing plants can hold it, changing marginal desert land to full-blown desert. Desertification is a problem in many places in the world. Approximately one-third of the continental areas are dry-land or desert areas and marginal desert regions are home to over 1 billion people. In poorer countries where living conditions are marginal at best, desertification is a life-threatening problem. Drought in Africa during the 1960s and 1970s is estimated to have caused the deaths from starvation and disease of 150,000 to 250,000 people who had been subsisting entirely from self-sufficient herding and gardening. More efficient farming and grazing practices might have prevented many of the problems and tragedies brought about by the drought. In fact, droughts themselves might be reduced in their severity, but cultural practices, such as maintaining herds of goats that eat anything green, and basic human survival needs, such as cutting down nearby trees for firewood, have contributed greatly to desertification over the centuries.

31–2 CLIMATE CHANGE

All the subsystems of the hydrologic system change in response to changes in climate. One of the great scientific debates of the past few decades has gathered around the causes and processes of climate change. All scientists agree that the world's climate is always changing. Today it is apparent that Earth's climate is getting warmer, but what is not agreed upon by everyone is the cause of this global warming. Some claim that it is just part of a natural cycle of global warming that has nothing to do with man. Others are certain that it is the result of the recent increases in man's production of carbon dioxide and other so-called "**greenhouse gases**," following the industrial revolution. Still others believe that the warming trend began long before the industrial revolution and is related to the development of agriculture.

The second part of the problem is that if the Earth is warming, what should we do? Can we do anything to stop it? If so, should we try to stop it? How soon will this global warming start to cause problems and what will those problems be? We can take a look at some of the data that is available and see if we can make sense of it.

Figure 31.17
A desert pavement where all of the fine sand and silt have been blown away, leaving behind a surface coated with coarse pebbles and cobbles.

♦ **Desert Pavements**
A desert pavement is a surface of pebbles and cobbles created by the removal of all of the finer grains by wind.

♦ **Desertification**
The process of converting marginal dry lands into desert by overgrazing, farming, or other processes.

♦ **Greenhouse Gases**
Gases in the atmosphere that trap heat and keep the Earth warmer than it would otherwise be, just like the glass in a greenhouse traps heat inside the greenhouse.

Figure 31.18
Graph of average temperatures for the Northern Hemisphere over the past 1000 years. Notice that the trend is nearly horizontal (perhaps slightly declining) until about 1900 when a sharp increase in temperature began.

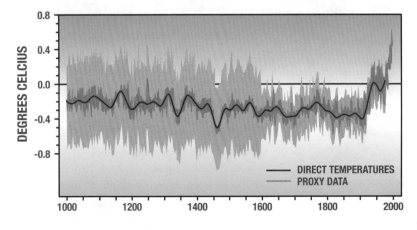

Temperature Changes Through Time

One of the most widely published graphs in recent years is shown in *Figure 31.18*. This graph, sometimes called the "hockey stick" because its shape somewhat resembles one, records a history of the Earth's average temperature over the past 1,000 years. Only the most recent data in the last 100+ years are from actual thermometer readings. The other data come from temperatures calculated from ice cores, tree rings, coral deposits and historical records that give indications of temperature. For example, historical records that refer to the time of latest and earliest frosts in different parts of the world can be used to estimate temperatures around the globe. Errors on the temperature estimates are quite large, particularly prior to about 1600, when historical records of an area's climate were seldom kept. However, one thing is quite obvious from the graph: over the past 100 years, Earth has on average become noticeably warmer, by about 1° C.

Orbital Variations

Since the 1970s, scientists have known that Earth's climate tends to follow three major cycles of cooling and warming, with periods of about 100,000 years, 41,000 years, and 23,000 years. The longest of these cycles is related to regular changes in the shape of Earth's orbit around the Sun. During one cycle of 100,000 years, Earth's orbit will change from being nearly circular to being slightly elliptical (*Figure 31.19*). The amount that Earth's orbit varies from circular is called its "**eccentricity**." When Earth's orbit is circular, it receives approximately the same amount of sunlight all year long. However, when that orbit becomes more elliptical, there is a difference in the amount of sunlight received when

Earth is close to the Sun and when it is farther from the Sun. This change can allow glaciers to develop and expand and cause global temperatures to fall.

The second cycle of 41,000 years is related to the tilt of Earth on its axis as it orbits the Sun (*Figure 31.20*). The amount of tilt varies from 24.5° to 21.5°; currently Earth's axis is tilted at 23.5°. It appears that as the tilt of Earth's axis decreases, solar energy is more evenly spread across the Earth, causing warmer, moister winters with more accumulation of snow and ice, followed by cooler summers when less ice can melt. This seems to trigger an advance of continental glaciers.

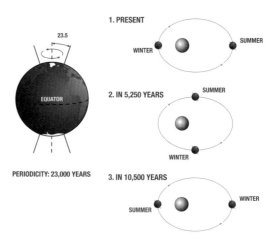

Figure 31.19

This figure shows how the shape of the Earth's orbit changes during its 100,000 year eccentricity cycle, going from a more elliptical orbit (exaggerated in this drawing) to one that is nearly circular.

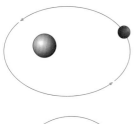

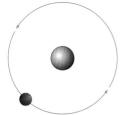

♦ **Eccentricity**

A measure of how elliptical the Earth's orbit is. Higher eccentricity means a more elliptical, less circular orbit.

Figure 31.21

As the Earth rotates on its axis, it wobbles a bit. The wobble, called precession, has a period of about 23,000 years. Because of this precession, the Earth receives different amount of solar radiation at different times in the 23,000 cycle. When solar radiation is high, the Earth is warm enough to prevent the formation and advance of large continental glaciers, but when solar radiation declines, continental glaciers form and expand.

The last of the three cycles lasts for about 23,000 years and is related to the wobble of Earth on its axis (*Figure 31.21*). Perhaps you have seen a spinning top and watched as it wobbles slightly back and forth as it rotates. This is caused by the force of gravity pulling down on the top as it spins. In the same way, Earth has the gravitational pull of the Sun acting on it as it spins. This causes Earth to wobble slightly on its axis as it spins. This wobble means that over 23,000 years Earth's northern hemisphere is tilted toward the Sun at different locations in Earth's orbit. During a cycle the northern hemisphere will change from being tilted towards the Sun when Earth is

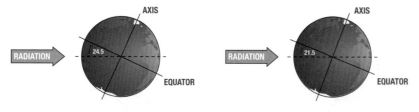

TIME: 41,000 YEARS

Figure 31.20

The axial tilt of the Earth toward the sun changes over a period of 41,000 years from about 24.5 degrees of tilt to about 21.5 degrees of tilt. This change in axial tilt has an affect on Earth's climate.

farthest from the Sun (producing cooler temperatures and an ice age), to being tilted toward the Sun when Earth is closest to the Sun (producing an interglacial period).

All these cycles work together to produce our climate and none of them is affected in the least by human activity. In a regular way the climate gets colder and then warmer and then colder again without any input from us. However, the shortest of these warming and cooling cycles is 23,000 years and the temperature changes we have measured in the last 100 years have taken place much faster than any natural change in the past that we have been able to discover.

Position of the Continents

Another factor that seems to play a critical role in Earth's climate is the positions of our continents. The continents are not fixed, but slowly move around on Earth's surface as part of its plate tectonic system. When the continents are mostly located close to the Equator, the world's climate is warmer and continental glaciers are slow to develop. However, when the continents are located nearer the Poles, as they are today, continental glaciers do form and expand or recede, depending on the cycles discussed above.

Greenhouse Gases

Certain gases in the atmosphere tend to trap solar radiation, keeping Earth warmer, just like a blanket (or a large, friendly dog) covering you on a cold night will keep you warm. The three most important of these so-called "greenhouse" gases are carbon dioxide, methane, and water vapor. When the Earth is receiving more sunlight, wetlands flourish. This encourages more bacterial action, which in turn creates more

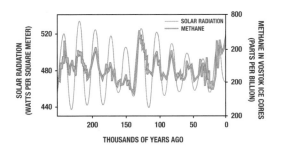

decaying vegetation. The rotting vegetation produces more methane (the most potent of the greenhouse gases) and the climate begins to warm. If we plot the concentrations of methane in the atmosphere for Earth's most recent 250,000 years (determined from gas bubbles trapped in ice cores) next to the solar radiation cycles, we can see that they follow each other very closely, until we get to the last 5,000 years. During this period methane amounts rise in opposition to the solar radiation cycle (*Figure 31.22*). The same thing can be seen in the global carbon dioxide curve; it follows the solar radiation curve until we get to the last 8,000 years, where they diverge. Our climate models will need to explain this discrepancy.

Where is the Climate Headed?

Predicting Earth's future climate, like predicting tomorrow's weather based on a farmer's almanac, turns out to be a very difficult question. There are so many factors that influence the climate and we have such a short record of actual climate data that we can't be sure what the future holds. However, we can make some pretty good guesses based on the trends in the data discussed above. First, it appears that something happened about 8,000 years ago to change the natural direction of the climate. Based on the solar radiation curve, 8,000 years ago is when the climate should have begun to cool, pushing

Figure 31.22

Graph of solar radiation and atmospheric methane concentration over the last 250,000 years of Earth's history. Note that the concentration of methane follows the solar radiation curve quite closely until just the last few thousand years.

Figure 31.23

History of human activities and greenhouse gases.

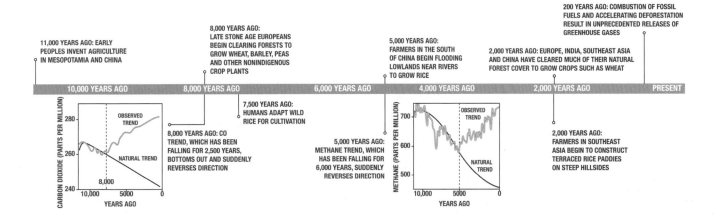

us back into another ice age by about 5,000 years ago. But this did not happen. Even though Earth was receiving less energy from the Sun, global temperatures remained fairly constant over most of this period because levels of carbon dioxide and methane were increasing.

One modern climate researcher, William Ruddiman, recently proposed in the Scientific American, March 2005, that the increasing levels of carbon dioxide noted at 8,000 years ago and increases in methane, starting at 5,000 years ago, were caused, respectively, by the start of substantial deforestation for farming at 8,000 B.P. and the development of rice agriculture in Southeast Asia at about 5,000 B.P. (*Figure 31.23*). If this theory is correct, then agriculture has kept

Earth warmer than it would otherwise have been. More recently, the rapid climb in worldwide temperature has been produced by a second event, the onset of the industrial revolution and the burning of fossil fuels. So an overall graph for the future climate might look something like *Figure 31.24*. This figure shows what the natural trend for the climate should have been without any human influence, plotted with the actual climate trend. It also shows what we might expect in the future as we continue to burn fossil fuels and what might happen when we run out of oil and coal. After all the fossil fuels are gone, Earth may return fairly quickly to its natural climate curve, plunging the world and future generations back into another ice age.

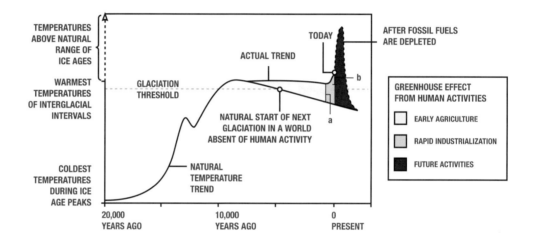

Figure 31.24

Temperature (climate) model for the last 20,000 years also showing the predicted trend for the next few hundred years. Agriculture has kept the Earth warmer than it would otherwise be, and now the burning of fossil fuels has caused a steep increase in temperature that will last until fossil fuels are depleted. When all the fossil fuels are gone, the Earth should cool down and return to the natural trend it has followed for many thousands of years.

Chapter Framework

A. The Hydrologic System

B. River System
2. Erosion and deposition
3. Flooding
4. Barriers created by man

C. Glacial System
1. Zone of accumulation
2. Zone of ablation
3. Sea level

D. Groundwater Systems
1. Porosity and Permeability
2. Water table
3. Sinkholes

E. Shoreline Systems
1. Wave energy
2. Dams and barriers

F. Eolian Systems
1. Erosion and deposition
2. Desertification

G. Climate Change
1. Impact on the hydrologic system
2. General trend

H. Temperature Changes Through Time
1. Graph of the past 1,000 years

I. Orbital Variations
1. Orbit
2. Tilt

J. Positions of the Continents

K. Greenhouse Gases

L. Where is the Climate Headed?
1. Agriculture
2. Industrial Revolution

Comprehension

True/False

1. _____ Gravity and buoyancy are the two forces that drive the hydrologic system.
2. _____ The Eolian system is a more effective form of erosion than the hydrologic system.
3. _____ Glaciers create V-shaped valleys.
4. _____ Flood plains are a great place to live because of the bountiful crops they yield.
5. _____ Groundwater is the third most abundant supply of water on Earth.

Fill in the Blank

1. All of the hydrologic subsystems change in response to changes in _____.

2. When Earth has an_____ orbit the temperature tends to cool.

3. Over the last 100 years, Earth's temperature has increased by_____.

4. _____ _____ supply a fresh source of sediment to the shoreline.

5. The less Earth tilts on its axis the more it triggers _____ glaciers.

Matching

1. _____ A measure of how elliptical Earth's orbit is.
2. _____ Where snow and ice accumulate in a glacial system.
3. _____ Surface of pebbles and cobbles created by the removal of fine-grained sand by wind.
4. _____ Part of glacial system where melting of snow and ice occurs.
5. _____ Measure of the connectedness of the porosity in a rock.
6. _____ Gases in the atmosphere that trap heat.
7. _____ Converting marginal dry lands into desert.
8. _____ Wonderful place to farm because of the enriched soil.
9. _____ Point in the subsurface where the rocks become saturated with water.
10. _____ The amount of pore space found in a rock.
11. _____ Created when an underground cavern collapses.
12. _____ During this period of time large continental glaciers can form and grow.
13. _____ Used to protect Holland by holding the ocean behind it.

a. Zone of accumulation
b. Ice age
c. Permeability
d. Floodplain
e. Porosity
f. Water table
g. Desertification
h. Zone of ablation
i. Sink hole
j. Levee
k. Desert pavement
l. Eccentricity
m. Green house gases

Analysis

1. The hydrologic system causes the most extensive changes on Earth's surface through
   a. running water
   b. glaciers
   c. shoreline processes
   d. wind

2. Rivers are largely responsible for the formation of
   a. Metamorphic rocks
   b. Marble
   c. Sedimentary rocks
   d. Igneous rocks

3. Mountain peaks carved by glaciers are called
   a. Aretes
   b. Antlers
   c. Moraines
   d. Horns

4. Which of the following affects the ability of water to flow through rock
   a. Porosity
   b. Hydrologic flow
   c. Permeability
   d. Static connectedness

5. If waves along the coast have high energy then

   a. Deposition occurs
   b. A tsunami is approaching
   c. A hurricane is imminent
   d. Erosion occurs

6. Which of the following would not directly affect temperature

   a. An elliptical orbit instead of a circular orbit
   b. The end of burning fossil fuels
   c. Flourishing wetlands
   d. A distant star dying

7. What has delayed the contemporary occurrence of an ice age?

8. What creates sink holes?

9. What effect do flourishing wetlands have on Earth's climate?

10. How does Earth's orbit affect the climate?

11. How do glaciers impact Earth's temperature?

12. List the different places where it may not be best to live as discussed in the chapter. What elements make these places a potential risk?

Synthesis

1. Discuss the different reasons people believe that Earth is getting warmer.

2. Based solely on the variable of continental position, explain what the general climatic condition might have been like on the super continent Pangaea?

3. How does a dam alter the normal behavior of a river? What benefits and problems do dams create?

4. When speaking of global cooling, glaciers are cited as impacting sea level depending on their size. Glaciers are just huge masses of ice on land. The North Pole is also a large mass of ice that floats in the ocean. Why does the chapter not mention the North Pole's size changing as impacting sea level? (Answering this question will require using principles of buoyancy from Chapter 6.)

5. The chapter explains that glaciers act like a viscous fluid, both eroding and depositing sediment. Rivers deposit their sediment when the kinetic energy of the water decreases. With this information, where and when would you expect a glacier to deposit the majority of the sediment that it carries?

6. The coast of California varies in it composition and structure. The south has very sandy beaches and the north has rock beaches. Why might this difference exist?

7. Levees are used to keep water from flooding over the riverbank and flooding homes built on the floodplain. What might be the consequences of building a Levee?

SURVIVING FINALS

*"When the time for decision arrives,
the time for preparation is past."*

Thomas S. Monson, First Counselor in the Presidency of the LDS Church

Preparing for and taking finals can be overwhelming. However, there are ways to make finals week less stressful and more manageable.

Before finals week begins:

- Start preparing for finals at the beginning of the semester. It is better to study regularly than to relearn all that you have covered before the final exam. It is easier to review difficult topics long before the test than to memorize vague concepts in a short amount of time.

- Make sure you know exactly when and where each final exam will take place. This information is available on AIM and is usually in your class syllabus.

- If a final exam is scheduled in the Testing Center, plan in advance which day you will take it. To avoid waiting for a long time (sometimes hours), check the line condition on the Testing Center web page. Also, spacing your unscheduled finals throughout the week might be a good way to lower stress levels.

- Many professors will provide study guides to aid in preparation for finals; it is a great idea to use them! If a professor does not give a study guide, make your own using old tests, class notes, and texts.

- Form study groups! Even if you haven't been participating in a study group, it is always useful to organize one before the final exam. In a study group you can compare notes, quiz each other, and clarify any misunderstandings about the material.

- Utilize the reading days. It is a great time to meet with others to focus on what you do not understand. If you are feeling overwhelmed, you might also want to take the opportunity to relax and do an activity you enjoy.

- Attend any study sessions offered by TAs and professors. Take advantage of these opportunities to ask any questions you might still have and to concentrate on material which may be covered on the final exam.

During finals week:

- Take care of your body. Eat a healthy diet with lots of fruits and vegetables instead of having too much sugar and caffeine. A burst of energy might feel good initially, but it will not be beneficial to your overall health and endurance.

- Get enough sleep! It may seem helpful to study all night, but sleep deprivation decreases your ability to remember and concentrate. Falling asleep during a test will bring you very little joy.

- Try to avoid studying one subject for long periods of time. Your brain will retain more information if you allow it to process what you have studied.

- To relieve additional tension, it might be helpful to take a snack or water, and to dress comfortably when you take an exam. If you are mentally relaxed, you will perform better.

- Final exams are not the most important part of your existence. Despite popular opinion, neither your graduate school nor your future career is decided solely by finals week.

- Be sure to practice good test-taking strategies.

Courtesy of Freshman Academy, BYU.

BEYOND THE EARTH

CHAPTER 32

"And he beheld many lands; and each land was called earth, and there were inhabitants on the face thereof. . . . And worlds without number have I created; and I also created them for mine own purpose; . . . But only an account of this earth, and the inhabitants thereof, give I unto you."

~ Moses 1:29, 33, 35

The scriptures above suggest that there may be many other planets in the Universe, but further indicate that scripture only provides detailed information about the Earth on which we live. Astronomers have found that there are many planets orbiting around other stars scattered throughout the Universe. The previous six chapters have focused solely on the planet Earth and cover topics such as the formation, history, and ongoing dynamic processes of the Earth. This chapter discusses what lies beyond the Earth. This textbook will conclude with chapters that examine the realm of stars and galaxies to see what conclusions we can draw concerning the nature of our Universe and its possible future.

ters. A **star cluster** (*Figure 32.1*) contains anywhere from a few dozen stars to upwards of a million individual stars. A million stars may seem like a lot of material. However, the size of a star cluster pales in comparison to a **galaxy**. A typical large galaxy (*Figure 32.2*) contains enough matter to form more than a trillion individual stars. It would take about a million of the largest star clusters known to equal the number of stars in one large galaxy! The study of very large objects such as galaxies and clusters of galaxies becomes very important in the field of cosmology, which will be discussed in the final chapter of this book.

It is apparent that the Universe around us is complex and contains a wide variety of materials. Very small objects such as protons, neu-

32–1 THE SCALE AND SCOPE OF THE UNIVERSE

The Sun is the only object in our solar system that gives off large quantities of light and other forms of electromagnetic radiation, making the Sun a clearly different class of object from the planets. The next chapter compares the Sun with other stars, and discusses stars in general. Stars are also seen in large groups known as clus-

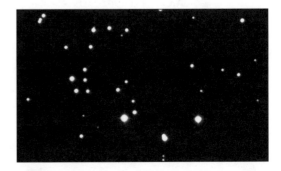

Figure 32.1
The central region of the old open star cluster M67. Note that the stars all appear to differ in both brightness and color.

trons, and electrons form atoms. We have already discussed how these tiny particles combine to form the familiar elements that are the building blocks for all the matter that we observe throughout the Universe. The Earth is part of a much larger system, our solar system. Our Sun and its planets belong to an even larger system known as a galaxy. Galaxies are the fundamental constituents of the Universe as a whole. When we discuss the nature of the Universe, nothing smaller than a galaxy is even worth noting. Objects the size of the Earth or the Sun are

Figure 32.2

The spiral galaxy M51 and a smaller companion galaxy, NGC 5195, as seen by the Hubble Space Telescope. Note that the structure in M51 clearly contains glowing gas clouds and dark gas clouds that closely follow the spiral pattern.

◆ Star Cluster

A group of stars that formed from the same cloud of material and have been held together in a cluster by gravitational forces. A small open cluster can consist of only a few dozen members while a large globular cluster can contain more than a million individual stars.

◆ Galaxy

A large collection of stars, dust, and gas that is found in a wide variety of sizes ranging from a few million solar masses for a small galaxy to large galaxies with more than a trillion solar masses of material.

◆ Comet

A small body composed of ice and dust that orbits our Sun. As a comet comes close to our Sun, some of the material is vaporized and a tail forms opposite the direction of the motion of the comet.

◆ Asteroid

One of many thousands of small rocky objects that orbit our Sun. The orbits of asteroids generally lie between the orbits of Mars and Jupiter, although some are in orbits that bring them close to our Sun. Asteroids are much smaller than a planet and are sometimes called minor planets.

◆ Meteoroid

A small rock found in the space between the planets.

all but invisible on such a scale. When discussing the Universe from an astronomical viewpoint, it is necessary to talk about objects that are almost inconceivably large when considered from our perspective here on the Earth.

32–2 THE NATURE OF OUR SOLAR SYSTEM

Before we begin studying more distant reaches of the Universe, we should note some qualities of the planets, moons, and other objects that make up the solar system. Planets and moons are not self-luminous objects. Although some of the planets (especially gas giants) give off small amounts of energy, mostly in the form of radio waves, it is important to remember that the planets, in general, do not produce their own radiant energy. A planet's glow is the result of reflected sunlight.

Our solar system is composed of the Sun and the nine known planets, including Earth, that orbit the Sun, along with millions of other objects that include moons, **comets**, **asteroids**, and other small pieces of space debris. Despite the great variety of objects and orbital motions that are observed in our solar system, astronomers have found the solar system to be a place of great order that has endured in much the same form over geologic time scales.

The Sun is a star and contains far more than 99% of all the matter in our solar system. These various objects include the dozens of moons that orbit many of the planets and thousands of asteroids that revolve around the Sun in a wide variety of orbital paths. There are also uncounted millions of comets and smaller pieces of space debris that move throughout the solar system.

Detailed observations of craters on planets and moons indicate that collisions between objects were frequent in the solar system's early history. Scientists believe that the planets were formed by accretion resulting from collisions in the material that formed our Sun. It is important to remember that the solar system contains numerous other objects that are in general much smaller than even the planets. Several hundred tons of extraterrestrial material still strike the Earth every day. Fortunately, most of these impacts are made by debris the size of dust particles or grains of sand. Astronomers commonly refer to these pieces of debris, whether large or small, as **meteoroids**.

Occasionally, larger pieces of space debris plummet through the atmosphere and smash into Earth's surface. Craters found on the Earth appear to be the result of large, ancient impacts. One of the most geologically recent large impact sites is the Barringer Crater near Winslow, Arizona (*Figure 32.3*). This crater resulted from a meteoroid impact that occurred within the last 50,000 years. Apparently, the meteoroid measured approximately fifty meters in diameter. This large mass, hurtling down at a high velocity, hit Earth's surface with so much force that the energy it released at impact has been compared to the simultaneous detonation of many hydrogen bombs. The crater that resulted is more than a kilometer across and about 200 meters deep.

The Planets of Our Solar System

In order of their distance from the Sun, the known planets in our solar system include Mercury, Venus, Earth, Mars, Jupiter, Saturn, Uranus, Neptune, and Pluto. A comparison of the planets' orbital properties indicates that the planets probably all formed during the same epoch. Each of the planets revolves around the Sun in the same direction. The orbits of the planets are just slightly elliptical in shape and lie on approximately the same plane as the Earth's orbit around the Sun. These common properties among the planets' orbits present strong evi-

Figure 32.3
The Barringer Crater in northern Arizona. This is one of the more recent impact craters (of less than 200 that can be identified) on the surface of our Earth.

dence that the material that formed our solar system originally had some motion in common. Despite the similarities, a closer examination of the planets shows some striking variations throughout the solar system.

Mercury, Venus, Earth, and Mars are the four inner planets, which are often called the **terrestrial worlds**. Mercury, Venus, and Mars each have densities similar to that of the Earth. The similar densities of the terrestrial planets mean that each inner planet is four or five times more dense than water. The terrestrial worlds are composed of rocky materials similar to those found on the Earth. The same elements common to rocks on Earth's surface also compose the rocks on the other terrestrial planets. However, Earth appears to be unique in its geologic activity caused by the movement of its tectonic plates.

Jupiter, Saturn, Uranus, and Neptune are the next four planets, which are commonly referred to as the **Jovian worlds**. These are giant gaseous planets composed mainly of hydrogen and helium, with smaller amounts of carbon, nitrogen, and other elements. Carbon and nitrogen often combine with hydrogen to form molecules such as methane and ammonia. The gas composition of the Jovian worlds makes their densities much lower than the densities found on the terrestrial planets. Typically, the gas giants have densities similar to the density of water, which is also much like the average density of the Sun.

The gaseous planets are many times more massive than a typical terrestrial planet such as Earth. Because of the Jovian planets' greater mass, their internal pressure is many times greater than the internal pressure of the terrestrial worlds. We do not yet know for certain if any Jovian planet has a rocky core similar to those of the terrestrial planets. However, each of the four Jovian worlds has a ring system. Saturn is well-known for the spectacular system of rings (see *Figure 32.4*) in orbit around its equator. The other planetary ring systems are difficult to observe because they are not nearly as extensive or as highly reflective as the rings around Saturn.

Pluto is believed to be the outermost planet in our solar system. Pluto is unlike either the terrestrial planets or the Jovian planets. Its lack of similarity to any other planet in the solar system is the cause of much debate among plane-

tary scientists as to whether Pluto should continue to be considered as a planet within the solar system.

The debate over Pluto's classification as a planet is based on specific discrepancies between Pluto and the rest of the solar system. Pluto's orbit is more than seventeen degrees out of alignment with the rest of the solar system. This orbital tilt is greater (by a factor of two) than any of the other planets in our solar system. Additionally, while all the planets in the solar system follow approximately circular orbits, Pluto's orbit clearly shows the greatest departure from being circular. Also, Pluto's density is somewhere between the average density of the terrestrial worlds and the Jovian worlds. In many ways Pluto is more similar to one of the Jovian planets' icy moons than either a terrestrial or Jovian planet. For these reasons, future planetary scientists may determine that Pluto is not actually a planet but is rather more representative of a different class of objects located in the outer reaches of the solar system.

The discovery of an object known as 2003 UB_{313} was announced in 2005. This object is apparently at least as large as Pluto, but currently lies about twice as far away from the Sun. This object is in a highly elliptical orbit that is tilted 44 degrees to the plane of the solar system. It is not certain at this time whether this object will be designated as a planet. Discoveries such as this will certainly influence future debates as to whether Pluto should remain classified as a planet.

32-3 THE NATURE OF EARTH AND ITS PLACE IN THE SOLAR SYSTEM

Today, many people have the misconception that Columbus' voyage in 1492 was the first

◆ **Terrestrial Worlds**
The rocky planets, which include Mercury, Venus, Earth, and Mars.

◆ **Jovian Worlds**
The gas giant planets, which include Jupiter, Saturn, Uranus, and Neptune.

Figure 32.4
The second of the Jovian worlds, Saturn, as observed by the approaching Cassini probe in 2004.

attempt to prove the Earth's spherical nature. In reality, most scholars and philosophers realized the spherical nature of the Earth as early as 600 B.C. For example, when sailors first navigated around the southern tip of Africa, they noted that as they traveled south the northern stars appeared to be lower in the sky. Also, as they sailed southward, new stars not previously seen became visible in the southern sky. Finally, as the sailors crossed the equator on their journey south, the North Star dipped below the northern horizon and was no longer visible from their latitude on the Earth's surface.

Aristotle, a remarkably gifted scholar and philosopher who lived approximately 300 B.C., believed the Universe could be explained through the use of mathematically based physical laws. During a lunar eclipse, Aristotle noticed that the Earth cast a circular shadow on the surface of the Moon. This observation strongly added to existing evidence for Earth's spherical nature.

A philosopher-scientist named Eratosthenes measured the Earth's circumference in approximately 200 B.C. To measure the Earth's circumference, one must first accept Earth's spherical nature. Eratosthenes obtained this measurement by an ingenious use of basic geometry.

Eratosthenes heard reports from the city of Syene that on the longest day of the year, the noonday sun would shine directly down the shaft of a well and cast no shadow. Eratosthenes realized that the city where he lived, Alexandria, lay almost due north of Syene. On the longest day of the year, an object in Alexandria, such as a post or an obelisk, would clearly cast a shadow that could be measured. From this, Eratosthenes realized that the Sun in Alexandria was a little more than seven degrees away from being directly overhead on the longest day of the year, as it was in Syene. By forming a simple proportion—that is, 7 degrees is to 360 degrees as d is to the circumference of the Earth—it became very easy to solve for the total distance around the Earth (*Figure 32.5*). The only number Eratosthenes had to measure was the distance between Alexandria and Syene. After measuring the distance between Alexandria and Syene, Eratosthenes calculated the Earth's circumference to be about 42,000 kilometers. This calculation is remarkably close to the current accepted value for the

circumference of the Earth—about 40,000 kilometers.

Approximately 80 years before the time of Eratosthenes, another Alexandrian astronomer named Aristarchus made geometric calculations that estimated the distance between the Earth and the Moon as being about 1/20 of the distance between the Earth and the Sun. However, Aristarchus made mistakes in measuring the angles formed by the Earth-Sun-Moon system, and as a result his estimate for the distance between the Earth and the Sun is about 20 times smaller than the actual distance. Nonetheless, this method proved to be a very powerful technique that was used over 2,000 years ago in order to ingeniously estimate incredibly large distances.

Aristarchus also estimated the actual size of the Moon. He did this by observing the time required for the Moon to pass through the Earth's shadow during a lunar eclipse. Using this technique, Aristarchus concluded that the Earth's diameter was about three times larger than the Moon. His measurement is a good estimate of the actual size ratio between the Earth and the Moon. Using the Moon's estimated size, Aristarchus then looked at how large the Moon appeared in the sky and calculated how far away the Moon must be in order to have that apparent size. Aristarchus' estimation of the distance between the Earth and the Moon was accurate to within about 10% of the true distance. Because his estimate of the Earth-Sun distance was off by a factor of 20, his calculated estimate for the distance to the Sun was also off by a factor of 20. However, this is an incredible measurement for the time period in which it was done.

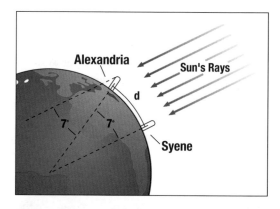

Figure 32.5

A representation of Eratosthenes' method for measuring the Earth's circumference from the cities of Alexandria and Syene located in Africa.

The Earth's Motion in Space

Even though the early Greek and Alexandrian astronomers determined the spherical nature of the Earth and estimated sizes and distances with a fair degree of precision, their philosophy about the Earth's motion was fundamentally flawed. Scientists from the time of Aristotle up until the 16th century A.D. believed the Earth remained stationary in the Universe. They also believed the Earth was the center of the entire Universe. The scientists based these conclusions on the absence of any experiment they could conduct to prove that the Earth moved.

From our own individual senses, we can easily understand why early scientists and philosophers concluded that the Earth doesn't move. We know they had concluded that the Earth was incredibly large. Being unaware of the principle of motion symmetry, they assumed that if the Earth was in motion then people on the surface of the Earth should be able to detect the effects of that motion. An object thrown into the air should move off rapidly in the direction opposite the motion of the Earth. People should feel the effects of continuous high winds. These were all issues that were examined, and the easiest conclusion for early astronomers to reach was that the Earth was indeed a stationary point at the center of the Universe. This conclusion persisted for at least 2,000 years.

Their incomplete understanding of science made it necessary for astronomers of this era to construct very elaborate models to explain the observed motions of the Sun, the Moon, the planets, and the stars. Astronomers could easily explain the motions of the stars, as they simply moved around the Earth as night slowly turned into day. However, simple explanations did not work well for other celestial objects such as the Sun, the Moon, and the five known planets of antiquity (Mercury, Venus, Mars, Jupiter, and Saturn). To ancient observers, these objects appeared to have a very complex set of motions when viewed from the surface of the Earth relative to the background stars. Sometimes the planets moved from west to east relative to the background stars. At times they appeared to stop, and sometimes they appeared to move from east to west. This phenomenon was very difficult to explain from a fixed observation point

located at the center of a spherical coordinate system. The Earth-centered model continued to become more and more complex as observations of the planetary motions became increasingly more accurate.

By the 16th century, the Earth-centered model of the Universe had become very complex indeed. Around this time, Nicolaus Copernicus suggested that a Sun-centered model could do a much better job of explaining the observed motion of the Sun, the Moon, and the five planets. The Sun-centered model was a much simpler explanation, so the principle of Occam's Razor (Chapter 26) suggested that it was likely the better explanation for the true nature of the motions in the solar system. Observational evidence supplied later by Galileo Galilei, using the first astronomical telescope, provided additional support for the validity of a Sun-centered model.

Early in the 17th century, scientists still felt that even if Earth and the five other known planets orbited the Sun, they did so in perfect circular motion. The idea that planets orbited in perfect circles was one of the last remaining tenets of the old Earth-centered model. About the same time that Galileo made his visual observations, a young mathematician named Johannes Kepler demonstrated that the planets actually traveled around the Sun in slightly elliptical orbits. The planets' elliptical motions around the Sun explained all the previously collected data showing the positions of the planets in the sky relative to the Earth. After this discovery, the scientific stage was now set for the development of a basic set of physical laws that would clearly explain orbital motion and determine the laws of gravity. This was accomplished by the well-known scientist, Sir Isaac Newton, in the late 17th century. Chapters 3 and 4 of this book discuss the physical laws discovered by Sir Isaac Newton.

32–4 GEOLOGICAL COMPARISONS OF THE EARTH AND ITS MOON

The Moon is our Earth's closest neighbor. With the aid of a telescope, we can examine the Moon in great detail from the surface of the

Earth. Telescopic observations allow us to observe detail of the Moon's surface (*Figure 32.6*) on the scale of about one kilometer. This offers sufficient resolution to see that the Moon is covered with many mountains and craters. Observations of the Moon also indicate an absence of clouds, atmosphere, or liquid water anywhere on its surface.

Figure 32.6

In December 1992, during its flight to Jupiter, the *Galileo* spacecraft returned this image of the Moon. Many surface features are clearly visible including the bright rayed craters Tycho (near the bottom of the image) and Copernicus (left of center), along with the dark lava-filled basins known as maria that are common on the side of the Moon facing Earth.

♦ **Maria**

The large, generally crater-free lava plains commonly found on the side of our Moon that faces Earth.

♦ **Lunar Highlands**

The old, heavily cratered terrain on our Moon that is thought to contain material from the original lunar surface.

The Moon is relatively close to the Earth. The Earth has more than 80 times the mass of the Moon. As a result, the Earth dominates the Moon's motion through space. In fact, the Earth's gravitational pull on the Moon is the reason that the same side of the Moon always faces the Earth. The side of the Moon facing the Earth has some interesting features called **maria**, which are much darker than the surrounding terrain. Telescopic examinations show far fewer craters are visible in the maria than in the surrounding terrain.

Mapping the Moon

Mankind first glimpsed the far side of the Moon in October of 1959, when a camera in an unmanned probe named Luna 3 launched by the Soviet Union took the first photographs of the previously unseen portion of the lunar surface. As is often the case in scientific discovery, the new data contained some unexpected results. Although maria are common on the side of the Moon facing the Earth, an examination of the photographs showed almost no maria exist on the far side of the Moon. The Moon's surface facing away from the Earth has a lighter color and is much more heavily cratered than the side of the Moon that lights our night sky.

Since the first photos of the far side of the Moon, a variety of unmanned probes have mapped the lunar surface with resolution that allows us to view lunar features only a few tens of meters across. These observations reveal that craters and the debris ejected by crater-forming impacts vary widely in size. The mapping observations also reveal that although craters exist in the maria, they are much less common than in the lighter-colored and heavily cratered terrain known as the **lunar highlands**.

Lunar mapping probes also show no evidence for plate tectonics on the Moon. The surface of the Earth is constantly reshaped by erosion, seafloor spreading, subduction, and mountain building. These processes are not present on the Moon, so scientists believe that the lunar highlands are composed of material from portions of the original lunar crust. This is why scientists believe the highland regions of the Moon are the best places to search for rocks dating back to the origin of the solar system.

Scientists believe the maria are impact basins that were created by large impacts long ago, when collisions between space debris and the planets and their moons occurred more frequently. These basins were then flooded with lava from the Moon's interior. The dramatically lower numbers of craters in the maria are strong evidence that the maria were covered by lava flows at a time after most of the impact craters were formed. The smooth surfaces of the lava flows also indicate that the lunar highlands represent terrain that is significantly older than the lava flows in the maria.

Exploring the Moon

Between 1969 and 1972, six manned Apollo lunar landing missions were flown by astronauts from the United States. These missions enabled astronauts to place reflectors at several landing sites. NASA still uses these reflectors to accurately measure the changing Earth-Moon distance. Astronauts also conducted numerous experiments to measure everything from the occurrence of tiny moonquakes to the composition of particles that flow out into space from the surface of the Sun. One of the most significant accomplishments of the manned exploration of the Moon was the collection of almost 400 kilograms of rocks from the lunar surface in more than 2400 carefully documented samples, which were brought to Earth for further study.

On Earth we commonly find igneous, sedimentary, and metamorphic rocks. Virtually no erosive forces exist on the Moon, so the absence of any sedimentary or metamorphic rocks among the astronauts' samples should come as no surprise. Each lunar rock sample has been found to be some variety of igneous rock, which provides strong evidence that the entire lunar surface was molten at one time. Comparisons of samples brought back from different landing sites clearly show the differences between the maria basins and the lunar highlands.

Analysis of lunar samples shows that rocks from the maria are often found in a form called **mare basalt** (*Figure 32.7*), which is similar in composition to dark terrestrial lava often found at volcanic sites on Earth. Overall, mare basalt contains higher concentrations of iron than is found in the material from the lunar highlands. Later Apollo missions exploring areas close to the lunar highlands identified a type of igneous rock called **anorthosite** (*Figure 32.8*). This is a light-colored rock that is less dense than the common mare basalt and contains a lower percentage of iron. Samples of anorthosite that were submitted to radiological dating proved to be

much older than material in the maria. For this reason, scientists believe that these light-colored rocks represent material from the original lunar crust. Another type of material brought back by the Apollo astronauts is a type of anorthosite called **impact breccias** (*Figure 32.9*). This material is the result of rocks that were broken apart and fused together again during the long history of meteorite impacts on the Moon. Although impact breccias are quite rare on Earth, there is an abundance of this material in the lunar samples collected by the astronauts. Numerous samples of impact breccias were brought back by the astronauts as they searched for anorthosite in hopes of finding samples of the oldest rocks in our solar system.

32–5 EXPLORING THE SOLAR SYSTEM

During the last half of the 20th century, numerous unmanned space probes were sent into space to explore different objects within the solar system. Though our Earth has a combination of properties that make it unique in the solar system, we are not certain that it is unique in the Universe or even in our Galaxy. Many of the individual properties of our Earth that in combination make it so unusual are seen to some degree on other bodies scattered throughout our solar system.

Figure 32.7

A sample of mare basalt that was returned to Earth by the crew of Apollo 15. Basalt from lava flows is common on the Moon and is comparable to basalt found on the Earth.

Figure 32.8

A specimen of lunar anorthosite returned by the astronauts from Apollo 16. This light gray colored rock from the lunar highlands is believed to be ancient material from the original crust of the Moon.

- **Mare Basalt**

A common igneous rock found in abundance on the lunar lava plains.

- **Anorthosite**

A rock found in the area of the lunar highlands that is thought to be an ancient remnant of the original surface of our Moon.

- **Impact Breccias**

Rocks that have been formed as other rocks have been broken apart, mixed, and then fused together during a series of meteoroid impacts. Impact breccias are rare on Earth but common on the surface of our Moon.

Figure 32.9

These rocks are pieces of impact breccias returned to Earth from the surface of the Moon. Astronauts exploring the Moon often confused impact breccias for anorthosite when gathering samples for later study. Although rare on the Earth, impact breccias are quite common on the Moon and provide abundant evidence of the long period of bombardment from space that was part of the early history of the Moon.

The exploration of the solar system with unmanned probes began with the first satellites that orbited our Earth and then studied our Moon starting in the late 1950s. This exploration continues even now, and we will discuss some of the most significant discoveries below.

Mapping Venus

Through a small telescope, the planet Venus appears to be completely covered with thick clouds. Historically, there has been considerable speculation about what might lie below the clouds of Venus. Many people felt that Venus was a warm and humid planet where plant and animal life could exist in great abundance.

In 1962, the unmanned U.S. spacecraft *Mariner 2* examined Venus using infrared light. *Mariner 2* found that the surface temperature was in excess of 400° C and that the atmosphere contained virtually no water vapor. In fact, Venus's atmosphere is composed almost entirely of carbon dioxide. During the 1970s the former Soviet Union had some success with robot landers that were sent to the surface of Venus. These probes confirmed the data from the earlier fly-by missions and also returned new data indicating that the atmospheric pressure of Venus is over 90 times greater than the air pressure found on Earth. These results eliminated all previous thoughts of the existence of life on Venus.

A remarkable probe named *Magellan* was sent to Venus and went into orbit in 1990. The clouds surrounding Venus are so thick that it is always impossible to observe the surface in visible light. *Magellan* used sophisticated radar-ranging techniques (discussed later in this chapter) to map more than 98% of Venus's surface with a resolution of about 100 meters (*Figure 32.10*). These results can be reconstructed into three-dimensional maps that show a wealth of detail about the surface of Venus. The *Magellan* probe discovered that Venus is covered with more than 1,000 major volcanic features. Although Venus is similar in size and composition to the Earth and has been shown to be volcanically active, the *Magellan* maps reveal no evidence of a surface re-shaped by plate tectonics like those observed on our Earth.

Exploring Mars

Through a small telescope, the planet Mars appears to have polar caps and other surface features that apparently change with the seasons (*Figure 32.11*). Also, since the rotation period of Mars is only about 40 minutes longer than that of the Earth, a day on Mars is almost the same as one day on Earth. These early observations led many to imagine the possibility that there may be Martians!

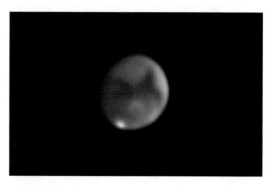

Figure 32.11
The planet Mars as seen through a telescope on the surface of the Earth, near opposition in early October 2003. The south polar cap is clearly visible in the photo, along with the dark triangular-shaped surface marking known as Syrtis Major.

The *Mariner 4*, *Mariner 6*, and *Mariner 7* spacecraft flew past the planet Mars between 1964 and 1969. These first probes were very disappointing for people who had hoped to find evidence for life on Mars. The probes showed that Mars was a very cold planet with an atmosphere over 100 times less dense than that of Earth. Photographs from various probes sent to Mars showed no hint of any vegetation or other evidence for life. Instead, we found that Mars is pockmarked with numerous impact craters of various sizes, much like the surface of the Moon.

Since the 1960s, many additional probes have been sent to Mars on a variety of missions. These probes have shown that, while Mars is not by any stretch of the imagination a comfortable place to live, it is still an intriguing planet with a wide variety of terrain. For example, Valles Marineris is a gigantic rift in the Martian surface that extends east to west across the planet for more than 4,000 kilometers, which is roughly the distance from New York to Los Angeles.

Figure 32.10
The *Magellan* spacecraft used imaging radar to look through the dense clouds of Venus in order to create this map. The colors indicate elevations. Red shows the mountains and highest plains, while blue denotes lower valleys and basins.

Probes have also found a region on Mars known as the Tharsis rise that contains many prominent volcanoes thought to be extinct. The largest of these is Olympus Mons. This mountain is about 600 kilometers in diameter and rises to a height of almost 25 kilometers above its surroundings (*Figure 32.12*). This is believed to be the largest volcano in the solar system. Olympus Mons covers an area about the size of the state of Utah with an altitude almost three times higher than Mt. Everest. Probes have occasionally observed wisps of clouds in the thin Martian atmosphere near the volcanic mountains of the Tharsis rise.

The Martian polar caps are real, even though they differ from the polar caps found on Earth. The polar caps on Mars are composed of a combination of both water ice and frozen carbon dioxide. This is in stark contrast to our Earth, where the polar caps are composed solely of water ice and the temperature is too high for carbon dioxide to freeze.

Some of the most interesting studies of Mars have come from robotic probes such as the *Spirit* and *Opportunity* rovers that landed on Mars early in 2004. These rovers have moved over the

Figure 32.13
A view into the distance toward the rim of Gusev crater from a point in the Columbia Hills, as seen by the *Spirit* rover from the surface of Mars in 2004.

surface of Mars (*Figure 32.13*), carefully searching for evidence that liquid water might be present or was present on the Martian surface sometime in the past. Although the evidence is not entirely conclusive, it appears that water has flowed on the Martian surface at times in the history of this fascinating planet. This may be another way in which other planets have similarities to our Earth.

Glimpsing the Asteroids

Most of our knowledge about asteroids within the solar system comes from a few carefully planned accidents. This is because most asteroids can barely be seen to have a shape, even when using a powerful instrument such as the Hubble Space Telescope.

The first detailed glimpse of an asteroid came from the *Galileo* probe that was sent to study Jupiter. Scientists realized that during the voyage to Jupiter the probe would pass fairly close to a couple of the medium-sized asteroids which follow orbits between Mars and Jupiter.

In 1991 *Galileo* flew by the asteroid Gaspra and returned the first detailed photos of one of these irregularly-shaped pieces of space debris (*Figure 32.14*). Two years later, the *Galileo* probe

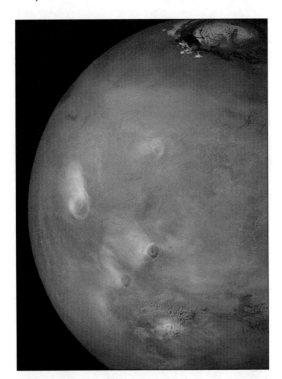

Figure 32.12
This photo mosaic of Mars was assembled from images taken by the Mars Global Surveyor. The northern polar cap is visible along with four large volcanoes in an area known as the Tharsis rise. The largest of the volcanoes is Olympus Mons. Note the layer of high clouds prominently seen around each of the volcanoes.

Figure 32.14
The asteroid 951 Gaspra orbits in the main asteroid belt between Mars and Jupiter. This is one of the best images of an asteroid ever recorded. It was taken by the *Galileo* spacecraft in 1991 as it flew past on its long journey to study Jupiter. Gaspra is only about 20 kilometers long.

passed by another asteroid named Ida. Interestingly, *Galileo* found that Ida had a tiny companion asteroid that orbited it like a moon. Details of the size, composition, and surface features of these asteroids provide scientists with clues to the formation of planets during the early history of our solar system.

Exploring Jupiter's Moon System

Jupiter is the largest planet in the solar system and the first of the gas giants known as the Jovian planets. When Galileo first observed Jupiter in a telescope, he saw that it had four visible moons that orbited Jupiter in regular intervals. We have since learned from probes sent to Jupiter that each of these moons is quite distinct.

The differences between the moons are the result of each moon's distance from Jupiter. The two large inner moons are named Io and Europa. They are close enough to Jupiter that gravitational forces cause the moons to stretch and flex as they orbit the planet. The final result is slightly different for each of these two moons.

In 1979 the *Voyager* spacecraft flew through Jupiter's moon system. The inner moon, Io, was shown to be a yellow and brown object with surface features unlike any seen before. One of the unusual things about the surface of Io was that there were no impact craters visible. This is because Io is continually resurfaced by volcanoes in a very short period of time.

Careful examination of many images of Io shows that this moon has giant volcanic plumes continually erupting from its surface (*Figure 32.15*). Io was studied in much greater detail by the *Galileo* spacecraft as it orbited through the

Jupiter system from 1995 through 2003. Some observations from *Galileo* were taken when the probe came within 200 kilometers of Io's surface, revealing a massive network of volcanoes scattered over the entire surface of Io. As Io orbits Jupiter, it is repeatedly stretched and squeezed by the tidal forces exerted by the giant planet. This adds energy to Io, and this energy is released through Io's volcanoes.

Europa is the next moon of Jupiter as you move outward from Io. Europa is close enough to Jupiter that it also receives energy from tidal forces. When the first *Voyager* pictures were returned to Earth, scientists were surprised to see that Europa appears to be covered with ice and a dense pattern of cracks instead of numerous impact craters. The images from the *Galileo* probe showed the same features in much greater detail (*Figure 32.16*). We know that Europa has a surface that is completely covered by ice sheets. The few impact craters that are visible show evidence of being filled with water that is then frozen. This suggests that Europa may receive enough energy from the tidal forces exerted by Jupiter to maintain an ocean of liquid water beneath Europa's thin icy crust. Europa appears to have an alternative form of plate tectonics. Instead of chunks of rocky crust being moved by magma, pieces of Europa's icy crust are moved by liquid water. It is possible, although not likely, that some forms of life could exist in an ocean of water that is warm enough to remain a liquid.

Exploring Saturn's Moon Titan

Saturn is a planet in a very cold region of the solar system. The average temperature at

Figure 32.15

The volcanically active moon of Jupiter known as Io. One of the many volcanic plumes visible on the left edge of Io is Pillan Patera. When this image was recorded in June of 1997, the plume was seen to extend more than 100 kilometers above the surface of Io.

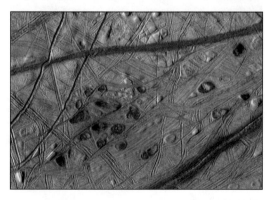

Figure 32.16

Detailed view of the surface of Jupiter's moon Europa as seen by the *Galileo* probe. Many cracks are visible in the ice sheets that are believed to cover a liquid water ocean. The dark domes visible on the surface are thought to be material that has risen up from the warmer interior onto the cold surface.

the cloud tops of Saturn is about −180° C. Saturn has numerous icy moons in addition to the extensive and beautiful system of bright rings that orbit the planet. Titan is the largest of Saturn's moons, and is unusual because of its thick atmosphere composed of compounds such as ammonia and methane.

Data from the *Voyager 1* spacecraft was used to determine that Titan's atmosphere has a pressure at the surface that is approximately 50% greater than that of Earth. *Voyager* data also confirmed the composition of the atmosphere of Titan. The infrared instruments of the *Voyager* spacecraft found that, in addition to methane, the atmosphere of Titan contains traces of other hydrocarbons such as propane and ethane.

In 1997 the *Cassini* mission was launched to study the planet Saturn. The *Cassini* spacecraft carried a probe named *Huygens* that was designed to descend by parachute through Titan's atmosphere and land on the surface where data could be obtained and returned to Earth for later analysis. In early 2005 the *Huygens* probe descended through the murky atmosphere of Titan and took an amazing sequence of photos like the one shown in *Figure 32.17*. It is amazing to examine these photos and see scenes that appear familiar, but are really very different from anything we observe on Earth. For example, Titan's beaches are likely composed of solid ammonia, while its lakes and rivers are possibly filled with liquid ethane.

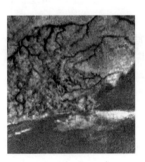

Figure 32.17
Detailed view of a coastal region on Saturn's moon, Titan, as seen by the *Huygens* probe in January 2005 as it descended through the atmosphere to the surface after being released by the *Cassini* spacecraft. River channels and lakebeds are apparently visible in this picture. Exactly what is flowing in those channels is still unknown, but it is much too cold to be water.

32-6 ASTRONOMICAL DISTANCES

One key concept in the study of planets, stars, and galaxies involves the measurement of distance. Many techniques are routinely used to measure the enormous distances between objects in space. We discuss below some of the basic techniques used for measuring solar system distances. Variations of the triangulation method can be used to find distances to the closest stars.

Radar and Laser Ranging

Objects close to us, such as the Moon or a nearby planet, can have their distances measured using a technique known as **radar ranging**, in which a signal is sent towards the object whose distance is being measured (*Figure 32.18*). A small amount of the radiation from that beam is reflected back from the object, returning to the point of origin. Radar is a form of electromagnetic radiation (electromagnetic waves, or radio waves) and its velocity is the same as the velocity of light. It is very easy to determine the distance to an object if you know the radar signal's velocity and its round trip travel time to the object.

This technique is only useful for objects that are relatively close to Earth, such as those planets and moons found in our solar system. This is because the radar signal loses a great amount of energy as it propagates out into space. Only a small fraction of the outgoing signal actually reflects off the object back to the Earth. When the signal returns to the Earth, it can be diminished millions of times. Measuring such a faint signal requires a very sensitive detector.

A slightly more efficient variation of this technique is **laser ranging**. The Apollo astronauts left several highly polished reflectors on

- **Radar Ranging**
A technique for measuring distance where pulses of microwaves (radar) traveling at the speed of light are sent to a nearby object and the reflected pulse is timed in order to determine the distance.

Figure 32.18
The technique used for radar ranging measures the time required for a signal to bounce off an object like the Moon and return. It only takes about 2.6 seconds for a signal to travel to the Moon and then return to the Earth.

- **Laser Ranging**
A technique for measuring distance that is similar to radar ranging but instead of reflecting microwaves, laser light is reflected off of a nearby surface and the time for the reflected pulse is observed.

the surface of the Moon in the late 1960s and early 1970s. For this ranging technique, an energetic coherent beam of light known as a laser is sent from Earth, bounces off the Moon's reflectors, and returns to its point of origin. The laser beam, unlike the radar signal described above, does not lose as much energy while traveling to and bouncing back from the Moon. Pulse detection is aided by the reflectors, so a stronger return pulse is detected. Laser ranging makes it possible to determine the distance between the Earth and the Moon to within a few centimeters.

Radar ranging and laser ranging are of no use when measuring distances to stars. Stars do not reflect enough of the signal's energy back to the Earth, and such a weak signal cannot be detected with the technology available today. Also, stars are vast distances away from the Earth. Typical experiments with radar and laser ranging take anywhere from a few seconds to an hour or two for the signal to return, depending on the distance the measured object is from Earth. Even if the return signal from a star could be detected, the signal would take over eight and one-half years to travel to the closest star in the sky and return to Earth.

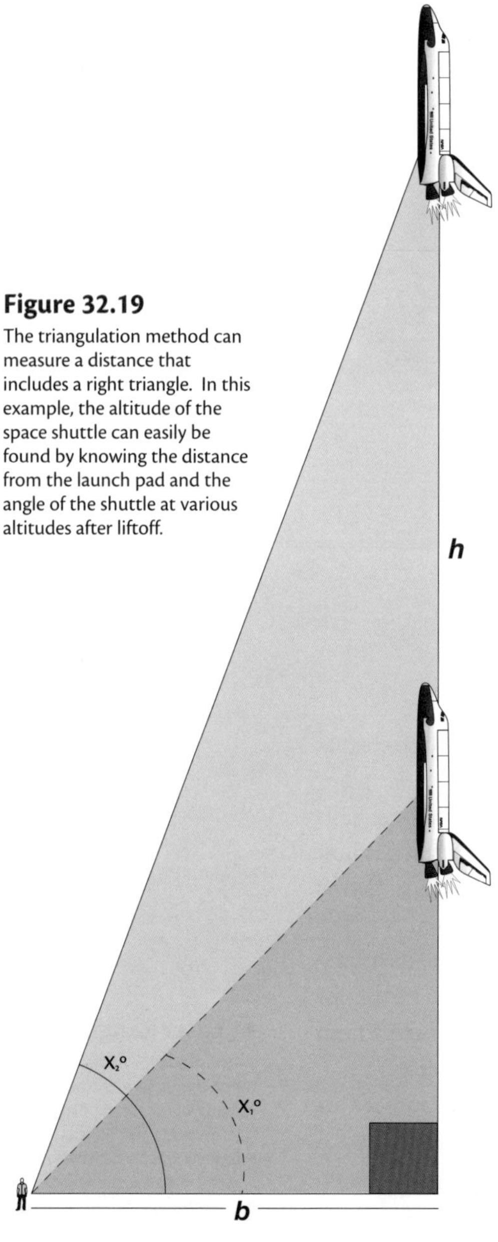

Triangulation

Another method of measuring distance is called **triangulation**. Measurements by triangulation are very accurate and are employed in many situations, not all of them scientific. Your eyes and brain subconsciously use triangulation all the time. Our sense of depth perception is an example of this principle. Your two eyes are set several centimeters apart in the front of your skull. This distance is called a baseline.

Although a few centimeters form a very short baseline, over time we unconsciously train ourselves to estimate distances to objects by comparing the view the brain receives from one eye with the view sent to it by the other eye. The muscles around our eyes must move very small amounts to keep each of the two images precisely aligned. That minute movement is sensed and then interpreted by our brains as the distance to a given object. Some people actually get quite good at making these distance estimates. For example, a baseball player or a person playing ping pong must constantly judge distances, and do so both accurately and instantly, in order to perform the skills required by their sport.

Triangulation can also be used to measure the height reached by the space shuttle (*Figure 32.19*) or to calculate the distance across a river. When calculating distance with a triangle containing a right angle, geometry tells us that the ratios of the triangle's sides that contain the same angles are always in the same proportion. These ratios are totally independent of the size of the triangle. With a right triangle, it is important to remember that if we measure an angle and the length of one side, we can exactly determine the remaining angles and the lengths of the other two sides. This method can easily determine distances to objects in the solar system, such as the Moon or other planets. We carefully measure a baseline between two points at some known distance apart on the surface of the Earth and perform the corresponding geometry.

Using triangulation to measure distance has certain limitations. It is critical to remember that the more distant an object is from the baseline point of measurement, the narrower the angle used to measure the object becomes. No baseline on the surface of the Earth is wide enough to use triangulation to measure the distance to even the nearest stars. An elegant solution to this problem involves the use of a baseline formed by Earth's orbit around the Sun (*Figure 32.20*). Using observations obtained over several years, it is possible to apply triangulation to measure the distance to nearby stars. However, even for the closest star to the Sun, the resulting triangle becomes so tall and skinny that the angle measured for the apex of the triangle is less than one second of arc. This is an extremely tiny measurement, because one second of arc equals

- **Triangulation**

A distance measuring technique that involves observing the angle to a distant object from at least two different locations with a known separation. It is then possible to determine the unknown distance by comparing the observed angles.

Figure 32.19

The triangulation method can measure a distance that includes a right triangle. In this example, the altitude of the space shuttle can easily be found by knowing the distance from the launch pad and the angle of the shuttle at various altitudes after liftoff.

h

$x_2°$

$x_1°$

b

just 1/3600 of one degree. It was not until the 19th century that optics, telescope mounts, and timekeeping methods improved enough to precisely measure these tiny angular shifts and calculate the distance to nearby stars.

Triangulation from the Earth's surface can measure the distance from Earth to about 1,000 of the stars closest to our Sun. It can be disappointing to realize that this is less than one percent of the distance across our Galaxy. If the limited nature of these measurements is a little disheartening, please remember that the distance to the closest star beyond the Sun is about 40 trillion kilometers.

The Earth's atmosphere distorts stellar images, smearing and blurring them as they are imaged. The size of the angles that can be measured is therefore severely limited by turbulence in the atmosphere. This is why measurements must be taken above the Earth's atmosphere in order to determine greater distances using triangulation.

Atmospheric turbulence can be overcome by the use of a space-based device that precisely measures the positions of stars relative to each other. In 1989, a satellite observatory named Hipparcos was launched to perform such measurements. Hipparcos contained a small telescope that was placed in orbit above the atmosphere where it could very accurately measure the positions of several hundred thousand stars over a period of several years. With multiple observations of these stars, astronomers determined distances up to 3,000 light years away for approximately 120,000 of the stars nearest to our Sun.

In order to measure greater distances, however, it is necessary to use other distance-measuring techniques. The technique of triangulation and that of laser and radar ranging have areas of overlap where the distances measured by both techniques can be compared. As increasingly sophisticated technological devices allow scientists to probe ever-greater distances into the Universe, each technique that extends our distance scale overlaps with a previous technique that has been calibrated by yet an earlier technique. The overlapping techniques that verify previous measurements build what astronomers refer to as a **distance ladder** as measurements extend to increasingly larger distances far away from the familiar surroundings of our solar system. In the next chapter, we will consider some extensions to the distance ladder necessary for stars whose distances are far greater than we can measure using the method of triangulation.

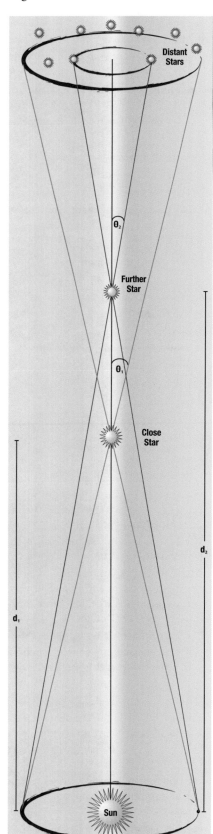

Figure 32.20

The triangulation method can also measure distances to objects such as stars. Even with a baseline the size of our Earth's orbit, the observed angles seen from nearby stars are difficult to measure because they are so small. Note that more distant stars have a smaller apparent motion relative to the background stars.

♦ **Distance Ladder**

A method used in astronomy where greater and greater distances are determined using many different measuring techniques that overlap to establish a sequence of increasing distances.

Chapter Framework

A. The Nature of Our Solar System

B. The Planets in Our Solar System
1. *The four Terrestrial worlds*
2. *The four Jovian worlds*
3. *Pluto*

C. The Scale and Scope of the Universe
1. *The size, composition, and main elements of a galaxy*

D. The Nature of Earth and Its Place in the Solar System
1. *First indications of Earth's spherical nature*
2. *Eratosthenes*

E. Earth's Motion in Space
1. *Greek scientists and Earth*
2. *Sun-centered model*

F. Geological Comparisons of Earth and Its Moon
1. *Features of the Moon*

G. Mapping the Moon
1. *Characteristics of the Moon*
2. *Maria*
3. *Lunar highlands*

H. Exploring the Moon
1. *Tests on the Moon*
2. *Rock samples collected on the Moon*

I. Astronomical Distances
1. *Radar and Laser Ranging*
2. *Triangulation*

Comprehension

True/False

1. ____ Radar and laser ranging can measure distances to the outer reaches of the Galaxy.
2. ____ Earth's gravitational pull makes the same side of the Moon face Earth.
3. ____ The Moon's tectonic system causes small moonquakes to occur.
4. ____ Astronauts' rock samples from the Moon lacked metamorphic and sedimentary rocks.
5. ____ The Jovian worlds are much more massive than the terrestrial worlds.
6. ____ Pluto is considered a terrestrial world.
7. ____ Eratosthenes measured Earth's circumference using shadows that the Sun cast.

a. *Galaxy*
b. *Earth-centered model*
c. *Jovian worlds*
d. *Meteoroids*
e. *Terrestrial worlds*
f. *Radar and laser ranging*
g. *Sun-centered model*
h. *Maria*
i. *Triangulation*

Matching

1. ____ Considered the better model of our solar system because of Occam's razor.
2. ____ Extraterrestrial materials that enter Earth's atmosphere.
3. ____ Method to measure distance using fundamental principles of geometry.
4. ____ Massive gas planets.
5. ____ Earth does not move in this model of the solar system.

6. ____ Mercury, Venus, Earth, and Mars.
7. ____ Fundamental constituent of the Universe as a whole.
8. ____ Impact basins filled by lava.
9. ____ Method that can only measure distance to planets in our solar system.

Fill in the Blank

1. The _____ model replaced the Earth-centered model.

2. Instead of orbiting in a perfect circle, planets actually have _____ orbits.

3. With radar and laser ranging, the signal _____ as the distance to the object being measured increases.

4. The _____ formed by Earth's orbit allows us to measure distance using triangulation to the nearest stars.

5. Earth's atmosphere limits the _____ of angles that can be measured in triangulation.

6. Extensions of the _____ allow us to measure distances greater than what triangulation can measure.

7. Craters are much more common in the _____ than in the maria.

Analysis

1. Which of the following is not a **known** characteristic of the Jovian worlds?

   a) A rocky core similar to the terrestrial worlds
   b) Composed mainly of hydrogen, helium, carbon, and nitrogen
   c) Many times more massive than the terrestrial planets
   d) Large internal pressure
   e) All of the above are characteristics

2. What would be the best method to determine the distance to Mars?

   a) Bounce a radio wave off of it and time how long it takes to make the round trip
   b) Take pictures of it 6 months apart and measure how much it has shifted relative to more distant background stars
   c) Use triangulation
   d) Examine its spectrum to see how much it has been shifted toward the red
   e) All of the above would work equally well

3. Which of the following is not a characteristic of **all** the terrestrial worlds?

   a) Densities that are several times denser than water

b) Composed of rocks similar to those found on Earth

c) Tectonic plate system

d) Four planets closest to the Sun in the solar system

e) All of the above are characteristics of the terrestrial worlds

4. Which of the following is **not** a difference between Pluto and the rest of the planets?

   a) Pluto's orbit is out of alignment with the rest of the solar system

   b) Pluto's orbit differs more from a circle than the other planets' orbits do

   c) Pluto has an average density between the terrestrial worlds and the Jovian worlds

   d) All of the above are differences

5. Which of the following provides evidence that the surface of the Moon was molten at one time?

   a) Igneous rocks

   b) Lunar highlands

   c) Moon dust

   d) Sedimentary rocks

   e) All of the above

6. Radar ranging and laser ranging can measure distance for all of the following except:

   a) The Moon

   b) Mars

   c) Saturn

   d) The Sun

7. Which of the following is mentioned as distorting triangulation from Earth's surface?

   a) The atmosphere

   b) The Moon

   c) City lights

   d) Overhead airplanes

Synthesis

1. What is a characteristic that most of the planets in our solar system hold in common?

2. What do the characteristics that the planets in our solar system share suggest about the solar system's formation?

3. Why can't radar ranging be used for planets beyond the solar system?

4. With triangulation, what was the solution to overcome atmospheric turbulence?

5. Radar ranging can be used for measuring the distance to nearby planets. Why can't radar ranging be used to measure distances to stars, far beyond our Sun?

6. What evidence would we expect to find on the Moon if it had been subjected to plate tectonics and an atmosphere? Do we find such evidence?

7. Compare and contrast the Jovian planets with the terrestrial planets.

8. Why do scientists consider the lunar highlands a great place to look for rocks that date back to the origin of the solar system?

THE HISTORY OF A STAR

CHAPTER 33

*"Canst thou bind the sweet influences of Pleiades,
or loose the bands of Orion?"*

~ Job 38:31

In the Biblical quote above, Job is being questioned about having a knowledge and control of the vast numbers of stars and star clusters along with other aspects of nature that mankind still has to learn. It is a good point to consider such questions since the previous seven chapters of this textbook have, almost exclusively, discussed the nature of our planet Earth along with a few local objects for comparison. This chapter extends beyond Earth itself and studies the history and life of our own Sun and its fellow stars far beyond our solar system. Viewing our Universe on the scale of stars involves measuring unbelievably great distances. However, the same physical laws discussed in previous chapters still apply, regardless of whether we discuss Earth's seas and land masses or the Sun, Moon, and stars.

Many billions of stars populate the space around us. Some of those stars are similar to our Sun in size, while others are much larger or smaller and differ in other ways as well. In general, all stars are composed of the same elements in similar proportions, but careful examination reveals that considerable diversity exists from star to star. These differences create such a great variety of stellar characteristics that each of the myriad stars we can observe from Earth may be said to be individually unique in some way.

Astronomers often say "birth," "life," "middle age" and "death" when they discuss the changes that occur between the time a star forms and the time that the star stops radiating energy. This terminology can be confusing because these phrases generally describe biological processes. However, if you are careful to remember that stars are not living organisms, these terms provide an easy way to examine the formation and eventual changes that happen to all stars.

Understanding the life history of a star first requires a discussion about the birth of that star. Our knowledge of stars is based on centuries of astronomers' observations of objects in the vast space beyond our Earth. We therefore know that star formation commonly occurs even now, throughout our Galaxy. This chapter describes what we now know about the history and life of individual stars.

33–1 FORMATION: FROM INTERSTELLAR MEDIUM TO PROTOSTAR

What we call "outer space" isn't exactly "empty" space. The vast area beyond our Earth's protective atmosphere and beyond the farthest

When you have finished studying this chapter you will:

- Know about the formation of protostars within the interstellar medium and understand that this is an ongoing process.

- Learn about the equilibrium between the force of gravity pushing inward and the pressure from energy generation pushing outward to form a stable star.

- Know the different phases in the life of a typical star.

- Understand how the mass of a star determines the length of each phase in the star's life.

- Identify the three different possible end states of stellar life.

- Know how a supernova enriches the interstellar medium and starts a new epoch of star formation.

- Describe H-R diagrams and understand how they are used to estimate the distance to a star or cluster of stars.

planets in our solar system still contains matter composed of elements that are common here on Earth. About three-fourths of all matter in the Universe is hydrogen. Virtually all the rest of the matter in the Universe is helium. The other naturally occurring elements in the periodic table appear only in trace amounts. Not surprisingly, ordinary stars consist of elements with approximately these same relative ratios.

The space between stars, which contains low-density clouds of material, is called the **interstellar medium**. Galaxies contain regions where the hydrogen gas and traces of other elements (*Figure 33.1*) are generally more abundant than is usual in the space between stars. If there

Figure 33.1

A high resolution Hubble Space Telescope view of the Sombrero galaxy. This is a spiral galaxy similar to the Milky Way. Note that the galaxy's disk shows considerable material that blocks the light from stars. The disks of spiral galaxies show evidence of continual star formation.

- **Interstellar Medium**

Gas and dust found in the space between stars.

- **Emission Nebula**

A gaseous cloud that is glowing from the energy radiated by nearby hot stars.

Figure 33.2

A young open star cluster, NGC 6611, and star forming region M16, located along the disk of the Milky Way. Also known as the Eagle Nebula, this region of space is known to contain clouds of cold dark gas and glowing emission nebulae.

- **Dark Nebula**

A cold cloud of dust and gas that blocks the light from background stars.

- **Protostar**

An object that will become a star in the early stages of formation before it begins to produce energy from fusion.

are hot stars close enough to this denser area to heat its gas, the gas will glow much like the light radiated from the gas in a fluorescent light bulb. This type of interstellar gas cloud is called an **emission nebula**. *Figure 33.2* shows a good example of this type of gas cloud, which is often found among the spiral arms in the flat disks of nearby galaxies. We observe emission nebulae most frequently in the disk of our own Galaxy, which is called the Milky Way. We use this name for the Galaxy because its enormous number of stars appears to viewers here on Earth as an awesome band of light that extends across the clear night sky.

The glowing gas in emission nebulae is clearly visible, unlike most hydrogen gas spread throughout space. Much of the matter in the interstellar medium exists in cold, dark regions of space far away from abundant sources of energy such as hot, young clusters of stars. In these cold areas of space, hydrogen frequently occurs as an H_2 molecule. The hydrogen gas in these regions of space does not give off visible light like the glowing emission nebulae. Therefore, these immense clouds of molecular hydrogen are often referred to as **dark nebulae**. The gas in a dark nebula emits low-energy radio waves that allow astronomers to locate such nebulae in isolated regions of space. *Figure 33.2* shows several dark nebulae as dark patches among the glowing clouds of emission nebulae.

Most portions of the interstellar medium

contain only tiny amounts of matter. In most areas of space, a measurement of only one to ten atoms of matter per cubic centimeter is not unusual. Densities of material like this present a far better vacuum than we could possibly create in any laboratory here on Earth. In the dark nebulae and emission nebulae, atoms are far more abundant. In these denser regions of interstellar space, there are anywhere from thousands to billions of atoms of matter per cubic centimeter. This amount of matter still forms an excellent vacuum, but such nebulae can be hundreds of trillions of kilometers across—and an object this large is so opaque that light from background stars can't shine through it.

For many decades, astronomers observed that stars in the process of formation or stars belonging to extremely young star clusters were closely associated with material in the interstellar medium. In fact, the interstellar medium can be regarded as the birthplace for all newly formed stars.

We do not know or fully understand all the mechanisms that trigger star formation. Stellar birth occurs most frequently in portions of the interstellar medium where the atoms are cold and relatively abundant. Under these conditions, many events form small condensations of matter within a dark nebula. Some events include another star passing through a region of nebula; the shock wave from an exploding star, such as a supernova; or the collision of several cold gas clouds.

For matter to collapse and eventually become a **protostar**, the force of gravity that pulls atoms closer together must exceed the resulting pressure that pushes them apart. Cold temperatures keep internal pressure low, making the process much easier in a dark nebula. In this type of environment, gravity quickly causes the initial clumps of material to increase in size.

33–2 BIRTH: FROM PROTOSTAR TO STAR

Atoms in a protostar mutually attract one another through gravitational force. As a result, each atom experiences a net force toward the center of the condensation. The atoms all move together in the direction of the net gravitational force, causing the volume of the condensing gas cloud to collapse. This causes individual atoms to lose gravitational potential energy and gain kinetic energy, so that each atom's speed inward increases as the protostar shrinks. Protostars continue to attract more material as their centers continue to contract.

Stars range in size from one-tenth of the mass of our Sun to approximately 100 times the mass of our Sun. This range appears consistent with the laws of nature. A collapsing object larger than 100 solar masses experiences high internal pressures that overpower gravitational collapse. The high pressure makes the formation of a stable star impossible. Protostars smaller than about one-tenth solar mass never reach pressures and temperatures high enough to initiate the production of energy. Such objects radiate energy while contracting by releasing gravitational potential energy, but never generate energy like regular stars. These "failed stars" are referred to as **brown dwarfs**.

The amount of time required for a protostar to contract depends almost entirely on the amount of matter in the surrounding region of space. Astronomers armed with the computing power now available can actually calculate the time needed for a protostar to shrink and become an ordinary star. As one might imagine, for an object of one solar mass, this process takes tens of millions of years. A very large protostar requires only thousands of years before it contracts and becomes a star. In contrast, a really small condensation of material requires over a billion years to become a star. A large star collapses rapidly because its larger mass exerts a greater gravitational force on the surrounding region of space. The opposite holds true for a small star. The matter is much less dense to begin with, so the gravitational forces are weaker.

The average velocity of a group of atoms most directly relates to temperature. The movement of atoms accelerates during the collapse of a protostar, which is detected by astronomers as an increase in temperature of the collapsing stellar body. The energy radiated by this increase in temperature is difficult to observe in the visual part of the electromagnetic spectrum. For that reason, visual images of active star-forming regions often show little evidence of new star formation. However, when the same region is imaged in infrared light (which reveals internal

Visible Light

Infrared Light

Figure 33.3

Images of the 30 Doradus region secured with the Hubble Space Telescope in both visible light (upper image) and in infrared light (lower image). There are six sources marked in the infrared image that are either not seen or are much fainter in the visible light image. This is due to the fact that the infrared light can penetrate the dust and gas that absorbs the visible light.

heat sources), we see numerous protostars in various stages of development. This is clearly shown in *Figure 33.3*.

As the protostar's interior experiences increasing temperature, high-speed particles exert increasing force on the collapsing layers above them. The heating results in considerable outward pressure that slows the contraction of the protostar. This ongoing relationship between gravity pushing inward and pressure pushing outward holds the key to understanding how stars become stable and why they change at different times during their existence. Thus, the continual interaction of these two forces determines the rest of the star's history.

As the protostar shrinks, its core increases in density and all atoms in the protostar's central region become ionized. The frequent collisions associated with increased temperatures become so energetic that the electrons no longer bind to the atoms. Atomic nuclei (mainly just individual protons) remain as free particles in the interior of the protostar. The protostar is on the verge of becoming a stable star.

At this size the protostar is still several times larger than it will be when the internal pressure balances the gravitational force pushing inward. The protostar appears hot and radiates considerable energy. This radiated energy is the result of gravitational collapse, which is very different from the way a typical star produces energy.

Because of gravity, the protostar continues its slow collapse until its internal temperature reaches about 10 million degrees Kelvin. Now a

● **Brown Dwarf**

An object that is like a star except for the fact that it is too small to sustain fusion reactions in its core.

• **Nuclear Fusion**
The process by which elements heavier than hydrogen are formed by adding protons and neutrons to existing atomic nuclei.

new process begins that will dominate and control all the other processes in the object throughout the remainder of its life. The process that dominates the life of a star is **nuclear fusion**. Due to the electromagnetic force, particles such as protons repel one another because they have like charges. This repulsive force exceeds the pull of gravity. At temperatures and densities found within collapsed protostars, the nuclear collisions are so energetic that the strong nuclear force pushes positively charged nuclei together. The protons bind or fuse together to form larger atomic nuclei. Nuclear fusion in this form produces considerable energy. The ongoing process of fusion in the protostar's core marks the time when astronomers begin to refer to the object as a star.

The hydrogen-fusion process in the core of a new star generally occurs in what is known as the **proton-proton cycle**. The nuclear reactions in the proton-proton cycle do not need to be described in detail. However, you should know that four protons combine to form a helium nucleus. In a typical fusion cycle, as the nucleus forms, helium emits positrons, neutrinos, and gamma rays. During this formation, there is a measurable reduction in nuclear potential energy. The reduction releases thermal energy into the core of the young star. The thermal energy is distributed throughout the star's core and the result is an increase in temperature and pressure in the stellar interior.

Prior to the generation of large amounts of energy within the core of the collapsing protostar, gravity acted as the dominant force in controlling conditions in the object's center. The

• **Proton-proton Cycle**
A process by which the protons in hydrogen nuclei combine in stars like our Sun to form the element helium.

onset of fusion now provides a force to push back and eventually balance the inward pull of gravity. All the objects in the size range for protostars reach an equilibrium point when fusion begins. With fusion active in the core, a balance is reached between the inward gravitational pull and the outward pressure from the energy released in the center of the star. This balance regulates the star's size (*Figure 33.4*). This balance continues and the star remains stable as long as the star's core continues generating energy.

33–3 Adult Life: Hydrogen Fusion in a Star

A star spends most of its life in this equilibrium state between internal pressure and gravity. Fusion reactions create the sources of internal pressure in most stars that bind hydrogen nuclei (protons) together to form heavier helium nuclei. This transformation occurs in the hot core of each star. Although the continuous cycle of nuclear fusion may seem out of control, the balance of energy and pressure makes a star stable year after year, for at least many millions of years.

As time passes, the nuclear reactions that form helium nuclei eventually exhaust the proton fuel. As the star's core slowly becomes dominated by helium, the ratio of hydrogen to helium gradually shrinks. A star's adult lifetime depends entirely on how fast hydrogen fuses to generate energy in the core. The time required to exhaust a star's fuel will be discussed in more detail later in this section.

Each occurrence of fusion produces a precise amount of energy. We can measure our Sun's total energy output to estimate the lifetime of a typical star. Also, physical laws that govern orbital motion within our solar system allow us to easily measure the Sun's mass. By accounting for the Sun's total energy output, the rate of fusion can easily be calculated. This calculation's results are almost unimaginable: several hundred million metric tons of the Sun's hydrogen converts into helium each second! At this rate of fusion, some worry about a possible fuel crisis for our Sun. However, our Sun's total mass is about 2×10^{30} kilograms. When estimating the lifetime of a star like our Sun, we only consider

Figure 33.4
In a stable star, the inward force of gravity is balanced by outward pressure due to the generation of energy. This type of equilibrium exists in our Sun.

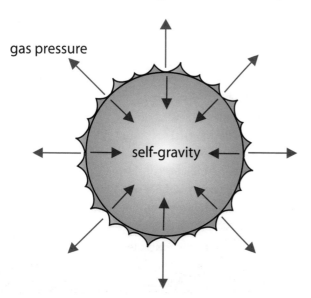

gas pressure

self-gravity

the 10% of mass where fusion takes place in the core. Simple arithmetic shows that it will take over ten billion years for our Sun to exhaust the hydrogen fuel in its core. The age of the Earth and the age of the oldest materials found in our solar system are estimated to be less than half this figure, so astronomers often refer to our Sun as a star that has reached middle-age.

Temperature, pressure, and density at the center of a star govern the rate at which fusion occurs. As they increase, the rate of fusion also increases. Massive stars have the shortest lives because their higher interior pressure and temperature balance the stronger gravitational compression associated with more mass. The nuclear fusion rates increase rapidly with temperature. Larger stars fuse hydrogen to helium at a much higher rate than stars with less mass. As a result, the more massive stars use their nuclear fuel much faster than their less massive counterparts. Definitely a striking result for stellar lifetimes, a star with 25 times the mass of our Sun lives only four million years (a lifespan several thousand times *less* than our Sun). On the other hand, a star with four-tenths our Sun's mass lives more than a trillion years (100 times longer than our Sun).

Incidentally, we never see light directly from a star's interior. The star's outer layers absorb the light over and over again as it travels outward from one layer to the next. The actual light emitted comes from a comparatively cooler layer at the star's surface, known as the **photosphere**. The nuclear reactions only take place in the high-temperature center of the star, a region that contains just a small fraction of the star's total volume.

33-4 OLD AGE: THE STAR BECOMES A RED GIANT

When hydrogen fuel in the center of a star is exhausted, the star will have a core of almost pure helium. The hydrogen-fusion region extends from the central core where nuclear reactions have stopped and expands to surrounding layers. The shell of hydrogen fusion around the core results in the release of large quantities of energy. For the first time since the initial contraction of the protostar, the pressure

outside the hydrogen-burning region exceeds the inward gravitational pressure and the star expands to 50 times its normal size over a period of several million years. As the star expands, its outer layers cool as the same quantity of radiant energy now passes through a much greater surface area. Since the visible surface of the giant star is now cooler, it will also appear redder in color. During this stage, the star is called a **red giant** (*Figure 33.5*). This term aptly describes the physical changes that occur as the star expands and the photosphere becomes cooler.

As the red giant phase continues, the massive helium core contracts under the influence of gravity because no nuclear fusion reactions occur in this region of the star to hinder its collapse. As the helium core contracts, the core's temperature increases. In a low-mass star, the temperature never increases enough to start a new cycle of fusion in the core. For stars with a higher mass, the temperature continues to increase to approximately 200 million degrees Kelvin. At this point, helium can begin fusing into carbon. The increase in energy from the new hot core causes the outer layers to expand even more. During this time, reactions proceed much more rapidly than during the hydrogen-fusion phase. The massive star quickly builds up a core that is mostly composed of dense carbon nuclei.

Depending on its mass, the star may go through one or more red giant phases as described above. During each phase the nuclei in the core become more massive than before. Fusion can occur in several different layers of the core in very massive stars. The end result

• **Photosphere**

The visible surface of our Sun or another star. This is the region where visible energy is radiated into space.

• **Red Giant**

A large, bright, cool star that has exhausted most of the hydrogen fuel in its core.

Figure 33.5

When a star like our Sun has used most of the hydrogen in its core it changes into a cooler, much larger, and brighter star called a red giant.

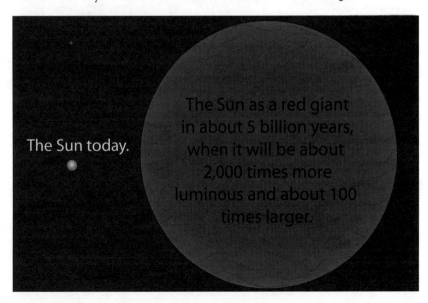

The Sun today.

The Sun as a red giant in about 5 billion years, when it will be about 2,000 times more luminous and about 100 times larger.

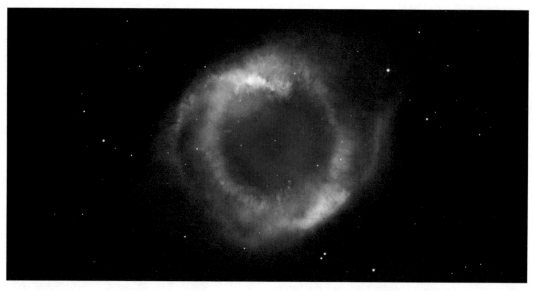

Figure 33.6
The Helix Nebula as seen by the Hubble Space Telescope. This object is known as a planetary nebula. The expanding shells of gas visible in the planetary nebula are being expelled by a star similar to our Sun that has already passed through the red giant phase.

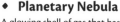

♦ **Planetary Nebula**
A glowing shell of gas that has been blown off an old star.

resembles the layers of skin on an onion. Hydrogen builds up a layer of helium. Helium fusion builds up carbon that can lead to a dense layer of neon, then to oxygen and eventually to silicon. Nuclear potential energy resists gravitational collapse for the last time when silicon fuses to form iron nuclei. Each successive fusion cycle occurs in shorter time periods, so that the nuclear furnaces go out a few million years after helium fusion first begins. Silicon fusing to form iron is the last process of fusion that produces excess energy. If we desired to build up elements heavier than iron, the stellar core would need additional energy. Without this extra energy, the nuclear furnaces go out and the star is left without an internal source of energy.

During the red giant phase the star undergoes considerable mass loss. Astronomers see the mass loss as expanding bubbles of glowing gaseous material surrounding stars. The expanding bubbles are referred to as **planetary nebulae**. A planetary nebula is the shell of gas from the surface of a star that has completed the red giant phase of its existence. At this stage the star will lose much of its original mass into space. The outer layers of the star blow off during the different expansions caused by renewed fusion in the stellar core. The cloud of material expands into space and leaves behind only the dense core of a dying star.

People commonly make the mistake of assuming that a planetary nebula must be associated with a planet. The name comes from the early days of telescopic observations. Through a small telescope, a planetary nebula looks like a faint round object similar in appearance to a

distant gas planet like Neptune. *Figure 33.6* shows a planetary nebula in the constellation of Aquarius imaged with the Hubble Space Telescope. The image clearly shows that the object is not a planet. Even though planetary nebulae have no connection with planets, the name has remained popular and is unlikely to change.

33–5 DEATH: WHITE DWARFS, NEUTRON STARS, AND BLACK HOLES

Three different classes of stars end their stellar "lives" in different ways. The first group of stars is made up of the Universe's "small" stars. These stars are the most common in the Universe and include stars like our Sun. Small stars are those that measure from one-tenth the mass of our Sun to as large as eight times the mass of our Sun. The second group of stars is much less common and represents middle-sized stars. These stars range in size from the largest of the small-sized stars to stars 25 times the mass of our Sun. The final group of stars is made up of the really large stars. These stars are very rare. The large stars range in size from masses greater than the most massive middle-sized stars up to the largest stars observed. The largest stars that form in nature have masses around 100 times the mass of our Sun.

A small star fuses helium into carbon but does not proceed further into the fusion cycle. After a small star loses mass and forms a planetary nebula, its outer layers are gone. The core remains as a small hot sphere with a central region composed mainly of carbon nuclei, a layer in which helium fusion still occurs, plus an outer layer where no nuclear fusion takes place. Such a star is about the size of our Earth and is known as a **white dwarf**.

Nuclear fusion gradually stops as helium disappears from the old stellar core. The core continues to collapse until the electrical repulsion of the particles balances the inward gravitational force. As the nuclear fusion diminishes, the white dwarf gradually cools for a very long time until it no longer emits energy. Because the star's core is so densely packed with material, it requires many billions of years for the white dwarf to cool. When the white dwarf finally cools and no longer emits light, it is known as a **black dwarf**. A black dwarf's density is extremely high. After all, it is approximately the same diameter as our Earth, but with a mass almost equal to that of our Sun. The density of matter in a white or black dwarf is approximately a million times greater than the density of water!

The middle-sized stars do not die as calmly and gradually as a fading white dwarf. After a middle-sized star's hydrogen and helium fuels fuse to form heavier elements, it continues to collapse gravitationally and go through multiple red giant cycles of fuel consumption, expansion, and contraction. Each of those cycles passes more rapidly than the one just completed. Such processes continue until iron nuclei form. Atoms with nuclei heavier than iron require energy to be added in order for fusion to occur. Thus, iron represents the last element in which energy is produced during the fusion process. Further fusion only occurs if energy is absorbed from the stellar core. With the formation of iron, fusion no longer supplies surplus energy to stop the gravitational collapse of the star's dense core. With no active energy source in the massive star the core catastrophically collapses and then rebounds, sending a shock wave toward the surface of the star. The shock wave that propagates through the star releases a tremendous quantity of energy that destroys the star as the energy quickly moves outward. This event is known as a **supernova**. When a star explodes as a supernova, a hundred times more energy is released in just a few minutes than our Sun has generated since it was formed! At the peak of its brightness, a supernova appears over a billion times more luminous than our Sun. Modern astronomers observe and record supernovae over great distances because they shine so brightly.

During a supernova, large quantities of protons, neutrons, and energy necessary for the formation of heavy elements are all present in the same location. When the energetic shock wave rips through the outer layers of the star, a new cycle of fusion begins. At this time energy production is not an issue and so, with great surpluses of materials present, all the elements (even those heavier than iron) found in nature are formed and spread throughout the interstellar medium by the supernova explosion. The planets in our solar system contain all these heavy elements, so we may assume that these elements probably formed in the explosion of a supernova that happened long before the birth of our Sun.

When a supernova explosion occurs, a shock wave crushes the core of the star before rebounding outward into space. The remnant of the original star has been compacted to only a few tens of kilometers in size. This remnant, known as a **neutron star**, contains a type of matter impossible to recreate in any laboratory on Earth. The neutron star's tiny size indicates that gravitational forces are strong enough to crush the electron orbits so that electrons and protons combine to form neutrons. The resulting object can best be described as a giant nucleus of pure neutrons, although it contains up to several times the mass of our Sun. If a pinhead-sized ball of such matter could be brought to the Earth's surface, it would weigh in at about one billion tons, thanks to its incredible density. Another way to imagine a neutron star's density is to think of the amount of matter in an average person. If all the material in that person could be compacted to the density of a neutron star, the resulting object would be much smaller than a single cell from the original person!

Neutron stars have seldom been observed directly through a telescope. However, astronomers have seen indications of neutron stars called **pulsars**. A few of these pulsars emit rapid flashes of light. Most often, however, astronomers observe that pulsars emit periodic and precisely timed bursts of radio waves and high-energy x-rays. These emitted waves flash from precise locations in the sky. Astronomers

- **White Dwarf**

A small star that no longer sustains nuclear fusion and has shrunk to become a dense object about the size of our Earth.

- **Black Dwarf**

A black dwarf constitutes the remains of a Sun-sized star which has evolved to a white dwarf and subsequently cooled down such that it no longer emits light.

- **Supernova**

A rare celestial phenomenon involving the explosion of most of the material in a star, resulting in an extremely bright, short-lived object that emits vast amounts of energy.

- **Neutron Star**

The remnant of a supernova explosion that is composed almost totally of neutrons. It is so dense that the entire mass of our Sun could be contained in a sphere only a few tens of kilometers in diameter.

- **Pulsar**

A variable radio source that is thought to be a rapidly rotating neutron star.

Figure 33.7
The inner regions of the Crab Nebula as seen by the Chandra Observatory and the Hubble Space Telescope. This picture of the famous supernova remnant from 1054 AD combines high energy x-ray data (blue) with visible light (red) images in order to produce an enhanced view. The energetic pulsar at the center of the image is known to flash 30 times each second.

◆ **Black Hole**
Any object where gravity is so strong that not even light can escape from its surface.

have long believed that these regular energy flashes result from rapidly spinning neutron stars.

Why would a neutron star spin so rapidly? Almost all observed stars rotate, some rapidly and others slowly. Our Sun rotates with a period of about one month. If we collapsed a solar-sized star down to the size of a neutron star, the angular momentum of that star would not disappear. Instead, as the star collapsed, the angular velocity we observe would increase to the point that the small compact object would rotate many times every second. The same process occurs with pulsars. Neutron stars also have super-strong magnetic fields. As the object spins, these magnetic fields cause charged particles to accelerate. The charged particles are then emitted from the object's magnetic poles as beams of radiation. Once again, this explains the unusual pulses of energy we observe from these objects.

Scientists believe neutron stars are one possible end product of a supernova explosion. People observed supernovae with the naked eye in the years 1054, 1572, and 1604. Chinese astronomers observed the supernova of 1054 in the area of the sky where astronomers now see a rapidly expanding cloud known as the Crab Nebula (*Figure 33.7*). Astronomers using optical, radio, and x-ray equipment also report detecting a pulsar that flashes every 0.033 seconds at the center of the Crab Nebula. Supernovae often occur in other galaxies and are usually only visible by telescope. Because of their distance from Earth, they are difficult to study in detail. A supernova that occurs within our galaxy will always be bright enough to observe without a telescope. Most historical observations of supernovae visible without a telescope are described as stars that are bright enough to see during the day!

A massive neutron star has a powerful gravitational field that easily deflects the straight-line path followed by photons as they radiate from the object's surface. It is logical to question what would happen if we were to imagine a progression of neutron stars, with each one containing more mass than the previous one. This is the result we encounter when we consider the remnant left behind by the most massive stars in the Universe after they have exploded as supernovae.

Black holes are even more massive and exotic than neutron stars. They are the massive remnants that are left behind after supernovae explosions in the largest stars. In a neutron star, the final gravitational collapse is halted by the pressure from neutrons being tightly packed together with no remaining space. If the remnant of the stellar core contains more matter than about two or three solar masses, even the pressure from the tightly packed neutrons cannot resist the inward force of gravity. A final collapse is certain. As the stellar remnant collapses, its surface gravity increases and the path of emerging light bends more severely until it eventually closes and no light can escape. In this visualization, it is as if the space-time region is

Figure 33.8
The deflection of light from the surface of various objects. The gravity from a neutron star is strong enough to bend the light path to a significant degree. In a black hole, the light is bent so far that it can never escape out into space.

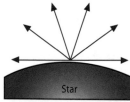
A supergiant star has relatively weak gravity, causing emitted photons to travel in straight lines.

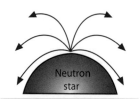
After collapsing into a neutron star, the surface gravity of the star becomes stronger causing the photons to follow curved paths.

As the star continues to shrink into a black hole, the photons follow paths which curve back into the black hole allowing no light to escape.

pinched off and no longer exists as part of our Universe (*Figure 33.8*).

A black hole can't be directly observed because it doesn't emit light. In principle, however, we can see matter in the space just outside the black hole. Also, the gravitational fields surrounding a black hole are extremely intense. In those instances where another star is orbiting a black hole, gas may be pulled from the other star into the black hole. The process is so violent that enormous amounts of energy are radiated in parts of the radio and x-ray regions of the spectrum. Even though astronomers can't directly see a black hole, they have observed several interesting objects that show evidence of an unseen massive companion.

The life cycle for stars of various masses is illustrated in *Figure 33.9*. Remember that the vast majority of stars have life cycles similar to our Sun. In comparison, stars that experience supernovae explosions and end up as neutron stars or black holes are quite uncommon.

33–6 ASTRONOMICAL DISTANCES

Measures of distance are critical to understanding all types of astronomical observations. If we know the distance to some source, we can determine the object's size by measuring how large it appears in the sky. Similarly, if we know the distance to some object that radiates energy, we can measure the amount of energy we receive from that object and then determine how much actual energy that object radiates into space.

Chapter 32 discussed how simple and reliable techniques can build a distance ladder with overlapping steps. However, these basic methods are often difficult to use for observations of stars and galaxies that are great distances beyond the Earth. This section discusses how the distance ladder can be extended by combining our knowledge of nearby stars with observations of similar stars that are much more distant.

More than 200 years after Galileo first used the telescope to make astronomical observations, the method of triangulation was used to successfully measure the distance to a nearby star. In 1837, Friedrich Wilhelm Bessel found that the distance to a faint star known as 61

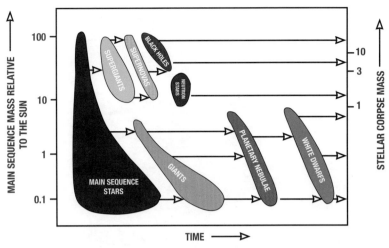

Figure 33.9
This chart shows the expected life cycle for stars of various masses. The most massive stars that eventually form neutron stars and black holes are rare compared to stars that are the size of our Sun or smaller.

Cygni was about ten light years. Ten light years is about 95 trillion kilometers—an incredibly large distance. This distance becomes even more difficult to fully comprehend when one realizes that this star is among those that are the closest to our Sun.

After Bessel determined the distance from our Sun to 61 Cygni, astronomers started to accurately determine distances for other nearby stars like Vega and Alpha Centauri. One problem they encountered was the difficulty involved in determining which stars to observe in order to calculate the distance. In the late 1800s, astronomers did not know that giant stars can radiate thousands or hundreds of thousands of times more energy than our Sun. This lack of knowledge caused many astronomers to mistakenly assume that all bright stars were nearby. Because of this error, astronomers were surprised at their inability to use triangulation to measure distance to many of the bright stars and later realized that these stars appeared so bright only because they really were many thousands of times more luminous than our Sun.

Astronomers found that triangulation is only applicable to the few thousand stars that are Earth's nearest neighbors. Chapter 32 mentioned that refinements in the triangulation method, including observations from above the blur of our atmosphere, allow us to measure distances for about 120,000 stars (including some that are up to 3,000 light years away). However, this distance stretches only a few percent of the total distance across our Galaxy. To measure distances farther into space, other methods and techniques to estimate those enormous distances would have to be developed.

Two astronomers, Ejnar Hertzsprung from

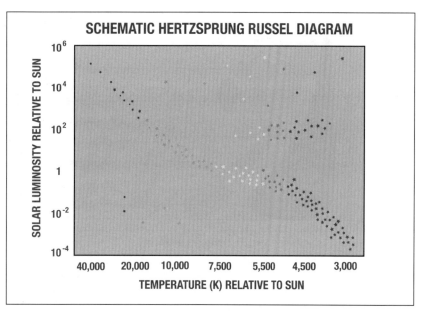

SCHEMATIC HERTZSPRUNG RUSSEL DIAGRAM

Figure 33.10
A plot of luminosity and temperature for various stars. This is known as a Hertzsprung-Russell (H-R) diagram. Most stars are plotted on the diagonal line that runs across the H-R diagram. This line is called the main sequence. Other areas of the H-R diagram are the red giant region (upper right) and white dwarf region (lower left) of the plot.

• **Luminosity**
Roughly equal to brightness or the rate at which energy is radiated from an object.

• **H-R Diagram**
A plot used for individual stars where luminosity is plotted on the y-axis and surface temperature is plotted on the x-axis.

• **Main Sequence**
A line of stars that runs diagonally from the upper left corner to the lower right corner of the H-R diagram. Stars on the main sequence are generating energy from hydrogen fusion in their cores.

Denmark and Henry Norris Russell from the United States, found that the properties of individual stars revealed surprising order. In the early 1900s, they independently discovered that the brightness of a star corresponds to its temperature. In retrospect, this relationship is not surprising. We already know that more massive stars are hotter and use the fuel in their cores more rapidly. Thus, they produce more energy and probably produce more light than a smaller, cooler star. Hertzsprung used a slightly different method than did Russell to make the same important deduction. Both astronomers made plots of **luminosity** and temperature for a large variety of different stars. These plots clearly illustrate order among the many types of observed stars. This type of luminosity and temperature plot (*Figure 33.10*) is known as a Hertzsprung-Russell diagram (or **H-R diagram**) in honor of its discoverers.

The H-R diagram provides a wealth of information about stars in general. Most of the stars graphed in the diagram fall on a roughly diagonal line running from the upper left portion of the diagram to the lower right part of the plot. This line in the H-R diagram is known as the **main sequence**. Stars on the main sequence are known to be in the adult stage, where hydrogen fusion is the primary source of radiated energy.

A star's actual brightness depends on both its temperature and its diameter. The temperature of a star can be measured by careful observation of its color. A hot star appears white or blue in color, and a cool star appears orange or red. Stars above the main sequence have the same temperature as a main-sequence star but appear to be more luminous. Therefore, the stars above the main sequence in the H-R diagram must be much larger than stars of the same temperature on the main sequence. This portion of the H-R diagram is filled by stars in the various giant phases discussed in Section 33.4. A typical star above the main sequence is usually found on the right side of the H-R diagram and is thus cool or red in color. The name red giant is appropriate for these stars.

Similarly, stars in the lower left portion of the H-R diagram have high temperatures like the most massive stars on the main sequence, but they are not nearly as bright. Because they have high temperatures, their lower luminosities are caused by their smaller diameters. We can see that the name given to these types of stars, white dwarf, is also quite descriptive.

The H-R diagram provides the basis for an indirect but powerful method of finding astronomical distances. A simple relation describes how luminous objects appear fainter with increasing distance. This brightness-distance relation makes sense when you think about it for a moment. Suppose two identical flashlights are shining at you from different distances. You would be correct in concluding that the one that appeared the brightest is the light closest to you. If you had previously measured the brightness of the flashlights at some standard distance, you would be able to use the same equipment to measure how bright the flashlights appeared at the unknown distances. You could then use the brightness-distance relation to determine how far each of the flashlights must be from your location.

The distance to a star can be found by using the H-R diagram to estimate the true brightness of a star in the following manner. We can determine many of the properties of our Sun because it is close enough to be studied in detail. Since we accurately know the distance of our Sun, we can measure its brightness at a known distance. When we observe other main-sequence stars with the same temperature or color as our Sun, we find that they also have the same luminosity. Thus, we can use the properties of our Sun to calibrate an H-R diagram.

Observing the color of a star and inferring its temperature is not difficult. When observing an entire cluster of stars (*Figure 33.11*), we can distinguish stars with different masses and temperatures. The main sequence of that cluster is often well defined. Measuring how bright the individual stars appear in the heavens is also easy. We can find the true brightness of any observed star by using the standard H-R diagram that has been calibrated with information from our Sun and other nearby stars.

When we compare the star's *apparent* brightness with its *true* brightness, we can calculate the distance to the star just as we did with the flashlight analogy above. In the case of a cluster of stars, we can find the distance to hundreds of individual stars that are approximately the same distance away from our Earth. The average of these many individual determinations will produce an excellent estimate for the actual distance. Most stellar distances are calculated by using some variation of this method.

Figure 33.11
This is a Hubble Space Telescope photo of a globular cluster known as M80 that contains several hundred thousand individual stars. Most of the visible stars are red giants many times more luminous than our Sun. It is possible to make an H-R diagram for an entire cluster of stars such as this and use that plot to find the distance to the stars in the cluster.

33-7 SUMMARY

Individual stars are not the unchanging and eternal beacons of the heavens we often imagine as we gaze into the night sky. Instead, they continually develop and change during an orderly process that can last millions or even billions of years. The time scale for the history and life of a star is determined by the amount of matter that initially formed each star. Although more massive stars form relatively quickly, they also exhaust the fuel supply in their cores more rapidly. As a result, massive stars move rather quickly to the next stage in their progression.

The way stars form and change during their period of existence is almost entirely due to the force of gravity. A star appears constant for long periods of time because the force of gravity pushing inward to make the star smaller is balanced against the pressure force from energy generation pushing outward to make the star expand. As long as these forces are in balance, the star will remain stable.

Each star will either slowly change into a red giant and then into a white dwarf, where it will slowly fade away, or else the star will eventually explode as a supernova. The end for more massive stars comes either in the form of a small and dense ball of neutron matter known as a neu-

tron star or, for only the most massive stars, an even more exotic object known as a black hole. Each of these possible outcomes is entirely dependent on the amount of matter contained in the star when it was first formed out of the interstellar medium.

Virtually all the elements found in the Universe today, other than hydrogen and helium, were formed during fusion in the cores of large stars where density and pressure reach levels far beyond our earthly experiences. After a large star explodes as a supernova, its matter enriches the surrounding interstellar medium and provides the raw materials for the formation of succeeding generations of stars. This process provides unimaginable quantities of protons, neutrons, electrons, and energy needed to form the heavy elements in a chain of natural events. The explosion itself spreads these materials throughout the star-forming regions of a galaxy. In fact, the supernova may itself act as a trigger for a new generation of stars to form in a large cloud of material in the interstellar medium, as small condensations form after the passage of the shock wave from the explosion.

This chapter also discussed other ways to measure large astronomical distances. Even though the simple method of triangulation can directly measure distances to a few stars, in practice it is difficult to make these observations and the method is only reliable for the stars that are relatively close to our Sun. Most stellar distances are estimated using the basic laws that govern the way light travels through space. Thus, if we can observe the apparent brightness of an object and compare that observation with an estimate of the object's actual brightness, we can accurately determine the true distance to the object.

Chapter Framework

A. Formation: From Interstellar Medium to Protostar
1. Composition of gas clouds
2. Nebulae
3. Stellar birth

B. Birth: From Protostar to Star
1. Stages of a Protostar
2. Gravity *vs.* Pressure
3. Fusion

C. Adult Life: Hydrogen Fusion in a Star
1. Rate of fusion
2. Radiation from stars

D. Old Age: The Star Becomes a Red Giant
1. Hydrogen-fusion region
2. Red giant phases
3. Planetary nebula

E. Death: White Dwarfs, Neutron Stars, and Black Holes
1. Small stars
2. Middle-sized stars
3. Large stars

F. Astronomical Distances
1. Triangulation
2. H-R diagram
   a. *Apparent brightness*
   b. *True brightness*

Comprehension

Matching

1. _____ Gas that glows from being heated by a nearby hot star.
2. _____ The small hot core that remains after a small star forms a planetary nebula. The star is about the size of Earth at this stage.
3. _____ Remnant of a star composed entirely of neutrons because gravity pulled the electrons into the protons.
4. _____ The final stage of a very massive star that no longer emits light and pinches off the space-time region.
5. _____ The space between stars.
6. _____ Glowing bubbles of gaseous material that expand out from a small star into space.
7. _____ Cool layer that the star's light comes from.
8. _____ When the star collapses and rebounds, creating a massive shock wave that destroys the star.
9. _____ Gas in cool, dark locations of space. The gas emits low-energy radio waves.
10. _____ The name of a white dwarf after it cools and no longer emits energy.
11. _____ Process that dominates the life of a star.
12. _____ In this stage, the star expands to about 50 times its normal size.
13. _____ Neutron star that emits precisely-timed bursts of radio waves and high-energy x-rays.
14. _____ Chart that provides star's luminosity and temperature for a variety of different stars.
15. _____ Beginning phase of a star when gravity begins to condense the surrounding matter.

a. *Interstellar medium*
b. *Protostar*
c. *Nuclear fusion*
d. *Neutron star*
e. *Pulsar*
f. *Emission nebula*
g. *Planetary nebula*
h. *Photosphere*
i. *Black hole*
j. *Dark nebulae*
k. *White dwarf*
l. *H-R diagram*
m. *Red giant*
n. *Black dwarf*
o. *Supernova*

True/False

1. _____ Scientists consider the interstellar medium the birthplace of stars.
2. _____ Fusion provides a force that balances the inward force of gravity.
3. _____ For a protostar to form, the force of pressure has to exceed the force of gravity.
4. _____ As the temperature of the star increases, the pressure within the star also increases.
5. _____ The light we see from the Sun comes directly from the center where fusion occurs.
6. _____ The amount of time required for a protostar to collapse depends on the amount of matter in the surrounding region of space.

Fill in the Blank

1. _____ cannot be directly observed because they don't emit light.

2. Three-fourths of all matter in the Universe is _____.

3. The fundamental interaction of _____ and _____ determines to a large extent the life of a star.

4. The _____ shows plots of luminosity and temperature for a large variety of stars and helps estimate astronomical distances.

5. _____ in the protostar's core marks the time when astronomers begin to refer to the object as a star.

6. We can use the properties of our _____ to calibrate an H-R diagram.

7. With a star's _____ brightness and its _____ brightness, its distance from us can be calculated.

Analysis

1. The ultimate source of light energy emitted by a protostar is

   a) the conversion of gravitational potential energy to other form(s) of energy that indirectly give rise to light
   b) the nuclear fusion of hydrogen into helium
   c) the nuclear fusion of helium into carbon
   d) the combination of hydrogen and oxygen to form water
   e) the fission of helium into protons and neutrons

2. Our sun is now in the state in which it will spend most of its active life. Which of the following best describes the current stage of the Sun?

   a) A protostar
   b) A middle-age star
   c) A red giant star
   d) A white dwarf star
   e) A neutron star

3. Our Sun will eventually become a

   a) white dwarf
   b) neutron star
   c) black hole
   d) protostar
   e) cloud of hydrogen gas

4. A neutron star is the final stage of what size star?

   a) Small star
   b) Medium star
   c) Large star
   d) Super massive star
   e) Two of the above

5. At what stage does fusion no longer occur in a small star?

   a) Protostar
   b) Middle-life
   c) Neutron star
   d) Main sequence star
   e) White dwarf

6. A type of neutron star that scientists can see because of the radiation it emits is a

   a) pulsar
   b) supernova
   c) black hole
   d) radiator
   e) none of the above

Synthesis

1. Why do brown dwarfs form?

2. What happens when fusion first begins to occur in a star?

3. How does a neutron star form?

4. What mistake did early astronomers make with triangulation?

5. What are pulsar stars and how do they help us locate neutron stars?

6. Outline the life of a small, medium, and large star. Describe what occurs in each stage of the star's life and the underlying forces responsible for each event in the different stages.

7. Why is hydrogen the first element that fuses in a star?

   a. What force fuses two elements together?
   b. What force needs to be overcome for the elements to fuse?
   c. How does this force that needs to be overcome for fusion compare between hydrogen and the other elements?

8. Why does the amount of matter originally present during the formation of a protostar so greatly affect the different stages that a star goes through?

9. How do astronomers use the H-R diagram to measure distance?

10. Two similar motorcycles travel towards you in the middle of the night. All you know about the two motorcycles is what you observe as they travel towards you. You observe that motorcycle A has a brighter light than motorcycle B. Which of the motorcycles is closer to you?

    a. What does their apparent brightness indicate?
    b. Do you know their true brightness?

CHAPTER 34

COSMOLOGY: THE HISTORY OF THE UNIVERSE

"Only two things are infinite, the Universe and human stupidity, and I'm not sure about the former."

~ Albert Einstein

It is interesting that Einstein would express doubts about the infinite nature of the Universe as voiced in the opening quote for this chapter. Well into the 20th century, virtually all scholars, scientists, and philosophers believed that our Universe was both infinite and static. For centuries, science's best minds were adamant that our Universe held no bounds and that it had existed in its present state since the first stars formed. They further argued that the Universe would continue in the same state until the distant future when nothing was left but a dead universe where no energy-changing processes could occur. This is just as predicted by the Law of Increasing Disorder, as discussed in Chapter 18.

So many people believed that our Universe was infinite and static that in 1915, as Albert Einstein developed his **General Theory of Relativity,** he was surprised to discover that his equations indicated that we should be living in an expanding universe. To remove this unexpected result from his theory, Einstein added what became known as a **cosmological con-**stant to his equations. Because of this unnecessary addition, Einstein missed making a prediction that would have quickly brought additional support to his ideas. Only a decade later, the astronomer Edwin Hubble reported observational evidence of a dynamic and expanding Universe. Einstein has often been quoted by secondary sources as saying that his addition of the cosmological constant to his General Theory of Relativity was "the greatest blunder of my life."

Centuries before Einstein, Isaac Newton and many other scientists considered the implications of living in a Universe that was infinite. Around 1610, Johannes Kepler questioned why the sky was dark at night if our Universe were indeed infinite. This question may seem silly, but many scientists and astronomers have wondered about this simple observation. Heinrich Olbers, an amateur astronomer in the 1800s, correctly reasoned that if space were indeed endless and contained stars randomly distributed in every direction, then no matter where we looked our line of sight would eventually fall on a star. If this were the case the night sky would not be dark, but would rather

LEARNING OBJECTIVES

When you finish this chapter, you should be able to

- Describe the general structure of the Milky Way and understand why determining the position of our Sun within the Galaxy was difficult.

- Understand the period-brightness relation for Cepheid variables and know how the relation is used to estimate distances to star clusters and galaxies.

- Recognize galaxies as the major constituents of the Universe and be familiar with the various types of galaxies.

- Describe the cosmological red shift and understand how the Hubble Law provides a description of the expanding Universe.

- Know what the Big Bang model of cosmology means and be familiar with the observations that support this model.

- Describe the discovery of cosmic microwave background radiation and be familiar with detailed observations from probes such as COBE and WMAP.

- Describe how methods that use supernovae or the Hubble Law are used by astronomers to estimate the vast distances at the edge of the Universe.

look like the visible surface of a typical star. The fact that the night sky is dark became known as **Olbers's paradox**. Many students and scientists alike falsely believe that the discovery of an expanding Universe resolved Olbers's paradox. Actually, the resolution of this paradox lies in our Universe's finite age and in the fact that the observed density of matter is grossly insufficient to provide enough energy to cover the entire night sky with a continuous blanket of starlight.

34–1 OUR GALAXY: THE MILKY WAY

Until the mid-1920s, the majority of astronomers believed that the **Milky Way**, of which our Sun is just one star in an enormous system of stars, clusters of stars, and nebulae, constituted the entire Universe. This idea of a cluster of matter located within an infinite space became known as the "one-island universe model." In a book published in 1890 Agnes Clerke, an astronomer and historian, stated this

view as absolute when she wrote, "No competent thinker, with the whole of available evidence before him, can now, it is safe to say, maintain any single nebula to be a star system of co-ordinate rank with the Milky Way." She believed that virtually all astronomers accepted that the Milky Way was the entire Universe, and even the somewhat mysterious spiral nebulae were simply part of that one great ensemble of matter.

Many have attempted to determine both the size of the Milky Way and where our Sun was located within this immense concentration of stars and matter, but this turned out to be a dif-

• General Theory of Relativity

Albert Einstein's description of gravity that was published in 1915. This theory explains the relationship between the geometry of space and the flow of time in our Universe.

• Cosmological Constant

A constant introduced into the equations of general relativity by Albert Einstein in an attempt to cancel the predictions of the expanding nature of our Universe.

• Olbers's Paradox

A fundamental question in cosmology centered around the observed fact that the sky appears dark at night.

• Milky Way

The galaxy of over a hundred billion solar masses to which our Sun belongs. As we observe it in the night sky, it refers to the faint band of light that marks the disk of our Galaxy.

ficult problem. A good analogy is to think of describing the apartment building where you live. Your description must be made from your vantage point in the living room, without being able to leave the living room to explore the rest of the apartment or go outside the building. You might be able to see part way down the hall or note that your apartment has a kitchen. You may be able to look out a window and see other buildings and determine that those buildings have different apartments and rooms. You may even assume that your building is similar to the buildings you see out the window. This may prove to be a good assumption or you may quickly realize that each of those apartments could be entirely different from the apartment with which you are most familiar. If you then try to draw a map of your apartment building with such limited knowledge, you will understand the difficulty of mapping the system of stars and pinpointing the area where our Sun is located. It is difficult to map an area so vast in every direction that a person could travel for thousands of years at speeds approaching the velocity of light and still not have a significant change in the view!

In 1920 Harlow Shapley, a young astronomer working in the Mount Wilson Observatory in California, made a great discovery about the size and shape of the Milky Way. He plotted the distribution of almost one hundred globular star clusters in the space around our Sun. The distribution conclusively demonstrated that the system of globular clusters associated with the Milky Way definitely does not center on our Sun. Instead, Shapley found that the center of the globular cluster distribution was a point in space in the direction of the constellation Sagittarius, many thousands of light years distant from our Sun. He also found that some of the most distant globular clusters were located more than 100,000 light years away. Shapley concluded that a huge spherical halo of material containing this collection of globular clusters completely surrounds the Milky Way. He was the first to show that our Sun is nowhere close to the center of the Milky Way. This discovery was significant because, at that time, scientists believed the Milky Way was the one island of matter in an infinite Universe of otherwise empty space.

Shapley had incorrectly estimated his distances, but his ideas and general conclusions about the Milky Way and the location of our Sun were correct. Further study has shown that the star system we know as the Milky Way is a relatively thin, disk-shaped concentration of stars and other material about 150,000 light years across. Our Sun is about one-third of the way out from the center to the edge of the disk, about 26,000 light years from the center of the Milky Way. The general shape of our Galaxy and the location of our Sun is shown in *Figure 34.1*. Even though it is a difficult problem to solve, years of clever observations and careful study have allowed astronomers to determine much about the size and shape of the Milky Way, despite the fact that we are observing from the inside while remaining stuck in one location.

Figure 34.1

An artist's conception of the Milky Way. It is clear that the Sun is not in the center of the Galaxy but is located among other stars in the galactic disk.

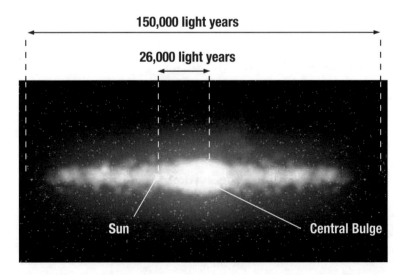

Astronomical Distances Close to the Milky Way

Great distances to points within the Milky Way or areas just beyond it can be measured using some of the techniques already covered in this textbook. One of the most powerful techniques used by astronomers is to compare how bright an object appears to observers on the Earth with an estimate of the actual luminosity of the object. This is the basis for determining stellar distances using physical properties as inferred from the H-R diagram discussed in Chapter 33.

By the early part of the 20th century, astronomers observed and catalogued a class of stars whose brightness changed regularly over a period of time. These stars, called **Cepheid variables**, continually go through cycles of pulsation with periods of days or months. The change in observed brightness is plotted against time for a typical Cepheid variable star in *Figure 34.2*. The time required for each pulsation can be measured with the precision of a fine clock. The North Star (Polaris) is a Cepheid variable whose brightness has been observed to vary by around 10% over a period of about four days. Polaris may be one of those extremely rare stars that allow us to observe its transition from one stage in its stellar life cycle to another. For several decades, the pulsations in the North Star have been slowly diminishing to the point where they are now barely noticeable.

Thousands of other Cepheid variables can be seen in our Galaxy and are sometimes located within star clusters. A star cluster is made up of many stars relatively close together when compared to the much greater distance from Earth to the cluster itself, so we can assume that all stars within the cluster are about the same distance from our Earth. If this assumption holds true, then any differences in the observed brightness of the individual stars relate directly to differences in the actual brightness of those stars. In 1912, Henrietta Leavitt was in the southern hemisphere observing distant star systems when she discovered a simple relationship between the time required for a full pulsation cycle and the true brightness of Cepheid variables. Her observations showed that the longer the pulsation period, the brighter the star's appearance. The scale of true brightness was calibrated by observing Cepheid variables with distances that could be checked using other methods. It became clear that measurements of the pulsation period alone for a Cepheid variable allowed astronomers to closely estimate a star's true brightness or luminosity.

With the total luminosity determined using the **period–brightness relation** and with the apparent brightness found from the observation, astronomers can quickly estimate the distance to any Cepheid variable. *Figure 34.3* clearly illustrates this relationship for regular Cepheid variable stars. Cepheid variables have enabled astronomers to add another rung to the distance ladder. The astronomer Harlow Shapley used this method, along with several other techniques, to find the distances to the globular clusters and

• **Cepheid Variables**

A type of pulsating variable star that changes brightness in a regular and predictable manner. The changes in brightness are directly related to observed changes in the size and temperature of the variable stars.

• **Period–brightness Relation**

A simple physical relationship that has been found for certain types of pulsating variable stars (including Cepheids) that indicates that the actual brightness of a pulsating star can be determined from a measurement of its pulsation period.

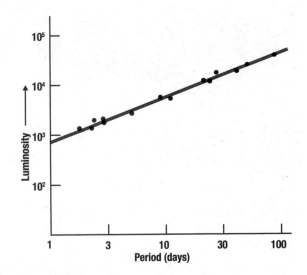

Figure 34.3

The period-brightness relation for Cepheid variable stars. This relation shows that the true brightness of a Cepheid variable star can be accurately predicted by observing how much time is required for the star to complete one pulsation cycle. Also note that the stars with the greatest luminosity require longer time periods to complete a pulsation cycle.

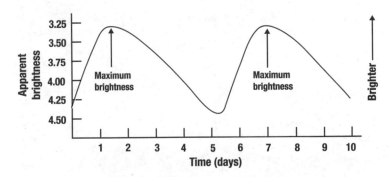

Figure 34.2

A plot of brightness variations for a typical Cepheid variable star. Stars such as Cepheids change brightness in a regular and predictable fashion over periods of time that are constant from cycle to cycle.

thus determine the shape of our Milky Way galaxy and the position of our Sun and Earth within it.

34–2 A VAST UNIVERSE OF GALAXIES

Philosophers like Immanuel Kant, along with some scientists, speculated that small diffuse patches (known as the spiral nebulae) scattered among the stars of the Milky Way were themselves giant conglomerations of stars outside the Milky Way. However, the majority of scientists at the time still believed in a one-island universe, with the Milky Way and its various components being the source of all radiant energy.

Ideas about the nature of the Universe were presented at a special meeting of the National Academy of Sciences in Washington D.C. in 1920. This event is known in science history as the Shapley-Curtis Debate, although the event was not really a debate in the formal sense. However, evidence for the one-island universe model was presented by scientists who believed, like Harlow Shapley, that the material in the Milky Way constituted the entire Universe. Some astronomers in attendance, including Heber Curtis, disagreed, claiming that the Milky Way was just one of an uncounted number of vast islands of matter spread throughout an even larger Universe. In the end, the Shapley-Curtis debate did not resolve any questions concerning the nature of the Universe because available evidence simply did not conclusively favor either point of view.

In 1923, Edwin Hubble used the then-largest telescope in the world to observe the Andromeda nebula. He found that individual stars could be resolved in the nebula and concluded that the nebula was not simply a luminous cloud of gas. Even more important was Hubble's discovery that some of the brightest stars visible in the Andromeda nebula are actually Cepheid variables. After applying the period-

Figure 34.4
A spectacular photograph of the nearby Andromeda galaxy. Note the two smaller and fainter companion galaxies that are visible in the photograph. The spiral structure and star-forming regions are clearly visible in this photograph. Determining that this was an independent system of stars and not a whirlpool of gas within the Milky Way was a major breakthrough in understanding how matter is organized in our Universe.

brightness relation, Hubble found that the stars within the Andromeda nebula were at least a million light years away from our Sun. This distance was at least ten times greater than the distance to the edge of the Milky Way. These results, announced at the end of 1924, resolved the unanswered questions from the Shapley-Curtis Debate by proving the one-island universe model was incorrect. The spiral nebulae became known as spiral galaxies, and scientists realized that our Universe contained much more matter than previously imagined. The Andromeda galaxy is pictured in *Figure 34.4.*

Galaxies in General

A new era in observational astronomy began with the discovery that many of the fuzzy nebulae visible in the heavens are actually vast systems of stars. Some of these star systems equal the Milky Way in size, and others are many times larger. As scientists built larger telescopes and discovered new ways to detect faint light from distant objects, they learned that our Universe is filled with galaxies as far as can be seen in every direction. Detailed observations of galaxies allowed scientists to classify them. Early in the history of studying galaxies, Hubble found most galaxies could be sorted into just a few distinct groups. In general, these groups simply describe the visual appearance of the galaxies. Astronomers once mistakenly believed that galaxies, like stars, change from one type to another as they age. Galaxies may have times when they produce greater quantities of energy in their nuclear regions, and some galaxies may go through many different eras of star formation. However, astronomers now generally believe that galaxies do not alter their basic structure as they age.

Elliptical galaxies, as the name suggests, are giant star systems with elliptical shapes. The degree to which they differ from being spherical in shape can be considerable. Remember that we are talking about a three-dimensional shape. Because galaxies are viewed from a random angle here on Earth, we often cannot determine how we see an individual galaxy projected onto the plane of the sky. For example, an elliptical galaxy could appear to us to be quite flattened along one axis, but if we look at it from the right angle it could appear to be spherical. In general,

elliptical galaxies have a dense core of stars at the center but lack spiral arms, dust, gas, star-forming regions, or other distinctive visible features (see *Figure 34.5*).

Elliptical galaxies have a wide variety of sizes. A **dwarf elliptical galaxy** can be approximately the same mass and size as a large globular cluster. These galaxies are so small that only those near our own galaxy can be seen. They simply do not include enough stars to be visible at large distances. The small companions of the Andromeda galaxy (refer back to Figure 34.4) are examples of dwarf elliptical galaxies. At the other end of the scale are the **giant elliptical galaxies**. A giant elliptical galaxy can contain over a trillion stars and have a mass much greater than the Milky Way. A giant elliptical galaxy (again, see Figure 34.5) is one of the most luminous objects in the Universe and can thus be observed from incredibly large distances.

Another group of galaxies are called **spiral galaxies**. Our Milky Way galaxy is thought to be a spiral galaxy similar to the spiral Andromeda galaxy discussed earlier in this chapter. Spiral galaxies do not show the same wide variety in

- **Elliptical Galaxy**
  A galaxy with an elliptical shape and little dust or gas.

- **Dwarf Elliptical Galaxy**
  A small elliptical galaxy with only a few million stars.

- **Giant Elliptical Galaxy**
  A large elliptical galaxy that may contain more than a trillion stars.

- **Spiral Galaxy**
  A galaxy flattened into a disk shape with a pattern of spiral arms wound about a central nucleus. Spiral galaxies usually include dust, gas, and active regions of star formation.

Figure 34.5
A nearby elliptical galaxy in the Virgo cluster. Elliptical galaxies are clearly symmetric, but lack the structure that is evident in spiral galaxies. Also, elliptical galaxies are typically more yellow in color. This indicates an older and cooler generation of stars, along with the general lack of active star-forming regions. There is seldom evidence of dust or gas in elliptical galaxies.

Figure 34.6

A nearby spiral galaxy known as M33. Note the numerous emission nebulae that lie along the spiral arms. These are regions of active star-formation.

◆ **Barred Spiral Galaxy**

A galaxy that is similar to a spiral galaxy, except that the spiral arm pattern originates from a bar of material that passes through the nucleus of the galaxy.

◆ **Irregular Galaxy**

A non-symmetric galaxy that does not have a well-defined shape like either the spiral or elliptical galaxies. Irregular galaxies generally include dust, gas, and active star-forming regions.

sizes as do elliptical galaxies. A spiral galaxy has a bulge in its nuclear region, a flattened disk containing dust and gas, and a spiral arm structure with active star-forming regions similar to the spiral galaxy shown in *Figure 34.6*. Ample evidence shows that the region around the disk of a spiral galaxy is a halo of material composed of globular star clusters, old red stars, and almost no material with which to form new stars. A typical spiral galaxy contains enough material to form 100 billion stars like our Sun. Although all spiral galaxies are similar in shape and appearance, considerable variation exists from one to another, depending on the viewing angle, the overall size of the nuclear region, and the number and structure of the individual spiral arms.

Barred spiral galaxies (*Figure 34.7*) appear similar to the spiral galaxies just discussed. The only significant difference thus far determined between a spiral galaxy and a barred spiral galaxy is that the spiral arms in a barred spiral start at the ends of a dense bar-shaped region of material running through the nuclear region of the galaxy. Computer simulations indicate that a bar through the nuclear region simply represents one "normal" way a spiral galaxy can form.

Regardless, the same variety is observed with respect to the overall mass, sizes of the nuclear region and structure of spiral arms in the barred spiral galaxies as in the regular spiral galaxies. A recent survey of more than 30 million stars observed in the infrared by the Spitzer Space Telescope indicates that if we could observe our Galaxy at a great distance, we would see a prominent bar through the nucleus with a length of more than 25,000 light years.

Irregular galaxies (*Figure 34.8*) are the remaining class of galaxies to be discussed here. The irregular galaxies do not exhibit the organized structure found in the elliptical, spiral, and barred spiral galaxies. They appear to be a minority of the observed galaxies. Among the large catalogs of galaxies that astronomers have compiled, approximately 75% are spirals, 20% are elliptical, and less than 5% are irregular. These numbers are only an estimate, of course, because the number of dwarf elliptical galaxies in the Universe are unknown due to their relatively (in astronomical terms) small size and low luminosity. The irregular galaxies usually contain dust, gas, and active star-forming regions as well as young star clusters. The average irreg-

⇧

Figure 34.7

The barred spiral galaxy NGC 1300. Except for the bar of material running through the nucleus, barred spiral galaxies are similar in size and structure to regular spiral galaxies.

⇦ **Figure 34.8**

The irregular galaxy NGC 1427. Irregular galaxies show evidence of recent star formation, but lack the structural symmetry that is clearly seen in elliptical and spiral galaxies.

Figure 34.9

A distant cluster of galaxies known as Abell 2218. Galaxies are nearly always gravitationally bound to other galaxies in clusters like the one shown here. Clusters of galaxies are almost unimaginably large, with each cluster containing many thousands of galaxies and each galaxy containing hundreds of billions of individual stars.

◆ **Local Group**

A small group of about two dozen galaxies that is associated with our Milky Way.

◆ **Cluster of Galaxies**

A group of galaxies that is gravitationally bound together into a cluster, which vary greatly in size. A small cluster may have just a few members, while a large cluster may have several thousand.

◆ **Supercluster**

Clusters of clusters of galaxies. It appears uncommon for these groups of clusters to be held together by gravity.

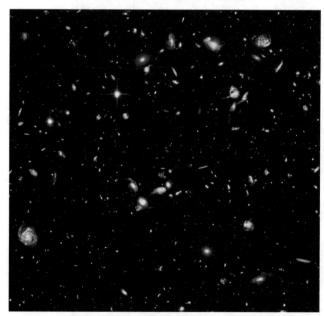

Figure 34.10

This figure shows a small section of the Hubble Ultra Deep Field. These are the faintest objects ever observed. Every image visible is of a distant galaxy, each of which contains hundreds of billions of stars. Some of the galaxies visible are more than ten billion light years away from Earth.

ular galaxy is usually only slightly smaller than the average spiral galaxy. Our Milky Way has two satellite galaxies (both irregular galaxies) that can be observed from the southern hemisphere. These well-known examples of irregular galaxies are called the Large Magellanic Cloud and the Small Magellanic Cloud.

Many different peculiar galaxies can also be observed. These include galaxies that have interacted with other galaxies over time to the point that their structures are greatly distorted. These galaxies are difficult to recognize as belonging to one of the regular classes of galaxies. Other galaxies undergoing an abnormally vigorous burst of star formation produce large quantities of radio energy or have exceptionally energetic emissions in their nuclear regions. These unusual objects add variety to our Universe and make the study of galaxies a challenge.

As astronomers have observed more and more distant objects, they find increasing levels of order in our Universe. Galaxies are almost incomprehensively large objects, but they seldom exist in isolation. Our Milky Way belongs to a small group of galaxies that contains a couple dozen members. Several dwarf elliptical galaxies and a couple of other spiral galaxies, including the Andromeda galaxy, are associated with the Milky Way. This small collection of galaxies is known as the **local group**. Other **clusters of galaxies** (*Figure 34.9*) may contain dozens or even thousands of large galaxies. Somewhat surprisingly, there are even clusters of clusters of galaxies. These are often called **superclusters**. A supercluster can contain tens of thousands of galaxies and span areas of space over 100 million light years across.

Our Universe is much larger and more complex than scientists ever suspected only 100 years ago. To image the most distant objects, the Hubble Space Telescope (HST) has taken several pictures that required exposure times of more than a month. In early 2004, a nearly three-month long exposure of a photograph now known as the Hubble Ultra Deep Field (*Figure 34.10*) was completed. Almost every image captured in that photograph, however faint, is of an unimaginably distant galaxy that contains hundreds of billions of stars. The vast majority of these galaxies are so far away that their radiated light has been traveling for billions of years before reaching our Earth.

34–3 AN EXPANDING UNIVERSE

The discovery that there exist uncounted galaxies beyond our Milky Way was of great interest to Hubble and other astronomers interested in the nature and extent of our Universe. After Hubble announced his results, increasingly careful observations were made of distant galaxies. In 1929, Hubble published a new discovery as surprising as his earlier discovery of external galaxies. Hubble found that the Universe was not static and eternal. The new observations clearly showed that the Universe was expanding.

We learned in Chapter 11 that light can be described as a series of electromagnetic waves. We also learned in Chapter 10 that the motion of either the sender or receiver of waves alters their frequency. This is the Doppler effect. For sound it means that the pitch changes with motion. Thus, a piano may be playing a constant tone of a perfect middle C, but if the piano were moving toward you the note would sound "sharp." Conversely, if the piano were moving away from you the note would sound "flat." In fact, if you knew with certainty what tone the piano was playing at rest and then measured what tone you actually received, you could cal-culate the exact speed that the piano moves toward or away from you.

This concept works the same way with light waves as it does with sound waves (*Figure 34.11*). If the source moves toward the observer, the waves appear to squeeze together. The observer sees this squeezed light as being shifted toward the blue end of the spectrum. If the source moves away from the observer, then the waves appear to stretch out and the light is observed to be shifted toward the red end of the spectrum.

In our research of stars within our own Galaxy, we use this method to measure the speed of stars either toward or away from the Earth. We can see that stars move through the space around us with a wide variety of speeds. About half the stars move away from us and the other half move toward us. Edwin Hubble did not find this to be true as he observed and recorded information about distant galaxies. A few of the closest galaxies to the Milky Way move toward us at low speeds, but all the rest of the millions of galaxies observed over the years move away from the Earth. Because nearly all galaxies are observed to be moving away, the Doppler shift is usually described as a cosmological redshift. What is even more remarkable is that there is a direct relation between the speed at which a galaxy is receding and how far away that galaxy is located!

The Hubble Law

Generations of astronomers have confirmed Hubble's observations that distant galaxies are all receding from us at ever increasing speeds, and that those speeds are related to the distance

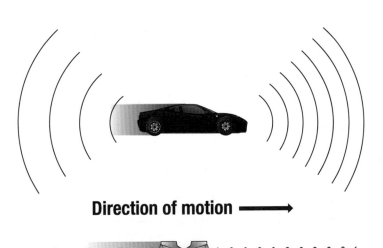

Direction of motion

Figure 34.11

An illustration of the Doppler shift for sound and light. As with sound waves, light waves emanating from an object moving relative to an observer will experience a shift in frequency and a corresponding change in wavelength.

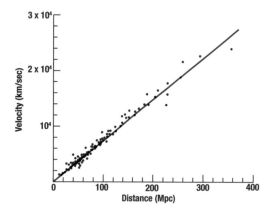

Figure 34.12
This plot shows that the speeds with which galaxies recede from Earth are proportional to their distance from us. The observed relation is direct evidence that the Universe is expanding.

♦ **Hubble Law**
An observed relation between the observed recessional velocity of a galaxy and the distance to that galaxy.

♦ **Hubble Constant**
A constant that is part of the Hubble Law; it gives the rate at which our Universe is expanding.

from our Earth to the observed galaxy. The speeds at which the galaxies recede from us have been worked out as a formula now known as the **Hubble Law**. The discovery of the Hubble Law is quite remarkable because the relation provides many clues about the creation, nature, and eventual fate of our Universe.

For example, the slope of the line in the speed versus distance plot shown in *Figure 34.12* gives a value known as the **Hubble constant.** The Hubble constant is the rate at which our Universe expands. Normal observational scatter in the data (due to the faint nature of distant galaxies) makes this constant especially hard to determine with high accuracy. However, in recent years giant telescopes have added a great deal of new information about the most distant galaxies, and the error in the value of the Hubble constant is now known to be less than 5%. New data suggest that the rate of expansion might be slowly increasing with time. If this is correct then an unknown force must exist to cause this to happen. If the Universe expands at a faster rate as time goes by, then obviously the Hubble constant would not actually be "constant."

If, as it appears, the Universe is expanding and if scientists have accurately determined the rate of that expansion, we can think of a time when all the material was in one place and the Universe had a beginning. Imagine running time backwards to a point when the expansion began. The best information currently available suggests that our Universe is around 14 billion years old. The age itself is a notable result because it indicates that our Universe is not infinitely old, but that an actual moment of creation occurred at some time in the past. These data also strongly suggest that our Universe has a distant horizon 14 billion light years away in all directions

beyond which we cannot view anything else since light beyond this has not had time to reach us. This important idea will be discussed in greater detail in the next section.

Because we see all the galaxies moving away from our Galaxy, we can imagine that we live in some special or preferred location. A first glance at the observations could easily make us believe that the Milky Way is really important, since it is obviously located at the center of the Universe! However, be careful! Sometimes, a quick look at the data can lead to an erroneous conclusion.

Imagine galaxies laid out on a grid (*Figure 34.13*). Now choose just one. The galaxy you choose as "home" does not make a difference in what you would observe as your universe expands at a constant rate. You will find that a neighboring galaxy that was only one unit away will be two units distant after the expansion. One that was two units away will now be four units

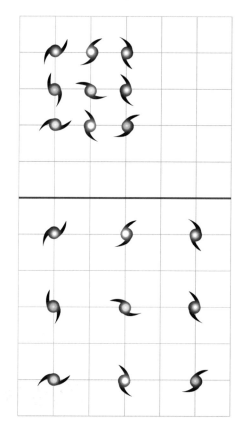

Figure 34.13
This figure illustrates that there is no preferred location, or center, within an expanding universe. To demonstrate this fact, choose any one of the nine galaxies as your home and measure the distance to each of the other galaxies before and after expansion. You will find in every case that galaxies that were more distant to start with also appear to move away from you at a greater rate, even though the expansion has been constant.

Figure 34.14
Have we found the center of the Universe? This wonderful sign refers to an astronomical education center located on Vancouver Island in British Columbia, Canada. One could argue that this is the center of the Universe as much as any other place you might select.

away. You can even use the diagonals, since a neighbor that was 1.4 units away in the first frame will be 2.8 units away after a period of expansion.

Note also that the most distant galaxies will appear to have moved at a greater speed during the expansion, because they have traveled a greater distance during the time interval. We can conclude from this thought experiment that an observer in any galaxy would observe the same Hubble Law (rates of expansion). This concept can also be observed tangibly, in three dimensions in a non-cosmic kitchen, by noticing how chocolate chips move away from one another during the expansion of a loaf of zucchini bread during the baking process. The primary conclusion here is that there is no way to find the center of the Universe. And contrary to the picture in *Figure 34.14*, it is probably not in British Columbia!

The ideas that the Universe has essentially the same basic structure regardless of one's location, and that it generally appears the same no matter what direction one looks, are two assumptions that together form the **cosmological principle**. Any successful cosmological model must be able to explain the available observations and conform to the cosmological principle.

34–4 THE COSMIC MICROWAVE BACKGROUND

In the early 1960s two scientists, Arno Penzias and Robert Wilson, worked with microwave antenna systems at Bell Telephone Laboratories in New Jersey to improve communications with Earth-orbiting satellites. They were surprised to find that no matter where they pointed their sensitive receiver, they always detected an easily measurable background noise. This background signal remained an irritating mystery until Penzias and Wilson became aware of theoretical work that astronomers had been doing just a few miles away at Princeton University. The two men found that the theoreticians had predicted a few years earlier that this type of microwave signal should be present if the expanding Universe had begun with a hot, explosive event. The microwave background signal represents the remnants of that initial creation. We see the residual radiation in the long-wavelength microwave region because it originated so long ago that all the short wavelengths have been stretched out and appear to have an even greater redshift than the light reaching us from the most distant galaxies.

This ever-present signal is referred to as the **cosmic microwave background** (CMB). Since its discovery, many careful observations have been made of the CMB. The atmosphere that blankets our Earth is not transparent at wavelengths where the CMB is the most intense. As a result, the most precise observations of the CMB have been made by detectors carried by specially designed balloons at high altitudes, or orbiting space probes, where there is little or no atmospheric interference. The first orbiting observatory designed to observe and record the CMB in detail was launched in 1989. This satellite, known as the Cosmic Background Explorer (COBE), provided detailed observations of the energy distribution of the CMB. The observations showed that the glow of radiation that apparently originates from the creation of the Universe looks the same in every direction. Significantly, the cosmological principle had already predicted this outcome. Another result from the COBE observations showed that the spectrum of the CMB almost exactly matched the spectrum an observer would expect to see

♦ Cosmological Principle
The concept that the large-scale structures of our Universe are the same no matter what direction you observe or where you are located.

♦ Cosmic Microwave Background
A uniform radiant field with an apparent temperature of 2.725 K that is observable in every direction.

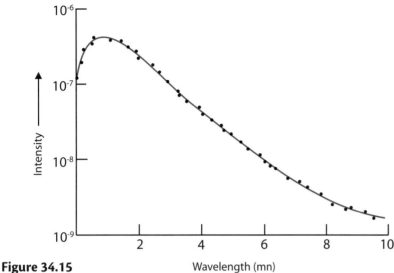

Figure 34.15

Data meets theory in these observations from the COBE satellite. The black dots represent actual data points, while the red line is from a theoretical model of how the radiation left over from the creation of the Universe should appear today. This figure shows remarkable agreement between theory and observation.

coming from an object with a temperature of only 2.725 degrees above absolute zero. The observed spectrum from the COBE satellite is plotted along with the theoretical spectrum for an object of 2.725 K in *Figure 34.15*.

In a map of the entire sky as viewed by the COBE satellite, the only patterns seen in the CMB down to the precision of a few thousandths of a degree Kelvin are those caused by the motion of our Galaxy through the background at a speed of about 370 km/s (*Figure 34.16*). Even these tiny variations are not actual variations in the CMB. Rather, they are from a doppler created shift as the Earth moves through space in the direction of the constellation of Leo. This causes the microwaves to compress a bit in that direction, and we thus record a slightly warmer average temperature. At the same time, we are moving away from the constellation of Aquarius in the other half of the sky. The microwave background radiation stretches out (redshifts) a little,

Figure 34.16

This is an all-sky map showing the CMB data collected by the COBE satellite. The colors indicate a departure from the average temperature of the CMB of only a few thousandths of a Kelvin. The blue area is slightly cooler and the red area is slightly warmer than the average temperature. The Earth's motion through the CMB is toward the red region, which is located in the general direction of the constellation of Leo.

and the temperature appears a few thousandths of a degree cooler than the average we observe.

One of the COBE results worried theoreticians. The observed temperature of the CMB is uniform to surprisingly high levels of precision. This causes concern because scientists have observed a considerable level of large-scale structure in our Universe. If the observed super clusters formed early in the history of the Universe, as suspected, some lumpy areas should still be observed in the CMB. Scientists believed that small variations in the CMB would show the areas where the first clusters of galaxies were formed. By the end of the COBE mission, the observations showed the presence of tiny irregularities in the CMB. These irregularities were at the limit of what COBE could detect. In 2001, scientists launched a specially designed satellite named the Wilkinson Microwave Anisotropy Probe (WMAP). This orbiting observatory had the mission to study the CMB and map any areas where the CMB was found to be non-uniform.

The WMAP results were released in 2003 and provided a greater source of information about our Universe than cosmologists had ever imagined. The detail in the WMAP results is nothing short of spectacular. Careful study of the WMAP results has allowed cosmologists to make surprising predictions about the density, age, geometry, and formation of stars and galaxies during the Universe's early history. Maps of the entire sky showing the CMB as seen by COBE and WMAP are shown in *Figure 34.17*. The largest variations are seen by both satellites. The largest temperature variations seen in either map are only about two ten-thousandths of a degree Kelvin above or below the average temperature of the CMB.

34–5 THE BIG BANG COSMOLOGICAL MODEL

The understanding of how elements heavier than hydrogen form during fusion processes in the cores of stars was a significant discovery for astronomers in the last century. The previous chapter of this textbook focused on the synthesis of these elements as in the life cycle of a typical star. The abundance of helium observed in even the oldest stars provided evidence that much of this material was formed even before the first stars existed. This is why so many theorists speculate that the Universe's early history included an era when all matter had a temperature at least as hot as the core of our Sun. If this speculation holds true, the helium that accounts for about 25% of the mass in stars like our Sun can be explained as the result of fusion that occurred during this hot era before the Universe expanded enough to cool to the point where fusion was no longer possible.

Scientists already knew about our Universe's expansion when they realized that a hot epoch was needed to explain the existence of so much helium. By combining the ideas of expansion and a hot early Universe, cosmologists derived the idea now known as the **Big Bang model** to explain the origin of the Universe. The Big Bang model received its catchy name from astronomer Fred Hoyle, who was making fun of the theory, but that little joke title has lasted for decades!

Hoyle disliked the Big Bang theory because this type of cosmological model supported the idea that our Universe had a finite age, and thus a specific moment of creation. The idea of a creation was so distasteful to Hoyle that he spent the remainder of his career working unsuccessfully to develop alternative cosmological models that would explain the flood of increasingly precise observations. The discovery of the CMB provided additional support to explain the observational evidence that our Universe is still expanding after an epoch marked by creation and high temperatures. The staggering detail in the most recent observations continues to be best explained by the model still known as the Big Bang.

34-6 MEASURING COSMOLOGICAL DISTANCES

The distances encountered in the study of cosmology are many hundreds of times greater than anything that can be measured using star clusters or Cepheid variable stars. These great distances make it impossible to see light from ordinary individual stars. Progress was made on this problem with the discovery of the Hubble Law. When the recessional velocity is measured for a distant galaxy, scientists can then determine a good estimate for the distance, using the Hubble diagram. To be accurate, this method requires that we know the value of the Hubble Constant with great precision. However, even if we do not know the value of the Hubble Constant, the Hubble Law can still be used to find relative distance. For example, if one galaxy moves away with a velocity of 10,000 km/s and a different galaxy has a recessional velocity of 20,000 km/s, the Hubble Law tells us that the second galaxy is twice as far away as the first. If we know a value for the Hubble Constant, then we can actually calculate a distance for each galaxy. We would still note that the second galaxy is twice the distance of the first.

This application of the Hubble Law became important when scientists first discovered that some galaxies emit unusually large quantities of energy from their nuclear regions. These galaxies are much more luminous than typical galaxies, and can thus be seen at much greater distances. Some of these distant objects were mistaken for nearby stars because they were so far away that telescopes on Earth's surface

• **Big Bang Model**
A cosmological model that indicates that our Universe had a hot beginning at the instant of creation.

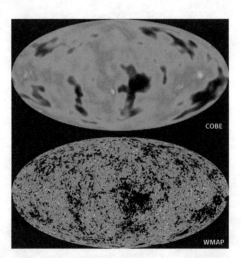

Figure 34.17
Two all-sky maps are shown in this figure. The upper panel is data from the COBE satellite and the lower panel is the high-resolution observations returned by the WMAP satellite. In both cases, the motion of the Earth seen in Figure 34.16 has been removed so that all that remains are the actual small variations within the CMB. It is believed that these tiny bumps in the CMB represent density variations in the early Universe that are responsible for the formation of the first galaxies and clusters of galaxies. This is a remarkable result, since the largest variations visible in either map are less than 0.0002 Kelvin above or below the smooth background.

revealed objects that appeared like an ordinary star. These objects were originally called quasi-stellar objects because of their star-like appearance. They are now called QSOs, or **quasars**. Analysis of the light from QSOs showed they had the largest redshifts of any objects ever observed. When the Hubble Law was used to find the distance to quasars, scientists found them to be the most distant objects ever seen. Many of these objects have had their true nature revealed by observations from orbiting telescopes such as the Hubble Space Telescope. These observations reveal that quasars are actually distant galaxies with an incredibly bright nucleus.

Another method of extending the distance ladder to cosmological distances makes use of the predictable properties and luminosities of some types of supernovae. Some supernovae are more than a billion times brighter than our Sun. This is why a supernova explosion is sometimes as bright as the entire galaxy (*Figure 34.18*) where it is located, and can be seen from an incredibly great distance. By observing many supernovae in many different galaxies with distances known from other methods, scientists can accurately predict the luminosities of some supernova types. These special types of supernovae can be observed out to distances of more than a billion light years. The distance measured from a supernova explosion is independent of the distance observed from the Hubble Law. Fortunately, even at the greatest distances that can be observed, different methods can be used to verify the results.

A truly surprising result in recent years has been found for the most distant supernovae

observations. The most distant supernovae appear just a little fainter than expected from distances determined using the Hubble Law. One interpretation of this unexpected result is that the expansion of our Universe does not remain constant, but actually speeds up over time. Astronomers are not certain that these results will prove to be correct, but if they do show a change of the Hubble constant with time, it would mean that some presently unknown force causes the expansion of our Universe to increase. Ironically, this would be just the opposite of what Einstein thought he had eliminated with the use of a cosmological constant!

34–7 SUMMARY

Our Universe is full of surprises. The results that scientists find through observation and experimentation may not always be expected. In studying the largest structures in our Universe, scientists have sometimes found it necessary to study the smallest particles that exist in order to answer the questions that may be uncovered. Even then, many objects still remain unexplained. We sometimes find that forces not completely understood are at work.

Scientists will continue to make progress. We may find that some of the details we observe change over time. Still, science appears to have reached a point where the major outline for studies in physical science is well in place and we will proceed to gather new information and illuminate the details of the Universe in which we live.

• **Quasar**
A luminous galaxy with a large redshift and star-like appearance when viewed through a telescope.

Figure 34.18
Supernova 1994 D as observed with the Hubble Space Telescope in a spiral galaxy. Notice how the single star in the lower left corner of the picture is as bright as the nucleus of the entire galaxy. A few days before this picture was taken, the supernova was not even visible. This particular supernova was one of the first to provide data indicating that the Hubble Constant may in fact be changing with time.

POSTSCRIPT: THE HUBBLE SPACE TELESCOPE

from hubblesite.org

The Hubble Space Telescope was named after Edwin P. Hubble. He revolutionized cosmology by proving that the clouds of light astronomers saw in the night sky were actually other galaxies beyond our Milky Way.

His greatest discovery was in 1929, when he identified the relationship between a galaxy's distance and the speed with which it is moving. The farther a galaxy is from Earth, the faster it is moving away from us. This is known as Hubble's Law. He also constructed a method of classifying the different shapes of galaxies.

Edwin Powell Hubble was born in Marshfield, Missouri. In 1910 he received his undergraduate degree from the University of Chicago and studied law under a Rhodes Scholarship at Oxford University. Later he changed his mind and completed his Ph.D. in astronomy at Chicago's Yerkes Observatory in 1917. He also served in the infantry during World War I.

The Hubble Space Telescope (HST) is a space-based telescope that was launched in 1990 by the space shuttle. From its position 380 miles above the Earth's surface, the HST has expanded our understanding of star birth, star death, and galaxy evolution, and has helped move black holes from theory to fact. It has recorded over 100,000 images in the past eight years. The Hubble Space Telescope whirls around Earth at a speed of five miles per second. If cars moved that fast, a coast-to-coast trip across the continental U.S. would take only 10 minutes.

The telescope's instruments are the astronomer's eyes to the universe. Its instruments include the Wide Field Planetary Camera 2 (WFPC2), Space Telescope Imaging Spectrograph (STIS), Near Infrared Camera and Multi-Object Spectrometer (NICMOS), Advanced Camera for Surveys (ACS), and Fine Guidance Sensors (FGS).

When first launched, the HST's primary mirror was out of shape on the edges by 1/50 of a human hair. This very small defect made it difficult to focus faint objects being viewed by the Hubble. Because the HST is in low Earth orbit, it could be serviced by a shuttle. The defect was corrected in one such servicing mission.

Servicing Mission 4, the last scheduled flight of the space

The Hubble Space Telescope being deployed out of the shuttle bay into space. All photos courtesy Hubble Space Telescope, NASA.

shuttle to the Hubble Space Telescope, has been cancelled. The mission would have performed maintenance work and installed new instruments. On Jan. 16, 2004, then-NASA Administrator Sean O'Keefe announced his decision to call off the mission, which would have performed Hubble maintenance work and installed new instruments. O'Keefe cited the new safety guidelines set out following the Columbia tragedy as the primary basis for his decision. New NASA Administrator Mike Griffin has promised to revisit the decision based on the success of upcoming shuttle flights. A mission, were it approved, could take place around mid-2007 or early 2008. While the telescope is operating normally now, the lack of routine repair work will eventually bring operations to an end.

Perhaps you will be able to visit the Hubble Space Telescope at the National Air and Space Museum someday. For more information about the Hubble Space Telescope visit www.hubblesite.org.

An astronaut removes the High Resolution Spectrograph in preparation for a new instrument during the second servicing mission in 1997. Hubble's science instruments are large and complex. The telescope can hold four telephone-booth sized instruments and four piano-sized instruments.

The Hubble Space Telescope floats against the background of Earth after a week of repair and upgrade by Space Shuttle Columbia astronauts in 2002.

Chapter Framework

A. Introduction
1. Nature of the universe
2. Olbers's paradox

B. Our Galaxy: The Milky Way
1. One-island universe model
2. Shapley's discovery

C. Astronomical Distances Close to the Milky Way
1. Cepheid variables
2. Period-brightness relation

D. A Vast Universe of Galaxies
1. Shapley-Curtis debate
2. Edwin Hubble

E. Galaxies in General
1. Elliptical galaxies
2. Spiral galaxies
3. Irregular galaxies
4. Local groups and superclusters

F. An Expanding Universe
1. Movement that alters waves
2. Measuring speed and distance

G. The Hubble Law
1. Speed and distance
2. Hubble constant
3. Center of the Universe

H. The Cosmic Microwave Background
1. Cosmic microwave background radiation
2. Cosmic Background Explorer (COBE)
3. Wilkinson Microwave Anisotropy Probe (WMAP)

I. The Big Bang Cosmological Model
1. Helium evidence
2. Fred Hoyle

J. Measuring Cosmological Distances
1. Hubble Law and quasars
2. Supernovae

Comprehension

Matching

a. *Cosmological constant*
b. *Cepheid variable*
c. *Milky Way*
d. *Elliptical galaxy*
e. *Irregular galaxy*
f. *Period-brightness relation*
g. *Olbers's paradox*
h. *Giant elliptical galaxy*
i. *Cluster of galaxies*
j. *Hubble Law*
k. *Barred spiral galaxy*
l. *Spiral galaxy*
m. *Cosmological principle*
n. *Supercluster*
o. *Local group*
q. *Big Bang model*
r. *Hubble constant*

1. _____ The sky appears dark at night.
2. _____ A small group of about two dozen galaxies that is associated with our Milky Way.
3. _____ A group of galaxies that is gravitationally bound together.
4. _____ Star system with an elliptical shape.
5. _____ A constant introduced by Einstein into his equations in an attempt to cancel the predictions of an expanding Universe.
6. _____ An observed relation between the recessional velocity of a galaxy and the distance to that galaxy.
7. _____ Elliptical galaxy that contains over a trillion stars and has a mass much greater than the Milky Way.

8. _____ The galaxy of over a hundred billion solar masses to which our Sun belongs.
9. _____ A simple relation where the actual brightness of stars can be determined by observing the pulsation period of a star.
10. _____ A galaxy flattened into a disk shape with a pattern of spiral arms wound about a central nucleus.
11. _____ Part of the Hubble Law that gives the rate at which our Universe is expanding.
12. _____ A non-symmetric galaxy that does not have a well-defined shape.
13. _____ A cosmological model that indicates that our Universe had a hot beginning when first created.
14. _____ A group consisting of clusters of clusters of galaxies.
15. _____ A pulsating star that changes brightness in a regular and predictable manner.
16. _____ Concept that the Universe's large-scale structures are the same no matter what direction you look or where you are located.
17. _____ Galaxy where the spiral arm pattern originates from a bar of material that passes through the nucleus of the galaxy.

True/False

1. _____ The idea that the Milky Way galaxy was the only cluster of matter located within infinite space became known as the one-island universe model.
2. _____ With the advancements in science and technology, knowing the shape of the Milky Way and our location in it has become a relatively easy task.
3. _____ Polaris is a Cepheid variable.
4. _____ The Shapley-Curtis debate ended with the conclusion that the one-island universe model of the Universe was correct.
5. _____ A barred spiral galaxy is one of the many variations of elliptical galaxies.
6. _____ Galaxies commonly exist in isolation.

Fill in the blank

1. Einstein's equations originally indicated that we live in an _____ universe.
2. Discoveries made by _____ _____ resolved the issues in the _____ _____ debate.
3. The uniform temperature of the _____ worried theoreticians.
4. The Big Bang Model helps explain the _____ that accounts for about 25% of a star's mass.
5. Measurement of Cepheid variable's pulsation periods allow scientists to estimate a star's _____ brightness.

Analysis

1. Which statement is true about the Big Bang model?

   a) The galaxies are, on the average, moving away from each other. The more distant the galaxies, the slower they are moving away from each other.

   b) The microwave background radiation that fills the Universe is left over from the fireball present in earlier stages of the expansion process.

   c) A certain amount of new matter is continually being created in space.

   d) The Universe has always been pretty much as we see it today, and it always will be.

   e) The heavy elements, like uranium, found on the Earth were created in the first few seconds of the Big Bang.

2. New data about the expansion of the Universe indicates that the majority of galaxies are

   a) moving toward the Milky Way galaxy with those farthest away moving the slowest.

   b) moving away from the Milky Way galaxy with those farthest away moving the slowest.

   c) moving away from the Milky Way galaxy with those farthest away moving the fastest.

   d) moving toward the Milky Way galaxy with those farthest away moving the fastest.

   e) not moving with respect to the Milky Way galaxy.

3. When the spectrum of light from distant galaxies is measured, what is found?

   a) The lines in the spectrum are shifted towards the blue end of the spectrum, with light from the most distant galaxies being shifted by the largest amount.

   b) The lines in the spectrum are shifted towards the blue end of the spectrum, with light from the closest galaxies being shifted by the largest amount.

   c) The lines in the spectrum are shifted towards the red end of the spectrum, with light from the most distant galaxies being shifted by the largest amount.

   d) The lines in the spectrum are shifted towards the red end of the spectrum, with light from the closest galaxies being shifted by the largest amount.

   e) The spectrum has lines in exactly the same place.

4. Which of the following causes some to speculate that our Universe included an era when all matter had a temperature at least as hot as the core of our Sun?

   a) The presence of planets with elliptical orbits in the solar system

   b) The helium gas that visibly escapes stars when solar flares occur

   c) The abundance of helium in older stars

   d) The abundance of hydrogen in older stars

   e) Two of the above

5. Two Cepheid variables, A and B, are seen in a cluster. Cepheid variable B has a longer pulsation period and appears much brighter than Cepheid Variable A. Which of the following is true?

   a) A has greater luminosity and apparent brightness than B

   b) A has greater luminosity but less apparent brightness than B

   c) B has greater luminosity but less apparent brightness than A

   d) B has greater luminosity and apparent brightness than A

   e) None of the above are true

Synthesis

1. What makes it so difficult to know our location in our Galaxy and what the rest of the Galaxy looks like?

2. List and describe the different types of galaxies.

3. Explain why we cannot assume that our Galaxy is the center of the Universe?

4. What were the accomplishments of COBE and WMAP?

5. How do Cepheid variables help determine distance to stars?

6. Observations from distant supernovae have recently surprised scientists. The supernovae appear fainter than normally expected. These results cause some to conjecture that an unknown force causes our Universe to expand at an increasing rate. If the Universe's rate of expansion is increasing, why do scientists assume that some unknown force accompanies this type of expansion?

7. Why would a one-island universe model better resolve Olbers's paradox than the presence of multiple galaxies spread throughout space?

8. What evidence suggests that the Hubble constant may not be constant?

9. What did Hoyle dislike so much about the Big Bang theory? How could the Big Bang theory be reconciled with the belief of a creation?

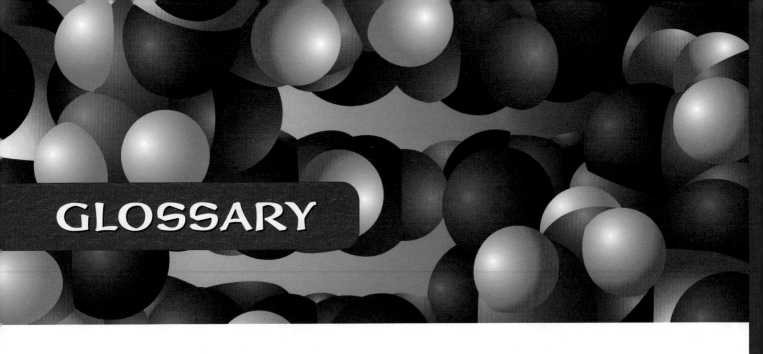

GLOSSARY

— A —

Absolute Time: A numeric or quantitative measure of time.

Abyssal Hills: Mounds of basalt on the deep ocean floor.

Abyssal Plains: Broad, flat areas on the ocean floor.

Acceleration: When an object either speeds up or slows down or changes direction.

Acidic: Having a pH value less than 7, meaning that the hydronium ion concentration is greater than in pure water.

Activation Energy: The difference between the energy of the isolated reactant molecules and energy of the transition state. If the activation energy is added to a set of reactant molecules, it is possible for them to reach the transition state and go on to form products. Reactants with less than the activation energy do not normally form products.

Activation Entropy: The difference between the entropy (or disorder) of the isolated reactant molecules and the entropy (or disorder) of the transition state. Frequently, the activation entropy is unfavorable so that colliding molecules do not always react even if they have sufficient energy to react.

Alloy: A combination of two or more metals into a single homogeneous substance.

Alpha Decay: The radioactive decay of an atomic nucleus by emission of an alpha particle.

Alpha Particles: A positively charged particle that is given off by some radioactive materials including uranium, plutonium, and polonium. Alpha particles are now known to be nuclei of helium atoms.

Alternating Current: A current of electrons that changes direction of flow.

Amine Group: The grouping of NH_2 attached to a carbon atom.

Ammonite: The name given to the fossil-shell remains of animals that lived in the oceans millions of years ago, but are now extinct. They were squid-like animals whose closest modern-day relatives are the nautilus.

Amplitude: The maximum amount that a particle will displace from its normal, undisturbed position when a wave passes through it.

Amu: The abbreviation for atomic mass unit. One atomic mass unit = 1.660559×10^{-27}kg. This is the average mass of the protons and neutrons in a 12C atom. Because protons and neutrons are so small, it is more convenient to measure their mass in units of comparable size.

Angular Momentum: Angular momentum is a quantity that measures the amount of rotation motion an object has.

Anions: Atoms, or groups of atoms bound together, that have a net negative charge. In an anion, the number of electrons is greater than the number of protons in the atom or group of atoms.

Anorthosite: A rock found in the area of the lunar highlands that is thought to be an ancient remnant of the original surface of our Moon.

Anti-Bonding Molecular Orbitals: Molecular orbitals that have low (or no) electron probability between atomic nuclei in a molecule and high electron density in areas not between the nuclei. When anti-bonding orbitals are occupied by electrons, the resulting electron density in the anti-bonding orbital helps pull the nuclei apart, weakening any chemical bond that may exist between them.

Antinode: A location of maximum vibration in a standing wave.

Asteroid: One of many thousands of small rocky objects that orbit our Sun. The orbits of asteroids generally lie between the orbits of Mars and Jupiter, although some are in orbits that bring them close to our Sun. Asteroids are much smaller than a planet and are sometimes called minor planets.

Asthenosphere: A soft, plastic, partially-molten mechanical layer in Earth located below the lithosphere.

Atoll: An ocean island that has no remaining central volcanic edifice, but exists only as a coral reef almost completely at or below sea level.

Atom: The fundamental unit of an element.

Atomic Mass Number: The total number of protons + neutrons in the nucleus of an atom.

Atomic Matter: Matter that exists in the solid, liquid, and gaseous states as single atoms.

Atomic Nuclei: The positively charged central region of an atom, composed of protons and neutrons.

Atomic Number: The number of protons in a nucleus. This number defines an element.

Atomic Size: An estimate of the volume occupied by an atom. The number is obtained from the density of the solid state of the element.

Atomic Theory: The model that matter is made up of atoms.

Authority: An accepted source of expert information or advice.

— B —

Band Gap: The band gap is the energy difference between the top of the valence band and the bottom of the conduction band in insulators and semiconductors.

Barred Spiral Galaxy : A galaxy that is similar to a spiral galaxy, except that the spiral arm pattern originates from a bar of material that passes through the nucleus of the galaxy.

Basal Drive: May help the plates to move. As the asthenosphere flows along under a plate, it may help to pull the plate along like a conveyor belt.

Basalt: An igneous volcanic rock that is composed of calcium-rich feldspar and other iron-rich minerals.

Basement: What geologists call the igneous and metamorphic rock found in the continental shields and under the sedimentary rock cover in the stable platforms.

Basic: Having a pH value greater than 7, meaning that the hydronium ion concentration is less than in pure water.

Beta Decay: The radioactive decay of an atomic nucleus accompanied by emission of a beta particle. (This process is also known as "electron capture" since it happens when a proton in the nucleus absorbs one of the atoms 1S electrons.)

Big Bang Model : A cosmological model that indicates that our Universe had a hot beginning at the instant of creation.

Black Dwarf: A black dwarf constitutes the remains of a Sun-sized star which has evolved to a white dwarf and subsequently cooled down such that it no longer emits light.

Black Hole: Any object where gravity is so strong that not even light can escape from its surface.

Bonding Molecular Orbitals: Molecular orbitals that have high electron probability between atomic nuclei in a molecule. When bonding molecular orbitals are occupied by electrons, the high electron density between the nuclei helps hold the nuclei together, contributing to a bond between the atoms.

Brown Dwarf: An object that is like a star except for the fact that it is too small to sustain fusion reactions in its core.

Brownian Motion: The constant, irregular motion of very fine particles (such as fine dust or smoke) suspended in a fluid and observed with a microscope. Brownian Motion is taken as evidence for molecules, which collide with the observed particles and cause the jittery motion.

Buoyant Force: A force pushing upward on objects immersed in a fluid.

— C —

Calcite: A mineral that is usually the main component of limestone. Calcite has the chemical formula $CaCO_3$.

Catalyst: A chemical whose presence increases the rate of a chemical reaction without being consumed by the reaction. Catalysts make the energy and/or entropy of the transition state more favorable, without affecting the energies or entropies of the initial reactants or final products.

Cations: Atoms, or groups of atoms bound together, that have a net positive charge. In a cation, the number of electrons is less than the number of protons in the atom or group of atoms.

Causality: Cause must always precede the effect.

Centrifugal Force: The force, required by the Third Law, of an object pushing back against the centripetal force.

Centripetal Acceleration: The acceleration of turning or changing the direction of motion.

Centripetal Force: A force sideways to the motion of an object. Centripetal forces cause objects to turn toward the center of a circle.

Cepheid Variables: A type of pulsating variable star that changes brightness in a regular and predictable manner. The changes in brightness are directly related to observed changes in the size and temperature of the variable stars.

Chain Reaction: A chain reaction is one that is self sustaining or increasing once it has started. Dominoes knocking each other over is a classic example of a chain reaction.

Chemical Bond: The attractive force between nuclei and electrons that hold atoms together in molecules or atoms and ions together in network substances.

Chemical Formula: Way to represent the the kind of atom and its number in a molecule. The chemical formula of a water molecule that contains two hydrogen atoms and one oxygen atom is given by H_2O. The subscript to the right of the atomic symbol indicates the number of that kind of atom in the molecule.

Chemical Potential Energy: The form of internal energy associated with the physical and chemical states of matter. The type of energy stored in a car battery.

Chemical Properties: Properties associated with the chemical reactivity of a material. Some examples: Does an substance combine with oxygen or react with water?

Chemistry: Chemistry is the discipline in which the interactions of atoms with each other are studied.

Cluster of Galaxies: A group of galaxies that is gravitationally bound together into a cluster, which vary greatly in size. A small cluster may have just a few members, while a large cluster may have several thousand.

Comet: A small body composed of ice and dust that orbits our Sun. As a comet comes close to our Sun, some of the material is vaporized and a tail forms opposite the direction of the motion of the comet.

Compounds: Matter that contains two or more atoms in a fixed, definite proportion. New compounds form when the relative proportions of atoms change.

Compression Force: A force that is applied in such a way as to compress a material.

Conduction: The transmission of an electric charge or heat through a conducting medium without perceptible motion of the medium itself.

Conduction Band: The range of electron energy, higher than that of the valence band, sufficient to make the electrons free to accelerate under the influence of an applied electric field and thus constitute an electric current.

Conductor: A material that allows electrons to flow through it.

Connectivity: The details of how atoms connect to one another in molecules or extended structures.

Conserved Quantity: Unchanging in time. A quantity is "conserved" if the amount of that quantity does not change in time, even though processes may be changing its form.

Constructive Interference: When two or more waves passing through the same space at the same time both disturb the medium in the same way so that the resultant amplitude is larger than the amplitude of each individual wave separately.

Contact Force: The force arising between objects when they touch. Contact forces are a repulsion caused by the electromagnetic interaction.

Continent: The granite part of the earth's crust. The continent is divided into three major structural parts: shield, stable platform, and folded mountain belts.

Continental Accretion: The process by which continents grow. When continents collide with island arcs or with other continents, new material may be added and the continent grows.

Continental Shelf: Part of the continent that is under a shallow cover of water.

Continental Shields: The oldest parts of the continents. They represent the roots of very ancient mountains, long since eroded away.

Continental Slope: The boundary between the continents and the ocean basins. It marks a distinct change in the composition of the rocks near Earth's surface.

Continuous Spectrum: A spectrum in which the colors blend gradually together without noticeably abrupt changes or missing colors.

Convection: The process by which energy is moved from one place to another by being stored in matter as internal energy, then moving the matter from one place to another.

Core: The deepest or central compositional layer of Earth. It is composed mostly of iron.

Cosmic Microwave Background: A uniform radiant field with an apparent temperature of 2.725 K that is observable in every direction.

Cosmological Constant: A constant introduced into the equations of general relativity by Albert Einstein in an attempt to cancel the predictions of the expanding nature of our Universe.

Cosmological Principle : The concept that the large-scale structures of our Universe are the same no matter what direction you observe or where you are located.

Coulomb: The unit of measure for charge. Named after Charles Augustin de

Coulomb, formulator of the Electric Force Law. The amount of electric charge possessed by a single electron or a proton is 1.6 x 10⁻¹⁹ coulombs.

Covalent: Materials characterized by chemical bonds that involve sharing electrons. Typically, the bonds in covalent substances occur between non-metal atoms.

Covalent Bonding: Bonding between atoms accomplished by sharing electrons to achieve low-energy arrangement of the electrons between the nuclei.

Crest: The part of a wave where the particles are displaced a maximum amount above or in front of their equilibrium position.

Critical Mass: The minimum amount of material necessary for each fission to result in one additional fission.

Crust: The uppermost compositional layer of Earth. It is very thin and composed of two parts: granitic continental crust and basaltic oceanic crust.

Crystal: A solid with a regular repeating arrangement of molecules or ions.

Crystalline : Crystalline matter is solid matter in which the constituent atoms or molecules are arranged in an orderly, repetitive pattern. For example, a crystal of sodium chloride has the regular pattern that every Na+ ion is surrounded by six Cl− ions and every Cl− ion is surrounded by six Na+ ions.

Curie Temperature: The temperature at which a material loses its magnetism.

— **D** —

Dark Nebula: A cold cloud of dust and gas that blocks the light from background stars.

Deceleration: Acceleration against the direction of motion.

Delocalized Electrons: Electrons in metallic orbitals are not confined to be near a specific nucleus, but have comparable probabilities of being around many different nuclei.

Dense Oxides: Minerals that form deep in the Earth's mantle due to the enormous pressures.

Density: An object's mass divided by its volume.

Desert Pavements: A desert pavement is a surface of pebbles and cobbles created by the removal of all of the finer grains by wind.

Desertification: The process of converting marginal dry lands into desert by overgrazing, farming, or other processes.

Destructive Interference: When two or more waves passing through the same space at the same time both disturb the medium in opposite ways so that the resultant amplitude is smaller than the amplitude of each individual wave separately.

Diatomic Molecule: A molecule containing only two atoms of the same kind of element. Hydrogen, nitrogen, oxygen, fluorine, chlorine, bromine, and iodine exist in nature as diatomic molecules.

Diffraction: The changing of direction of waves to bend around corners and spread as they encounter obstacles.

Dipole: The separation of positive and negative charge in a polar bond or molecule.

Direct Current: A steady flow of electrons in one direction through a wire.

Discrete Spectra: A spectrum of separate and distinct colors in which not all colors are present.

Dispersion Forces: Weak intermolecular attraction arising from the formation of temporary dipoles in non-polar molecules. Also known as Van der Waals forces.

Distance Ladder: A method used in astronomy where greater and greater distances are determined using many different measuring techniques that overlap to establish a sequence of increasing distances.

Domain: A small section in a magnet where the magnetic force from all the atoms add together.

Doppler Effect: A change in the observed frequency of a wave occurring when the source and observer are in motion relative to each other.

Double Bond: A covalent bond involving two pairs of electrons shared between the two bound atoms. In chemical structure drawings, double bonds are represented by double lines.

Double Bond: Atoms connected by two bonds. Double bonds usually involve four electrons, two per bond.

Dwarf Elliptical Galaxy : A small elliptical galaxy with only a few million stars.

— **E** —

Eccentricity : A measure of how elliptical the Earth's orbit is. Higher eccentricity means a more elliptical, less circular orbit.

Elastic Potential Energy: The form of internal energy associated with stretching or compressing material.

Elastic Rebound: The point at which stress in Earth's lithosphere is strained to a point where it can bend no further and the lithosphere ruptures and rebounds somewhat like a rubber band that has just been pulled apart.

Electric Current: Electric charges flowing through a conductor.

Electric Force Constant: A number relating the strength of the electric force to the charges involved and their distance apart.

Electric Force Law: The mathematical formula F=kqQ/d² which describes the strength of the force between two objects of charge Q and q separated between their centers by the distance d.

Electrical Conductivity: A measure of the degree to which a substance conducts an electrical current.

Electrical Potential Energy: The form of energy associated with the relative positions of charged objects. Objects with opposite charges have maximum electrical potential energy when they are separated by greatest distance, but objects with the same charge have maximum electrical potential energy.

Electrolytes: A chemical compound that ionizes when dissolved in water to produce an electrically conductive medium.

Electromagnetic Interaction: The interaction between charged objects that gives rise to the electromagnetic force.

Electromagnetic Radiation: Radiation originating in a varying electromagnetic field, such as visible light, radio waves, x-rays, and gamma rays.

Electromagnetic Spectrum: The entire range of radiation including, in order of decreasing frequency, cosmic-ray photons, gamma rays, x-rays, ultraviolet radiation, visible light, infrared radiation, microwaves, and radio waves.

Electron: An elementary particle in atoms having a negative charge. Electrons are located outside atomic nuclei.

Electron Configuration Diagram: An enumeration of how electrons populate atomic orbitals that is consistent with the "lowest-energy filled first" and "exclusion" principles.

Electron Volt: A small amount of energy used to measure energies of particles in atoms and nuclei. It is equal to 1.6 x 10⁻¹⁹ joules.

Electronegativity: A measure of how strongly atoms attract electrons. Both ionization energy (the energy required to remove an electron from a neutral atom) and electron affinity (the energy gained when an electron is added to a neutral atom) contribute to electronegativity. Electronegativity increases from left to right across rows and decreases down columns of the Periodic Table.

Element: A substance composed of atoms which have an identical number of protons in each nucleus. Elements cannot be reduced to simpler substances by normal chemical means.

Elliptical Galaxy : A galaxy with an elliptical shape and little dust or gas.

Emission Nebula: A gaseous cloud that is glowing from the energy radiated by nearby hot stars.

Emission Spectrum: An emission spectrum is the set of colors of light given off, or emitted by, an object.

Entropy: A quantitative measure of disorder. It increases as the disorder increases. It can be calculated mathematically from the probability of obtaining the system in its current state.

Enzymes: Protein molecules that function as catalysts in biochemical reactions.

Epicenter: The point on Earth's surface directly above the focus of an earthquake.

Equilibrium: The condition where the forward and reverse rates of a chemical reaction are equal, so the system experiences no net change. Equilibrium is also the state of most favorable energy and entropy for a chemical system.

Equilibrium Position: The place where a molecule will reside when no unbalanced forces are acting upon it.

Eras: The largest subdivision of geologic time.

Event: Something that has happened in the Earth's history. Some examples might be the eruption of a volcano, the building of a mountain range, the deposition of sedimentary layers in the ocean, or the metamorphosis of rocks because of changes in pressure and temperature.

Excited States: Electronic states with quantum number n greater than 1.

Exclusion Principle: The rule that two electrons cannot be in exactly the same state in an atom. In other words, no two electrons in the same atom can have exactly the same shell, orbital, and spin values.

Existence: The fact or state of having actual or real being.

— F —

Families or Groups of Elements: Elements that were grouped together because they had very similar chemical properties and are now known to have the same number of valence electrons. An element family occupies a vertical column in the Periodic Table.

Fats and Oils: Fats and oils are substances that do not dissolve in water, but can dissolve in hydrocarbon liquids. Fats are solid at room temperature; oils are liquid at room temperature.

Fatty Acids: A molecule with a long hydrocarbon tail and an acid group –COOH at the other end.

Fault: A break in the Earth where rocks on one side of the break have slipped past the rocks on the other side. Faults are created by earthquakes.

Feldspar: The name of a family of silicate minerals that are the most abundant minerals in the Earth's crust.

Ferromagnetism: Metal alloys that are attracted to magnets or are capable of being transformed into a permanent magnet are called ferromagnetic.

Field Lines: Lines coming from an object representing the strength of the force. The denser the lines, the stronger the force.

Fission: A nuclear reaction in which an atomic nucleus, especially a heavy nucleus such as an isotope of uranium, splits into two fragments of comparable mass, releasing energy.

Fission-track Dating: A type of radioactive decay clock that uses the trails or tracks created by uranium fission decay to determine the age of geologic events.

Floodplain: A relatively flat region around a river where rich sediment has been deposited by the river's floods.

Fluid: Anything that flows. This refers to gases such as air and liquids such as water.

Focus: (plural–foci)The focus of an earthquake is the point within Earth where an earthquake starts. The focal depth is the depth from the surface of Earth down to the focus.

Force: A push or pull on an object.

Freefall: The act of always falling under the pure influence of gravity.

Frequency: The number of wave amplitude crests that pass a particular point in space every second.

Fusion: A nuclear reaction in which nuclei combine to form more massive nuclei with the simultaneous release of energy.

— G —

g: The symbol representing the acceleration caused by gravity. It is equal to 22 mi/hour per second or 32 ft/second per second or 9.8 m/sec per second depending on the units.

Gabbro: An igneous plutonic rock made of the same minerals as basalt, but, because the minerals cooled slowly underground, they are coarse-grained.

Galaxy: A large collection of stars, dust, and gas that is found in a wide variety of sizes ranging from a few million solar masses for a small galaxy to large galaxies with more than a trillion solar masses of material.

Galilean Relativity: The notion that a final speed vector can be computed by directly adding all individual velocity vectors together according to the rules of Euclidean geometry.

Gas: A physical state of matter that readily changes both shape and volume to match its container.

Gedanken Experiment: A situation of logic contrived to illustrate a particular effect.

General Theory of Relativity: Albert Einstein's description of gravity that was published in 1915. This theory explains the relationship between the geometry of space and the flow of time in our Universe.

Geologic Column : A chart that shows the subdivisions of geologic time.

Giant Elliptical Galaxy : A large elliptical galaxy that may contain more than a trillion stars.

Glossopteris Flora: The Glossopteridales are an extinct group of seed plants that arose during the Permian Period. These plants went on to become a dominant part of the flora on the southern part of the supercontinent Pangaea through the rest of the Permian, though they dwindled to extinction by the end of the Triassic Period.

Gneiss: A banded or foliated metamorphic rock, usually of the same composition as granite.

Granite: An igneous plutonic rock that is made mostly of quartz along with sodium and potassium-rich feldspar.

Gravitational Constant: A number relating the strength of the gravitational force to the masses being attracted and their distance apart.

Gravitational Potential Energy: The energy stored in an object that has the potential to fall. Near the surface of the earth, the increase of gravitational potential energy of an object that is lifted is given by GPE = weight x height.

Gravity: The interaction between anything with mass that gives rise to the gravitational force.

Greenhouse Gases: Gases in the atmosphere that trap heat and keep the Earth warmer than it would otherwise be, just like the glass in a greenhouse traps heat inside the greenhouse.

Guyots: Flat-topped seamounts that once were above the surface of the ocean, but have now subsided below it.

— H —

H-R Diagram: A plot used for individual stars where luminosity is plotted on the y-axis and surface temperature is plotted on the x-axis.

Half-life: The time required for half the nuclei in a sample of a specific isotopic species to undergo radioactive decay.

Heat: That portion of internal energy that is associated with the kinetic energy of molecules.

Heisenberg Uncertainty Principle: The product of the uncertainty in an object's position and the uncertainty in its momentum must be greater than or equal to Planck's Constant.

Hot Spots: Volcanoes that result from the lithosphere moving over a mantle plume. Hawaii is an example of an island-formed hot spot. As the plate moves over the mantle, a line of volcanic structures (such as the Hawaiian chain of islands) marks the passage. The trail of volcanism is called a hot-spot trail.

Hubble Constant : A constant that is part of the Hubble Law; it gives the rate at which our Universe is expanding.

Hubble Law : An observed relation between the observed recessional velocity of a galaxy and the distance to that galaxy.

Hydrocarbon Molecules: Molecules that contain only carbon and hydrogen atoms. The compounds that make up gasoline are examples.

Hydrogen Bonding: Interactions between hydrogen atoms bound to oxygen, nitrogen, or fluorine with other oxygen, nitrogen, or fluorine atoms. Hydrogen bonds are among the strongest intermolecular interactions.

Hypothesis: A tentative explanation for an observation, phenomenon, or scientific problem that can be tested by further investigation.

— I —

Ice Age: A time in Earth's history when conditions are such that large continental glaciers can form and grow.

Igneous Rock: Rocks that have been formed by solidification from a molten state.

Impact Breccias: Rocks that have been formed as other rocks have been broken apart, mixed, and then fused together during a series of meteoroid impacts. Impact breccias are rare on Earth but common on the surface of our Moon.

Inertia: The tendency to resist changing a state of motion.

Inertial Frame of Reference: A place of being that is experiencing no acceleration. The laws of nature are the same when looking at the universe from an inertial frame of reference.

Inner Core: The lower part of the core that is made of solid iron.

Insulator: A material that does not permit electrons to flow through it.

Interaction: Any of four fundamental ways in which elementary particles and bodies can influence each other.

Interference: The canceling and enhancing effect that occurs when two waves move through the same space at the same time.

Intermolecular: Between molecules (as opposed to intramolecular, within molecules).

Internal Energy: A name given to energy hidden within matter but manifest by the temperature of the matter, the shape of the matter, the physical state of the matter (solid, liquid, gas), the chemical composition of the matter (i.e., the kind of energy that might be released).

Interstellar Medium: Gas and dust found in the space between stars.

Intuition: The act or faculty of knowing or sensing without the use of rational processes; immediate cognition.

Ionic Bonding: The model used to explain the bonding in ionic compounds. Metal atoms lose electrons, forming positive ions. Non-metal atoms gain electrons forming negative ions. In the salt, positive metal ions are surrounded by negative non-metal ions, and vice versa. Because electrostatic forces are strong and long-range, each ion experiences attractive interactions with many ions of the other type. The extended interactions give rise to the high melting points.

Ionic Compound: A compound formed between a metal and a non-metal. Ionic compounds are crystalline solids at room temperature. They conduct electricity when molten or dissolved in water.

Ionic Conductors: Materials that do not conduct electricity in the solid state, but do when molten or dissolved in water.

Ionization Energy: The amount of energy needed to completely remove an electron from an atom. The energy need to remove the first electron from a neutral atom varies periodically with atomic number.

Iron Meteorites: Meteorites thought to represent the type of material found in Earth's core.

Irregular Galaxy: A non-symmetric galaxy that does not have a well-defined shape like either the spiral or elliptical galaxies. Irregular galaxies generally include dust, gas, and active star-forming regions.

Irreversible: An irreversible process is one which goes in only one direction; its effects often cannot be undone. Most processes which occur in nature are irreversible.

Island Arcs: Arc-shaped chains of volcanoes that are always found associated with an ocean trench.

Isostasy: Equilibrium in the earth's crust such that the buoyant forces elevating landmasses balance the gravitational forces that depress them.

Isotope: An isotope is determined by the number of neutrons: the atomic mass number minus the atomic number.

— J —

Jovian Worlds: The gas giant planets, which include Jupiter, Saturn, Uranus, and Neptune.

Junction: The interface between two different semiconductor regions in a semiconductor device.

— K —

Kinetic Energy: The form of energy associated with motion. The kinetic energy of an object in motion is given by KE = $\frac{1}{2}$mass × speed^2.

— L —

Laser Ranging: A technique for measuring distance that is similar to radar ranging but instead of reflecting microwaves, laser light is reflected off of a nearby surface and the time for the reflected pulse is observed.

Law: A well-tested theory, so firm as to be unquestioned by science.

Law of Constant Composition: Substances contain a fixed, definite proportion of elements by mass.

Law of Gravity: The mathematical formula F=GmM/d^2 which describes the strength of the force of gravity between two objects of mass M and m separated between their centers by the distance d.

Law of Increasing Disorder: Changes occurring in natural systems always proceed in such a way that the total amount of disorder in the universe is either unchanged or increased. If total disorder is increased, the process is irreversible.

Length Contraction: The shortening of an object along its direction of motion as its speed approaches the speed of light, as measured by an observer not moving with the object.

Levees: Broad embankments built up along the banks of a river channel. These may be naturally created by floods or they can be artificially constructed to keep a river in its banks.

Limestone: A sedimentary rock usually formed from the precipitation of the mineral calcite in the ocean.

Linear Momentum: An object's mass times its velocity. Measures the amount of motion in a straight line.

Liquid: A physical state of matter that readily changes shape to match its container but that resists changes in volume.

Lithosphere: The rigid outer shell of Earth, which consists of the crust and the outermost part of the mantle that is too cool to be partially molten. It is brittle and is the only layer in which earthquakes can occur.

Local Group : A small group of about two dozen galaxies that is associated with our Milky Way.

Longitudinal Wave: A wave in which the molecules of the medium vibrate in the same direction as the wave propagates.

Low Velocity Zone: A region of the upper mantle where seismic waves travel slower than expected.

Luminosity: Roughly equal to brightness or the rate at which energy is radiated from an object.

Lunar Highlands: The old, heavily cratered terrain on our Moon that is thought to contain material from the original lunar surface.

Lystrosaurus: Lystrosaurus was a sturdily built, plant-eating reptile (not a dinosaur). Scientists disagree on whether it spent most of its time in water browsing on plants like a modern hippo, or whether it lived mostly on land. An adult would have been about 3 feet long and weighed about 200 pounds.

— M —

Macroscopic Kinetic Energy: The kinetic energy possessed by moving objects given by 1/2mass x (speed)^2.

Magma: Hot, liquid rock. It is called lava when it erupts onto the Earth's surface.

Magnetite: An iron oxide mineral found in basalt. The magnetic field of the magnetite aligns with Earth's magnetic field as molten basalt cools to solid form and makes a permanent record of the direction of Earth's magnetic field when the rock formed.

Magnitude Scale: A measure of the size of an earthquake. The first widely used magnitude scale was developed by Richter and was called the "Richter Scale." Today the most widely used scale is called the "moment magnitude scale." All of these scales have one thing in common: they are non-linear logarithmic scales. As you increase the magnitude from, for example, a 7.0 to an 8.0, the amount of energy released goes up by 30 times.

Main Group: The set of metal and non-metal elements designated with A column headings. They have valence electron configurations involving only s and p electrons.

Main Sequence: A line of stars that runs diagonally from the upper left corner to the lower right corner of the H-R diagram. Stars on the main sequence are generating energy from hydrogen fusion in their cores.

Malleability: The characteristic of substances that allows them to be worked into desirable shapes or drawn out into wires.

Mantle: The middle compositional layer of Earth. It is a thick layer made up of peridotite in the upper part and higher density rocks of peridotite composition in the lower part.

Mantle Plume: A buoyant mass of hot rock rising through the Earth's mantle. As it nears the surface of the Earth some of the plume melts and erupts at the surface forming a "hot spot."

Mantle Resistance, Plate Collision, and Transform Fault Friction: Forces that resist plate motion.

Marble: Metamorphosed limestone.

Mare Basalt: A common igneous rock found in abundance on the lunar lava plains.

Maria: The large, generally crater-free lava plains commonly found on the side of our Moon that faces Earth.

Mass: A measure of how a body resists accelerating.

Maxwell's Equations: A set of four fundamental laws, expressed in mathematical form, than govern electricity and magnetism and their interrelationship. The Electrical Force Law is included in Maxwell's Equations.

Mechanical Wave: A vibration in material that transports energy.

Mesosaurus: Mesosaurus was a fresh-water dwelling reptile that lived from the late Pennsylvanian Period to the early Permian Period. It had an elongated head and snout with nostrils near its eyes and a flattened tail used for swimming. Typically it would have been about 1.5 feet long.

Mesosphere: A term we use here to describe the mechanical layer between the asthenosphere and the outer core. It is solid, but still plastic and able to flow.

Metallic Bond: The chemical bond that binds metal atoms to other metal atoms in forming metal substances.

Metals: Elements that are good electrical and thermal conductors and can be hammered into thin sheets or drawn into fine wires.

Metamorphic Rock: Rocks that have been subjected to intense heat and pressure that cause the minerals in them to undergo chemical reactions, forming a "new" rock.

Meteoroid: A small rock found in the space between the planets.

Microscopic Kinetic Energy: The kinetic energy associated with atomic and molecular motions. A stationary object can have microscopic but not macroscopic kinetic energy.

Milky Way: The galaxy of over a hundred billion solar masses to which our Sun belongs. As we observe it in the night sky, it refers to the faint band of light that marks the disk of our Galaxy.

Mineral: A naturally occurring, inorganic solid that has a specific chemical formula.

Mixtures: Matter that contains multiple substances. Many mixtures can be physically separated into their pure components.

Model: A schematic description of a system, theory, or phenomenon that accounts for its known or inferred properties and may be used for further study of its characteristics.

Modified Solar System Model: The Bohr model with restricted circular orbits of electrons around a dense nucleus.

Moho: The seismic discontinuity at the base of the Earth's crust.

Molecular Ions: Groups of atoms covalently bound to each other that have a net charge because electrons have been lost or gained to facilitate formation of the covalent bonds. Also called polyatomic ions.

Molecular Model: The essential defining characteristics of the Molecular Model are: 1. Matter consists of tiny particles called molecules. 2. Each different kind of matter consists of a different kind of molecule. 3. The molecules in matter are in constant motion. 4. Molecules move and interact in accord with laws of motion, the laws of force and the laws of conservation.

Molecular Orbitals: Standing electron probability waves for molecules. These standing wave shapes and sizes are different from those for individual atoms because of the multiple atomic nuclei.

Molecular Substances: Matter that exists as molecules in the solid, liquid, and gaseous states.

Molecule: The smallest unit into which matter can be divided without loosing its chemical properties.

Monounsaturated Fats: Mono = 1 in Greek. Fats containing fatty acids with a single double bond, such as oleic acid.

Mountain Belts: Regions of the continents where the rocks have been highly deformed by enormous forces. These belts usually lie along the edges of the continents.

— N —

Net Force: The sum of all the forces present on a body.

Network or Extended-Bonding Substances: Substances in which every atom or ion interacts strongly with many neighbors. An extended network of linked atoms or ions form. Distinct molecules or ion pairs do not exist in these materials.

Neutron: A composite, strongly-interacting particle made up of three quarks, but which carries no net electrical charge. Neutrons are a constituent part of the nucleus of atoms.

Neutron Star: The remnant of a supernova explosion that is composed almost totally of neutrons. It is so dense that the entire mass of our Sun could be contained in a sphere only a few tens of kilometers in diameter.

Noble Gases: Gaseous elements in the rightmost column of the periodic table (helium, neon, argon, krypton, xenon, and radon) that exist in nature as individual atoms. They are quite unreactive and are very unlikely to form chemical compounds.

Node: The part of a wave where the particles are at their equilibrium position. A location of no vibration in a standing wave.

Non-conductor: An image of iron atoms deposited on a layer of copper atoms spelling the word "atom" in Japanese. The copper atoms are only visible as the ripples in the blue background.

Non-inertial Frame of Reference: A place of being that is undergoing an acceleration.

Non-Metals: Elements that do not conduct electricity.

Nuclear Fusion: The process by which elements heavier than hydrogen are formed by adding protons and neutrons to existing atomic nuclei.

Nuclear Potential Energy: The energy stored in the nucleus of an atom.

Nuclear Strong Force Law: F = ? Scientists are still trying to figure out what the equation for the strong force looks like. Compare this with the Electric Force Law equation: $F = kqQ/d^2$. The electromagnetic force pushes the protons in the nucleus apart.

Nucleon: A generic name for either a proton or a neutron.

Nucleus: The atomic nucleus is the very dense, positively charged center of the atom.

— O —

Occam's Razor: The rule that where two or more explanations exist for the same physical phenomenon, we should choose the simplest one that satisfies all of the observations.

Oceanic Ridge: Mountain ranges that are under the oceans. They form very long mountain chains that essentially encircle Earth.

Octet Rule: An atom will most likely form an ion that has the ns^2np^6 configuration of the closest noble gas atom.

Olbers's Paradox: A fundamental question in cosmology centered around the observed fact that the sky appears dark at night.

Opacity: The opposite of being transparent. Visible light is absorbed by an opaque object.

Orbital: A standing wave giving the probability of finding an electron in various locations around the nucleus of an atom.

Organic Acid: A molecule that contains the fragment CO_2H attached to another carbon atom.

Organic Molecules: Molecules that have a central framework of carbon atoms. Originally, it was thought that organic molecules could only be produced in living organisms, hence the name. Now it is clear that the molecules can be produced abiologically.

Outer Core: The upper part of the core that is made of liquid iron.

— P —

P-Waves: Compressional waves produced by an earthquake. They travel the fastest in Earth and so are the first to arrive at any seismic wave detectors.

Paleoclimatology: Paleoclimatology is the study of ancient climates.

Paleomagnetism: Magnetism preserved or fossilized in rocks. It can often tell us about changes in the orientation of rock bodies after their formation.

Paleontologists: Scientists who study ancient life preserved as fossils in the rocks.

Pangaea: The name Alfred Wegner gave to the large continental mass that existed before the continents began to drift apart about 200 million years ago.

Parent & Daughter Isotopes: The result of radioactive decay, in which one element decays to form another element. The element we start with is called the parent and the new element formed in the decay process is called the daughter.

Period: A subdivision of geologic time. Smaller than an era, but still several 10's of millions of years long.

Period–brightness Relation : A simple physical relationship that has been found for certain types of pulsating variable stars (including Cepheids) that indicates that the actual brightness of a pulsating star can be determined from a measurement of its pulsation period.

Periodic Law: The properties of the elements are a periodic function of their atomic masses.

Peridotite: A rock made up mostly silicon, oxygen, iron, and magnesium that is denser than the basalt and granite that make up Earth's crust.

Periods: Horizontal rows in the periodic table within which physical and chemical properties change systematically.

Permeability: A measure of the connectedness of the porosity in a rock.

Perpetual Motion Machine: A perpetual motion machine is something that keeps moving forever without any energy being added.

pH: A logarithmic measure of the concentration of hydronium (H_3O^+) ions in water. pH values less than 7 describe acidic solutions, pH = 7 is neutral (that is, the pH of pure water is 7), and pH values greater than 7 indicate the solution is basic.

Photoelectric Effect: The ejection of electrons from metals when light is shined on the metal's surface.

Photon: A particle of light. It is characterized by energy, frequency, and wavelength. It has neither mass nor charge.

Photosphere: The visible surface of our Sun or another star. This is the region where visible energy is radiated into space.

Physical Properties: Properties like melting or boiling temperature, density, ionization potential.

Planck's Constant: A value when multiplied by the frequency of light, gives the energy of the photon of light at that frequency.

Planetary Nebula: A glowing shell of gas that has been blown off an old star.

Plasma: A physical state of matter characterized by fluid properties but in which positive and negative charges move independently.

Plutonic Rocks: Igneous rocks that solidify underground.

Polar: Bonds or molecules having an unequal distribution of charge (one end being positive, the other negative).

Polyunsaturated Fats: Poly = many in Greek. Fats containing fatty acids with many double bonds, such as linolenic or arachidonic acid.

Porosity: The amount of open space found in a rock.

Position Symmetry: The laws of the universe are not different at different locations.

Potential Energy: Energy that depends on the position of an object or on the positions of an object's constituent parts.

Potential Energy Surface: A diagram plotting the total energy of reactants and products as a function of the "completeness" of a chemical reaction. For all but the simplest reactions, these are multidimensional hypersurfaces that are difficult to visualize.

Pressure: The force on an object divided by the area over which the force is applied.

Principle of Noncontradiction: Of two contradictory propositions, both cannot be true.

Probability Curve: A curve giving the probability of where an object might be detected. The particle is likely to be found where the curve is high and unlikely to be found where the curve is low.

Probability Wave: A probability curve that moves in time. At a given moment in time, the places where the wave is high are where the object associated with the wave is most likely to be found.

Products: Material(s) produced in a chemical reaction, written on the right-hand side of a chemical equation.

Proton: A composite, strongly interacting particle made up of three quarks. The proton carries a positive electrical charge and is a constituent part of the nucleus of atoms.

Protostar: An object that will become a star in the early stages of formation before it begins to produce energy from fusion.

Pulsar: A variable radio source that is thought to be a rapidly rotating neutron star.

Pure Substance: Chemical matter that has a defined, unchanging chemical composition.

— Q —

Quantum Mechanics: The branch of physics used to describe the wave properties of light and matter.

Quark: The elementary particles of which protons and neutrons consist. A proton and a neutron each consist of three quarks.

Quartz: A common mineral that has a chemical formula of SiO_2.

Quartzite: A metamorphic rock composed of sand grains that have been welded tightly together, unlike sandstone where the sand grains rub off in your hand.

Quasar : A luminous galaxy with a large redshift and star-like appearance when viewed through a telescope.

— R —

Radar Ranging: A technique for measuring distance where pulses of microwaves (radar) traveling at the speed of light are sent to a nearby object and the reflected pulse is timed in order to determine the distance.

Radial Shape: A cross section of what an orbital would look like if it were sliced in two.

Radiation: The process by which energy is moved from one place to another in the form of light or related forms such as X-rays, gamma rays, microwaves, etc.

Radioactive: A term referring to atoms whose nuclei can spontaneously change under the influence of the weak nuclear force.

Radioactive Decay: Spontaneous disintegration of a radionuclide accompanied by the emission of ionizing radiation in the form of alpha or beta particles or gamma rays.

Rate of Reaction: The speed at which reactants are consumed and products are produced in a chemical reaction per unit time.

Reactants: The starting material(s) in a chemical reaction, written on the left-hand side of a chemical equation.

Reason: The capacity for logical, rational, and analytic thought; intelligence.

Red Giant: A large, bright, cool star that has exhausted most of the hydrogen fuel in its core.

Reflection: The act of bouncing off a surface.

Reflectivity: The characteristic of being capable of or producing reflection.

Refraction: The act of changing direction when passing from one medium to another.

Relative Time: The determination of the sequence in which events occurred, relative to each other.

Relativity: The idea that motion is only defined relative to other objects, which may have their own motion. There is no such thing as an "absolute" motion measured against objects that are absolutely at rest.

Resistivity: The capacity for or tendency toward electrical resistance.

Resonance: The creation of an amplitude of oscillation in a system exposed to a periodic infusion of energy.

Reversible: A reversible process goes both forward and backward at the same time. Reversible processes are relatively rare in nature.

Rhyolite: A volcanic rock that has the same composition as a granite, but has erupted and cooled at the surface, rather than underground.

Ridge Push: Helps move the Earth's plates. The ridge is high and has gravitational potential energy which is converted into kinetic energy as the plate moves.

Rift Valley: A long, linear depression that commonly forms along a divergent plate boundary as two plates pull apart.

— S —

S-Waves: Shear waves produced by an earthquake. They are slower than P-waves and so arrive later at seismic wave detectors.

Salts: An other name for ionic compounds.

Sandstone: A sedimentary rock made up mostly of grains of sand.

Saturated Fat: A triglyceride containing three saturated fatty acid molecules.

Seafloor Spreading: The theory that the ocean floor grows on either side as the mid-ocean ridge moves apart. The rift created in this process is filled in with basalt as magma squeezes up into the fractures created by rifting.

Seamounts: An underwater mountain rising from the ocean floor and having a peaked or flat-topped summit below the surface of the sea.

Sedimentary Rock: Rocks formed by the deposition of sediment.

Seismic Discontinuity: A place where the velocities of seismic waves change abruptly.

Seismic Waves: Waves produced by earthquakes.

Seismograph or Seismometer: A seismic wave detector.

Self-ionization: The reaction of certain neutral molecules (such as water) with other identical molecules to produce cations and anions.

Semiconductors: A solid crystalline substance, such as germanium or silicon, that conducts electricity better than insulators, but not as well as metals. Unlike metals, they become better conductors as their temperature increases.

Sensory Data: Knowledge obtained through the senses.

Shadow Zone: A region of the Earth where seismic waves cannot be detected by seismometers.

Shale: A sedimentary rock made up of fine particles of clay and mud.

Shear Force: A force that is applied in such a way as to twist or deform a material.

Shell: A group of orbitals having similar energies and sizes.

Silicates: Minerals that contain silicon and oxygen bonded together.

Siltstone: A sedimentary rock made up mostly of grains of silt (smaller than sand size particles, but still gritty, not smooth like clay or mud).

Single Bond: A covalent bond involving one pair of electrons shared between the two bound atoms. In chemical structure drawings, single bonds are represented by single lines.

Sink Hole: A depression created at the Earth's surface when an underground cavern collapses.

Slab Pull: Helps move the tectonic plates. As an oceanic plate becomes old, cold, and dense, it sinks back into the mantle, pulling the rest of the plate along with it.

Slate: Metamorphosed shale. It still breaks into thin layers like shale, but the layers are much harder and more durable. In fact, slate is hard enough to use for roofing tile.

Solar System: The sun and all planets, comets, asteroids, and other bodies that orbit about it under the pull of gravity.

Solar System Model: A model of the atom in which the electrons orbit the small, dense, positively-charged nucleus in elliptical paths. The model proposed by Rutherford.

Solid: A physical state of matter that is characterized by rigidity and resistance to changes in size and shape.

Solutions: A liquid mixture containing two or more compounds.

Solvent: A material (typically a liquid) in which another material dissolves.

Special Principle of Relativity: Another name for motion symmetry.

Special Theory of Relativity: The theory of how objects in inertial frames of reference behave at high speeds.

Spectroscopy: The study of the brightness and wavelengths of the different frequencies of light emitted by excited atoms and ions.

Spin: A characteristic of an electron, giving the direction of its intrinsic magnetic field.

Spiral Galaxy : A galaxy flattened into a disk shape with a pattern of spiral arms wound about a central nucleus. Spiral galaxies usually include dust, gas, and active regions of star formation.

Stable Platform or Covered Shield: An area of the continent where the old rocks of the shield have been covered by relatively flat-lying sedimentary rocks.

Standing Wave: A wave characterized by lack of vibration at certain points, between which areas of maximum vibration occur.

Star Cluster: A group of stars that formed from the same cloud of material and have been held together in a cluster by gravitational forces. A small open cluster can consist of only a few dozen members while a large globular cluster can contain more than a million individual stars.

State of Motion: The condition of an object when no unbalanced forces act upon it. A state of motion always refers to being at rest or in uniform motion.

Stony Achondrites: Meteorites thought to represent material from small planetary bodies that had differentiated into layers and then were broken up.

Stony Chondrites: Meteorites thought to represent the primitive material from which the planets were made.

Strong Nuclear Interaction: The interaction between nucleons that gives rise to the strong force.

Structural trends: Structural trends are the orientations of major geologic features such as mountain belts, continental shields, stable platforms, and areas of folded and deformed rocks.

Subduction: What geologists call the process that occurs at the trenches where old oceanic lithosphere is sinking back into the mantle. The trench area is also called a "subduction zone" and as the plates sink, they are said to be subducting.

Supercluster: Clusters of clusters of galaxies. It appears uncommon for these groups of clusters to be held together by gravity.

Supercritical Fluid: Materials dissolve more easily in a liquid than in a gas. A super-critical fluid has the property of filling the volume of its container like a gas, but dissolving materials like a liquid. Both carbon dioxide and water can be put into super-critical states at temperatures and pressures that are pretty close to room temperature and pressure. Cola and coffee beans are decaffeinated by passing one of these supercritical fluids over them. The caffeine dissolves in the fluid, leaving most of the other chemicals in the beans behind. Advertisers proclaim the process is "natural" because both carbon dioxide and water occur in nature.

Supernova: A rare celestial phenomenon involving the explosion of most of the material in a star, resulting in an extremely bright, short-lived object that emits vast amounts of energy.

Surface Wave: A wave that travels along the surface of a medium. In this wave particles travel in a circular motion.

Surroundings: Everything outside what we have defined to be the system.

System: A small piece of the world around which we mentally draw a box and upon which we focus our attention. It may be a beaker containing an ice cube and warm water or a refrigerator or a living organism.

— T —

Tectonic Plates: The brittle, rigid but thin outer part of Earth is divided into sections called tectonic plates.

Tension Force: A force that is applied in such a way as to stretch a material.

Terrestrial Worlds: The rocky planets, which include Mercury, Venus, Earth, and Mars.

Theory: A set of statements or principles devised to explain a group of facts or phenomena, especially one that has been repeatedly tested or is widely accepted and can be used to make predictions about natural phenomena.

Theory of Plate Tectonics: The model of Earth in which the rigid outer layer of the Earth (lithosphere) is fractured into separate pieces (plates) that move relative to one another carried by convection currents originating in the mantle and driven by heat released by radioactivity. The plates move on a partially molten layer (asthenosphere) underneath them and may push against one another (convergent boundary), move away from one another (divergent boundary), or slide past one another (transform boundary). The model unifies the ideas of continental drift and seafloor spreading.

Thermal Conductivity: A measure of the degree to which a substance conducts heat. Metals have a high thermal conductivity.

Time Dilation: The slowing of a clock as its speed approaches the speed of light as measured by an observer not moving with the clock.

Time Symmetry: The laws of the universe do not change with time.

Trans-fatty Acids: A non-natural form of unsaturated fatty acids in which H atoms are on opposite sides of the double bond.
Cis fatty acids are the natural form. H atoms are on the same side of the double bond.

Transform Fault: The break in the Earth's lithosphere that connects segments of ridges or trenches together. These are plate boundaries where the plates are sliding past each other.

Transition Metals: The set of metal elements designated with B column headings. They have valence electron configurations involving d electrons.

Transition State: The critical point that separates reactants from products on a potential energy surface. Usually this corresponds to the point on the path from reactants to products where the energy is highest.

Transverse Wave: A wave in which the molecules of the medium vibrate at right angles to the direction the wave propagates.

Trenches: Long, narrow, deep places on the ocean floor. They are usually found near or next to continents.

Triangulation: A distance measuring technique that involves observing the angle to a distant object from at least two different locations with a known separation. It is then possible to determine the unknown distance by comparing the observed angles.

Triglyceride: A large molecule created by reacting three fatty acids with glycerol.

Trilobites: A common animal that lived in the Earth's oceans during the Paleozoic Era. They are most closely related to the modern Horseshoe Crab.

Triple Bond: A covalent bond involving three pairs of electrons shared between the two bound atoms. In chemical structure drawings, triple bonds are represented by triple lines.

Trough: The part of a wave where the particles are displaced a maximum amount below or behind their equilibrium position.

Tsunami: A water wave produced by an earthquake. They can be extremely dangerous for people living near the coast.

Turbidity Flow: A mass of water and sediment that flows down off of the continental shelf into the deep ocean. Because the sediment mixed with water is denser than plain water, these flows move along the bottom of the ocean.

— U —

Unbalanced Forces: The portion of the total force that is unopposed by other forces and so will cause an acceleration.

Unconformity: A break or gap in the geologic record.

Uniformitarianism: The idea that the laws of nature do not change with time. This idea is also called the principle of "Time Symmetry."

Universe: The combination of system plus surroundings.

— V —

Valence Electrons: One or more electrons in the outermost populated electron shell of an atom. Valence electrons determine an element's chemical properties.

Valence Shell: The outermost, highest-energy set of orbitals in an atom. The arrangement of electrons in the valence shell determines how the atom interacts chemically with other atoms.

Van der Waals Forces: Weak intermolecular attraction arising from the formation of temporary dipoles in non-polar molecules. Also known as dispersion forces.

Velocity: The speed and direction of a moving body.

Volcanic Arc: A chain of volcanoes, shaped like an arc, that form at some convergent plate boundaries.

Volcanic Rocks: Igneous rocks that cool and solidify at the Earth's surface.

— W —

Water Table: An underground surface that marks the level at which the rocks become saturated with water.

Wavelength: The distance between successive similar parts in a repeating wave.

Wave-Particle Duality: The state of possessing both wave and particle properties.

Wave Speed: The rate at which a specific wave disturbance travels from point to point.

Weak Nuclear Interaction: The interaction between nucleons that gives rise to the weak force.

Weight: A measure of the force of gravity pulling on an object.

White Dwarf: A small star that no longer sustains nuclear fusion and has shrunk to become a dense object about the size of our Earth.

Work: The technical name given to the process by which energy is transferred to or from an object by an agent that exerts force on the object and the object moves along the direction of the force.

— Z —

Zone of Ablation: The part of a glacial system where melting of snow and ice occurs faster than accumulation.

Zone of Accumulation: The part of a glacial system where snow and ice are accumulating faster than they are melting away.

SELECTED ANSWERS

Chapter 1

True/False
1. T
2. F
3. T
4. F
5. F

Fill in the Blank
1. Noncontradiction
2. Charged
3. Atom
4. Theory
5. Molecules

Matching
1. j
2. k
3. g
4. h
5. o
6. f
7. i
8. n
9. d
10. l
11. c
12. b
13. m
14. a
15. e

Analysis
1. c
2. b

Chapter 2

True/False
1. F
2. T
3. F
4. T
5. T

Fill in the blank
1. Galileo
2. Mass
3. Velocity
4. Velocity

Matching
1. a
2. b
3. b
4. c
5. a
6. c
7. b
8. a.
9. c.

Analysis
1. b
2. b
3. c

Chapter 3

True/False
1. F
2. T
3. F
4. F
5. F

Fill in the Blank
1. Law of Gravity
2. Universal Law of Gravitation
3. Curvature
4. Gravitational

Matching
1. b
2. c
3. a

Analysis
1. b
2. d
3. c
4. d
5. e

Chapter 4

True/False
1. T
2. F
3. F
4. T
5. T

Fill in the Blank
1. charge
2. electrons,
3. electrons, negartive
4. alternating
5. domains
6. field lines.

Matching
1. f
2. a
3. c
4. k
5. g
6. b
7. l
8. e
9. h
10. i
11. d
12. j

Analysis
1. c
2. a
3. b
4. e

Chapter 6

True/False
1. T
2. T
3. T
4. F
5. F

6. T

Matching
1. h
2. c
3. d
4. f

5. e
6. b
7. a
8. g

Fill in the Blank
1. Depth
2. Convection
3. The displaced liquid, the weight of the floating object
4. Weight

Analysis
1. b
2. d
3. d
4. b
5. d

Chapter 7

Matching
1. c
2. b
3. f
4. d
5. g
6. i
7. a

8. h
9. e

True/False
1. T
2. T
3. F
4. T
5. F

6. T
7. T
8. T
9. F
10. F

Fill in the Blank
1. contracts, dilates
2. space-time contin-

uum
3. high
4. accelerated, non-accelerated
5. spinning
6. time, space

Analysis
1. d

2. b
3. f
4. d
5. c
6. a

Chapter 8

True/False
1. T
2. T
3. F
4. T
5. T
6. F

7. T
8. F
9. T
10. F

Matching
1. c
2. d

3. a
4. f
5. b
6. e

Fill in the Blank
1. conserved
2. charge

3. angular momentum
4. quarks
5. momentum
6. mass, speed
7. direction
8. inside
9. equal, opposite

Analysis
1. d
2. e
3. d

Chapter 9

Matching
1. a
2. c
3. d
4. b
5. g
6. e
7. f
8. h

9. j
10. m
11. k
12. l
13. i

True/False
1. T
2. F
3. T
4. F
5. T
6. T
7. T

Fill in the Blank
1. mass, speed
2. increases
3. hot, cold
4. radiation
5. conduction
6. convection
7. energy, mass, the speed of light

Analysis
1. c
2. a
3. b
4. d
5. b
6. c
7. c
8. d

Chapter 10

Matching
1. k
2. l
3. j
4. n
5. f
6. h
7. d
8. i

9. c
10. a
11. m
12. g
13. e
14. b

True/ False
1. T
2. T
3. T
4. F
5. F
6. F

Fill in the Blank
1. medium
2. solids
3. Earthquake or seismic
4. wave
5. wavespeed
6. longitudinal

Analysis
1. c
2. e
3. b
4. c
5. e
6. d
7. b
8. d

Chapter 11

Matching I
1. b
2. b
3. a
4. a
5. a
6. a

Matching II
1. g
2. d
3. e
4. b
5. a
6. f
7. c

True/ False
1. F
2. T
3. F
4. T

Fill in the Blank
1. two-slit
2. speed of light

3. electromagnetic field
4. detected, measured, observed
5. travels
6. electromagnetic waves

Analysis
1. b
2. d
3. a
4. a
5. c

Chapter 12

Matching
1. i
2. n
3. h
4. j
5. g
6. f
7. b
8. a
9. o
10. l
11. k
12. d
13. c
14. m
15. e

True/False
1. T
2. F
3. F
4. F
5. T
6. F
7. F

Fill in the Blank
1. reflects
2. model
3. compression, tension
4. supercriticalfluid
5. insulator

Analysis
1. e
2. e
3. b
4. d
5. e

Chapter 13

True/False
1. T
2. F
3. T
4. T
5. F
6. F
7. F

Fill in the Blank
1. molecules
2. less
3. increases
4. stays the same
5. internal potential energy

Matching
1. e
2. d
3. f
4. b
5. a
6. c

Analysis
1. b
2. d
3. d
4. c
5. e
6. b

Chapter 14

True/False
1. F
2. T
3. T
4. F
5. T
6. T
7. T
8. F
9. F
10. T

Matching
1. a
2. d
3. e
4. c
5. b

Fill in the Blank
1. energy
2. electrical
3. elliptical, circular
4. far away from, lots of
5. Bohr

Analysis
1. a
2. d
3. b
4. c
5. c
6. b
7. a

Chapter 15

True/ False
1. F
2. F
3. F
4. T
5. F
6. F

Matching
1. f
2. e
3. a
4. b
5. c
6. d
7. g

Fill in the Blank
1. wave-particle
2. Davisson, Germer
3. neutrons
4. wavelength
5. destructive

Analysis
1. b
2. e
3. a
4. c
5. e

Chapter 16

True/False
1. T
2. T
3. F
4. F
5. T

Matching
1. d
2. c
3. f
4. b
5. a
6. e

Fill in the Blank
1. nucleus
2. up, down
3. more
4. shell, orbital, spin
5. three

Analysis
1. d
2. e
3. c
4. c
5. d
6. e

Chapter 17

Matching
1. f
2. a
3. j
4. i
5. d
6. c
7. e
8. h
9. g
10. b

True/False
1. T
2. F
3. T
4. T
5. T

Fill in the Blank
1. metals, non-metals
2. scandium
3. weight, volume
4. proportions
5. oxide combining ratios

Analysis
1. b
2. c
3. c
4. e
5. c & e
6. d
7. d
8. c

Chapter 18

True/False
1. T
2. F
3. F
4. F
5. T

Fill in the Blank
1. irreversible
2. lower
3. disorder
4. system, surroundings
5. equilibrium

Matching
1. e
2. c
3. d
4. a
5. b
6. f

Analysis
1. a
2. c
3. c
4. d
5. e
6. d
7. e
8. The ice in the ice-box naturally changes from a solid to a liquid. As the ice melts, the temperature increases with the increasing entropy. The temperature will never become cooler than 0° C without increasing disorder elsewhere.
9. During the expansion portion, the fluid transforms from a high-pressure liquid to a low-pressure evaporated gas. As the pressure lowers, so does the temperature.
10. a) The salt solution
    b) Water in the gaseous state
    c) The balloon at sea level
    d) The mixed chamber
11. Aluminum changing between a solid and a liquid state is a reversible process. Aluminum naturally changes from a liquid to a solid as the temperature cools, but to "reverse" this process, heat must be applied, increasing overall entropy.

Chapter 19

True/False
1. T
2. T
3. F
4. F
5. F

Fill in the Blank
1. C_4H_{10}
2. $C_2H_4O_2$
3. $C_6H_8O_6$
4. $C_8H_{10}O_2N_4$
5. a) 4
   b) 4
   c) 1
   d) hydrocarbon

Matching
1. d
2. e
3. f
4. c
5. a
6. b

Analysis
1. d

Chapter 20

True/False
1. F
2. T
3. T
4. F
5. F

Matching
1. b
2. a
3. d
4. c
5. e

Fill in the Blank
1. activation energy
2. catalyst
3. identical
4. uphill
5. increase
6. equilibrium

Analysis
1. a, c, e
2. To the first student: This equation is incorrect because the two sides are not balanced. On the left side, there are 2 hydrogen and 2 oxygen atoms, on the right side, there are 2 hydrogen and only 1 oxygen atom. To the second student: Although the number of molecules matches on each side, the right side forms a compound other than water (the ratio that forms water: 2 hydrogen to 1 oxygen).

3. d
4. a) A favorable entropy change (atoms are mixing and heat is given off in the explosion)

b) Both (states change from a liquid to a liquid and a gas, and energy is given off)
c) A favorable entropy change (states stay the same, energy is given off)

d) Both (state changes from a solid and a liquid to only a liquid, atoms increase in movement, and energy is absorbed)

Chapter 21

True/False
1. F
2. F
3. F
4. F
5. F
6. T
7. T

Fill in the Blank
1. wave
2. sizes, energies, valence
3. fluid-like, lubricant
4. band gaps
5. junction

Analysis
1. b
2. c
3. b
4. d

Chapter 22

True or False
1. F
2. F
3. T
4. T
5. T
6. F

Matching
1. c
2. e
3. b
4. d
5. a
6. d

Fill in the Blank
1. transition metals
2. lowest
3. large, small
4. electrons
5. interactions
6. opposite
7. metal, non-metal

Analysis
1. Two factors are responsible. The sodium nucleus has only 11 protons to pull on the electrons while Cl has 17 electrons. The greater charge means the Cl nucleus exerts a stronger force on the valence electron. Secondly, the Cl valence electron is closer to the nucleus. Because the nucleus-electron distance in Cl is smaller than in Na, the force is also greater. A stronger attractive force corresponds to a lower potential energy.
2. Sodium chloride
   a) Na forms +1 ions; Cl forms -1 ions
   b) NaCl
   c) $2Na + Cl2 = 2 NaCl$
   d) See Figure 22.a
   e) 1) electrons have wave-like and particle-like characteristics; 2) only certain electron energies are allowed, the particular values depend upon the charge on the atom's nucleus; 3) one can only talk about probably locations of an electron in a particular energy level; 4) the standing wave of probability associated with each energy level is called an orbital; 5) electrons emit or absorb photons as they fall down to a lower energy level or jump up to a higher energy level, respectively; 6) the photon energy matches the difference in energy of the two levels.
   f) Electrons arrive in lumps, like particles, but the probability of arrival of these lumps is determined as the intensity of waves would be.
2. Magnesium chloride
   a) Mg forms +2 ions; Cl forms -1 ions
   b) MgCl2
   c) $Mg + Cl2 = MgCl2$
   e) see response for NaCl
   f) see response for NaCl
3. Ionic compounds form between metals, which can easily lose electrons, and non-metals, which have a strong affinity for electrons. Positive ions are formed by metals and negative ions formed by non-metals. Ionic bonds form between the positive and negative ions.
4. Electrostatic forces are long-range forces. They stay strong for long-distances. Each positive ion feels the attractive force of many negative ions, and vice-versa. It is hard to pull away one or two individual ions, which is the beginning of melting. A lot of thermal energy is needed.
5. When an ionic compound is hammered, layers of ions slide over each other. Ions with like charges come in contact with each other, leading to large repulsive forces. These large repulsive forces essentially blow the crystal apart.
6. c.
7. A heap of small bits of crystals scatter light; no colors of visible light are absorbed. All colors get reflected back at you and so the crystals appear white.
8. Rubies contain Cr3+ ions which absorb blue and green photons; sapphires contain Ti4+ and Fe2+ ; the combined effect of the absorption of visible light by these two transition metal ions is to give a blue color.

Chapter 23

True or False
1. T
2. F
3. F
4. F

Matching
1. e
2. g
3. h
4. i
5. f
6. a
7. c
8. d
9. b

Fill in the Blank
1. covalent bonds
2. valence
3. ion

Analysis
1. Molecular ions are groups of atoms covalently bonded to each other, having a net charge because electrons have been lost or gained to allow the formation of covalent bonds.
2. Hydrocarbons are made of hydrogen, oxygen, and carbon. When a hydrocarbon is burned, these elements form into more stable compounds such as H_2O and CO_2
3. b
4. c, e, g
5. c

Chapter 24

Matching
1. h
2. b
3. f
4. a
5. g
6. d

7. c
8. e

True or False
1. T
2. F
3. F
4. T

5. F
6. T
7. T
8. F
9. T
10. F
11. T

Fill in the Blank
1. triglyceride
2. saturated
3. crystalline
4. tetrahedron
5. trans-fatty, cis-fatty

Analysis
1. b
2. c
3. b
4. d

Chapter 25

True/ False
1. F
2. T
3. T
4. T
5. T

Fill in the Blank
1. less
2. isotopes
3. radioactive decay
4. fusion
5. fission
6. element

Matching
1. d
2. e
3. a
4. g
5. f
6. b

7. h
8. c

Analysis
1. c
2. a
3. d
4. c

5. c
6. d

Chapter 26

True/False
1. F
2. F
3. T
4. T
5. F

Matching
1. f
2. i
3. a
4. c
5. l
6. g
7. b
8. m
9. e
10. h
11. k
12. d
13. j

Fill in the Blank
1. uniformitarianism
2. Principle of inclusions
3. unconformity
4. fossils
5. faunal succession

Analysis
1. d
2. b

3. c
4. a
5. c
6. b
7. c

8. The Geologic Column evolved over a period of many years, before there was a way to determine absolute ages. The periods of the Column were calculated on the basis of the appearance and disappearance of particular fossils in the rock record, but there was no way to know whether the fossils chosen yielded periods of anywhere near uniform length. We now know they didn't.

9. Carbon-14 has a half life of only 5,730 years—far too short to use for dating anything older than very recent materials (70,000 years old at most). In addition, Carbon-14 measures the time since an object died and stopped replenishing its complement of radioactive carbon, so objects dated in this way must once have been alive.

10. Relative dating compares events according to when they happened. For example, we know that a couple must meet before they can date. They must date before they get engaged and they must get married only after they have been engaged. Absolute dating is an exact date o f when events happen. To use the same example: A coupe first met in the beginning of January, started dating at the end of January, became engaged in April, and married in July.

11. The same decay curve can be used for all radioactive isotopes because when the time length of the half-life is reached, half of the isotope is decayed. After the time length of the half-life is reached again, half of the remaining isotope has decayed. Therefore, the same decay curve can be used for all radioactive isotopes by simply changing the half-life time along the horizontal axis.

12. Uniformitarianism states that the laws of nature do not change over time. This is essential to understanding the history of the Earth because it states that other principles, such as inclusion, cross-cutting relationships, and superposition happen identically today as they did at the foundation of the earth.

13. 1) Principle of Original Horizontality
    2) Principle of Superposition
    3) Principle of Inclusion
    4) Principle of Cross-Cutting Relationships
    5) Principle of Faunal Succession

14. Refer to page 333.

15. (Answers may vary) One early method used by James Ussher was to use the genealogy from the Bible. The error with this method is the assumption that the Earth was literally created in one week. Other early attempts consist of Lord Kelvin's cooling rates method, calculating the salt accumulation, and the accumulated thickness of sedimentary rock. Problems with these attempts include radioactive decay at the Earth's core causes heating, salt has precipitated out of the ocean, and sedimentary rock contains numerous unconformities, respectively.

Chapter 27

True/ False
1. F
2. F
3. T
4. T
5. F

Matching
1. n
2. f
3. o
4. g
5. j
6. c
7. h
8. i
9. l
10. k
11. a
12. e
13. b
14. m
15. d

Fill in the Blank
1. trenches
2. hydrologic system
3. metamorphic
4. limestone
5. sedimentary

Analysis
1. c
2. a
3. d
4. Igneous rocks form from molten material (lava if it erupts onto the surface of the earth, magma if it remains below the surface) that cools and crystallizes. Sedimentary rocks consist of debris deposited in layers and cemented together, either by chemicals dissolved in groundwater or by heat and pressure from the weight of overlying layers. Metamorphic rocks are made from igneous, sedimentary, or other metamorphic rocks whose mineral composition is changed by a combination of heat, pressure, and fluids.
5. The continents are made of a great variety of rock types, but if the chemical composition pf all of them are averaged together; the result is close to the chemical composition of granite, an igneous rock. The rocks on the ocean floor are all of essentially one type—basalt, another type of igneous rock.
6. Typically, a high ridge winds through the ocean basin, near the middle of the ocean floor, and is bordered on either side by abyssal hills. These hills become smaller the further one moves away from the ridge, because they become covered with sediment that has accumulated on the seafloor. Given enough sediment, the hills are completely covered and this results in abyssal plains. Generally, far

from the ridges are deep trenches. These are always adjacent to island arcs (or volcanic mountain ranges if the ridge is adjacent to a continent).
7. Composition and Texture
8. The plate tectonic system continually alters the shape and size of continents and oceans. The hydrologic system changes the face of the continents and moves large amounts of rock through erosion and deposition. These two systems have made the Earth's appearance drastically different from what it was initially.
9. An island protrudes above the surface of the water, whereas a seamount does not (although it may have in the past).
10. Both are igneous rock and have similar mineral composition. Geologists name them differently because differences in the speed at which they cooled have created different textures.
11. Both are hot, liquid rock that forms igneous rocks, however, magma becomes lava when it surfaces.
12. Metamorphism is when igneous or sedimentary rocks are changed by some combination of heat, pressure, and fluids to become rocks made of new mineral compositions. Examples are granite into gneiss , or shale into slate.
13. Three main rock types are 1) Igneous rock, such as granite or basalt. 2) Sedimentary rock such as sandstone or shale. 3) metamorphic rock, such as marble or quartzite.

Chapter 28

True/ False
1. F
2. T
3. F
4. T

Matching
1. h
2. l
3. n
4. b
5. g
6. k
7. m
8. i
9. d
10. c
11. e
12. f
13. a
14. o
15. j

Fill in the Blank
1. seismometer or seismograph
2. Curie temperature
3. focus, epicenter
4. liquid, solid
5. Moho

Analysis
1. b
2. d
3. d
4. d
6. The asthenosphere is composed of a soft, plastic, partially-molten mechanical layer in the Earth located below the lithosphere. We know the composition through studying seismic waves traveling through Earth's center.
7. The lithosphere, the asthenosphere, the mesosphere, the outer core, and inner core.
8. Iron meteorites are thought to represent the type of material found in the Earth's core.
9. Remember the Silly Putty example? Plastic means non-rigid, deformable, and capable of

flowing in response to pressure.
10. Compositional layers differ in the kind of material they are made of. They are the crust, mantle, and core. Mechanical layers differ in the behavior of the material. These layers are lithosphere, the asthenosphere, the mesosphere, and the outer and inner core.
11. The inner core is at a higher temperature than the outer core, but it is also under higher pressure. The pressure is so large that, at the prevailing temperatures, the core is solid iron.
12. Earth's interior is differentiated (meaning it has different distinct layers) both mechanically and compositionally. As one goes deeper, the composition and behavior of the material of the Earth changes several times.
13. Seismic waves make abrupt changes when traveling through Earth's interior when they encounter an abrupt change in elasticity of the rock and refract. Waves travel in curved paths when the density changes slowly with depth.
14. P-waves are compressional waves. They travel

the fastest in the Earth and so are the first to arrive at any seismic wave detectors. S-waves are shear waves produced by an earthquake. They are slower than P-waves and so arrive later at seismic wave detectors. S-

waves cannot travel through the liquid outer core.

15. The focus is the place inside the Earth where an earthquake originates and the epicenter in the point on the

Earth's surface directly above the focus.

16. The process by which the lithosphere ruptures and returns to its normal form after being bent under pressure.

Chapter 29

True/ False
1. F
2. T
3. F
4. T
5. F

Matching
1. h
2. e
3. j
4. l
5. a
6. i
7. g
8. b
9. f
10. k
11. c
12. d

Fill in the Blank
1. Paleoclimatic
2. normal, reverse
3. basalt, sediment
4. margins or edges
5. parallel

Analysis
1. c
2. d
3. a
4. The continental shelves are those portions of the continents that happen to be below the sea level at this time. They consist of continental rock and are not part of the ocean basin.
5. If the directions of the inherent magnetic fields of ancient lava flows on different continents are measured, it is found that they do not all point towards the same north pole. However, if the continents have rearranged so that their continental shelves fit best, then the

magnetic directions all point towards a single location. In answering this question, you should discuss the origin of magnetic fields in rocks, including the concept of the Curie temperature.
6. The parallelism of the Atlantic coastlines and the similarities fossils on different continents.
7. The increasing age of the seafloor rock from the ridges, and the presence of guyots.
8. The supercontinent that broke up at the start of the Mesozoic Era to form the continents we have today.
9. Wegener and his colleagues gave evidences such as the jigsaw fit of the continents, continuity of structural trends, fossils of similar ages and type on different continents, Permian glaciation on multiple continents, and Paleomagnetic evidence.
10. If the continents are assembled into Pangea, all the glaciation grooves align in a logical and consistent manner.

Chapter 30

True/ False
1. F
2. F
3. T

Fill in the Blank
1. mantle plumes
2. convergent plate
3. denser

Analysis
1. c
2. b

3. b
4. a
5. a
6. Fold mountain belts come into existence when a continental mass located on a plate boundary becomes involved in a plate convergence—particularly a continent-continent collision. As two continents collide, they do so along a relatively long, narrow collision zone.
7. Answers should include ridge push and slab pull working together to slide a plate towards the trenches and what role basal drive plays, if

any. Also include how this results in new ocean floor being created and how the age of the plate increases away from the ridges.
8. Island arcs are always found in association with ocean trenches, but islands chains are formed over hot spots. Trenches are larger than mantle plumes, thus islands arcs tend to be larger.
9. The lithosphere is young and warm and it has hot, low-density asthenosphere welling up beneath it.

Chapter 31

True/False
1. T
2. F
3. F
4. F
5. T

Fill in the Blank
1. climate
2. elliptical
3. 1° C
4. Undammed rivers
5. continental

Matching
1. l
2. a
3. k
4. h
5. c
6. m
7. g
8. d
9. f
10. e
11. i
12. b
13. j

Analysis
1. a
2. c
3. d
4. c
5. d
6. d

7. According to William Ruddiman, increasing levels of carbon dioxide, methane, deforestation, the use of fossil fuels in particular, have delayed the contemporary occurrence of an ice age.
8. When underground caverns are created too close to the surface of the Earth, they can collapse and create a sink hole.
9. When the Earth receives more sunlight, wetlands flourish, which encourages bacteria action and leads to decaying vegetation, which pro-

duces more methane and warms up the climate, methane being the most potent of the green house gases.
10. The "wobble" created because Earth is on an axis, called precession, has a period of 23,000 years. During this cycle, Earth receives different amount of solar radiation at different times during the cycle. This allows Earth to be warm enough to prevent the formation of large continental glaciers at the warmer parts of the cycle.
11. Glaciers expand during cooler

months and melt during warmer periods. During an ice age, ocean water can be frozen, lowering the ocean level by hundreds of feet. During warmer periods, just the opposite can occur. This affects our climate because the Earth is currently warming by 1°C per year.
12. (Answers will vary and should be creative) Some suggested places are: near a dam or levee of a river, or a flood plain, in Florida above a sinkhole, or in the center of the Sahara Desert.

Chapter 32

True/False
1. F
2. T
3. F
4. T
5. T
6. F
7. T

Matching
1. g
2. d
3. i
4. c
5. b
6. e
7. a
8. h
9. f

Fill in the Blank
1. sun-centered
2. elliptical
3. diminishes or weakens
4. baseline

5. size
6. distance ladder
7. lunar highlands

Analysis
1. a
2. a
3. c
4. d

5. a
6. d
7. a

Chapter 33

Matching
1. f
2. k
3. d
4. i
5. a
6. g
7. h
8. o
9. j
10. n
11. c
12. m
13. e
14. l
15. b

True/False
1. T
2. T
3. F
4. T
5. F
6. T

Fill in the Blank
1. Black holes
2. hydrogen
3. gravity, pressure
4. Hertzsprung-Russell diagram
5. Fusion
6. Sun
7. apparent, true or absolute

Analysis
1. a
2. b
3. a
4. b
5. e
6. a

Chapter 34

Matching
1. g
2. o
3. i
4. d
5. a
6. j
7. h
8. c
9. f
10. l
11. r
12. e
13. q
14. n
15. b
16. a
17. k

True/False
1. T
2. F
3. T
4. F
5. F
6. F

Fill in the Blank
1. expanding
2. Edwin Hubble, Shapley-Curtis Debate
3. Cosmic Microwave Background (CMB)
4. helium
5. absolute

Analysis
1. b
2. c
3. c
4. c
5. d

FIGURE CREDITS

Chapter 1

Splash Jennifer Berry
1.1 Brent Laker
1.2 Kelli Rane
1.3 BYU
1.4 Kelli Rane
1.5 Chris Henderson
1.6 Jennifer Berry
1.7 © 1992 The Harold E. Edgerton Trust.
1.8 Courtesy NASA
1.9 Photos.com
1.10 Chris Henderson
1.11 Chris Henderson

Chapter 2

Splash Courtesy NASA
2.1 Photos.com
2.2 Chris Henderson
2.3 Chris Henderson
2.4 Chris Henderson
2.5 Kelli Rane
2.6 Chris Henderson
2.7 Chris Henderson
2.8 Courtesy NASA
2.9 Courtesy American Lumberjack Association
Kilogram Courtesy BIPM.org

Chapter 3

Splash Modified from Photos.com and presse.splash-festival.de/bildarchiv.php
3.1 Chris Henderson
3.2 Chris Henderson
3.3 Chris Henderson
3.4 Chris Henderson
3.5 Chris Henderson
3.6 Chris Henderson
3.7 Chris Henderson
3.8 Courtesy NASA

Chapter 4

Splash Photos.com
4.1 Kelli Rane
4.2 Kelli Rane
4.3 Chris Henderson
4.4 Chris Henderson
4.5 Photos.com/Kent Minson
4.6 Chris Henderson
4.7 Photos.com
4.8 Kelli Rane
4.9 Chris Henderson
4.10 Kelli Rane
4.11 R. V. Coleman and G. G. Scott
4.12 Courtesy W. M. Hess

Chapter 5

Splash Kent Minson. Modified from Photos.com
5.1 Chris Henderson
5.2 Chris Henderson
5.3 Courtesy Mark Philbrick and BYU
5.4 Chris Henderson
5.5 Chris Henderson
5.6 Chris Henderson
5.7 Chris Henderson
5.8 Chris Henderson
5.9 Courtesy NASA
5.10 Courtesy NASA
5.11 Photos.com
5.12 Kent Minson

Chapter 6

Splash Rear Admiral Harley D. Nygren. Courtesy NOAA
6.1 Chris Henderson
6.2 Kelli Rane
6.3 Kent Minson
6.4 Chris Henderson
6.5 Chris Henderson
6.6 Chris Henderson
6.7 Chris Henderson
6.8 Chris Henderson
6.9 Chris Henderson
6.10 Chris Henderson
6.11 Chris Henderson
6.12 Chris Henderson
6.13 Kent Minson
6.14 Chris Henderson
6.15 Chris Henderson

Chapter 7

Splash Courtesy NASA
7.1 Kent Minson
7.2 Kent Minson. Courtesy NASA
7.3 Photos.com
7.4 Kent Minson
7.5 Kent Minson
7.6 Kent Minson
7.7 Chris Henderson
7.8 Chris Henderson
7.9 Courtesy SLAC
7.10 Chris Henderson
7.11 Chris Henderson
7.12 Chris Henderson
7.13 Kent Minson
7.14 Kent Minson
7.15 Chris Henderson

Chapter 8

Splash Kent Minson. Modified from Photos.com

8.1 Kelli Rane
8.2 Kent Minson
8.3 Courtesy CERN
8.4 Kelli Rane
8.5 Chris Henderson
8.6 Kelli Rane and Kent Minson
8.7 Chris Henderson
8.8 Kelli Rane

Chapter 9

Splash Courtesy NASA

9.1 Jennifer Berry
9.2 Jennifer Berry
9.3 Kelli Rane
9.4 Chris Henderson
9.5 Jeffrey Berry
9.6 Kelli Rane
9.7 Jennifer Berry
9.8 Kent Minson
9.9 Jeffrey Berry
9.10 Kelli Rane
9.11 Kent Minson
Table 9.1 Stephen Berry and Photos.com

Chapter 10

Splash Photos.com

10.1 Brent Laker
10.2 Kent Minson
10.3 Kelli Rane
10.4 Kelli Rane
10.5 Kelli Rane
10.6 Kent Minson
10.7 Kelli Rane
10.8 Kelli Rane
10.9 Kelli Rane
10.10 Kelli Rane
10.11 Chris Henderson
10.12 Kelli Rane
10.13 Kent Minson
10.14 Kelli Rane
10.15 Kelli Rane
10.16 Kent Minson
10.17 Kelli Rane
10.18 Chris Henderson
10.19 Chris Henderson

Chapter 11

Splash Photos.com

11.1 Kelli Rane
11.2 Kelli Rane
11.3 Kelli Rane
11.4 Kelli Rane
11.5 Kelli Rane
11.6 Kelli Rane
11.7 Kelli Rane
11.8 Kelli Rane
11.9 Chris Henderson
11.10 Chris Henderson
11.11 Chris Henderson
11.12 Chris Henderson
11.13 Chris Henderson
11.14 Chris Henderson
11.15 Chris Henderson
11.16 Kelli Rane
11.17 Kelli Rane

Chapter 12

Splash Photos.com

12.1 Chris Henderson
12.2 Courtesy NASA and Photos.com
12.3 Kelli Rane
12.4 Chris Henderson
12.5 Chris Henderson, Kelli Rane, and Kent Minson
12.6 Chris Henderson
12.7 Chris Henderson
12.8 Jennifer Berry
12.9 Chris Henderson

Chapter 13

Splash Photos.com

13.1 Chris Henderson
13.2 Kelli Rane
13.3 Courtesy of IBM
13.4 Courtesy of IBM
13.5 Chris Henderson
13.6 Chris Henderson
13.7 Chris Henderson
13.8 Chris Henderson
13.9 Chris Henderson
13.10 Kent Minson
13.11 Chris Henderson

Chapter 14

Splash Kent Minson. Modified from Photos.com

14.1 Kelli Rane , Chris Henderson
14.2 Kelli Rane
14.3 Chris Henderson
14.4 Kelli Rane
14.5 Kelli Rane
14.6 Kelli Rane
14.7 Kelli Rane
14.8 Kelli Rane

Chapter 15

Splash Modified from Photos.com

15.1 Kelli Rane
15.2 Chris Henderson
15.3 Kent Minson
15.4 Chris Henderson
15.5 Kent Minson
15.6 Kent Minson
15.7 Courtesy of Hitachi
15.8 Kelli Rane
15.9 Kent Minson
15.10 Kelli Rane
15.11 Courtesy Richard Vanfleet
15.12 Kelli Rane
15.13 Kelli Rane
15.14 Kelli Rane
15.15 Kelli Rane
15.16 Kelli Rane
15.17 Kent Minson
15.18 Paul Ehrenfest

Chapter 16

Splash Modified from Photos.com

16.1 Kent Minson
16.2 Kent Minson
16.3 Kent Minson
16.4 Kent Minson
16.5 Kent Minson
16.6 Kent Minson
16.7 Kent Minson
16.8 Kent Minson
16.9 Kent Minson
16.10 Kent Minson
16.11 Kent Minson
16.12 Kent Minson
16.13 Kent Minson
16.14 Kent Minson

Chapter 17

Splash Chris Henderson, Kent Minson

17.1 Kelli Rane
17.2 Kelli Rane
17.3 Greg Allen and Mark Clayton
17.4 Kelli Rane
17.5 Courtesy GSI
17.6 Chris Henderson
17.7 Kent Minson
17.8 Kent Minson
17.9 Kent Minson
17.10 Kent Minson
17.11 Kent Minson
17.12 Public Domain

Chapter 18

Splash   Kent Minson. Modified from Photos.com
18.1   Chris Henderson
18.2   Chris Henderson
18.3   Kelli Rane
18.4   Kelli Rane
18.5   Kelli Rane
18.6   Chris Henderson
18.7   Chris Henderson
18.8   Kent Minson and Photos.com
18.9   Chris Henderson
18.10   Copyright Sydney Harris. Reprinted with permission.

Chapter 19

Splash   Kent Minson
19.1   Reprinted with permission
19.2   Kent Minson
19.3   Kent Minson, Chris Henderson
19.4   Kent Minson, Kelli Rane. Courtesy Mark Philbrick and BYU
19.5   Tyler K. Meldrum
19.6   Kent Minson
19.7   Kent Minson
19.8   Tyler K. Meldrum
19.9   Tyler K. Meldrum
19.10   Kelli Rane
19.11   Chris Henderson
19.12   Tyler K. Meldrum. Source: Japanese Spectral Database
19.13   Tyler K. Meldrum. Source: Japanese Spectral Database
19.14   Courtesy Dr. Steven Herron, BYU Department of Chemistry and Biochemistry

Chapter 20

Splash   Photos.com
20.1   Chris Henderson
20.2   Chris Henderson
20.3   Kent Minson, Photos.com
20.4   Chris Henderson
20.5   Chris Henderson
20.6   Chris Henderson
20.7   Chris Henderson, Kent Minson
20.8   Kelli Rane
20.9   Chris Henderson
20.10   Kent Minson
20.11   Chris Henderson

Chapter 21

Splash   Photos.com
21.1   Photos by Jon Hazen. Courtesy of SALEMOREGON.COM ©2005.
21.2   Chris Henderson
21.3   Chris Henderson
21.4   Chris Henderson
21.5   Chris Henderson
21.6   Kent Minson
21.7   Keli Rane
21.8   Kent Minson
21.9   Chris Henderson

Chapter 22

Splash   Kent Minson. Modified from Photos.com
22.1a   Courtesy InternationalCrystal.net
22.1b, c   Kelli Rane
22.2   Jennifer Berry
22.3   Juliana Boerio-Goates
22.4   Chris Henderson
22.5   Jennifer Berry
22.6   Chris Henderson
22.7   Kelli Rane

Chapter 23

Splash   Kent Minson
23.1   Kent Minson
23.2   Kent Minson
23.4   Kent Minson
23.5   Kelli Rane
23.6   Kent Minson
23.7   Kent Minson
23.8   Kelli Rane
23.9   Kent Minson
23.10   Kelli Rane
23.11   David Dearden
23.12   David Dearden
23.13   Kent Minson

Chapter 24

Splash   Kelli Rane
24.1   Juliana Boerio-Goates
24.2   Kelli Rane
24.3   Kelli Rane
24.4   Kelli Rane
24.5   Tyler K. Meldrum
24.6   Kent Minson
24.7   Tyler K. Meldrum
24.8   Chris Henderson
24.9   Chris Henderson
24.10   Kent Minson
24.11   Tyler K. Meldrum
24.12a,b   Kelli Rane
24.12c   Kent Minson
24.13   Kent Minson
24.14   Kent Minson
24.15   Juliana Boerio-Goates
24.16   Kelli Rane
24.17   Kelli Rane

Chapter 25

Splash   Courtesy NASA
25.1   Jeanette Lawler and Jennifer Berry (data courtesy NIST)
25.2   Chris Henderson
25.3   Courtesy rollercoasters.com
25.4   Chris Henderson
25.5   Bill Watterson. Reprinted with permission of Andrews McMeel, a Universal Press Syndicate Co.

Chapter 26

Splash   Photo of Rock Canyon by Kelli Rane
26.1   Bart Kowallis
26.2a   Chris Henderson
26.2b   Jennifer Berry
26.3   Chris Henderson
26.4   Bart Kowallis
26.5   Bart Kowallis
26.6   Jennifer Berry
26.7   Bart Kowallis
26.8   Bart Kowallis
26.9   Bart Kowallis
26.10   Chris Henderson
26.11   Jennifer Berry
26.12   Bart Kowallis
26.13   Chris Henderson
26.14   Chris Henderson
26.15   Chris Henderson
26.16   Chris Henderson

Chapter 27

Splash   Photo of Earth by Apollo 17 astronuats. Courtesy NASA
27.1   Courtesy NASA
27.2a   Bart Kowallis
27.2b   Bart Kowallis
27.3   Chris Henderson
27.4   Kelli Rane
27.5   Kelli Rane
27.6   Kent Minson
27.7   Chris Henderson
27.8   Chris Henderson
27.9   Courtesy the National Geophysical Data Center (NGDC)

27.10   Courtesy the NGDC
27.11   Courtesy the NGDC
27.12   Courtesy the NGDC

Chapter 28

Splash   A lava flow spilling into the ocean. Modified from Photos.com

28.1   Kelli Rane
28.2a   Kelli Rane
28.2b   Courtesy NSF and WUSTL
28.2c   Courtesy Matteo Chinellato and www.mcomemeteorite.info
28.3   Chris Henderson
28.4   Chris Henderson
28.5   Chris Henderson
28.6   Chris Henderson
28.7   Chris Henderson
28.8   Chris Henderson
28.9   Chris Henderson
28.10   Chris Henderson

Chapter 29

Splash   Global Relief Map courtesy the NGDC

29.1   Chris Henderson
29.2   Chris Henderson
29.3   Chris Henderson
29.4   © Ken Lucas/ Visuals Unlimited
29.5   Chris Henderson
29.6   Chris Henderson
29.7   Chris Henderson
29.8   Courtesy the NGDC
29.9   Chris Henderson
29.10   Chris Henderson
29.11   Chris Henderson
29.12   Chris Henderson

Chapter 30

Splash   Crustal Ages of the World's Ocean Floor—Müller, R.D., Roest, W.R., Royer, J.-Y., Gahagan, L.M., and Sclater, J.G., A digital age map of the ocean floor. SIO Reference Series 93–30, Scripps Institution of Oceanography

30.1   Kelli Rane
30.2   Kelli Rane
30.3   Courtesy Peter Swenson
30.4   Kelli Rane
30.5   Kelli Rane
30.6   Kelli Rane
30.7   Courtesy Bart Kowallis
30.8   Kelli Rane

30.9   Courtesy the NGCD
30.10   Chris Henderson, Kelli Rane
30.11   Chris Henderson, Kelli Rane
30.12   Chris Henderson, Kelli Rane

Chapter 31

Splash   A waterfall. Modified from Photos.com

31.1   Chris Henderson
31.2   Courtesy NASA
31.3   Courtesy KSL News
31.4   Courtesy NASA
31.5   Courtesy Ken Hamblin
31.6   Bart Kowallis
31.7   Bart Kowallis
31.8   Bart Kowallis
31.9   Chris Henderson
31.10   Courtesy Brandon Kowallis
31.11   Courtesy Volusia County
31.12   Bart Kowallis
31.13   Courtesy NASA
31.14   Chris Henderson
31.15   Courtesy NASA
31.16   Courtesy NASA
31.17   Courtesy Ken Hamblin
31.18   Chris Henderson
31.19   Chris Henderson
31.20   Chris Henderson
31.21   Chris Henderson
31.22   Chris Henderson
31.23   Chris Henderson
31.24   Chris Henderson

Chapter 32

Splash   The first Earthrise as viewed from the Moon by Apollo 8 astronauts. Courtesy NASA.

32.1   Michael Joner
32.2   Hubble Heritage Team, NASA
32.3   Courtesy D. Roddy and LPI
32.4   Cassini Imaging Team, NASA
32.5   Chris Henderson
32.6   The Galileo Project, NASA
32.7   Courtesy NASA
32.8   Courtesy NASA
32.9   Courtesy NASA
32.10   The Magellan Project, NASA
32.11   Michael Joner
32.12   Courtesy MSSS, JPL, NASA
32.13   Mars Exploration Rover Mission, JPL, NASA
32.14   The Galileo Project, NASA
32.15   The Galileo Project, NASA
32.16   The Galileo Project, NASA
32.17   Courtesy ESA, NASA

32.18   Chris Henderson
32.19   Jennifer Berry
32.20   Jennifer Berry

Chapter 33

Splash   Globular Star Cluster Messier 80 as seen by the Hubble Space Telescope. Courtesy NASA

33.1   Hubble Heritage Team, NASA
33.2   Michael Joner
33.3   Hubble Space Telescope, NASA
33.4   Kelli Rane
33.5   Kelli Rane
33.6   Hubble Space Telescope, NASA
33.7   Courtesy CXC, HST, NASA
33.8   Kelli Rane (data from Freedman-Kaufmann)
33.9   Kelli Rane
33.10   Kelli Rane
33.11   Courtesy AURA, STScI, NASA

Chapter 34

Splash   Gravitational lenses seen by the Hubble Space Telescope in a distant cluster of galaxies known as Abell 1689. Courtesy NASA

34.1   Kent Minson
34.2   Kelli Rane
34.3   Kelli Rane
34.4   Robert Gendler
34.5   Robert Gendler
34.6   Robert Gendler
34.7   Hubble Space Telescope, NASA
34.8   Hubble Space Telescope, NASA
34.9   Courtesy STScI, HST, NASA
34.10   Courtesy STScI, HST, ESA, NASA
34.11   Chris Henderson, Kent Minson
34.12   Kelli Rane
34.13   Kelli Rane
34.14   Michael Joner
34.15   Kelli Rane
34.16   Courtesy NASA
34.17   Courtesy NASA
34.18   Hubble Space Telescrope, NASA

Cover   Kent Minson
Original images courtesy NASA, Photos.com

Preface Header   Modified from Photos.com and NASA

Back Splash Headers   Photos.com and Courtesy NASA

INDEX

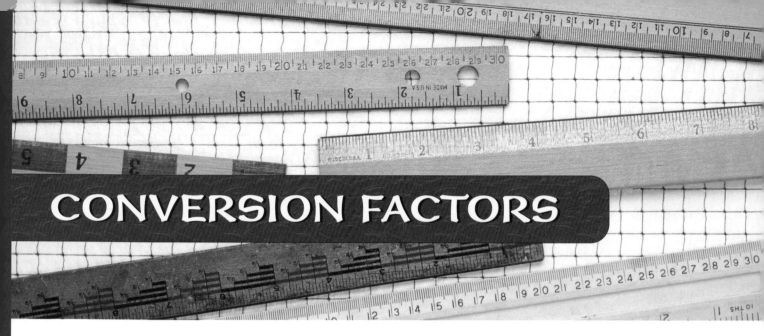

CONVERSION FACTORS

Length

1 m = 39.37 in. = 3.218 ft

1 in. = 2.54 cm

1 km = 0.621 mi

1 mi= 5280 ft = 1.609 km

1 lightyear (ly) = 9.461×10^{15} m

1 angstrom (Å) = 10^{-10} m

Mass

1 kg = 10^3 g = 6.85×10^{-2} slug

1 slug = 14.59 kg

1 u = 1.66×10^{-27} kg

Time

1 min = 60 s

1 h = 3600 s

1 day = 8.64×10^4 s

1 yr = 365.242 days = 3.156×10^7 s

Volume

1 L = 1000 cm^3 = 3.531×10^{-2} ft^3

1 ft^3 = 2.832×10^{-2} m^3

1 gal = 3.786 L = 231 $in.^3$

Speed

1 km/h = 0.278 m/s = 0.621 mi/h

1 m/s = 2.237 mi/h = 3.281 ft/s

1 mi/h = 1.61 km/h = 0.447 m/s = 1.47 ft/s

Force

1 N = 0.2248 lb = 10^5 dynes

1 lb = 4.448 N

1 dyne = 10^{-5} N = 2.248×10^{-6} lb

Work and Energy

1 J = 10^7 erg = 0.738 ft·lb = 0.239 cal

1 cal = 4.186 J

1 ft·lb = 1.356 J

1 Btu = 1.054×10^3 J = 252 cal

1 J = 6.24×10^{18} eV

1 eV = 1.602×10^{-19} J

1 kWh = 3.60×10^6 J

Pressure

1 atm = 1.013×10^5 N.m^2 (or Pa) = 14.70 lb/$in.^2$

1 Pa = 1 N.m^2 = 1.45×10^{-4} lb/$in.^2$

1 lb/$in.^2$ = 6.895×10^3 N/m^2

Power

1 hp = 550 ft·lb/s = 0.746 kW

1 W = 1 J/s = 0.738 ft·lb/s

1 Btu/h = 0.293 W

rad

THE ELEMENTS

By Symbol

Ac	Actinium	Mn	Manganese
Ag	Silver	Mo	Molybdenum
Al	Aluminum	N	Nickel
Am	Americium	N	Nitrogen
Ar	Argon	Na	Sodium
As	Arsenic	Nb	Niobium
At	Astatine	Nd	Neodymium
Au	Gold	Ne	Neon
B	Boron	No	Nobelium
Ba	Barium	Np	Neptunium
Be	Beryllium	O	Oxygen
Bi	Bismuth	Os	Osmium
Bk	Berkelium	P	Phosphorus
Br	Bromine	Pa	Protactinium
C	Carbon	Pb	Lead
Ca	Calcium	Pd	Palladium
Cd	Cadmium	Pm	Promethium
Ce	Cerium	Po	Polonium
Cf	Californium	Pr	Praseodymium
Cl	Chlorine	Pt	Platinum
Cm	Curium	Pu	Plutonium
Co	Cobalt	Ra	Radium
Cr	Chromium	Rb	Rubidium
Cs	Cesium	Re	Rhenium
Cu	Copper	Rh	Rhodium
Dy	Dysprosium	Rn	Radon
Er	Erbium	Ru	Ruthenium
Es	Einsteinium	S	Sulfur
Eu	Europium	Sb	Antimony
F	Fluorine	Sc	Scandium
Fe	Iron	Se	Selenium
Fm	Fermium	Si	Silicon
Fr	Francium	Sm	Samarium
Ga	Gallium	Sn	Tin
Gd	Gadolinium	Sr	Strontium
Ge	Germanium	Ta	Tantalum
H	Hydrogen	Tb	Terbium
He	Helium	Tc	Technetium
Hf	Hafnium	Te	Tellurium
Hg	Mercury	Th	Thorium
Ho	Holmium	Ti	Titanium
I	Iodine	Tl	Thallium
In	Indium	Tm	Thulium
Ir	Iridium	U	Uranium
K	Potassium	V	Vanadium
Kr	Krypton	W	Tungsten
La	Lanthanum	Xe	Xenon
Li	Lithium	Y	Yttrium
Lr	Lawrencium	Yb	Ytterbium
Lu	Lutetium	Zn	Zinc
Md	Mendelevium	Zr	Zirconium
Mg	Magnesium		

By Element

Element	Symbol	Atomic Number	Atomic Mass*	Element	Symbol	Atomic Number	Atomic Mass*
Actinium	Ac	89	227	Mercury	Hg	80	200.59
Aluminum	Al	13	26.98	Molybdenum	Mo	42	95.94
Americium	Am	95	243	Neodymium	Nd	60	144.24
Antimony	Sb	51	121.75	Neon	Ne	10	20.179
Argon	Ar	18	39.948	Neptunium	Np	93	237.048
Arsenic	As	33	74.92	Nickel	Ni	28	58.70
Astatine	At	85	210	Niobium	Nb	41	92.906
Barium	Ba	56	137.34	Nitrogen	N	7	14.0
Berkelium	Bk	97	247	Nobelium	No	102	254
Beryllium	Be	4	9.01	Osmium	Os	76	190.2
Bismuth	Bi	83	208.98	Oxygen	O	8	15.9994
Boron	B	5	10.81	Palladium	Pd	46	106.4
Bromine	Br	35	79.90	Phosphorus	P	15	30.97
Cadmium	Cd	48	112.40	Platinum	Pt	78	195.09
Calcium	Ca	20	40.08	Plutonium	Pu	94	242
Californium	Cf	98	251	Polonium	Po	84	210
Carbon	C	6	12.011	Potassium	K	19	39.098
Cerium	Ce	58	140.12	Praseodymium	Pr	59	140.9
Cesium	Cs	55	132.9	Promethium	Pm	61	145
Chlorine	Cl	17	35.45	Protactinium	Pa	91	231.0
Chromium	Cr	24	51.99	Radium	Ra	88	226.02
Cobalt	Co	27	58.93	Radon	Rn	86	222
Copper	Cu	29	63.5	Rhenium	Re	75	186.207
Curium	Cm	96	247	Rhodium	Rh	45	102.9
Dysprosium	Dy	66	162.50	Rubidium	Rb	37	85.468
Einsteinium	Es	99	254	Ruthenium	Ru	44	101.07
Erbium	Er	68	167.26	Samarium	Sm	62	150.4
Europium	Eu	63	151.96	Scandium	Sc	21	44.95
Fermium	Fm	100	253	Selenium	Se	34	78.96
Fluorine	F	9	18.99840	Silicon	Si	14	28.086
Francium	Fr	87	223	Silver	Ag	47	107.868
Gadolinium	Gd	64	157.25	Sodium	Na	11	23.0
Gallium	Ga	31	69.72	Strontium	Sr	38	87.62
Germanium	Ge	32	72.59	Sulfur	S	16	32.06
Gold	Au	79	196.96	Tantalum	Ta	73	180.94
Hafnium	Hf	72	178.49	Technetium	Tc	43	98.906
Helium	He	2	4.002	Tellurium	Te	52	127.60
Holmium	Ho	67	164.93	Terbium	Tb	65	158.9
Hydrogen	H	1	1.0079	Thallium	Tl	81	204.37
Indium	In	49	114.82	Thorium	Th	90	232.038
Iodine	I	53	126.90	Thulium	Tm	69	168.9
Iridium	Ir	77	192.22	Tin	Sn	50	118.69
Iron	Fe	26	55.847	Titanium	Ti	22	47.90
Krypton	Kr	36	83.80	Tungsten	W	74	183.85
Lanthanum	La	57	138.9	Uranium	U	92	238.0
Lawrencium	Lr	103	257	Vanadium	V	23	50.9
Lead	Pb	82	207.2	Xenon	Xe	54	131.30
Lithium	Li	3	6.94	Ytterbium	Yb	70	173.04
Lutetium	Lu	71	174.97	Yttrium	Y	39	88.9
Magnesium	Mg	12	24.305	Zinc	Zn	30	65.38
Manganese	Mn	25	54.938	Zirconium	Zr	40	
Mendelevium	Md	101	256				

*based on the atomic mass of 12C = 12

PERIODIC TABLE OF ELEMENTS

	8 A					
	2 **He** 4.0 Helium					

7 A						
1 **H** 1.0 Hydrogen						
9 **F** 19.0 Flourine						
17 **Cl** 35.5 Chlorine						
35 **Br** 79.9 Bromine						
53 **I** 126.9 Iodine						
85 **At** 210 Astatine						
117						

2 A	3 B	4 B	5 B	6 B	7 B	8 B			1 B	2 B	3 A	4 A	5 A	6 A
4 **Be** 9.0 Beryllium											5 **B** 10.8 Boron	6 **C** 12.0 Carbon	7 **N** 14.0 Nitrogen	8 **O** 16.0 Oxygen
12 **Mg** 24.3 Magnesium	21 **Sc** 45.0 Scandium	22 **Ti** 47.9 Titanium	23 **V** 50.9 Vanadium	24 **Cr** 52.0 Chromium	25 **Mn** 54.9 Manganese	26 **Fe** 55.8 Iron	27 **Co** 58.9 Cobalt	28 **Ni** 58.7 Nickel	29 **Cu** 63.5 Copper	30 **Zn** 65.4 Zinc	13 **Al** 27.0 Aluminum	14 **Si** 28.1 Silicon	15 **P** 31.0 Phosphorus	16 **S** 32.1 Sulfur
20 **Ca** 40.1 Calcium	39 **Y** 88.9 Yttrium	40 **Zr** 91.2 Zirconium	41 **Nb** 92.9 Niobium	42 **Mo** 95.9 Molybdenum	43 **Tc** 98 Technetium	44 **Ru** 101.1 Ruthenium	45 **Rh** 102.9 Rhodium	46 **Pd** 106.4 Palladium	47 **Ag** 107.9 Silver	48 **Cd** 112.4 Cadmium	31 **Ga** 69.7 Gallium	32 **Ge** 72.6 Germanium	33 **As** 74.9 Arsenic	34 **Se** 79.0 Selenium
38 **Sr** 87.6 Strontium	57 **La** 138.9 Lanthanum	72 **Hf** 178.5 Hafnium	73 **Ta** 180.9 Tantalum	74 **W** 183.9 Tungsten	75 **Re** 186.2 Rhenium	76 **Os** 190.2 Osmium	77 **Ir** 192.2 Iridium	78 **Pt** 195.1 Platinum	79 **Au** 197.0 Gold	80 **Hg** 200.6 Mercury	49 **In** 114.8 Indium	50 **Sn** 118.7 Tin	51 **Sb** 121.8 Antimony	52 **Te** 127.6 Tellurium
56 **Ba** 137.3 Barium	89 **Ac** 227 Actinium	104 **Rf** 261 Rutherfordium	105 **Db** 262 Dubnium	106 **Sg** 266 Seaborgium	107 **Bh** 264 Bhorium	108 **Hs** 269 Hassium	109 **Mt** 268 Meitnerium	110 **Ds** 271 Darmstadtium	111 **Rg** 272 Roentgenium	112	81 **Tl** 204.4 Thallium	82 **Pb** 207.2 Lead	83 **Bi** 209.0 Bismuth	84 **Po** 209 Potonium
88 **Ra** 226 Radium											113	114	115	116

58 **Ce** 140.1 Cerium	59 **Pr** 140.9 Praseodymium	60 **Nd** 144.2 Neodymium	61 **Pm** 145 Prometium	62 **Sm** 150.0 Samarium	63 **Eu** 152.0 Europium	64 **Gd** 157.3 Gadolinium	65 **Tb** 158.9 Terbium	66 **Dy** 162.5 Dysprosium	67 **Ho** 164.9 Holmium	68 **Er** 167.3 Erbium	69 **Tm** 168.9 Thulium	70 **Yb** 173.0 Ytterbium	71 **Lu** 175.0 Lutetium
90 **Th** 232.0 Thorium	91 **Pa** 231.0 Protactinium	92 **U** 238.0 Uranium	93 **Np** 237 Neptunium	94 **Pu** 244 Plutonium	95 **Am** 243 Americium	96 **Cm** 247 Curium	97 **Bk** 247 Berkelium	98 **Cf** 251 Californium	99 **Es** 252 Einsteinium	100 **Fm** 257 Fermium	101 **Md** 258 Mendelevium	102 **No** 259 Nobelium	103 **Lr** 262 Lawrencium

Li 6.9 Lithium 3
Na 23.0 Sodium 11
K 39.1 Potassium 19
Rb 85.5 Rubidium 37
Cs 132.9 Cesium 55
Fr 223 Francium 87

metals ☐   non-metals ☐   artificially prepared ▨

Atomic Number 90 **Th** 232.0 Thorium ← Symbol / Atomic Weight / Name

91.22